THE FUNGI

VOLUME III

The Fungal Population

Contributors to This Volume

G. C. AINSWORTH

PETER K. C. AUSTWICK
J. A. BARNETT
C. G. C. CHESTERS
B. J. DEVERALL
C. L. DUDDINGTON
RALPH EMERSON
J. L. HARLEY
T. JOHNSON
T. W. JOHNSON, JR.
MORTEN LANGE
M. F. MADELIN
G. W. MARTIN

PETER MAZUR
DAVID PARK
CLAYTON PERSON
K. A. PIROZYNSKI
JOHN R. RAPER
D. B. O. SAVILE
H. P. R. SEELIGER
GEORGE SMITH
FREDERICK K. SPARROW, JR.
A. S. SUSSMAN
JOHN SAVILLE WAID
B. E. J. WHEELER

THE FUNGI

An Advanced Treatise

Edited by

G. C. AINSWORTH

COMMONWEALTH MYCOLOGICAL INSTITUTE
KEW, SURREY, ENGLAND

ALFRED S. SUSSMAN

DEPARTMENT OF BOTANY
UNIVERSITY OF MICHIGAN
ANN ARBOR, MICHIGAN

VOLUME III

The Fungal Population

1968

ACADEMIC PRESS New York San Francisco London

A Subsidiary of Harcourt Brace Jovanovich, Publishers

ACADEMIC PRESS INC.
111 Fifth Avenue, New York, New York 10003

United Kingdom Edition published by
ACADEMIC PRESS, INC. (LONDON) LTD.
24/28 Oval Road, London NW1

LIBRARY OF CONGRESS CATALOG CARD NUMBER: 65-15769

PRINTED IN THE UNITED STATES OF AMERICA.

List of Contributors

Numbers in parentheses indicate the pages on which the authors' contributions begin.

G. C. Ainsworth, *Commonwealth Mycological Institute, Kew, Surrey, England* (211, 505)

Peter K. C. Austwick, *Central Veterinary Laboratory, Ministry of Agriculture, Fisheries and Food, Weybridge, Surrey, England* (419)

J. A. Barnett,* *King's College, Cambridge, England* (557)

C. G. C. Chesters, *Department of Botany, The University, Nottingham, England* (517)

B. J. Deverall, *Botany Department, Imperial College, London, England* (129)

C. L. Duddington, *Biological Laboratories, The Polytechnic, London, England* (239)

Ralph Emerson, *Department of Botany, University of California, Berkeley, California* (105)

J. L. Harley, *Department of Botany, University of Sheffield, Sheffield, England* (139)

T. Johnson, *Canada Department of Agriculture, Research Station, Winnipeg, Canada* (543)

T. W. Johnson, Jr., *Department of Botany, Duke University, Durham, North Carolina* (95)

Morten Lange, *Institut for Sporeplanter, Copenhagen, Denmark* (625)

M. F. Madelin, *Department of Botany, The University, Bristol, England* (227, 253)

G. W. Martin, *Department of Botany, University of Iowa, Iowa City, Iowa* (635)

Peter Mazur, *Biology Division, Oak Ridge National Laboratory, Oak Ridge, Tennessee* (325)

David Park,† *Department of Botany, Manchester University, Manchester, England* (5)

Clayton Person,‡ *Department of Genetics, University of Alberta, Edmonton, Canada* (395)

* *Present address:* Food Research Institute, Norwich, England.

† *Present address:* Department of Botany, The Queen's University, Belfast, Northern Ireland.

‡ *Present address:* Department of Botany, University of British Columbia, Vancouver, Canada.

K. A. Pirozynski,* *Commonwealth Mycological Institute, Kew, Surrey, England* (487)

John R. Raper, *Department of Biology, Harvard University, Cambridge, Massachusetts* (677)

D. B. O. Savile, *Plant Research Institute, Central Experimental Farm, Ottawa, Canada* (649)

H. P. R. Seeliger, *Institut für Hygiene und Mikrobiologie der Bayerischen Julius-Maximilians-Universität, Würzburg, Germany* (597)

George Smith, *Department of Biochemistry, London School of Hygiene and Tropical Medicine, London, England* (273)

Frederick K. Sparrow, Jr., *Department of Botany, University of Michigan, Ann Arbor, Michigan* (41)

A. S. Sussman, *Department of Botany, University of Michigan, Ann Arbor, Michigan* (447)

John Saville Waid,† *Department of Botany, University of New England, Armidale, New South Wales, Australia, and Department of Agronomy, Cornell University, Ithaca, New York* (289)

B. E. J. Wheeler, *Imperial College Field Station, Silwood Park, Sunninghill, Berks, England* (179)

* *Present address:* Plant Research Institute, Ottawa, Canada.

† *Present address:* Department of Soil Science, University of Reading, Reading, England.

Preface

After having considered the fungal cell and the fungal organism in the first two volumes of this treatise in which what is known about fungi as fungi is summarized, a third traverse of the group is now made at the population level.

Attempts are made to relate fungi to their environment as saprobes, symbionts (as exemplified by mycorrhiza), and parasites, while the "domestication" of fungi for human ends is touched on. The effects of the interaction of fungi with their environment are considered from various points of view, and the summation of these effects as reflected in the geographical distribution and number of fungi is discussed. Finally, after considering the principal methods of approach to the taxonomy of fungi, there is some speculation on phylogeny and evolutionary trends.

The intention was that this should be the concluding volume of this treatise. However, in response to pressure, a fourth and final volume in which accounts will be given by specialists of the main fungal groups is now in preparation.

G. C. Ainsworth
Commonwealth Mycological Institute, Kew, Surrey, England

A. S. Sussman
University of Michigan, Ann Arbor, Michigan

June, 1968

Contents

ECOLOGY: RESULTS OF ADJUSTMENT IN NATURE

16. Effects of Adjustment to the Environment on Fungal Form

Peter K. C. Austwick

17. Longevity and Survivability of Fungi

A. S. Sussman

18. Geographical Distribution of Fungi

K. A. Pirozynski

19. The Number of Fungi

G. C. Ainsworth

TAXONOMY: TAXONOMIC CRITERIA

20. Morphology as a Taxonomic Criterion

C. G. C. Chesters

21. Host Specialization as a Taxonomic Criterion

T. Johnson

22. Biochemical Differentiation of Taxa with Special Reference to the Yeasts

A DISCUSSION OF THE BIOCHEMICAL BASIS OF THE NUTRITIONAL TESTS USED FOR CLASSIFICATION

J. A. Barnett

23. Serology as an Aid to Taxonomy

H. P. R. Seeliger

24. Genetical and Cytological Aspects of Taxonomy

Morten Lange

TAXONOMY: POSSIBLE EVOLUTIONARY PATTERNS

25. The Origin and Status of Fungi (with a Note on the Fossil Record)

G. W. Martin

26. Possible Interrelationships between Fungal Groups

D. B. O. Savile

27. On the Evolution of Fungi

John R. Raper

Contents of Previous Volumes

VOLUME I
THE FUNGAL CELL

VOLUME II
THE FUNGAL ORGANISM

THE FUNGI

VOLUME III

The Fungal Population

Ecology

SAPROBIC FUNGI AND THEIR HABITATS

CHAPTER 1

The Ecology of Terrestrial Fungi

DAVID PARK[1]

Department of Botany
Manchester University
Manchester, England

I. INTRODUCTION

It is widely recognized that in the field of ecology there are fundamental principles that apply to most organisms, including man as well as micro-organisms. Workers investigating a particular type of organism can define processes and formulate principles of application to ecology generally. Conversely work in a restricted field can often benefit from the application of ideas deriving from work on very different organisms. In many ways the ecology of fungi demonstrates these generalities and has great similarities to that of other groups; it has sometimes confirmed work in other fields and sometimes contributed to it. Fungi, because of their small size and their rapid activity permit a study on a smaller scale than do many more traditional ecological materials, and they can be particularly useful in this role. However, partly because fungi have certain special features of somatic morphology, of physiology and of genetics, as described in earlier accounts in these volumes, there are some important ways in which their ecology differs from that of higher plants and animals, and these differences will carry most of the emphasis in this account.

The large surface:volume ratio inherent in the hyphal growth form gives a large contact with the environment and greatly affects fungal biology. Ecologists studying root systems of higher plants have sometimes been impressed with the surface:volume ratio there, but in filamentous, and even more in unicellular, fungi the surface for contact with the environment is extremely high in relation to the total mass of protoplasm. Not only is the area of contact large, but there is no great distance between any point in the protoplasm itself and the environment. Whereas the higher

[1] *Present address:* Department of Botany, The Queen's University, Belfast, North Ireland.

multicellular organisms have much of their protoplasm protected from the environment by physical and physiological barriers, in fungi in the somatic condition such barriers are minimal. Except in plectenchymatous structures all the protoplasm is within a few microns of the outside environment, and only a thin cell wall and the plasmalemma separate the two states. For these reasons the environment plays a much more immediate and direct part in fungal behavior than in the behavior of many other organisms. Conversely, the fungus may in turn influence the environment rapidly, and the effect may be large in proportion to the amount of protoplasm present. Where the mycelium is extensive it is as though some of the environment were contained in rather large intercellular spaces of the organism, rather than the organism contained in the environment. Most fungi characteristically have a very rapid and active metabolism, and this also is related to the high surface:volume ratio. The maintenance of life processes in a protoplast involves a disequilibrium between that protoplast and its environment. Normal physical and chemical processes across the boundary act to cancel this disequilibrium, and the larger the boundary the greater the tendency toward equilibrium. The normal disequilibrium of life is maintained across this gradient by the utilization of energy in metabolic activities that hold the protoplasm in a state markedly different from that in the environment. The high rate of metabolism of fungi then is a necessary corollary of their somatic morphology. These relationships also help to explain the rapid and large effects on fungus behavior of apparently small changes in the environment, and further implement the sometimes relatively large effect of the fungus on its environment. Contributing further to these effects is the fact that in the somatic parts of most fungi all cells are metabolizing. In higher plants and animals some cells, often a large proportion, serve a supporting or protecting function and thus reduce the total amount of activity in relation to the total mass of the organism, while, with few exceptions, fungi do not possess such layers of cells that contribute little or nothing to overall metabolic activity. In fungi, in fact, much of cell metabolism occurs much closer to the environment than in higher animals and plants, in which it mostly occurs inside the cells. In fungi much of this activity occurs either outside the cell or just at the cell surface, which may increase the effective area by corrugation or involution. The production by cells of external metabolites or ectocrine substances (Lucas, 1947) is not confined to fungi, but because of the relationships just described such substances produced by fungi have a very obvious importance in their biology. They assist the fungus to exploit its environment even more thoroughly than is possible by surface contact. They also affect the environment, causing alterations and modifications to it, and part of the relevant altered environment may consist of other living organisms. There is adequate recognition of the importance in microbial ecology of synecological interrelationships. To a great extent these relationships are important because of the facts outlined in this paragraph.

Because an active fungal mycelium metabolizes rapidly and exploits its environment extensively, it is also usual for it to synthesize new protoplasm and to grow in length rapidly. These phenomena assist in the quick colonization of substrata[2] under suitable external conditions. However, because it is rapidly colonized and exploited, the environment may soon fail any longer to provide suitable conditions for growth of the fungus. There occurs a depletion of nutrients and an accumulation of waste metabolites that can reach toxic concentrations. When the mycelium in any area fails for reasons of this sort to maintain its disequilibrium with its environment, there is a tendency toward a slowing down in the rate of metabolism and toward a loss of organization in the protoplasm. Some fungi have a naturally slower rate of metabolism which avoids rather than counteracts the difficulty. Some fungi actually counteract the deficiency in the environment by a movement of the protoplasm forward within the hyphae, so that there is within the tubular cell wall a migration forward of the active protoplast to regions that permit or favor a higher rate of metabolism. With fungi that do not use this mechanism and that yet inherently need a high metabolic rate for survival, there are two possibilities. Either the metabolic rate slows down involuntarily and the protoplasm soon dies, or the metabolic rate slows down endogenously together with concurrent active and adaptive changes on the part of the fungus whereby physical and physiological barriers are erected between the protoplasm and the environment. These, by limiting the rate of exchange between the two phases, reduce the effects of the equilibrating forces, and allow the protoplast to retain viability without metabolizing much, and without much expenditure of energy and reserves. The change of metabolic condition may be associated with a morphological change. Sometimes swollen and thick-walled chlamydospores are produced, or special asexual structures producing conidia or sporangiospores may result. But similar physiological changes may occur also in superficially normal hyphal segments of one or a few cells, and these can also form a residual viable inoculum of the fungus in regions where it has been active but where most of the mycelium has subsequently died.

Because of the prevalence of study with artificial laboratory culture, it is common to think of fungal colonies as rather large and continuous,

[2] In this chapter *substratum* is used to designate the material medium in which the fungus occurs, *substrate* to designate the chemical substance acted upon by an enzyme.

but even in such large laboratory colonies it is usual to find that a relatively small proportion of the mycelium, normally the marginal zone only, is metabolically active. In parts of the colony individually older than 1 or 2 days the mycelium has arrived at the stage where somatic activity is at a low level, and usually propagules of some sort, either residual or dispersal, have been produced (Park, 1961). In nature, although fungi may not grow as colonies, a condition similar to this may be normal. Burges (1958) has estimated that some fungal hyphae in soil have a life of 1–3 days at the most. Other types of mycelium with an inherently slower metabolic rate, like that of some basidiomycetes, may of course be longer-lived in soil. However, from the fact that individual hyphal lengths may be very short-lived in nature as in culture it does not necessarily follow that natural death occurs at a high rate in fungi. The protoplasm from the dead hyphae may not itself have died, but may have been transferred to other parts of the fungus, either to actively metabolizing regions or to reproductive propagules. Fungi are rightly notorious for their extremely prolific reproduction, large numbers of dispersal spores often being produced very rapidly, and, equally important although less widely appreciated, large numbers of residual propagules being left behind in regions where mycelial growth has taken place. The cause for this prolific reproduction is partly the inexpendability of fungal protoplasm. Natural death of fungal protoplasm then is probably rather uncommon; it is mainly brought about by either enforced decline in metabolic activity by unfavorable environment in the absence of an appropriate response on the part of the fungus, or by a decline in the viability of inactive propagules by senescence. In nature any marked and rapid decline in the amount of viable fungal protoplasm is likely to be attributable to some environmental factor actively causing death. Factors having this action are considered later in this chapter.

It was indicated earlier that one consequence of the rapid and efficient colonization and utilization by individual fungi of substrata in nature is that their substratum may soon become unsuitable for those fungi. Natural substrata are often rather small, and almost always they are somewhat discontinuous in distribution. It is very rare for large amounts or areas of a particular decomposable material to be available at a site at the appropriate state of decay for any length of time. Where such a situation does exist, survival of a fungus might be ensured by continued somatic growth of hyphal apices, but since this situation is very rare the propagular modifications of fungal protoplasm serve a very important role in their ecology, and allow the transfer of the fungus from one available substratum to another. The nature, form, and position of dispersal propagules is often related to the habitat in a manner assisting efficient dispersal. Residual propagules are often larger than is the case with dispersal propagules since they are dispersed in time, remaining static while the environment changes round them. If the environmental change with seral succession is completely unidirectional and progressive, the same type of substratum may not again contact the residual propagules, which will eventually die. However, in many terrestrial habitats, particularly in the later stages of seral succession, changes are cyclical, and there is some chance that a suitable substratum at the right stage of decomposition will contact the residual propagule.

What has been discussed here helps to explain the ecological significance to fungi of their ability rapidly to take advantage of a substratum or situation and to exploit it quickly, their very thorough and intimate association with the immediate environment, biotic and nonbiotic, their ability to survive relatively large discontinuities in the environment appropriate for their activity, and the wide geographical range of individual species. While these characteristics are of general significance to fungi, not all species possess all in equal degree. Fungi especially active in the early stages of substratum succession, for instance species of *Neurospora* and *Rhizopus,* show exceptionally high rates of growth and utilization, and a correspondingly rapid and prolific production of dispersal propagules. Other species, particularly some ascomycetes and basidiomycetes, active in later stages of substratum succession, grow more slowly and have a generally low rate of metabolism and utilization, and are correspondingly more tardy about reproduction.

Of much advantage to fungi in their role of versatile opportunists is their high degree of adaptability. This is expressed in both morphologic and metabolic ways and can be mediated by three normal mechanisms—hybridization, genetic mutation, and environmentally induced, nongenetic variation—as well as by the two additional and peculiar mechanisms of parasexual recombination and the labile system conferred by heterokaryosis (Volume II, Chapters 18 and 19). Taken together these five mechanisms confer an unusually high degree of adaptability on fungi. Species can show variation in respect to the substrates suitable for supporting growth, tolerance to physical factors and different forms of biological antagonism, mode of somatic growth for different environmental conditions, and types of propagule produced under different conditions. Under the abnormally favorable conditions of normal laboratory culture fungal species exhibit a fair degree of constancy of form and physiology. In nature their lability may be much greater than the usual laboratory studies indicate. By altering the normal laboratory conditions, and by providing lower concentrations of nutrients, or more natural sorts of nutrients, even in axenic culture some idea of the potential range of behavior of a fungus can be obtained. In mixed culture in the laboratory a still wider range of behavior may be observed. In addition to being less variable in laboratory culture a species may even show characters that would not allow it to survive in nature, and conversely may fail to show characters that would be positively advantageous in nature. Thus cultural forms of fungi not only may be less variable than the same species in nature, but may be in some respects morphologically and physiologically quite different. On continued laboratory cultivation fungi may become more or less permanently altered in form and metabolic behavior in a direction adaptive to the laboratory environment, which is both specialized in particular and unusual directions, and also less variable than environments in nature. Thus the characters of a laboratory strain of a species may have little significance for the natural survival and behavior of that species, but the phenomenon itself may be relevant to conditions in nature. Thus two laboratories starting with the same wild type, but using different media, cultural methods, or modes of transfer during subculture, may soon possess different morphological and physiological entities. So in nature a species may, owing to the different selective pressures of different niches, come to exist in more than one form, each being adapted particularly to its individual niche. Genetical clones of a fungal species are known to occur in soil in distinct forms in different environments (e.g., Durbin, 1959; Papavizas and Davey, 1962). In other situations a fungus species may in nature form a heterokaryotic pool from which peculiarly suitable adapted forms may arise by selection by particular environments (Buxton, 1960). One result of these phenomena is that cultural features by themselves are inadequate to properly describe an organism, and there is a need with fungi, as Winogradsky envisaged with bacteria, for a taxonomic classification that takes into account ecological as well as cultural features.

II. IMPORTANT CONCEPTS

The study of terrestrial ecology of fungi has during its development been particularly aided by the formulation of several concepts explaining some of the significant processes that operate. These concepts can also be applied to the ecology of other types of organisms, and therefore contribute to general ecological theory. The more important of these concepts are outlined here.

A. Inoculum Potential

The term inoculum potential has been used in plant pathology in more than one sense and the history of the term is set out clearly by Garrett (1960). The most useful meaning is that which Garrett (1956) defined as "the energy for growth of a fungus (or other micro-organism) available for colonization of a substrate at the surface of the substrate to be colonized." The concept was first used in connection with the infection of hosts by pathogens. A host exerts a physical and chemical resistance to fungal penetration (the host resistance), and the chance of a fungal growing point successfully penetrating the host surface is better when it has a greater growth energy or inoculum potential. With active mycelium this may come about through better environmental conditions (for example, nutrition, or through more hyphae of the same sort attacking at one point). With a propagular inoculum larger propagules or more of them may give a higher inoculum potential.

Not only living hosts, but also dead substrata, can exert a resistance to colonization. This *substratum resistance* is equivalent in its ecological effect, if not in its mode of action, to the host resistance of a living organism. There are at least three possible sources of substratum resistance. First, it may be a residual host resistance carried over from the living host into moribund tissue for a limited period, in which case it will have its highest level initially and subsequently declne. Second, it may be a result of the production of external toxic metabolites by microorganisms already active in earlier stages of substratum succession, in which case it may fluctuate in intensity with time. Last, it may be due to an initial refractoriness in the substrate materials, and require a certain "starter" energy to be expended before any useful energy can be got from it. In this case the degree of substratum resistance may increase progressively during substratum succession as the more easily utilized substrates disappear. A saprophyte, in order to colonize the substratum, must have a sufficiently high inoculum potential to balance against the substratum resistance. The possession of a higher inoculum potential will permit the colonization of more difficult substrata.

B. Competitive Saprophytic Ability

This concept also has been discussed in detail by Garrett (1956, 1963). He defines it as "the summation of physiological characteristics that make for success in competitive colonization of substrates." The important point is that the colonization is competitive. Many fungi when in pure culture are able to utilize substrata that in nature they are unable to colonize. The reason for this failure in nature, and therefore for the more restricted range of activities there as opposed to laboratory culture, is that other more successful organisms are present, possibly gaining entry first, and certainly actively excluding the less successful organisms. This exclusion occurs as a result of antagonism, which is discussed on p. 13.

Garrett (1950) lists four general attributes that are likely to contribute to a high degree of competitive saprophytic ability. These are (1) rapid germination of spores and a high rate of hyphal growth, both favoring rapid colonization; (2) good enzyme production, which favors rapid and extensive substrate utilization; (3) production of substances toxic to other organisms, which may reduce competition for the available substrates; and (4) tolerance of antibiotic substances produced by other organisms, this property enabling the fungus to be saprophytically active even in the presence of competitors able to produce the substances mentioned in (3) above. The first two of these characteristics will be advantageous in any circumstance where sufficient amounts of utilizable substrates are available to support a high degree of activity. This means, in effect, the early to middle stages of substratum succession. It has already been indicated that where substrates are available only slowly or in small quantity a low rate of metabolism and a correspondingly low rate of growth may be an advantage. The third property is probably of particular advantage in the very early stages of substratum succession where there are still few organisms present, and where the readily available energy-yielding material is at its maximum and may support the vigorous growth that can produce these substances. In later stages of decomposition more organisms will be present in the substratum, and there may be a relatively high level of toxic substances residually present together with those concurrently being produced. Under such circumstances the fourth property listed will be of most importance, its possession being necessary for activity before any of the other three characters can be exhibited.

The concept of competitive saprophytic ability has been much used recently and has stimulated a great deal of valuable work. Generalized statements of competitive saprophytic ability in respect of individual fungi can have broad validity. Thus it can be said that fungi of very low competitive saprophytic ability do not survive as saprophytes in soil generally, and therefore need some protection against the antagonism that prevents their successful activity there. Many such fungi depend upon a host for this protection, the host acting as suitable substratum and also excluding potential antagonists. The fungus has here exchanged tolerance to antagonism for tolerance to host resistance. Such organisms have been described by Garrett (1956) as *ecologically obligate parasites* in that, like true obligate parasites, they have no soil ecology, apart from a declining phase after death of their host. Similarly, in a general way a spectrum of competitive saprophytic ability can be envisaged among terrestrial fungi, those with a low value occurring very early in substratum succession and being pioneer colonizers, those with a higher value being able to be active later when mixed culture conditions impose more intense antagonism. However, too often the concept has been used in a vague sense and applied as though each fungus could be assigned an invariable value to apply under all environmental conditions. In fact, the competitive saprophytic ability is not a fixed characteristic for each fungus, but may vary according to the particular environment presented. A fungus with a high competitive saprophytic ability in respect of the colonization of a newly dead plant root may have a low one for a newly available dead fly—different enzymes being involved. Similarly a leaf falling on a soil under one set of conditions of temperature and moisture may be colonized by quite a different microflora from that under other conditions. The immediate conditions influence the competitive saprophytic abilities of the different organisms available to colonize and thus affect the outcome of the selection. For many fungi that have been studied, and assigned on paper a high or low competitive saprophytic ability, we know next to nothing about the conditions under which the competitive saprophytic ability might in fact operate at that level, and how changed conditions might affect this level. A more precise statement of those conditions and how they do affect the competitive saprophytic ability is desirable in future work on this topic.

Competitive saprophytic ability works along with inoculum potential, each being a factor in the successful outcome of colonization. A high inoculum potential may allow a fungus to colonize successfully in the face of competition from another fungus of a higher competitive saprophytic ability under the given environmental conditions, but having a lower inoculum potential at that point.

C. *Antagonism*

Antagonism is the factor that makes for the difference between saprophytic colonization in pure culture and saprophytic colonization in nature where other microorganisms are present. Ecologically obligate parasites, unlike true obligate parasites, are, in axenic culture, capable of colonizing and utilizing dead substrata; it is only in mixed culture in nature that they are unable to colonize or survive saprophytically, and must depend on living hosts. Antagonism is important in terrestrial ecology also because of its role in substratum succession, during which substrata become progressively unsuitable for some colonizers. Along with affecting colonization and amount of activity after colonization, antagonism further affects fungal ecology by influencing survival after activity has ceased.

There are three main ways in which antagonism of one organism toward another can be expressed. *Antibiosis* occurs when one organism introduces into the environment a chemical substance that is toxic to and inhibits the second organism. *Competition* occurs when the two organisms compete for the supply of some feature of the environment that is present in quantities insufficient for both. *Exploitation* occurs when one organism utilizes directly as food the body or part of the body of the second organism. Parasitism and predation both belong to this form of antagonism. All these categories of antagonism exist among fungi in nature, and Park (1960) has discussed in detail their relative importance in fungal ecology. It might here be noted that competition is used in two senses in the literature, one the strict meaning defined here, and the other a general meaning more or less equivalent to antagonism as used here. In most contexts it is possible to know which meaning is intended, but some care should be taken to understand this bifarious usage. It is important also to appreciate that exploitation is the only mechanism that operates by a direct effect of one organism on the other and from which the antagonist obtains direct benefit as a result of its action. The other two mechanisms, antibiosis and competition, operate indirectly through the environment and may therefore influence any other organisms in that environment. In most situations in nature large numbers of microorganisms are present in the environment and the outcome of the antagonisms is, as a result, extraordinarily complex. Probably the most significant form of antagonism in soil is that of antibiosis, not necessarily by specifically active antibiotics but rather by more generally produced toxic external metabolites. The widespread soil fungistasis that has interested a number of workers in recent years is most probably a summation of the production of such substances by the activity of microbes generally in the soil. Park (1967) discusses and explains some of these points in more detail.

D. Saprophytic Survival

Like saprophytic colonization, saprophytic survival occurs specifically under conditions of antagonism. Garrett (1944) used the term in connection with a parasite that had colonized living host tissue to describe its survival in an active mycelial form after death of the tissues of the host. Saprophytic colonization, by contrast, refers to the entry into already dead substratum material in the presence of antagonism. Most parasites that are not true obligate parasites probably survive for some time in an active condition in the tissues after death of the host, but the duration varies enormously with the species of pathogen, and is related among other things to its competitive saprophytic ability. While Garrett defined this concept of saprophytic survival in respect of parasites it can also be applied to survival of fungi that have previously saprophytically colonized a material. Caldwell (1963), in a study of fungi that over a two-year period colonized woody substrata in soil, has shown that some species appear, fairly rapidly reach a peak, and then decline in the frequency with which they can be isolated from the material. Other species appear gradually and remain more or less constantly present throughout an extended period. As in the original concept, where some pathogens, in tissues colonized when living, continue activity after the tissue's death and show saprophytic survival, while others soon cease activity and persist, if at all, only by residual propagules, so saprophytic colonizers may be similarly differentiated in their behavior, some continuing saprophytic activity for long periods and so surviving, while others soon become inactive and produce resting structures.

Survival as inactive structures has been described as *dormant survival* as opposed to saprophytic survival, but it could be useful under certain circumstances to differentiate between survival of resting structures that on the one hand are truly dormant in the physiological sense of being incapable of germination owing to immaturity or to endogenous inhibition, and those that on the other hand could immediately germinate given favorable conditions but that remain inhibited by environmental antagonism (antibiosis). The term *inactive survival* can cover both these conditions, *dormant survival* being particularly appropriate for the first, and *inhibited survival* for the second. Related phenomena under the headings constitutional and exogenous dormancy are discussed by Sussman in Volume II, Chapter 23.

E. *The Half-Life Concept*

This concept was developed by Yarwood and Sylvester (1959). They stated that viruses and plant parasites in an unfavorable environment decline in numbers at a logarithmic rate, and that in such a situation there can be no accurate statement of the duration of total longevity. The size of the initial population, the slope of the curve, and the sensitivity of any methods for detecting numbers all determine the useful end point in the construction of a declining population curve. The sort of calculation made by these authors can be applied to a population of resting structures of a fungal saprophyte showing inactive survival in an antagonistic environment. There is no point at which one can say survival has ceased, but ecological survival will terminate when the inoculum potential of the population has fallen below that necessary for successful colonization of substrata that become available. In inactive survival, then, the effective time of survival is governed by the size of the initial population, the amount of antagonism and hence the rate of decline, the degree of suitability of substrata becoming available, their frequency, and the amount of competition for colonization of these substrata. During and soon after successful exploitation of substrata the inoculum will be high because residual propagules are produced by the mycelium. In nature, then, the numbers of an organism of this sort at a restricted site will, when represented as a graph with time, be a curve rapidly rising to a peak and then more slowly declining to a trough with abrupt transitions between the rising and declining phases. The distances between the troughs represents the time intervals between availability of successive substrata. A steep decline of numbers in a habitat will necessarily be matched in any successful fungus by a steep rise to a high peak or by a relatively frequent substratum availability. A slower decline will allow a fungus to survive when substrata are less frequently available. Thus high resistance of residual propagules to the effects of antagonism and enforced decline is an effective adaptation to survival just as is a high rate of metabolism and reproduction.

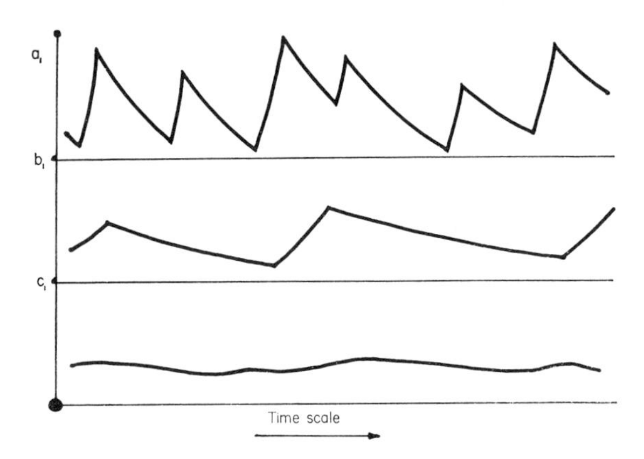

FIG. 1. Schematic population curves for fungi from different stages of substratum decomposition. Curve *a*: Fungi active in early stages of succession: high rate of metabolic activity and rapid reproduction, but rapid decline and need for frequent substratum availability. Curve *b*: Fungi characteristic of a later stage: less rapid reproduction matched by a slower decline and a greater resistance to antagonism. Curve *c*: Saprophytic survival in soil by fungi with somatic resistance to antagonism: no clear-cut logarithmic phases or half-life for inactive survival.

A high level of metabolism and reproduction is the adaptation shown by many early colonizers like *Neurospora* and *Rhizopus* described earlier, while the high resistance type of adaptation is that shown by species active somewhat later in succession and which take longer to mobilize substrates and to reproduce, but which also decline less rapidly. These types of behavior are diagrammed in Fig. 1.

High resistance to antagonism may be shown by somatic structures as well as by propagules, and this property may indeed allow lengthy saprophytic survival, in which case the half-life concept is not applicable. With organisms showing this adaptation the population curves with time may show some fluctuation but no clear-cut logarithmic trend. Warcup (1957), by isolating and identifying viable pieces of mycelium from soils and studying their distribution with time found that some species showed short periods of activity and persisted as inactive propagules between these periods, the periods of activity corresponding to the availability of readily decomposable material. Other species, by contrast, were present as viable and probably active mycelium constantly throughout the investigation and showed no marked increase in frequency during the decomposition of plant residues.

III. FACTORS INFLUENCING FUNGAL ECOLOGY

In any local environment there will normally be several types of substratum, and each of these may have a number of microhabitats each with its characteristic and peculiar microbial community. Reasons of this sort have led students of fungal ecology to be very much concerned with the factors influencing behavior within microhabitats. The overall environmental factors as influences have, in consequence, been somewhat neglected. But the major and obvious factors in a local environment are important and should be considered. Garrett (1963) says, "In the ultimate analysis, it is the physico-chemical characteristics of a habitat that determine the kind of community that will occupy it. But the precise composition of that community at any time will be the result of competition between different species of organisms." The first determinants of a community are the nature of the substratum and the conditions prevailing around it. These will select from among the organisms available, favoring some at the expense of others, and excluding some altogether. Only then, among those that are able to develop, will antagonism operate in the second and most studied phase of the organization of community structure. The factors that influence the course of these developments of a community are of course largely the same as those studied by ecologists of other groups of organisms. The effects of these factors on individual fungi have been described in previous articles in these volumes. Nutrition is the primary factor of course. In many substrata more than one type of material is available and many fungi may be potentially capable of development. In a few substrata the commoner nutrients may be absent, and the dominant nutrient be suitable for only a small number of fungi. The colonization of such restrictive substrata can be of particular interest, but it is simpler in principle than that of most substrata. The availability of nutrients within a substratum as a function of time is, of course, not constant, but generally undergoes movement in one direction, namely toward more and more intractable and refractory substrates, and eventually tends toward nil. A substratum with a nutrient content unsuitable for a particular fungus may, however, by the activity of other microbes, subsequently become suitable, as explained later, so that the trend is not uniformly toward lesser availability of food.

Temperature of the local environment has an important immediate influence in that fungi with limits outside the range are automatically excluded. There is also the less immediate effect whereby temperature will have some selective action among fungi whose acceptable range falls within that of the environment, those fungi whose optimum comes nearest to the prevailing temperature being favored most. In nature, of course, temperature is not static but fluctuates to some extent diurnally, and usually to a much greater extent seasonally. This contributes, along with fluctuations in other factors, to the common situation where habitats are rarely optimum for the same organism for very long, and may if the fluctuations are at all frequent and regular, give a cyclical pattern to the community.

Water is necessary for all forms of life. As an environmental factor it acts upon fungi in several ways, affecting directly as free water the growing mycelium. The amount of water also indirectly affects the availability of nutrients and the concentration of toxic substances. A drier situation may have a higher concentration of some nutrients, but also a higher concentration of some inhibitory factors. Humidity of the atmosphere is also important in affecting the morphogenesis of fungi. The nature and size of hyphae, their degree of branching, the intensity of sporulation, and even the type of reproduction, are affected by this factor. The nature of the substratum may also affect the water availability through its own attraction for moisture, some substrata allowing easier uptake by microorganisms than others of the same moisture content. Mycologists who have been interested in this factor have usually characterized a soil by its moisture-holding capacity, a property which allows for some differences of this sort. Recently Griffin (1963) has reviewed the importance of water in the ecology of soil fungi and has argued that moisture-holding capacity is a poor criterion for comparisons between substrata and that moisture characteristics of soils should be more clearly defined. The criterion of moisture characteristic allows both for moisture content and also for the suction tension of the soil. Apart from this overall measure for soil as a whole little is known about the water retentivity and characteristics of different substrata within the soil. This is obviously an important property and an understanding of it would seem important in ecological studies. Osmotic pressure of the soil solution is probably not an important influence but when it is excessively high it may inhibit some of the water molds that can occur in normally moist soils.

The water content of soil may inversely affect gaseous exchange in soil and associated substrata. Fungi, when active, consume oxygen and produce carbon dioxide. Gaseous diffusion in normal soil is somewhat restricted; in the presence of excess water the restriction is even greater. Penman (1940) has discussed these aspects in detail. Within soil the proportion of oxygen in the soil atmosphere is commonly lower than that in the air above the soil but, except under very wet or flooded conditions, is adequate for the growth and activity of most fungi. The lower concentration of oxygen in the soil atmosphere is less likely to be an important ecological influence than is the higher carbon dioxide concentration, which varies from 0.3 to 10% in reasonably porous, nonflooded, unamended soils but can rise higher on compaction, flooding, or with intense microbial activity (Griffin, 1963). Many fungi are markedly affected by higher carbon dioxide levels of the sort that have been recorded in soil, and this can be an important factor in selection of species composing communities (Durbin, 1959).

The pH of the substratum may have an important influence on fungal ecology. The overall composition of the microflora in respect of bacteria and actinomycetes, as against fungi, is related to this factor. The first two groups function better in neutral to alkaline conditions, whereas fungi show best activity under acid conditions. However, most fungi have a rather wide range of tolerance of pH and their growth curve over most of the range is somewhat flat-topped so that while an exceptional pH outside the range of some fungi may be an eliminative factor, within the range small changes may not have such a great effect as concurrent changes in other factors.

The overall physical and chemical characteristics of the soil may have a less direct effect than the characteristics of the substratum itself, but they are still extremely important in fungal ecology. Not only must temperature, moisture content, aeration, base-exchange properties, and pH be considered, but also mechanical properties such as soil texture, pore space, crumb structure and tilth which influence the magnitude of effect of some of the other factors, such as water and oxygen availability and temperature. In the case of this last factor a good tilth or a good organic content can shield the surface of the soil against the effects of insolation and can significantly reduce temperature at a short distance below the soil surface. It may also reduce in amount the deleterious effect of insolation acting as radiation, not simply as temperature. Direct radiation in high doses has a harmful and even lethal effect on fungi. Soil structure and texture also affect soil pore space. In respect to fungi not only is the total space important, but the size of individual pores and pore necks has an effect. With sufficiently large pore spaces fungi may reproduce more or less normally in soil as in laboratory culture, with condiophores, etc. Where pore spaces are small the development of these structures is not possible. Pore necks if very small may reduce the amount of spore dispersal in soil by water.

The biotic environment, which itself is also controlled in part by the physical and chemical factors listed, in turn influences the fungi present. Plants and animals may alter some of the other factors by providing or removing nutrients, substrata and water, by improving soil texture and tilth, by improving drainage and gaseous exchange, by increasing humidity and decreasing the water loss from the soil surface, and by reducing insolation at the soil surface. Larger organisms may also affect dispersal of fungal propagules, sometimes impeding dispersal and sometimes assisting it.

It has been pointed out that the factors operating in an environment are rarely constant but may fluctuate irregularly, oscillate cyclically, or show a progressive trend. The system is dynamic and the changes may be relatively great, with large alterations in the characteristics of microhabitats and hence of the microflora. Biotic influences in general confer a greater degree of stability on the microhabitats and reduce in amount the changes in factors within an environment. In other words the presence of other organisms has a buffering or damping effect. The result of plant and animal activities through root growth, leaf and stem shading, root secretions, burrowing, mixing, comminution and trituration, and the addition of debris as substrata is to reduce the spatial and temporal discontinuities which interrupt fungal activity, and to make environments more generally favorable for more fungi, and thus to increase antagonism. Man's actions fall into this category. However, the manipulation of soil by mankind tends even more than the activities of the other biota to make for uniformity by reducing the range of variation in microhabitats. It may even reduce the number of species that can survive, while allowing an increase in total biomass.

Not only do environmental factors act differently on different fungi, and thus operate in the selection of species available for community evolution, but they may also act differently upon different phases in the life history of a single species. Thus germination, growth, reproduction, dissemination and survival may not all be influenced in the same direction by a given factor at a given level. Germination is commonly more demanding in terms of many environmental conditions (but not always for nutrients) than is growth. Conditions inimical to growth may actually help to initiate and favor reproduction. Germination in dormant spores is sometimes stimulated by an extreme environment that would be most harmful to germ tubes and mycelium (see Chapter 17). Survival and dissemination occur under conditions that inhibit germination. An alteration of environmental conditions between the production of a spore and its germination is almost always necessary, since spores often fail to germinate in the identical conditions under which they are produced, even in culture.

It will be seen from some of these different relationships that individual species and even forms of fungi have adapted themselves to the changing dynamic environment in which they occur. This is often particularly obvious in the case of reproduction, dissemination, and survival. There are obvious relationships between fungal morphology for these processes and the local environmental conditions. The timing of the phases of life cycles is also often particularly appropriate to changes in environmental conditions, particularly seasonal fluctuations. Adaptation of growth processes of individual fungi to special conditions is also found and is responsible for some of the unusual tolerances to extreme conditions. For instance, a few fungi are able to make somatic growth at unusually low oxygen tensions, e.g., *Blastocladiella pringsheimiana, Penicillium roquefortii,* and a number of yeasts. Others, such as *Fusarium oxysporum,* may grow at unusually high carbon dioxide levels. Some species, i.e., *Rhizoctonia solani* [*Corticium solani*] (Durbin, 1959) show a clonal differentiation depending on tolerance to carbon dioxide levels, and different clones occur at different depths in soil. Adaptations to biotic factors is common. Disease-causing fungi exemplify this particularly well, but similar biotic adaptations may occur in nonpathogens. Adaptation to the seed-borne habit is very helpful to a fungus in assisting dispersal and the finding of a substratum, and not all seed-borne fungi are pathogenic for their carrier species. *Serpula lacrimans,* while not a pathogen, can cause considerable economic damage to man's economy by its destruction of timber, and this species is fairly uncommon outside man's economy. It is adapted to the more or less equable temperature and the protection from draughts that buildings provide. Pigmentation, particularly of dispersal spores, is an effective and rather common adaptation to tolerance to radiation, and the same adaptation occurs in mycelium of fungi growing habitually in situations where they are exposed to radiation (see Volume I, Chapter 24). In forests, where airborne dispersal may be less effective than in open communities, a number of characteristic basidiomycetes and ascomycetes fructify underground and are adapted to dispersal by subterranean animals rather than by turbulent air currents. On mountains at high altitudes some basidiomycetes have xeromorphic fruiting bodies which show spongy layers, small size, resupinate habit, hard context, and occur low on the host tree, particularly in clefts in the bark. By adaptations such as these particular fungi have extended their range of tolerance to certain environmental factors.

IV. DISTRIBUTION OF FUNGI

Review accounts of the geographical distribution of fungi have been written by Bisby (1933, 1943), and there is also a useful account by Wolf and Wolf (1947). These accounts and Chapter 18 of this volume should be consulted by anyone interested in the topic. It is, however, clear that relatively little detail is available that helps toward a general knowledge of fungal distribution in the world as a whole. Reliable information depends, of course, in the first place on the world distribution of mycologists, which itself is far from even, and many of these have special interests rather than general ones. A second limitation is that much of the information that is available comes from collections and records only, and little work has been done to supplement it by analytical studies of the factors affecting the activity and appearance of individual fungi or groups of fungi. Moreover for many fungi, particularly agarics, gasteromycetes, and many ascomycetes, the records or collection data are of sporulating stages only, and although these do depend on some prior activity this can be misleading since conditions for fructification may be rather different from those for vegetative activity and may give a one-sided picture. For some fungi even the habitat for fructification may be different from that for somatic and trophic activity. This is seen clearly in some of the slime molds which migrate to a suitable place for fruiting. Perhaps the one valid generalization on distribution that can be made is that many fungi are extremely widespread. An example of this is the fact that there are more total phanerogams in the world than described species of fungi, but in any one area there are almost always more fungi than phanerogams. Spores and propagules are produced and dispersed very efficiently (see Volume II, Chapters 21 and 22), and resting stages are often long-lived. The fungi are dispersed by the natural agencies of air and water, on seeds, by animals and human agencies over very large, often worldwide, areas. Where conditions are suitable the fungi arriving may be successful. Distribution therefore depends more than with most organisms on local conditions, and where favorable conditions occur, there the fungus is likely to be found. There is no good evidence that fungi are limited geographically by barriers to dispersal as is often the case with higher plants and animals. Even fungi of special habitats which, in consequence, are only occasional or even rare, may nevertheless be widespread. Pugh and Mathison (1962) discuss the widespread occurrence of certain keratinophilic fungi even in soils in which keratin is difficult of access. Some fungi are widely distributed even where the mode of dispersal would not seem obviously well adapted to this end. Thus the water mold *Allomyces arbuscula* occurs in soil from all continents. Although it is relatively rare to find endemic fungal species they do occur. *Phymatotrichum omnivorum* is a plant pathogen that is confined to the southwestern United States. Similarly the human pathogens *Histoplasma capsulatum* and *Coccidioides immitis* occur in restricted areas of the United States and elsewhere. In these examples, however, the extreme localization is related to particularly suitable local conditions for activity and survival, and not to any limitations of dispersal.

Substratum is one of the most obvious determinants of distribution and must be the primary factor in world distribution of fungi. This is seen very clearly in the case of pathogens where their range does not extend beyond that of the hosts and may be limited further by other environmental factors that are not favorable. Hosts are commonly able to grow in regions outside those favorable for the development of the pathogen. The same considerations apply also for saprophytes. The distribution of coprophilous fungi, for instance, is related to the distribution of herbivores of the correct habits and constitution. Saprophytes are usually less specific in substratum requirements than are pathogens, so saprophytes in general have a wider distribution than pathogens. But since the nutrient condition of the substratum is only one of the relevant factors a particular substratum may support different fungal populations in different areas. In this respect immediate local differences may be greater than continental differences. It has for instance been estimated that more than 70% of North American agarics and polypores are also found in Europe, but that latitude exerts an important influence on the distribution of particular common species within these two great areas. Thus *Stropharia depilata* is boreal in range while *Amanita caesarea* is temperate, each occurring in both continents. Gasteromycetes tend to be widely represented in both the Eastern and Western hemispheres, particularly in dryish areas, but the group shows a pattern whereby the Lycoperdales is mostly temperate while the Phallales is predominantly tropical. Similarly in the Ascomycetes members of the Xylariales in both hemispheres are more common in the tropical zone than in temperate and cooler regions. The fungus:bacterium ratio of the microflora of soils, independently of geographical area, increases from the equator toward higher latitudes. Temperature may be one of the factors in these general correlations, but few detailed studies of the conditions necessary for different phases of the life histories have been made. Such studies are essential for reasonable interpretation of some of the observations concerning geographical distribution.

Since it is local conditions that are primarily important in this connection, it is not surprising that large discontinuities occur in the distribution of some species. Where the appropriate conditions occur, the fungus is likely to be found despite its absence from intermediate regions. Desert soils all over the world have a basically similar fungal population, with a high proportion of species from the Dematiaceae and Sphaeropsidales. High mountains all show common features, the fungi of alpine regions in lower latitudes resembling those of the arctic regions, and showing more micromycetes than macromycetes.

Some of the recorded discontinuities in distribution are extremely large, and often mycologists have been impressed by the appearance of a fungus in one place at one time and then its absence or apparent absence for quite long periods before its next recorded appearance. *Urnula geaster,* an ascomycete with a very distinctive and striking fruit body, and a very obvious species, was recorded from Texas in 1893, and next in Japan in 1938. Another ascomycete, *Sarcoscypha minuscula,* is recorded only from Portugal and from California. Temporal discontinuities can be great, even in one continent. *Eremascus albus* was first described in Europe in 1883 and then not reported again until 1950. Although examples like this may represent extremes of the natural dynamic and changing situation, and be due to local and sporadic occurrence of conditions suitable for activity, it is more probable that incomplete recording is responsible. Other members of the family containing the two discomycetes mentioned above are far from frequently recorded fruiting. The reliance with many fungi upon records of fruiting structures is a serious disadvantage to their study. Distribution can be much more readily studied with those fungi that can easily be isolated in culture from active or resting stages in soil or other substrata. Such isolation methods give a much more reliable picture, and for many fungi where these methods have been used the history is one of wide distribution with only sporadic activity when conditions are appropriate and the substratum is in the right stage of decomposition. For the remainder of the time, survival occurs as a resting stage or by dispersal of a large number of usually small propagules which find the appropriate substratum at another site.

A number of commentators on fungal distribution have pointed out that some species show a considerable amount of permanence at a site while others are essentially transient. This may reflect a true state of affairs in that some sites provide a rapid succession of a fairly limited range of substrata, whereas others show wide fluctuations in the types of substrata that become available. This last condition of low site stability is particularly common in the early stages of environmental succession. Another factor that could contribute to these differences is that some fungi have broad limits for substratum and other conditions, whereas others are very restricted by the need for specific requirements. Differences of this sort could account for some of the differences between "settlers" and "tourists," but it is more than probable that some of the described contrasts are the result of differences in reliability of methods for detecting occurrence. Better methods for isolating and detecting individual fungal species could rapidly lead to a better understanding of their behavior in respect to breadth of distribution and constancy of occurrence in sites.

V. SPECIAL HABITATS AND HABITAT SELECTION

The variety of terrestrial habitats occupied by fungi is extremely large, since fungi are notorious as versatile opportunists, and almost anything that can be decomposed to yield energy will find some fungi able to colonize it. There is no point, therefore, in attempting to describe comprehensively the unusual habitats that are known to support fungi, but an account of some of these might be useful and illustrative of certain features. In this connection it should be emphasized that habitat is not substratum only, but includes other features. Any habitat that remains available for colonization for any length of time, say more than 1 or 2 days, develops a community that is more or less characteristic of it. This community comes about by selection, as described in more detail in the next section, but it is relevant here to note that the main selection may initially operate from the nonfungal part of the habitat. This is particularly the case when the habitat contains some unusual feature, such as a refractory substrate, or some toxic compound that limits or prevents the growth and activity of most fungi, but to which some fungi are or can become adapted. The study of such special habitats can be particularly interesting, and there are not usually any great difficulties since appropriate selective isolation techniques based on the special features of the habitat can generally be devised. An opposite type of situation arises in the development of community structure in relation to a habitat that is initially potentially suitable for any of a large number of available fungal species. Here the selection operates through factors from the fungi and other colonizing organisms, through processes of antagonism, so that some of the colonizers become successful and others are eliminated, while still others may be prevented from making any headway. Here, biological antagonisms, rather than habitat features, serve the formative role of integrating the community and determining its composition. It is in such habitats that the most complex biological interplay occurs, and its outcome may be very difficult to elucidate. Habitats of both sorts may progress through stages serally, and show a more or less well defined succession, but such a progression of stages is more particularly characteristic of environments in which the habitat itself initially exerts little significant selection. It is in such general habitats that the phenomenon has been most studied, and discussion of it is reserved for the following section.

Living tissues of organisms can be regarded as one special habitat of the type being considered here, the colonizers being parasites. Fungi that parasitize plants or animals have been extensively studied. The substratum here is clearly unfavorable for activity of most fungi, in fact, the host resistance of the animal or plant serves just that end, to eliminate by chemical or mechanical means most microorganisms in the environment. But certain fungi as well as some bacteria are able to overcome, avoid, or tolerate these defense mechanisms and to use the host as their substratum. Details of these relationships are given in Chapters 6, 7, 8 and 9. However, when the host defenses are completely overcome by the fungus, the invader may rapidly cause death of the tissues and the habitat then becomes general and open to colonization by other fungi. In associations where the fungus remains under a degree of control by the host defense mechanisms, yet is somewhat active, then it often occurs as the sole microbial occupant of that substratum. This is a very special habitat and one in which there is no microbial antagonism at all. Correlated with this is the fact that fungi adapted to this role are often found to be those most sensitive to microbial antagonism and appear therefore to depend on the host resistance as a protection from other more successfully competitive fungi. This situation may be true also of fungi from other "special" habitats. During evolution toward tolerance to rigorous and exclusive habitat factors, there has been a reduction or even an absence of selection pressure for tolerance to microbial antagonism, and such tolerance usually is found to be low in fungi typical of special habitats.

Fungi need not be parasitic and endophytic in a host organism to have a special habitat provided by that organism. At the surface of living organisms is a region that is intermediate in its selective action. Conditions here may favor some fungi and exclude others, so that special niches arise. Thus, at the surface of plant roots there is the rhizosphere effect giving an often characteristic flora. On leaves there occurs a similar and analagous phyllosphere effect. The rhizosphere has been a topic of interest since the turn of the century, and most work on it has been done with bacteria, but there is abundant evidence for selective effects of the rhizosphere on fungal populations about the roots of plants (Starkey, 1958). The roots of plants alter the soil by secreting substances that can act as major or minor nutrients, by sloughing off dead parts and by parts dying, by altering the pH, by altering the $CO_2:O_2$ ratio, by secreting toxic substances (host resistance), and by removing substances from the soil. The sum of these effects, each of which may be small, alters the soil and in turn the microflora. The most obvious result is a usually higher number of microorganisms in the rhizosphere region, and the difference between this number and that in normal soil is given as the R:S ratio. But there are qualitative as well as quantitative differences between the two populations. Thus some fungi are inhibited by particular secretions from plant roots, while others are able to develop and may be stimulated. These quantitative and qualitative differences may be important to the higher plant. Not only may different species of plants affect soil differently and therefore possess different rhizosphere floras, but different cultivars of one species may also have very different effects. There may be among the fungi comprising the rhizosphere flora a fairly high proportion potentially pathogenic to the supporting plant. Species of *Alternaria, Fusarium, Helminthosporium,* and *Pythium* are commonly isolated from this habitat. This might be expected on the basis that those organisms have some degree of tolerance to chemicals conferring host resistance. In some investigated cases, however, root secretions favor organisms antagonistic to pathogens and thereby promote the development of a rhizosphere flora that helps to protect against infection. In this way some forms of host resistance are based on the rhizosphere effect.

Plant leaves, like roots, secrete substances from their surface, and spores fall on leaves. There they may be inhibited or may be able to develop. Most do not develop but some do but without being able to penetrate internally or cause disease. These constitute the phyllosphere population, which appears to be more restricted in numbers of species than is the rhizosphere, and is certainly more clearly defined physically in that there is not a continuous gradient outward from the surface of the organ as there is in the rhizosphere which makes the delimitation of zones difficult. In the phyllosphere yeastlike, budding forms seem to have an advantage, and the commonly predominating fungi possess this property. The mirror yeasts, *Sporobolomyces, Bullera,* and *Tilletiopsis,* and the mycelial fungi *Aureobasidium* and *Cladosporium* are particularly common on leaf surfaces and occur also on the bark of twigs and branches. The number of the fungi in these habitats is relatively low during the early part of the life of the organism but increases rapidly with aging of the organ and reaches its maximum at death of the organ. The increase is probably connected with the increase in humidity in the lower, more crowded parts of the plant, with the increasing amount of nutrients excreted, and possibly with the decreasing potency of the host resistance mechanism. Ruinen (1961) has reviewed the facts published on this habitat.

The surface of animals can also form a special habitat. Most fungi are excluded from this type of site by chemical secretions, but a few find a favorable niche which is thereby relatively free from antagonism. Dermatophytes (see Chapter 8) that inhabit the keratin of hair, nails, or the horny layer of skin are often considered to be parasites, but are by analogy more like a dermosphere flora in their ecological relationships living on dead tissue at the surface and being protected from antagonism by an unusual site. A number of yeasts also inhabit animal surfaces. *Lipomyces starkei* can under moist conditions develop very quickly on man within a few hours of bathing. *Candida albicans,* while most dramatic in its disease-producing role, is usually a commensal on moist surfaces of the human body and is able to tolerate the chemical conditions that exclude most other fungi.

The special habitats discussed so far in this section represent selection by exclusion of the majority of available organisms by toxicity of the substratum. The second major category excludes by providing a substratum that is suitable for a few specially adapted fungi but unsuitable by its lack of appropriate nutrients for the majority. Lignin is a substance that fairly few microorganisms appear able to decompose on any significant scale. Nevertheless among the species of fungi that cause tree diseases and decay of timber there are, in addition to those causing brown rots (corrosion rots) by the removal of cellulose, those causing white rots (destruction rots) by removal of lignin as well as much, if not all, of the cellulose. White rot fungi are not usually found to be active in general habitats: timber and related substrata form their special habitat. Not only do they display special enzymatic properties, but they form strands or rhizomorphs that help to provide a high inoculum potential since some starter energy is commonly necessary to get the process of decomposition initiated. The fungi in this category are mostly basidiomycetes, particularly agarics and polypores.

Keratin is another substrate that in nature supports a rather limited and defined fungal flora. Feathers, hair, hoof, and horn occur infrequently but nevertheless consistently in some natural sites. Some chytrids are found inhabiting these materials but more characteristic are the ascomycetes, *Onygena equina, O. corvina, Gymnoascus gypseum, Ctenomyces serratus,* and those members of the Fungi Imperfecti associated with these perfect states, i.e., *Keratinomyces ajelloi, Microsporum gypseum,* and *Trichophyton terrestre.*

Paints and plastic surfaces are relatively resistant to decay, but, not uncommonly, in use they show some decomposition by a number of characteristic fungi, particularly *Aureobasidium pullulans, Phoma violacea,* and *Cladosporium herbarum.* At least one of the properties necessary for success in this habitat is resistance to desiccation and to radiation, a property needed in common with the population of the phyllosphere and of soils of deserts. The fungal flora of all three habitats have species in common. The fungal flora of paint must also be able to withstand toxic substances and to derive nutrients from it, although experiments have shown that at least some of the nutrients come from other sources such as wood underlying the paint. Thus painted glass surfaces were shown not to support fungal growth. References to this topic are given by Reynolds (1950) and Eveleigh (1961).

Fungi are extremely adaptable, and even for seemingly most unlikely substrata there is usually some fungus that can decompose them and make some growth. Particularly in laboratories is it easy to acquire a collection in almost pure culture without special precautions as to sterility, as for example, in reagent solutions exposed to contamination for some time. Recent collections by the author include fungi growing reasonably well in 0.1 *M* citric acid, in 1% tannic acid, and in 10% Tween 80. In cases like these not only is the fungus able to use some of the unusual substratum for energy, but also it has a tolerance for it that other fungi may not have. Under such conditions it is probable that partial starvation growth is occurring, the fungus moving the cytoplasm forward within the growing hyphal tips and synthesizing new cell wall material, leaving empty cell walls behind as described earlier. Some fungi are able to make visible growth under conditions often surprisingly low in nutrients. Under humid conditions apparently clean glass may support fungal growth in this way, and in the tropics lenses may be damaged permanently by the etching effect of secretions from fungal hyphae (Smith, 1946). At the opposite extreme there can be selection by high concentration of nutrients. A few fungi are osmophilic and can grow, and in fact sometimes grow best, in solutions of high osmotic pressure. Some species of *Aspergillus* and *Penicillium* show this well, and are found growing on substrata like jam, leather, paper, where there is little free water. *Aspergillus glaucus* is common on dried fruit in damp cellars and larders. Some species of yeasts are typically osmophilic, particularly species of *Zygosaccharomyces,* some of which can grow in saturated sucrose solutions and in the free water condensed on honey or sugars. *Eremascus albus,* which grows well in a 40% sucrose solution, is known from culture collections as isolates derived initially from moldy damp mustard powder in 1950. In the examples of low and high osmotic pressure of the substratum, it is not the type of nutrient that selects and determines the colonizers but its concentration. Nonnutrient selection may operate also in other special habitats. Thus special thermal substrata such as composts and hay, that under moist conditions show "spontaneous" heating, possess fungal colonizers that can be active at higher temperatures than most fungi. Species of *Chaetomium* are commonly found decomposing cellulose in hot compost heaps, and *Aspergillus fumigatus* is particularly characteristic of overheated hay. Thermophilic fungi are discussed in Chapter 4 of this volume.

Special habitats, then, seem to be characterized by having one or more features unsuitable for fungi generally but to which a relatively small number of fungi is adapted. Selection is thus immediate and is based on habitat factors; the community that arises does so by its species possessing in common certain properties adapting them to the special conditions. The selecting and limiting factors may be chemical, like nutrients and toxins, or physical, like temperature, moisture, or osmotic pressure. In some special habitats the initial limiting factors may fail to persist, either for natural reasons as when high temperature subsides in compost, or as an autogenic result of the microbial activities of the selected flora in the habitat, as when toxic factors are converted to inert compounds, or refractory substrates are converted to those readily available to more organisms. In such cases a special habitat may become converted into a general habitat and the potential flora is then no longer limited by the original habitat factors but may be selected from a wider field.

Most dead animal and plant remains or debris that become available contain a variety of carbon sources and other nutrients, and exist at a normal temperature, pressure, and range of moisture, and usually form a general habitat. However, deriving as they do from living and therefore special habitats these substrata may show the transition just described, and soon become colonized by typical members of general communities. Dung of herbivorous animals is a material typically of a sort available to most microorganisms yet it anomalously shows a very special flora that has interested large numbers of mycologists. The reason for this apparent anomaly is the treatment the material has had before being voided by the animal. The high temperature and the digestive enzymes have largely sterilized the material, leaving viable fungal spores of just a few resistant species that had been ingested with the plant food. These species contain members specially adapted, first in having devices to increase the chance of being present on the vegetation that is ingested, and second in their tolerance of conditions in the alimentary canal so that they begin to germinate while still in the hind gut. Thus when the dung is voided these fungi have already made some growth, and in fact are exposed to little antagonism from other organisms. The first colonizers have a large advantage, particularly when, like these forms, they have a rapid growth rate, enzyme production, and utilization of substrates. These special communities are of coprophilous fungi belonging to taxonomically very different groups and show wide morphological differences, but they have important biological and ecological features in common; these include (1) phototropic responses of the reproductive parts which assist in the dispersal of the spores from the humid crevices of the substratum to the surrounding vegetation; (2) large and often deeply pigmented spores, often in mucilage and difficult to germinate in the laboratory, but resistant to the digestive juices of the herbivores and, in fact, sometimes actively stimulated to germinate in the gut. This special community, then, develops not because of especially appropriate conditions of the habitat at the time they are visible to the mycologist, but because of the earlier history of that habitat.

Another habitat that would superficially appear to be generally favorable, but that commonly has a set of special fungi developing, is burnt trees or wood and burnt areas of ground. *Anthracobia* spp., *Pyronema* spp., *Daldinia vernicosa,* and *Nummularia bullardia* are typical examples of fungi having the pyroxylophilous habit. Here the partial sterilization effect of heat may be analogous to the situation described in dung. Again the habitat eventually becomes open to a wider variety of colonizers, and becomes a general habitat.

VI. GENERAL HABITATS AND SERAL SUCCESSION

A. *Substratum Succession and Seral Succession*

General habitats proper differ from special habitats in that they show little special selectivity for certain species initially. In the early phases of their colonization chance determines which species arrive at the surface of the substratum, and it is in the later stages that the community structure, through antagonism and symbiosis, arrives at a more or less integrated condition. The changes that occur may be complex and constitute a continuous process, with a balance among various different forces. Soil, with the litter and debris accumulating on and in it, serves as a good comprehensive example of the general type of habitat. The habitat develops serally from the initial or parent stages by succession, and an understanding of ecology in such a habitat can best be gained by first considering the process of this succession.

With microorganisms there are two distinct levels at which succession can be considered. When a potential substratum becomes available for colonization in an environment a succession of organisms usually colonizes it. This is *substratum succession* and occurs on a small scale within a larger environment. Substratum succession represents a cyclical and continually occurring series of events within the larger system. On the other hand, a whole habitat starting from parent rock material also passes through a succession of phases before arriving at a more or less mature stage. This is *seral succession* and within such a succession a procession of fungal changes occurs often concurrent with and correlated with the changes occurring in other biotic properties of the habitat. Such succession may be primary, when the basic substrata at the start contain no microbially converted material, or secondary, when such material does exist. Secondary seral successions usually occur following some sort of partial or complete sterilization of a habitat by agencies like fire or flood, and the course of succession and the main fungal participants may be very different from those occurring in a primary succession.

B. Primary Sere

The primary succession starting from bare parent rock is determined in its course, and the phases through which it progresses, by the following factors: (1) the nature of the parent rock, (2) the local climate, and (3) the organisms available. Fungal spores are among the first potential colonizers of parent rock since fungi have such efficient dispersal systems. Spores and other propagules are carried in by air currents, water (irrigation, flood, and drainage from higher areas), and birds, insects, and large and small soil animals. Some of these propagules may germinate and produce some mycelium, but mostly there will be very little in the way of suitable substrates, and in consequence spores and resting stages are the dominant elements of this initial phase, the fungal population being largely inactive. The species present at first are likely to be those in nearby habitats, particularly those with high spore production and with efficient spore dispersal, most especially dry spore forms carried in by air currents. Slime spore fungi and mycelial forms might be expected to be less frequent initially, being brought in later on wind-blown soil dust, on seeds as seed-borne fungi, and on debris carried by irrigation or flood, or by animals. From the random selection of the fungi casually available by these agencies there occurs further selection for those able to survive starvation conditions and the physically and chemically unfavorable factors that may exist. Extremes of temperature, water availability, radiation, pH, salt concentrations, and other toxic factors are very common in such habitats in the initial stages of colonization. The longer the period that elapses before the arrival of suitable substrata or of autotrophic organisms able to provide substrata, the greater the selective effect of the environmental factors and also the greater the range of species arriving on which these factors can act. In these early stages the habitat compares well with a special habitat in that selection of community is by extrinsic or habitat factors. Fungi tolerant of the existing unfavorable conditions will come to predominate. Selection here, however, will operate on inactive phases, rather than on the active phase as happens in special habitats. From these considerations it is seen that efficient and widespread dispersal, ability in the inactive state to withstand adverse physical conditions, and tolerance of starvation conditions will be the features most characteristic of the fungi found in this phase of succession.

The change from the bare parent rock and the increase in organic nutrients in the environment derives, of course, mainly from the activities of higher living organisms. In their effects on succession it is convenient to separate the effects of the dead organic nutrient material from the effects of living organisms themselves. Dead nutrient materials arrive in any of several ways. The larger animals pass over the area and die, leave droppings or shed parts of themselves. Smaller animals may from adjacent areas move through the soil and underneath the surface and similarly add their bodies or parts thereof to the rock material. Plant parts—leaves, twigs, fruits, and seeds—may be blown in from elsewhere. Along with available substrata of this sort there may come additional fungi, as in the case of dung or leaves, that may be well adapted to the substratum but not necessarily to the habitat. Thus specialized fungi may grow and fructify but may, in the absence of vegetation, find little future for survival. The fungi already in the habitat and lying inactive will be stimulated into activity and attempt to colonize such substrata as arrive. The number of species, as of individuals, present in the early stages will be quite low, but organisms able to germinate, grow rapidly, and utilize the readily decomposed substrates as quickly as possible will have an advantage, particularly if they can then produce a crop of further propagules able to rest until another substratum arrives. Possession of some of the properties contributing to comparative saprophytic ability are of direct advantage here. In addition if some of these organisms produce an antibiotic substance to which others are susceptible these producers may appropriate a greater share of the available energy. It follows, of course, that other organisms similarly tolerant of the antibiotic substances, though not themselves antibiotic producers, will also benefit by the removal of any potential competitors sensitive to the substance. The characters conferring an advantage in the early stages are those listed by Garrett for competitive saprophytic ability. Slow growers will be at a disadvantage unless they are able to utilize the more complex compounds after simple substrates have disappeared. Even then relative efficiencies will still be important in selecting among fungi having the ability to utilize more refractory substrates, but as substratum succession progresses fewer fungi will have such ability so the intensity of competition, and of antagonism in particular, may decrease. The secondary colonizers may include not only organisms able to decompose more difficult carbon sources, but also organisms requiring more specialized compounds, such as vitamins and growth substances not initially present in the substratum but synthesized by earlier colonizers. Kendrick and Burges (1962), in connection with the decomposition of pine needles on forest soils, have shown that the substrate conditions may improve for a time for some fungi. The mycelium of fungi active in the earlier stages will form substrata for yet other organisms; some fungi are parasitic on other fungi, and dead mycelium may be utilized in part by other microorganisms. Later colonizers may thus be dependent on early ones appropriately to modify the substratum. Animals such as nematodes, mites, the Collembola and millipedes may find in fungi a source of food. Other fungi in turn may utilize fecal pellets, dead bodies, and even the living animals as substrata. The community becomes more complex, and at the same time more sheltered from the bare physicochemical features of the environment. Fungi become less exposed to extrinsic environmental factors and more subject to intrinsic community or substratum factors. There arises a situation where organisms are dependent upon other organisms and influenced by them. The influences can be positive or negative, namely symbiotic or antagonistic; both are important in organizing the community.

The major substrata, of course, do not all arrive as dead materials, and living organisms in the environment play a very significant role in providing and modifying living conditions for fungi. Algae, animals, spores of thallophytes and archegoniates, seeds of higher plants, may all arrive. Some may be highly unsuccessful, particularly in the very early bare stages, and may die and therefore act merely as dead nutrient additions, but as the habitat becomes more and more modified from the parent rock, and fungi and bacteria convert dead nutrients finally into humus, the habitat becomes more favorable for autotrophic plants, and then for animals. The usual progression with ecological succession is to permit growth of more demanding organisms. These later colonizers are usually more complex and add more variety in the way of substrata.

Among the first successful autotrophic newcomers may be algal cells. Some may form lichens with fungi and thus contribute to the available energy in the area, others may grow without any such close association but nevertheless benefit fungi growing nearby by a sort of rhizosphere relationship. Then bryophytes and pteridophytes, and also more tolerant pioneer forms of angiosperms will appear. Subsequent arrivals are usually larger and more rapidly growing, and therefore provide more in the way of decomposable substrata. They provide a greater constancy in availability of substrata for fungi. Higher plants may also bring in with them, or be followed by, other fungi specially adapted to them. These include not just pathogens but also mycorrhizal species and commensals. As more organic materials appear, the environment can support more soil animals. The community evolves toward a more and more integrated complex, and the habitat becomes increasingly buffered from the physicochemical surroundings and more conditioned by the activities of organisms that are there. The sum of these activities, together with the residual effects of the original habitat and climate, gives a selective effect different from that originally obtaining, and with more emphasis on intrinsic factors. The first colonizers may not now survive since quite different properties are selected for. Resistance to desiccation, insolation, variations in salt concentration, and starvation, are much less important than the four characters of competitive saprophytic ability listed earlier. The environment, having less variability than in the first place, has, therefore, fewer species of fungi. There may, however, be a greater number of individuals, that is, a greater fungal biomass. This also intensifies the antagonisms in the environment, and emphasizes further the selective pressure on tolerance to antagonism rather than selection for efficient dispersal and long-lived resting stages which may, however, still have some importance.

As seral succession progresses there is usually a smaller fluctuation in the range of environmental factors, the organic material becoming available will also be more constant in type with the increasing integration of the higher flora and fauna, and there are likely to be fewer temporal and

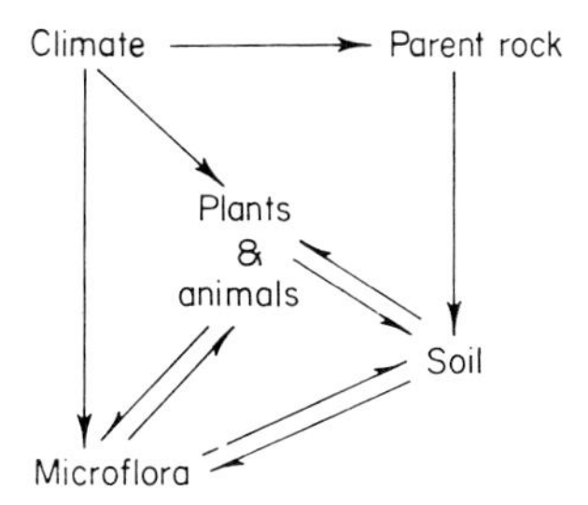

FIG. 2. Ecological interrelationships between soil microflora and the other components of the environment.

spatial discontinuities. At each seral stage the fungi present become, through selection, more and more related to the conditions, chance occurrence playing a smaller part so that the microbial community becomes integrated from within. There develops an intrinsic regulation of community structure. In this regulation the important operative influences of the habitat on the fungi include plant effects such as mycorrhizal and parasitic relationships, rhizosphere and phyllosphere effects, as well as the provision of dead plants and parts of plants. Also animal influences upon internal and external parasites and commensals, provision of substrata in droppings and shed parts, and dead animals take place. Both animals and plants also affect soil formation and thus the nonbiotic habitat factors. Humus formation and the accumulation of organic matter, aeration, drainage and mixing of soil are all affected. There is also the buffering effect of animals and plants on the climate of the habitat as described earlier.

During *seral* succession, therefore, there is an evolution toward a fairly characteristic sort of community, and toward what can be regarded as a climax, with an increase in biological energy and an increase in the total biomass within the habitat. The climax is often relatively stable, but a change in any part of it may be reflected through the whole of it, because its ecology is that of a single complex interlinking system. Figure 2 illustrates the interrelationships between the elements of this system.

C. Secondary Sere

A secondary sere occurs in an area where at least some of the changes from parent rock to mature soil have already taken place, but from which all or most living things have been removed by some agency, which may also have caused some alteration in the physical and chemical characteristics of the habitat. High temperature, extreme desiccation, anaerobiosis, flooding, and scouring are the principal agencies that convert primary seres into secondary ones. The habitat at the start of a secondary sere is of course very different from that at the start of a primary sere and is commonly more favorable for activity than is the bare parent rock. This leads to a higher degree of intrinsic selection at first, and a more rapid evolution away from the chance assemblage of species toward an adapted and fitted community. Since the underlying rock and the climate have usually not altered, the sere may move back into the lines that were being followed by the primary sere, but this is not always the case.

Tutin (1941) has defined the climax as "vegetation which is in complete equilibrium with its environment" but states that this is largely a theoretical concept and in practice is applied to communities that to the observer give the appearance of being stable. The short life cycles and rapid metabolism of fungi give them in individual substrata a low degree of stability. The changes are rapid, continuous, and readily observable. It is therefore difficult to find any validity in this concept of climax in respect to fungal succession in individual substrata. Garrett has said that fungal succession is a progressive depletion of a habitat, and moves not toward a climax but toward exhaustion of energy. In respect to the whole habitat, however, substratum succession is a fluctuating or cyclical process in that it is continually being repeated on the same type of substrata by the same species of fungi. In the larger habitat many different stages are present at one time, and on this scale the same overall picture is seen at different times, and there is a gross form of stability for the whole habitat and, therefore, for the fungal population in the habitat climax can have a significance as useful as for that of higher plants, since its overall pattern is relatively constant. This climax stage is characterized not just by relative stability but also by its higher total biomass for fungi as for higher organisms.

Studies of succession on substrata have been made for a few types of substratum (Caldwell, 1963; Griffin, 1960; Pugh, 1958; Watling, 1963;

Webster, 1956), but relatively few studies have been made of fungal habitat succession, though some indications of the type of phenomena discussed here are available in papers by Webley *et al.* (1952), Brown (1958), and Pugh (1962).

D. *The Community*

In the foregoing discussions and examples, some references have been made to specific fungal communities. But the real biological communities in nature comprise not just fungi, but also other organisms: microbes, and higher plants and animals, form a coherent system with a considerable amount of interdependence and interaction. The constituents of the community have all been selected from a considerably wider pool of available organisms by environmental features of the habitat, and by antagonistic and symbiotic features emerging from their existence together. Fungi are not only recipients of such influences but may make important formative contributions to the habitat through improving soil structure and making available or storing nutrients and thus affecting soil fertility. They may also exert major selective influences on the more apparent organisms in the habitat, most obviously by causing disease. But there are other ways in which fungi affect apparently more dominant organisms in an area. Fairy rings affect the vegetation at their site, and not always in a minor way. Ramsbottom (1926) has described gorse and bramble being driven back by advancing rings of *Tricholoma gambosum*. Much work is still needed on community relationships involving fungi. Most of what we do know of synecology as well as of autecology of fungi is incomplete, and usually it is based on some stage in the life history that is of economic interest. This has been largely because funds are more readily available for such work. Some of the facts that should be known about a fungus in order to understand its autecology, its relationship with the factors in its environment, and its role in the community, include the range of suitable substrata, the stage of colonization of and activity in these, the modes of survival, and how all these are affected by altering the conditions in the environment. Autecology and synecology cannot at this level be maintained as separate departments of knowledge because both are elements in the relationship of fungi with their full environment.

REFERENCES

Bisby, G. R. (1933). The distribution of fungi as compared with that of phanerogams. *Am. J. Botany* **20**: 246–254.

Bisby, G. R. (1943). Geographical distribution of fungi. *Botan. Rev.* **9**: 466–482.

Brown, J. C. (1958). Soil fungi of some British sand dunes in relation to soil type and succession. *J. Ecol.* **46**: 641–664.

Burges, N. A. (1958). "Micro-organisms in the Soil," 188 pp. Hutchinson, London.

Buxton, E. W. (1960). *In* "Plant Pathology" (J. G. Horsfall and A. E. Dimond, eds.), Vol. **II**, pp. 359–405. Academic Press, New York.

Caldwell, R. (1963). Observations on the fungal flora of decomposing beech litter in soil. *Brit. Mycol. Soc. Trans.* **46**: 249–261.

Durbin, R. D. (1959). Factors affecting the vertical distribution of *Rhizoctonia solani* with special reference to CO_2 concentration. *Am. J. Bot.* **46**: 22–25.

Eveleigh, D. E. (1961). The disfiguration of painted surfaces by fungi, with special reference to *Phoma violacea. Ann. Appl. Biol.* **49**: 403–411.

Garrett, S. D. (1944). "Root Disease Fungi," 177 pp. Chronica Botanica, Waltham, Massachusetts.

Garrett, S. D. (1950). Ecology of the root-inhabiting fungi. *Biol. Rev.* **25**: 220–254.

Garrett, S. D. (1956). "Biology of Root-infecting Fungi," 293 pp. Cambridge Univ. Press, London and New York.

Garrett, S. D. (1960). *In* "Plant Pathology" (J. G. Horsfall and A. E. Dimond, eds.), Vol. **III**, pp. 23–56. Academic Press, New York.

Garrett, S. D. (1963). "Soil Fungi and Soil Fertility," 165 pp. Pergamon Press, Oxford.

Griffin, D. M. (1960). Fungal colonisation of sterile hair in contact with soil. *Brit. Mycol. Soc. Trans.* **43**: 583–596.

Griffin, D. M. (1963). Soil moisture and the ecology of soil fungi. *Biol. Rev.* **38**: 141–166.

Kendrick, W. B., and N. A. Burges. (1962). Biological aspects of the decay of *Pinus sylvestris* leaf litter. *Nova Hedwigia* **4**: 313–432.

Lucas, C. E. (1947). The ecological effects of external metabolites. *Biol. Rev.* **22**: 270–295.

Papavizas, G. C., and C. B. Davey. (1962). Isolation and pathogenicity of *Rhizoctonia* saprophytically existing in soil. *Phytopathology* **52**: 834–840.

Park, D. (1960). *In* "The Ecology of Soil Fungi" (D. Parkinson and J. S. Waid, eds.), pp. 148–159. Liverpool Univ. Press, Liverpool.

Park, D. (1961). Morphogenesis, fungistasis and cultural staling in *Fusarium oxysporum* Snyder & Hansen. *Brit. Mycol. Soc. Trans.* **44**: 377–390.

Park, D. (1967). *In* "Soil Biology" (N. A. Burges and F. Raw, eds.), pp. 435–447. Academic Press, New York.

Penman, H. L. (1940). Gas and vapour movements in soil. *J. Agr. Research* **30**: 437–461 and 570–581.

Pugh, G. J. F. (1958). Leaf litter fungi found on *Carex paniculata* L. *Brit. Mycol. Soc. Trans.* **41**: 185–195.

Pugh, G. J. F. (1962). Studies on fungi in coastal soils. II. Fungal ecology in a developing salt marsh. *Brit. Mycol. Soc. Trans.* **45**: 560–566.

Pugh, G. J. F., and G. E. Mathison. (1962). Studies on fungi in coastal soils. III. An ecological survey of keratinophilic fungi. *Brit. Mycol. Soc. Trans.* **45**: 567–572.

Ramsbottom, J. (1926). *In* "Aims and Methods in the Study of Vegetation" (A. G. Tansley and T. F. Chipp, eds.), pp. 173–186. Brit. Emp. Veg. Comm. & Crown Agents for Colonies, London.

Reynolds, E. S. (1950). *Pullullaria* as a cause of deterioration of paint and plastic surfaces in south Florida. *Mycologia* **42**: 432–448.

Ruinen, J. (1961). The phyllosphere. I. An ecologically neglected milieu. *Plant Soil* **15**: 81–109.

Smith, G. (1946). Presidential address: Mycology and the war. *Brit. Mycol. Soc. Trans.* **29**: 1–10.

Starkey, R. L. (1958). Interrelations between micro-organisms and plant roots in the rhizosphere. *Bacteriol. Rev.* **22**: 154–172.

Tutin, T. G. (1941). The hydrosere and current concepts of the climax. *J. Ecol.* **29**: 268–279.

Warcup, J. H. (1957). Studies on the occurrence and activity of fungi in a wheat field soil. *Brit. Mycol. Soc. Trans.* **40**: 237–259.

Watling, R. (1963). The fungal succession on hawk pellets. *Brit. Mycol. Soc. Trans.* **46**: 81–90.

Webley, D. M., D. J. Eastwood, and C. H. Gimingham. (1952). Development of a soil microflora in relation to plant succession on sand dunes, including the 'rhizosphere' flora associated with colonising species. *J. Ecol.* **40**: 168–178.

Webster, J. (1956). Succession of fungi on decaying cocksfoot culms. *J. Ecol.* **44**: 517–544; **45**: 1–30.

Wolf, F. A., and F. T. Wolf. (1947). "The Fungi," Vol. II, 538 pp. Wiley, New York.

Yarwood, C. E., and E. S. Sylvester. (1959). The half-life concept of longevity of plant pathogens. *Plant Disease Reptr.* **43**: 125–128.

CHAPTER 2

Ecology of Freshwater Fungi[1]

FREDERICK K. SPARROW, JR.

Department of Botany
University of Michigan
Ann Arbor, Michigan

I. INTRODUCTION

The present account is of necessity a most generalized one, for work in this field is scanty and available data consist mainly of statements scattered in accounts of the morphology, taxonomy, and physiology of specific fungi. It is evident that the ecology of freshwater fungi has not attained the degree of prominence and sophistication reached, for example, by the ecology of soil fungi. This is understandable because the latter are of considerable significance in phytopathological studies and agriculture and have in consequence been accorded concentrated and long-time study (see Chapter 1). To be sure, zoosporic phycomycetes, which are the principal organisms with which we will be concerned, have been studied ecologically by a number of workers, notably, Harvey (1925, 1927, 1928), Harder (1948, 1954), Dick (1962, 1963), Dick and Newby (1961), Apinis (1964), Reinboldt (1951), and Gaertner (1954), but their work has been concerned with these organisms as they occur in the terrestrial habitat (soil). The extensive ecological work of Höhnk (1939, 1952, 1953, and other papers) should be given special mention. Höhnk, however, was primarily concerned with phycomycetes of high salt tolerance, usually in estuarine situations, as were Scholz (1958) and TeStrake (1959) (see Chapter 3).

The whole area of fungi in sewage and more or less polluted waters is rapidly growing—as the papers of Harvey (1952), Suzuki (1960f,g), Cooke and Bartsch (1959, 1960), Stjerna-Pooth (1957), and others will

[1] I am particularly indebted to L. G. Willoughby and to W. S. Benninghoff, R. Emerson, and other ecologically minded colleagues for various suggestions as to what to include in this chapter.

attest—and encompasses a special area of its own in the field of sanitary engineering. For the most part, the papers of Maurizio (1899), von Minden (1916), H. E. Petersen (1910), A. Lund (1934), Canter and Lund (1948, 1951, 1953), Willoughby (1961a,b, 1962a,b, 1965a), Collins and Willoughby (1962), Willoughby and Collins (1966), Suzuki (1960a–g, 1961a–j), Paterson (1960, 1967), and Roberts (1963) must be relied upon in the ecology of aquatic phycomycetes. Ingold (1942, 1943) in his many papers on aquatic imperfects has included ecological data, as have Ranzoni (1953), Van Beverwijk (1953), Glen-Bott (1951), Nilsson (1964), Tubaki (1957), and Suzuki and Nimura (1960a, 1961a,b). Ingold (1951, 1954, 1955), Ingold and Chapman (1952), Webster (1959a,b, 1961), Weston (1929), and others have given some ecological details of aquatic ascomycetes to be added to the classical accounts of such forms as *Vibrissea, Apostemidium, Mitrula,* etc. It is quite evident, however, that both the aquatic ascomycetes themselves as well as their ecology are in need of the concentrated study which in recent years has been accorded their marine counterparts. Indeed, even a cursory examination of old pilings, etc., in freshwater will indicate the presence of numerous lignicolous ascomycetes and imperfects. There are undoubtedly basidiomycetes in fresh waters, as the frequent findings of clamp connections in old water cultures of twigs, etc., indicate and as Ingold has stated (1959a,b), but it is not known to what organisms they belong.

Considerable thought was given to attempting here the application of the terminology of classical ecology as has recently been done for "microorganisms" by Brock (1966). The importance to science of precision in usage of terms and the danger here of misapplying them discouraged for the most part their use in this account.

The qualitative composition of the fungal population in fresh water is becoming fairly well known. In the course of somewhat more than a century of continued investigation, particularly in the last four decades, we have accumulated a considerable body of information on the diversity of types to be found among the Phycomycetes and Fungi Imperfecti, but less about the Ascomycetes. We have paid little attention, however, at least in print, to their ecology save, perhaps, for recording the substrata on which they were found, including the locality and date. As to their place and role in the aquatic environment, we know by their very nature that they are concerned with the utilization and reworking of organic materials which have been produced by autotrophs. Which ones accomplish which processes is less well known, and for their precise workings we must for the most part await the results of laboratory study. It is known with certainty, as Weston (1941) has pointed out, that fungi do initiate and carry out the destruction of living photosynthesizers as well as of non-photosynthesizers in the aquatic environment, for these attacks and predations have been closely followed by a number of reputable observers.

II. QUANTITATIVE STUDIES

Quantitatively we know very little about water fungi. Just how significant and effective a factor they are in the great cycle of decomposition and simplification of organic matter, particularly when compared with bacteria and protozoa, is at present an unanswered question. How many viable fungus units per liter of lake or pond water are there? What is their distribution in the lentic environment? Are they found in sufficient numbers to indicate that they are an effective component of the microbiota of bottom deposits where is found the bulk of decaying materials? These and other questions are asked by the limnologists when the significance of fungi in the aquatic habitat is considered.

The investigations of Canter and J. W. G. Lund (1948, 1951, 1953) on the parasitism by fungi of planktonic algae, present a clear demonstration of fungi at work in a lake parasitizing a primary producer. The papers of Schikora (1903, 1906, 1922), Nybelin (1931, 1934, 1936), Schäperclaus (1935), Rennerfelt (1936), Unestam (1965), and others attest to the devastation of the European crayfish populations by the water mold *Aphanomyces astaci*. Also, parasitism of the zooplankter *Leptodora* by *Leptolegnia* (H. E. Petersen, 1910) in Danish lakes might be considered (see page 52).

Canter and Lund show, for example, that parasitic fungi occur in sufficient numbers on planktonic diatoms to delay the time of the algal maximum in a lake and to cut down the number of individuals composing this maximum. The degree of infection of the population will depend upon the relative growth rates of host and parasite. If conditions favor the parasite, an epidemic will ensue at any time of the year, for the intruder is nearly always present. An arbitrary lower limit for epidemics has been set by J. W. G. Lund (1957) at one-quarter infection of the host population. Canter and Lund have also shown that parasitic fungi working in numbers can so reduce the population of their host that *other* phytoplankters, resistant to these parasites, replace the susceptible species.

It has also been shown that parasitic fungi can sometimes hasten the onset of algal decline in a lake, although in such instances the role of the fungus may be obscured. Thus, Paterson (1960) following the planktonic alga *Anabaena planktonicum* and its parasite *Rhizosiphon anabaenae*, outlined a somewhat different picture from the previous one, and one which is like that given by Canter and Lund (1951) for parasitism of a planktonic species of *Oscillatoria* by a chytrid. Paterson concluded with respect to *Anabaena* that the "senility of the declining population due to these (physical-chemical) causes is more likely to permit parasitism than for the parasite to initiate or even hasten the decline of the algal population."

A few attempts have been made to estimate numbers of saprophytic fungi, but so far as the strictly aquatic habitat is concerned these are either inadequate, still in the formative stage, or restricted in scope. Collins and Willoughby (1962), applying quantitative methods suitable for recovery only of mycelial forms such as the Saprolegniaceae, found that 11 of the 12 water molds recovered in their investigation of the distribution of bacterial and fungal spores in Blelham Tarn in the English Lake District were from the marginal water and only one from the surface water at the center of the lake. This kind of disparity has been found to be generally true in Lake Windermere, also in the English Lake District, where margin surface water has ranged from less than 25 to 5200 propagules per liter compared with less than 25 to 100 per liter for center surface water. On smaller Esthwaite Water there were less than 25 to 1040 per liter in margin surface water and less than 50 to 150 per liter in center surface water.

Suzuki (1960d, 1961d)[2] using limnological collecting methods has estimated fungus numbers, primarily phycomycetes, by counting the number of outgrowths emerging from a split hemp seed bait immersed in a water sample. The number of outgrowths represented to him the number of fungus propagules. It can readily be seen that a wide margin of error is possible by this method. Since cultures were not always set up immediately after collection of the water, many zoospores may have died en route to the laboratory, and gemmae or mycelial fragments might produce zoospores and hence give an incorrect picture of numbers. Furthermore, many zoospores might never achieve visible growth because of competition for the substratum. There is no proof that a single zoospore will produce only a single, unbranched outgrowth. It is also hard to see, as Suzuki recognizes, how common delicate water molds such as *Pythium* and *Aphanomyces* could be counted by this method.

Willoughby and Collins (1966) have proposed a somewhat more accurate method. Aliquots of water samples are plated with GYS tellurite (an antibacterial agent) agar[3] (Collins and Willoughby, 1962) at 45–48°C,

[2] Relying for the most part, as we do in Suzuki's papers, on English summaries which are lacking in essential data are not very satisfactory and are sometimes contradictory. The papers are included, however, since we know practically nothing about the important aspect of ecology studied by him. A rather complete bibliography of his papers and of Suzuki and Nimura are included, some of which are not referred to in the text.

[3] Composition: 10 gm of glucose; 5 gm of soluble starch; 2 gm of yeast extract;

just enough being added to solidify the sample aliquot. Dishes are incubated at 25°C for 2 days, when saprolegniacean colonies can be detected and counted. Estimates of these were calculated on the basis both of spores per liter for individual collections and mean spores per liter for various periods of sampling. If an isolate could not be at once recognized as being a zoosporic phycomycete, the colony was removed and placed in a drop of water under conditions suitable for zoospore production. This method is less laborious than one ("agar sector analysis") previously described by Willoughby (1962b), but it would still seem susceptible to quantitative error since some motile zoospores undoubtedly are killed by the warm agar. It is also possible that growth in the dishes is from some other type of propagule (mycelial fragment, gemma, germinating oospore) although when attention was given to this aspect, the evidence was that these consisted solely of zoospores. Also, as Willoughby and Collins are well aware, only filamentous forms are recovered by this technique. Fuller and Poyton (1964) have suggested the use of continuous flow centrifugation for concentrating fungal propagules for subsequent plating. They stated that the method has potentialities for yielding significant quantitative data on both mycelial and nonmycelial forms but must first be tested with known numbers of zoospores in suspension. Recently, Dick (1966), in connection with a study of soil fungi, has proposed a hemp seed–agar block method for estimation of propagules of saprolegnians in bottom samples. Appropriate samples (water, or "slurry") at suitable dilutions are incorporated into very transparent corn meal agar. After 24 hours of growth, a ruled grid of fifty 0.5 × 1.0 cm (later altered to 0.5 × 0.5 cm) blocks is drawn on the bottom of the plate. Twenty-five blocks of agar of this size are removed and each is placed in a drop of a sterile water with a hemp seed on top of the block. After 48 hours of growth, those not producing saprolegnians are discarded, those which do are counted and allowed to develop further for purposes of identification. Meanwhile, the 25 blocks left in the plate are examined after 24 hours and the number of colonies of saprolegniaceous mycelia is recorded.

For the bulk of aquatic fungi few reliable quantitative data exist, a lacuna which needs immediate attention.

III. OCCURRENCE

It is now common knowledge that so-called "aquatic fungi" or "water molds," e.g., zoosporic phycomycetes, are to be found not only in pools,

---

0.597 gm of $Na_2HPO_4 \cdot 12\ H_2O$; 2.043 gm of KH_2PO_4; 0.1 gm of potassium tellurite; 40 gm of agar per liter. Incorporated phosphate buffer with PO_4 molarity of 0.017 and pH of 5.9.

ponds, lakes, rivers, streams, and bogs, but also in marginal as well as strictly terrestrial habitats. Perhaps the best illustration of this type of occurrence [although others dealing primarily with soil fungi such as Apinis (1964) and Dick (1966) might be cited] is that provided by Willoughby (1961a). He studied the distribution at Esthwaite Water, a small lake in the English Lake District, of saprophytic chytrids along a transect extending from a field above recorded high lake level, through a marginal zone which was periodically inundated at times of high lake level, to a permanently submerged zone located at an approximately 2-meter depth in the lake. By means of a diversified group of baits (pollen excepted) he elicited representatives of a wide variety of groups of chytrids. Samples were taken monthly, starting in February and, for each of the three zones mentioned, 14 collections were made and the percentage of occurrence of each species in each zone was calculated. He presented two tables, one for those occurring 40% or more, the other for those of more infrequent occurrence. Willoughby states that "of the 36 species on both lists only 12 were obtained from field collections in contrast to 31 from the margin, and 23 from the permanently submerged mud." His tables indicate that of the 36 different taxonomic entities recognized, two were found *only* at the field site, three *only* in the submerged zone, and seven were confined to the marginal zone. Six occurred at all three sites. Most striking was the fact that 20 occurred in both marginal and submerged zones whereas ten occurred in both marginal and field zones. That is, of the components making up the rich and diverse marginal zone, twice as many aquatic as terrestrial forms occurred. This lends emphasis to Willoughby's statement that the field zone, in spite of the great numbers of individuals it supported, consisted of only a limited number of different species. A table of monthly occurrences of species with a 70% "frequency of occurrence," or better, over the years seemed to indicate that most were recoverable in that area (English Lake District) at all seasons.

We have made a preliminary study along a transect somewhat similar to Willoughby's and with comparable zones. This, however, is a mesotrophic lake (Burt Lake, Michigan) of glacial origin in a sandy terrain. We have used similar baits and, in addition, pine pollen. Only one set of samples was collected. We also have found the marginal zone, the recipient of great masses of aquatic insect exuviae, various flotsam and jetsam, etc., to be richest in variety of chytrids (13). Above this zone, the sandy terrain yielded little (1–3 species). At the opposite end from the marginal zone in up to 2 meters of water, bottom samples yielded less than half (5–6 species) the number of types found in the periodically inundated zone. Of interest was the fact that *Rhizophlyctis rosea,* considered to be a cellulose decomposer primarily occurring in soils, was found at all stations on the transect. Only one-quarter (3 species) the number of types was found in the surrounding sandy terrain at Burt Lake as were present in the agricultural fields bordering the English lake site.

Willoughby also provided some data on another point of ecological and general biological interest. It is difficult, if not impossible by direct examination, to say in what state (vegetative, sporangial, or resting spore) these fungi exist in soils, muds on lake bottoms, etc. This has been a source of considerable perplexity and interest to aquatic mycologists, both fresh water and marine. To supply at least a partial answer to this question in his marginal and soil sites, Willoughby placed 6-gm soil samples in 30-ml beakers, where they were covered with sterile water and held at 5 and 25°C. Half-hourly samples were taken from the surface of the water and examined for the presence of the strongly aerotactic chytrid zoospores. These are readily recognizable to an experienced observer. Willoughby found that at 5°C samples from the marginal zone produced zoospores in 3½ hours and at 25°C yielded zoospores in ½ hour. The field zone material at 5°C yielded zoospores in 7½ hours and at 25°C in 2 hours. He rightly pointed out that the shortness of time involved in the appearance of zoospores makes it clear that they have emerged from mature sporangia rather than from resting spores. If the latter were true, one would expect zoospores in a matter of days, not hours. Since no zoospores were recovered *immediately* after samples were set up for study, the fungi must be in an active growing stage, and, upon flooding with fresh water, sporangial formation and discharge were induced.

Willoughby's suggestion that it would appear that there is a microflora at the field site different from that in the permanently submerged mud, one not merely adventitious from the water, would seem to need study of more sites to ascertain its generality.

In seeking physical-chemical causes for the high population in the marginal zone, Willoughby compared the three sites. In this project he concluded that the high moisture, concentration of organic matter, and exchangeable cation content of the marginal mud collections were potent factors in determining the richness of the chytrid flora. The marginal zone also had the greatest variation in pH.

In a later study Willoughby (1962a) investigated in similar fashion a number of different sites in the English Lake District. At these the chytrid floras of only two zones were considered: (1) field zone just above highest lake level and (2) mud in submerged *Littorella* zone at a depth of 2 meters. Cellulose, chitin, and keratin baits were used. For all three types of bait distinct differences were demonstrated between the chytrid floras of field and submerged mud. *Rhizophlyctis rosea* was the most important soil cellulose decomposer, and a number of chytrids assumed this role in muds. There were few important chitinophilic species in soils compared with lake muds, *Rhizophlyctis ingoldii* and *Rhizophydium stipitatum* being dominant. These two species also decomposed keratin. Species of *Chytriomyces, Asterophlyctis sarcoptoides, Podochytrium chitinophilum,* and several other chytrids were important chitin attackers in muds. Although two of Willoughby's four soil fungi (1961a) were found in lake mud, two others were not. Nonetheless he considers these four (*Rhizidium richmondense, Rhizophlyctis ingoldii, R. rosea,* and *Rhizophydium elyensis*) valid and characteristic soil chytrids.

There is a wealth of ecological information in Willoughby's papers, only portions of which can be covered here.

IV. LOTIC ENVIRONMENT

Running waters, such as a stream or river, support a variety of fungi. The phycomycete flora has not been extensively studied, far less so than that of the fungi imperfecti. In cold streams of clear water in spring and early summer, growths of such ascomycetes as *Vibrissea* and *Apostemidium* [considered synonymous with the preceding by Sánchez and Korf (1966)] are common on submerged twigs. These disappear later in the growing season, possibly in response to rising temperature and associated chemical changes. Ingold (1942, 1943, 1958, 1960, etc.), Nilsson (1964), R. H. Petersen (1962, 1963a,b), Tubaki (1957), Cowling and Waid (1963), Ranzoni (1953), and others have called attention to the extraordinarily diverse hyphomycete flora living primarily in decaying leaves in stream bottoms. Conidia of these fungi are most easily found in foam and scum which collect in the eddies of streams and which function merely as traps. A further account of these fungi is to be found on page 69.

Creeks and rivers support a phycomycetous fungus flora, as we can personally attest and as Miss Waterhouse (1942) has shown in her study of Hogsmill River in England. This is a shallow stream originating in a series of springs; it is about 17 feet wide at collection point and 4–7 inches deep at bank to 10–13 inches deep in midstream with a 5–6 inch deep bed of soft black mud. The stretch studied for water molds is bordered by meadows and the banks are overhung by hawthorne, alder, and ash. Once a year it is cleared of aquatic angiosperms so that there are usually no large aquatic plants and few attached algae.

Waterhouse used restricted baiting techniques in recovering fungi. Employing only traps with cherry tomato bait, a method which would be limiting as to variety of types recovered, she obtained twelve phycomycetes. A seasonal rhythm in the occurrence of these was clearly detectable (see also page 78). Suzuki (1960f) examined the distribution of zoospores of aquatic phycomycetes in the Arakawa River in Japan from December, 1956, to August, 1957. They were scarce in the upper reaches of the river and increased in its lower part, becoming most abundant in its middle course near the city of Kumagaya, and diminished with the increase of pollutants in its lower reaches. *Leptomitus* was found only in the latter courses. Zoospores were distributed uniformly from surface to bottom layers, *Saprolegnia monoica* was found primarily on the surface, *Leptomitus* was seen on the bottom. The zoospores varied in amount, the maximum occurring in winter, minimum in summer. *Saprolegnia monoica, Achlya racemosa, A. flagellata,* and *Leptomitus* flourished in winter whereas *S. diclina* and *Pythium* sp. were found throughout the period observed.

As earlier indicated, a consideration of fungi in relation to sewage effluent, etc., is outside the scope of this chapter. Harvey (1952), Cooke (1961), Suzuki (1960g), Willoughby and Collins (1966), and others have given considerable information on the occurrence of fungi including zoosporic phycomycetes and fungi imperfecti in streams, rivers, etc., with effluent. It might be of interest here, to mention that in a stream polluted by municipal sewage waste, Suzuki (1960g) found that species of *Saprolegnia* and *Achlya* occurred below the sewage effluent, whereas species of *Aphanomyces* and *Pythium* were restricted to the cleaner portions of the stream above the entrance of the effluent. In other streams studied, which were polluted, *Aphanomyces* was found restricted to the cleaner waters, whereas *Pythium* was common in sewage-polluted water. Harvey and others have given information on the occurrence of aquatic phycomycetes in polluted waters and rivers. Such areas become loaded with propagules of terrestrial imperfects. Of interest here since it involves a well-known aquatic phycomycete is the impairment of several laboratory-activated sludge units by the interesting predaceous fungus *Zoophagus insidians* (Cooke and Ludzack, 1958). A special type of environment is that produced by the acid run-off of drainage from coal mines. Lackey (1939) first reported fungi present in such habitats, and recently Cooke (1966) has confirmed their presence in considerable numbers. Aquatic phycomycetes were found, but are not named by Cooke.

V. LENTIC ENVIRONMENT

A. Temporary Pools

Small temporary pools which may reappear over many years present rigorous conditions for life, but, nonetheless, are sources of aquatic fungi, sometimes very unusual ones. A. Lund (1934) found that such sites do not show a paucity of fungi. Dayal and Tandon (1962) found certain temporary pools in India (25° 26″ N. latitude) had two-thirds to one-half the variety of species that more permanent bodies of water supported.

Probably the richest site yet recorded for species of the rather rare genus *Monoblepharis* is a series of shallow ponds examined by Perrott (1955) in Wales. Spring rains produced pools, some of which dried out during summer but again filled up in autumn. At these sites all the previously described species of the genus were found, together with two new species and two new varieties. A shrubby swamp of similar seasonal characteristics has also been found in Michigan to be rich in species of *Monoblepharis* (Sparrow 1965a). A vernal pool we recently examined in Sonoma County, California, about 40 feet wide, which became completely dry by mid-May and presumably remained so throughout the summer, supported a variety of phycomycetes, particularly algal parasites. Other examples are known in the literature.

Rice paddies are man-made pools kept flooded for about four months of the year and are subject to inorganic nitrogenous fertilization. Nagai (1931) and others have found many saprolegnians on vegetable matter in this habitat. Ookubo and Kobayashi (1955) using keratin bait have isolated nine phycomycetes primarily from paddies, five of which were new taxa, an indication of the richness in variety of fungi of this habitat.

B. Ponds and Lakes

With respect to fungi in larger bodies of water such as ponds and lakes, both H. E. Petersen (1910) and A. Lund (1934), have emphasized that phycomycetes are to be found in calm water where there is little violent wave action, little mechanical damage, and near the shore where oxygen is available in abundance. Constant rolling of substrata by wave action close to shore will no doubt scour a substratum of phycomycetes, whereas ascomycetes and fungi imperfecti, which are partially or wholly immersed in cast-up reeds, and so forth, will probably be little affected. Protected waters do allow for undisturbed growth of fungi already on the substrata, and for nutrient-rich objects such as algae, dead insects, integuments of insects, etc., to accumulate, as has been pointed out by Kanouse (1926) and Miller (1961). There can be no doubt that shallow water, which by mild wave action has an abundance of readily available oxygen, favors growth and reproductive processes in fungi. Such conditions of high oxygen were shown by Maurizio (1899) in his laboratory studies of saprolegnians to favor both growth and reproduction. Very rough water, however, could as indicated be mechanically damaging and also act to saturate a floating substratum which would sink to the bottom where very different, possibly less-favorable conditions would prevail. Protected bays might also be considered in the category of ponds where motility of the larger water masses by wind action is not so pronounced.

Lakes and large ponds would seem to possess three different ecological areas, namely, the water mass itself, structures submerged in the water such as branches which may actually be attached to the bottom and extend upward in the water, and finally, the bottom itself.

1. Open Water Mass

The open water mass near its surface is the habitat where are typically found the planktonic populations and various other floating objects, such as pollen grains. It is here also that the so-called "general fungus spore population" at times makes its appearance. Collins and Willoughby (1962) and Willoughby and Collins (1966) have clearly established that this spora, primarily belonging to the Fungi Imperfecti, is of extraneous origin, is composed largely of terrestrial soil fungi washed in by rain action, and is transient in nature. The *bona fide* inhabitants of this area, as contrasted with these adventitious temporary inhabitants, include saprophytic water molds and the parasites of phytoplankton earlier mentioned. However, Skuja (1948), Willén (1958), and others have reported conidia of aquatic hyphomycetes in plankton samples, and we have found them with fair frequency in certain American lakes.

In a pioneering study of the distribution of Saprolegniaceae and Pythiaceae (*Pythium* and *Phytophthora*) in the "water column" of an oligotrophic 11 meter deep "heath-moor" acid lake near Bremen, Höhnk and Bock (1954) compared the density of colonization on a variety of baits along prepared east-west and north-south profiles. The baits in gauze sacks were suspended along the lines at different depths and were exposed for 4 days, after which they were taken into the laboratory for examination. The pH around the shore was taken (4.8–5.5) as well as temperature, oxygen, phosphate, nitrate, etc. During the period of full circulation of the lake in April, Saprolegniaceae (*Saprolegnia, Achlya, Isoachlya,* and *Aphanomyces*) made luxuriant to good growth down to the 4 meter depth. Fungi sporulating as *Saprolegnia* extended only to this depth. Below this level to the bottom only *Achlya* and *Aphanomyces,* i.e., fungi with clusters of primary zoospore cysts at discharge, were present of the Saprolegniaceae, and only in moderate degree of colonization density. *Pythium* and *Phytophthora* were everywhere in the water. It was noticed that zones of good and luxuriant growth corresponded to those zones having *Saprolegnia*-like type of zoospore discharge, although the *Achlya*-like type was also present and as indicated it and *Aphanomyces* extended to the bottom. With the establishment of the thermocline at 4–5 meters in depth in the summer a different distribution pattern of Oomycetes occurs. In the warm (22–27°C) surface layer with 100–110% oxygen content down to 2 meters, there was found along the east-west line a strong colonization of baits by *Saprolegnia, Achlya, Dictyuchus,* and *Aphanomyces.* Below this depth at 4 meters lies a zone of 15° water with diminished oxygen content. Here, only a moderate degree of colonization of baits occurred and no fungi with *Saprolegnia*-type of discharge were recovered. Only fungi with the *Achlya*-type of discharge occurred at 4 meters. *Pythium* was common throughout. Below the "isobath," at 11–13° virtually no fungi attacked their baits along either profile. Other interesting data are included.

Suzuki (1961c) and Suzuki and Nimura (1961d) have shown in lakes that viable phycomycete propagules are present and recoverable from the water mass. During periods of circulation they were distributed vertically and somewhat differently ("homogeneous") whereas in the stagnation period they were found only in the epilimnion. The numbers also differed with the type of lake. Beneke and Schmitt (1961, 1962), in a study of a site on Lake Erie, found more Oomycetes than members of the Chytridiales or Blastocladiales in the open waters of the lake.

a. Plankton. Distributed in the water mass are the planktonic organisms, both animals and plants. Important zooplanktonic forms are actively parasitized by true water molds. As an example of the latter, *Leptolegnia caudata* might be cited. This fungus was first reported by P. E. Müller and Wesenberg-Lund and later by H. E. Petersen (1910) from various lakes in Denmark, parasitizing the planktonic crustacean *Leptodora kindtii.* Petersen found that the fungus appeared in abundance on the cladoceran within a few days, toward the end of August. It multiplied so rapidly that it was very rare to meet with an animal which was not attacked, and in a week's time the species was exterminated from the lake under observation. He followed the course of the disease over three consecutive years, and each year it occurred at essentially the same time and with the same destructive effects. Petersen's observations showed that the attack on the cladoceran took place during the maximum period of the animal's abundance, which lasts from the middle of July until the middle of September. He observed a severe attack on July 22 in one year, and as early as July 7, single infected individuals had been seen. Petersen suggested that the animal was infected by way of the mouth. The mycelium within the animal rapidly spread and finally enveloped both the mother individual and the eggs with a thick meshwork of hyphae after killing them. The infection always seemed to be fatal. The extramatrical hyphae protruding from the cladoceran functioned as zoosporangia and produced a great number of zoospores, as a result of which the entire contents of the intramatrical mycelium (inside the animal) were used up. Within a very short time the infection was spread, presumably by the zoospores. Actually, zoospore formation took place continuously until near the end of the cycle of the fungus. Petersen noticed that the individuals bearing mycelium and zoosporangia sank only slowly to the bottom whereas those in which sexual reproduction and oospore formation were taking place sank very rapidly. The sexual reproductive structures formed only within the body of the animal and were not observed with great frequency. Resting spores, as Petersen pointed out, were not necessary for the spread of the infection owing to the abundant formation of zoospores. He suggested that the resting spores rise to the surface prior to their germination, which he thought probably took place the following summer. At all events, the fungus parasitism ceased by the middle of September. Petersen pointed out that this epidemic was probably of great importance to the life of the planktonic crustaceans in the lakes since it diminished the numbers of *Leptodora,* which is a pronounced predator of other planktonic crustaceans.

Petersen also recorded the presence in Danish lakes of another phycomycete which attacks the planktonic *Daphnia hyalina, D. cucullata,* and *Bosmina coregoni.* This fungus he termed *Pythium daphnidarum* H. E. Petersen. Here too, the fungus had been found earlier by Müller and Wesenberg-Lund. According to the latter (in H. E. Petersen, 1910), the attacks on *Daphnia* begin in the first generations of the *forma galeata* which takes place at the end of June or the beginning of July at about the time the maximum of the species begins. The epidemic terminates toward the beginning of September. According to Petersen's (1910) observations on the disease as it occurs on *Bosmina,* infection probably takes place by the germinating zoospore penetrating the dorsal valves. The fungus attacks both the body and the eggs, and the whole is enveloped in a thick mycelium and quickly killed. The zoospores are formed in the extramatrical parts of the mycelium but are never formed in such great numbers as in *Leptolegnia.* Nor does the infection of the population seem to be so extensive as in the cladoceran. A maximum of infection takes place toward the end of June or during the first half of July and lasts 8–10 days. Sometimes the maximum may occur without the attack thereafter ceasing; instead it continues sporadically until mid-September. The resting spores are formed at a somewhat earlier time in the epidemic than was true of the cladoceran parasite, about the middle of July, and Petersen has suggested that this circumstance helped in checking the further distribution of the fungus. Wesenberg-Lund noted that the epidemic on *Bosmina* had not been seen by him before Petersen's observations brought it to his attention. Petersen has suggested that it may be in fact a rare phenomenon that occurs only when circumstances in a year are favorable for the development of the fungus and when, for some reason, individuals are small in number on *Daphnia.* That is, *Bosmina* is only a secondary substratum for the fungus and in years in which *Bosmina* and *Daphnia* are equal in number the zoospores of the fungus evidently prefer *Daphnia* and only sparingly attack *Bosmina.* Scott (1961) has given accounts of zooplankton heavily infected with species of *Aphanomyces* (*A. patersonii, A. bosminae*). Prowse (1954) also described an *Aphanomyces* on *Daphnia,* and it is interesting to note that the formation and liberation of the zoospores occurred most frequently at night and that zoospore discharge proceeded typically only if the temperature did not exceed 20°C. At higher temperatures, the zoospores emerged and behaved in a manner characteristic of species of the genus *Leptolegnia.* That is, they emerged as rod-shaped bodies which, instead of encysting at the orifice of the zoosporangium, exhibited amoeboid activity and ultimately formed arrow head-shaped structures with two apically attached, forwardly directed flagella. They finally encysted as spherical bodies, and within a few hours the typical secondary zoospores emerged from each cyst. In view of these variations noted by Prowse, as well as those recorded by Scott in *A. patersonii,* it is possible that the fungus described from the Danish lakes as *Leptolegnia* may, in fact, be a member of the more common genus *Aphanomyces.*

Mention should be made here of the small but ubiquitous group of puzzling ectocommensal organisms represented by *Amoebidium parasiticum.* The latter was discovered over a century ago by Cienkowski (1861); it was attached to the outer surface of mosquito larvae. Whisler (1962), who found this organism on cladocera and cultivated it, concurs with others in allying *Amoebidium* with various endocommensals living in the hindgut of many types of arthropods, all termed Trichomycetes. *Oedogoniomyces lymnaeae* Kobayashi and Ookubo (1954b) on the outer surface of aquatic snail shells, although possibly mixed with a second fungus (*Allomyces*), is probably another related organism.

The association of water molds with diseased and moribund fish (adults and eggs), amphibians, etc., has been noted since the Middle Ages. Indeed, it is this aspect of aquatic fungi which has attracted the most general attention in the past and with which they are almost universally associated. Species of *Saprolegnia* (primarily *"S. parasitica"*) and *Achlya* are generally the fungi associated with such diseases in nature. From the careful work of Tiffany (1939a,b), Vishniac and Nigrelli (1957), and Scott and O'Bier (1962), and many others, there can be no question but that, once established, these fungi may hasten the demise of fish. The evidence for initiating primary infection on wholly uninjured fish, however, is not convincing. This is clearly shown in the experiments conducted by Vishniac and Nigrelli, where infection was obtained only after scraping scales from a selected area. They found that uninjured fish were not attacked. Scott and O'Brier in an extensive survey of aquatic fungi associated with diseased fish and fish eggs obtained 64 isolates. Of these, 14 were identified as *Saprolegnia parasitica,* and 14 as *Saprolegnia* sp.; the remainder were scattered among species of *Achlya, Aphanomyces, Pythium, Leptomitus,* and *Allomyces.* Their inoculation studies using wounded platyfish demonstrated that only *S. parasitica, S. ferax, S. delica, S. monoica, Achlya bisexualis,* and all isolates of *Saprolegnia* sp. would grow as wound parasites. They feel that, while their results lend weight to the parasitic role of the fungi associated with diseased fish, their use of platypus fish rather than hosts found in nature limits their conclusions.

Fungus invasion of phytoplankton has already been noted, and the instances might be multiplied. Thus, Paterson (1967) studied the variation in incidence of infection of chytridiaceous fungi attacking planktonic algae at various depths in Grand Traverse Bay, Lake Michigan. These studies were confined to parasites of diatoms, and the generic identity of the parasites was in doubt. Paterson's tables show that there were only one or two species of diatoms infested by fungi at 0, 5, 10, 15, and 20 meters on July 16, and at 2, 15, and 80 meters on July 22, whereas on July 16 at 25 meters and on July 22 at 30 meters there were four and five species of diatoms, respectively, supporting parasitic growths. Three species of diatoms were infested at 25 meters on July 16, and the number of fungal thalli found at that depth, at 30 meters on the same date, and at 30 meters on July 22 was strikingly greater than at all the other depths. Furthermore, there was a greater number of diatom cells of all forms at 25 and 30 meters on July 16, and at 30 meters on July 22, than at all other depths sampled. Of the three identifiable chytrids found in greatest abundance, *Zygorhizidium melosirae* occurred most frequently on July 16 in samples at the surface, 15, 25, and 30 meters. On July 22 this fungus was found only at 2 meters. Even though those thalli which occurred at the latter depth and date and at the surface on July 16 probably belong to the same fungus population, Paterson thinks it is possible that the chytrids at each of the other depths are members of different populations that have been separated by the thermal stratification of the lake. That thermal stratification can influence the distribution of the host thereby limiting the invasion by chytrid zoospores has been suggested by J. W. G. Lund (1957). It seems entirely possible, Paterson continues, that a thermal stratification by differences in water density may restrict the movement of zoospores from layer to layer. A major discontinuity layer existed at that time in Grand Traverse Bay at 10 meters, at which depth the temperature was 18.2°C, and at 11 meters, where it was 16.5°C. Thus, there was a thermocline between the population at the surface and the one at 15 meters. Further, Paterson (1966) states that the population may have been older at 15 meters than at the surface, since sexual stages and resting spores were abundant there and only zoosporangia were found at the surface. Thus, the population with sexual stages at 15 meters may have gone through the asexual stages earlier in the season and may have sunk below the layer of discontinuity before the next fungal infestation at the surface began. "The other two populations, one at 25 meters and the other at 30 meters may have originated in a similar manner but in deeper waters than those at 0 and 15 meters since there was a major discontinuity layer which could have separated them. The layer was between 16 meters where the temperature was 11°C and 17 meters where it was 10°C."

A similar situation involving more than one fungus population was found by Paterson (1967) to occur on the diatom *Fragilaria crotonensis* parasitized by *Rhizophydium fragilariae* and probably can be explained as in the preceding instance. The pattern of infection of *Tabellaria flocculosa* was also followed in Grand Traverse Bay. Although Paterson states that it was not certain that all fungus thalli found on this diatom were the same species, infested diatoms were found only at 20 and 30 meters on July 16 and 30 and at 80 meters on July 22. This distribution was not due to the occurrence of the host only at these depths since it was present at all depths on both dates. The infected diatoms seem to have sunk into the water from July 16 to July 22. Paterson states that except for the influence of temperature there appears to be little relationship between physical-chemical factors and the occurrence of fungi inhabiting diatoms in Grand Traverse Bay, for dissolved oxygen, total alkalinity, and pH are quite uniform from the surface to 80 meters. Many different chytrids were found in surface tows taken by Paterson in Lake Michigan, the hosts being mostly diatoms. The epilimnion of Grand Traverse Bay yielded several saprolegniaceous fungi and *Pythium,* but no saprophytic chytrids.

Paterson's (1960) account of an epidemic on the blue green alga *Anabaena planktonicum* caused by the chytrid *Rhizosiphon anabaenae* in a small Michigan lake included a study of the physical-chemical factors which seemed to influence parasitism, such as dissolved oxygen, pH, alkalinity, temperature. Paterson was able to show that the degree of parasitism by *Rhizosiphon* on the plankton population (*Anabaena planktonicum*) was related to the dissolved oxygen level in the water. Thus, the maximum number of *Rhizosiphon* individuals on the alga was present during a decline from the oxygen maximum. A striking decrease in the numbers of *Rhizosiphon* occurred when oxygen reached 77–82% of saturation, a finding that would seem to indicate that oxygen was a limiting factor. A decrease in pH and carbonate alkalinity occurred during periods of maximum parasitism, indicating an increase in carbon dioxide during these times of decreasing numbers of photosynthetic filaments of *Anabaena*. This increase in carbon dioxide is suggested as a factor in the occurrence of parasitism. Both spring and summer maxima of *Rhizosiphon* fell within a range of pH 8.5–9.8 of lake water indicating that an optimum pH exists for the parasite during its infection of the host.

Paterson (1960) also considered saprophytism for the first time in quantitative terms in the case of *Amphicypellus elegans* on the dinoflagellate plankter *Ceratium hirundinella,* and its relation to physical-chemical factors in the environment. He detected little relationship between pH, alkalinity, and maximum saprophytism. Correlations were found however, between temperature, dissolved oxygen, and the maximum of *Amphicypellus.* The peak of the saprophyte maxima occurred within a range of 2.5° (19.2–21.5°C) suggesting an optimum temperature for the fungus *Amphicypellus*, the temperatures below 19°C and above 21.5°C being limiting. Dissolved oxygen, however, seemed not to be very limiting since it ranged from 5.2–10.3 ppm (60–126% saturation) during saprophyte maxima.

b. Adventitious Plankters. Floating in the upper water mass are dead insects, unidentified bits of organic debris, and, in the spring, pollen, which become the normal substrata for various fungi, chiefly phycomycetes. No one who has noted the surface scum of pollen on lake surfaces or the windrows of it cast up on beaches in coniferous forest country can doubt that in the spring this material occurs in fantastic abundance, at least for a short time. These pollen grains are set upon by a myriad of chytrids which accomplish the primary opening of the grain for later bacterial and protozoal invaders. Even after the grains sink into beach sand and lake bottoms these depredations continue. Inasmuch as such pollen grains are attacked almost at once and the chytrid cycle is usually completed in 2 days, there can be no doubt that we are dealing with parasitic organisms. Indeed, in our experience pine pollen grains remain viable even in the dried state for some weeks or even months. Conidia of true aquatic hyphomycetes are often found in plankton (Willén, 1958), as has been mentioned earlier.

Recently shed integuments of aquatic insects offer another type of flotsam and jetsam which during periods of onshore winds are cast up by the millions in our northern lakes. These harbor a characteristic flora of phycomycetes which develops within 48 hours after exuviae are left behind by the insects in the water. Various chytrids, for example, *Asterophlyctis, Siphonaria, Rhizoclosmatium, Obelidium,* and the saprolegniaceous *Aphanomyces,* invariably develop within them (H. E. Petersen, 1903; Sparrow, 1937). In addition, there is always a scattering of integuments in which are unemerged dead insects; these are invaded by various coarse, saprolegniaceocus fungi, usually *Saprolegnia,* itself. All these materials are eventually washed into the marginal beach or sink to the bottom, where decomposition of the chitinous integument by various organisms continues. Fungi are, however, among the very first, if not the first, of the invaders. This disintegrated debris adds greatly to the organic content of the marginal zone and represents a contribution from the aquatic to the terrestrial environment.

2. *Submerged Structures*

Submerged branches, twigs, fruits, attached culms, leaves, etc., are frequently attacked by various groups of fungi. Twigs in particular support growth of saprolegnians as well as *Monoblepharis. Gonapodya, Blastocladia,* and *Pythiogeton;* further data are given on page 66. Fruits, usually floating and not completely submerged, are also well-known objects on which to search for phycomycetes. Dead culms of *Typha* and various sedges and rushes harbor ascomycetes and fungi imperfecti. Culms, leaves, etc., of *Carex, Phragmites,* etc., lying at the edges of lakes, streams, and other waters and frequently wholly submerged, or in such litter which is constantly saturated, have been found by Cunnell (1956, 1957, 1958) to be a rich source of fungi imperfecti belonging to the Sphaeropsidales. Ingold (1954, 1955) earlier found members of various ascomycetous genera below the lake surface on permanently submerged sedge, rush, and *Phragmites* culms. Species of the ascomycete *Loramyces* have been found on fallen *Juncus* culms by Weston (1929) and by Ingold and Chapman (1952), and we have encountered them in small Coastal Plain lakes in New England. Decorticated ash twigs which supported growths of *Ceriospora caudae-suis* have been dredged up from 3–5 feet of water by Ingold (1951), and he has, as noted, described a rich ascomycetous flora growing on submerged "reed" culms, water-logged twigs, etc. Ingold (1961) has also discovered in this habitat fungi, presumably basidiomycetes, with clamp connections. As earlier indicated, such are not uncommon in old laboratory gross cultures of twigs kept at low temperature for several years and overrun by various fungi imperfecti.

3. *Bottom*

Present evidence is somewhat confusing but suggests that this area supports a limited but diversified fungous flora, primarily of chytrids and fungi imperfecti. Depth of occurrence, temperature, and oxygen content will, however, most surely circumscribe both numbers and variety (see Paterson, 1967; Suzuki, 1961a).

Willoughby (1961a,b, 1962c), and Willoughby and Townley (1961a,b) have reported numerous chytrids from muds of English lake bottoms primarily in the shallow, littoral zone. In an investigation of the sites of fungal activity at Blelham Tarn, a small water body 13 meters in depth at its center, Willoughby (1965a) took collections of bottom mud and water immediately overlying the lake center and lake margin (2-meter depth) with a core sampler. Surface mud and mud at 1 cm below the surface of the core were taken while the lake was in full circulation. Quantitative methods designed to catch coarser fungi such as saprolegnians and mucors were employed. Neither site showed evidence of very pronounced activity of saprolegniaceous fungi, the estimated figures being well within the range previously established for Lake District water samples, namely, less than 25–5200 per liter. The high numbers of mucors recovered clearly indicated a general sedimentation of viable fungus propagules to the bottom mud, but such did not seem true of saprolegnians. A lake margin site on shore, however, gave evidence of high activity of saprolegnians, in mud which was essentially periodically inundated soil.

Recently, Paterson (1967) has reported data pertinent to benthic fungi obtained by different collecting methods and in waters up to 31 meters in depth. Instead of bringing into the laboratory samples of bottom mud, he placed at certain bottom sites wide-mouthed pint jars covered with plastic mesh of a size which would not impede zoospore entry. Within these jars were placed various baits such as pine pollen, hemp seeds, chitin, snake skin, cellophane, and grass blades. These traps were made so that they could be lowered to the bottom without the baits coming into contact with upper lake water. Once on the bottom, they were opened by remote control and the baits were exposed to fungi present in the water. Depths of 26 and 31 meters in Grand Traverse Bay, an arm of Lake Michigan, were examined. These traps were removed at intervals of 1–7 weeks. Subsequent to their removal, the jars and the baits were brought to the laboratory and an examination for fungi was conducted. A similar investigation was made of the benthos of Douglas Lake, using the same methods. The recovery of fungi at these two sites is given in Table I.

The data on bottom fungi given by Paterson and Willoughby seem to be in general agreement.

Roberts (1963) in a study of Saprolegniales from 21 natural waters in the United Kingdom found that, typically, more species were collected from the bottom than from surface waters. Suzuki (1961h) noted, however, that during the stagnation period aquatic fungi were scarce on the

TABLE I

DATES AND DEPTHS AT WHICH AQUATIC PHYCOMYCETES WERE FOUND IN TWO MICHIGAN LAKES[a]

	Douglas Lake, Michigan Date and depth																Grand Traverse Bay, Lake Michigan Date and depth						
	1961										1963						1961				1962		
	June 27 to July 7		June 27 to July 18		June 27 to July 28		June 27 to Aug. 4		Aug. 4 to Aug. 17		June 24 to July 10		June 24 to July 28		June 24 to Aug. 12		July 12 to Aug. 8		June 26 to July 11		June 26 to July 25	July 11 to Aug. 18	
Substrate and fungus	0.5 m	8 m	0.5 m	15 m	0.5 m	4 m	0.5 m	12 m	0.5 m	6 m	0.5 m	6 m	0.5 m	9 m	0.5 m	10 m	3 m	31 m	3 m	26 m	26 m	3 m	26 m
CHYTRIDIALES																							
Pine pollen:																							
?*Rhizophydium* spp.	+	+	+	−	−	+	−	−	+	+	−	−	−	−	−	−	−	+	−	−	−	−	−
Cellophane																							
?*Rhizophlyctis* sp.	−	−	−	−	−	−	−	−	−	−	−	+	−	−	−	−	−	−	−	−	−	−	−
Nowakowskiella hemisphaerospora	−	−	−	−	−	−	−	−	−	−	−	−	−	+	−	−	−	−	−	−	−	−	−
Mayfly exuviae:																							
Siphonaria sp.	−	−	−	−	−	−	−	+	−	−	−	+	−	−	−	−	−	−	−	−	−	−	−
?*Siphonaria* sp.	−	−	−	−	−	−	−	−	−	−	−	−	−	−	−	−	−	+	−	+	−	−	+
Obelidium mucronatum	−	+	−	−	−	−	−	−	−	−	−	−	−	+	−	−	−	−	−	−	−	−	−
Rhizoclosmatium aurantiacum	−	+	−	−	−	−	−	−	−	−	−	−	−	+	−	+	−	−	−	−	−	−	−
Asterophlyctis sarcoptoides	+	+	+	−	+	+	−	−	−	−	+	−	−	+	−	−	−	−	−	−	−	−	−
Chytriomyces hyalinus	−	−	−	−	−	+	−	−	−	−	−	−	−	−	−	−	−	−	−	−	−	−	−

Grass leaf blade:																							
Nowakowskiella elegans	+	+	+	+	−	−	−	−	−	−	−	−	−	−	−	−	−	−	−	−	−	−	−
BLASTOCLADIALES																							
Snake skin:																							
Catenaria anguillulae	−	−	−	−	−	−	+	−	−	−	−	−	−	−	−	−	−	−	−	−	−	−	−
LEPTOMITALES																							
Hemp seed:																							
Leptomitus lacteus	−	−	−	−	−	−	−	−	−	−	−	−	−	−	−	−	−	+	−	−	+	−	−
SAPROLEGNIALES																							
Hemp seed:																							
Saprolegnia diclina	−	−	−	−	−	−	−	−	−	−	−	−	−	−	−	−	−	+	+	+	−	−	+
Saprolegnia spp.	−	−	−	−	−	−	−	−	+	−	−	−	−	−	−	−	+	−	−	+	+	+	−
Achlya klebsiana	−	+	−	−	−	−	−	−	−	−	−	−	−	−	−	−	−	−	−	−	−	−	−
Achlya treleaseana	−	−	−	−	−	−	−	−	−	−	−	−	−	−	−	−	−	−	−	−	−	−	+
Achlya caroliniana	−	−	−	−	−	−	−	−	−	−	−	−	−	−	−	−	−	−	−	−	−	+	−
Achlya sp.	−	−	−	−	−	−	+	−	+	−	−	−	−	−	−	−	−	−	−	−	−	−	−
Mayfly exuviae:																							
Aphanomyces spp.	+	+	−	−	−	−	−	−	−	−	−	−	−	−	−	−	+	+	−	−	−	−	−
Snake skin:																							
Aphanomyces spp.	−	−	−	−	−	−	−	−	−	−	−	−	−	−	−	−	+	+	−	−	−	−	−
PERONOSPORALES																							
Grass leaf blade:																							
Pythium spp.	−	−	−	+	−	−	−	−	+	+	−	−	−	−	−	−	+	+	+	+	+	−	−

[a] Based on Paterson (1967); prepared by R. A. Paterson

bottom, only *Pythium* and *Aphanomyces* being recovered. Suzuki (1961a) studied aquatic fungi from the bottom mud of Lake Nakanuma over the period of about a year, noting seasonal changes and including certain parameters not supplied by others. The water temperature of the bottom layer here varied only 3°C in the course of the year and became practically anaerobic from May to December. The aquatic fungi in the profundal bottom mud showed seasonal changes. There was a distinct midsummer minimum and a midwinter maximum. This variation in fungi was correlated with the dissolved oxygen in the water of the bottom layer. *Pythium* sp. was seen throughout the year with the maximum in winter. *Achlya flagellata, A. racemosa, Dictyuchus* sp., *Aphanomyces* sp., and *Saprolegnia* spp. were obtained during the circulation and winter stagnation periods when the bottom layer of water contained oxygen. Suzuki reported that laboratory experiments on the relation of oxygen to fungus activity gave results that were in accordance with observations on the natural lakes. In other studies, Suzuki (1961i) reported that the bottom of lakes of the Nikko volcanic group was characterized by jet black reduced mud "resulting in the removal of oxygen from the contacting water." Here aquatic phycomycetes were very scarce, and *Pythium* sp. was the only one isolated from such a habitat. Suzuki and Nimura (1961f) stated that the frequency of aquatic phycomycetes in the bottom mud of the Lake Onogawa group, which are small basins on the surface of mud flows extruded from the volcano Bandai in 1888, was measured to be 90–100% of the total mud samples. Suzuki and Hatakeyama (1961) stated that aquatic fungi in the bottom deposit of Lake Yamanakako were rich in autumn in number of species, *Pythium* being the preponderant member at all seasons of the year. In a paper on anaerobic life of aquatic fungi in a lake bottom, Suzuki (1961h) stated that aquatic fungi in lake bottoms with an anaerobic layer were observed during the summer stagnation period. They were scarce both in kinds and quantity in the bottom muds. The genera *Pythium* and *Aphanomyces* were the only fungi present at this season of the year. The distribution of the aquatic fungi in the bottom mud showed a close relationship with the amount of dissolved oxygen in the bottom water. Laboratory experiments were carried out on the effect of low oxygen tension upon fungus activity. The results were in accordance with observations from the lake bottom samples. From the tables it appears that 12 meters was the greatest lake depth. In lakes of low pH and high mineral content, Suzuki (1960d) noted that aquatic phycomycetes were very scarce or lacking in the bottom mud but were very rich in neutral lakes. This same investigator (1961d), discussing the distribution of aquatic phycomycetes in some inorganic acidotrophic lakes (pH 1.9–2.9) in Japan, indicated that aquatic fungi were scarce or absent in the bottom mud of these lakes, occurring in 0–20% of the total mud samples, a very small figure compared with those of harmonious or dystrophic lakes. The bottom muds of these volcanic lakes often are very high in sulfur and iron minerals.

Blackened leaves which have been lying on lake bottoms for some time under more or less anaerobic conditions have been found by Glen-Bott (1951) and others to possess a characteristic, usually helicosporous, hyphomycete flora when allowed to develop under aerobic conditions in damp chambers. Indeed, it is probable there are no submerged materials of biological origin free from fungus invasion in this habitat.

VI. SPECIAL ENVIRONMENTS

A. Thermal Springs

According to Cooney and Emerson (1964) no fungi have been isolated from thermal springs. Considering the profusion of algae which occur in this habitat, it seems probable that fungi are present but as yet undetected. Indeed, Cooney and Emerson cited a paper by Loginova *et al.* in which many obligately thermophilic microorganisms, including true fungi, are reported to occur in the thermal soils of volcanic regions in the Ural Mountains.

B. Sphagnum Bogs

Although, as others have pointed out (A. Lund, 1934), sphagnum bogs have a paucity of substrata and present rigorous conditions of environment (primarily because of high acidity) there is every reason to believe that they support a variety of zoosporic fungi. Indeed it has been this writer's experience that sphagnum bogs are one of the richest sources of bizarre types of chytrids (Sparrow, 1966). A perusal of Lund's paper on the ecology of phycomycetes, and that of Miller (1965), shows a great percentage of sphagnum sites rich in fungi. It is becoming increasingly clear that species such as *Achlya treleaseana* and *Pythium undulatum* and a variety of chytrids including *Blyttiomyces helicus* and *Phlyctochytrium furcatum* are highly characteristic of such bogs. This habitat would well repay detailed investigation because of both the variety and number of forms it harbors. Kobayashi and Ookubo (1952, 1954a), for example, have studied the aquatic fungi of Ozegahara moor. This is a high moor about 1400 meters above sea level surrounded by mountains 2000–2300 meters high. The standing water ranged from pH 4 to 5 in the bogs. Twenty-eight species of water molds, including *Allomyces* were isolated, four of them being new. Furthermore, Ookubo (1954) isolated from a similar site 12 species, two of which were considered new.

C. *Inland Salt Lakes and Salt Pools*

The fungi present in such areas as the Salton Sea in California and in such extreme saline aquatic conditions as that provided by the small pool, called "Bad Water" in Death Valley, California, face rigorous conditions for life. Nonetheless, in the Salton Sea Anastasiou (1963) has found 8 ascomycetes and 10 imperfects. In our brief examination and sampling of this area three phycomycetes have been found (*Olpidium longicollum, Rhizophlyctis harderi, Phlyctochytrium semiglobiferum*), all of which have been heretofore described from the Adriatic Sea. In the Death Valley site a single phycomycete was discovered (*Thraustochytrium pachydermum*), one which had been found beneath salt crusts at the lower end of San Francisco Bay. It is evident therefore that these organisms in salt lakes have affinities with marine forms and indeed appear to be exact counterparts of them. These halophilic fungi are considered in the next chapter (Chapter 3). As an indication of the tolerance of saprolegnians of salts it is interesting to note the following. Höhnk (1952, 1953) found that the freshwater *Saprolegnia ferax* grew and reproduced best in fresh water. A salinity of 3% inhibited sex organ formation, 7% prevented sporangial formation, at 13% there were no gemmae, and at 25% only a feeble mycelium was developed.

D. *Acidotrophic Lakes*

Suzuki (1960d, 1961d) has described certain lakes in Japan associated with volcanoes which are strongly acid. These lakes are small and shallow, the water remarkably blue except where suspended iron granules may redden it. They are on the whole fairly transparent. The waters are strongly acid by reason of the sulfuric or hydrochloric acids from the rivers or springs of the volcanoes. The pH may vary from 1.9 to 2.9. Large amounts of mineral substances such as sulfate, chlorine, and calcium are present. Further, iron and manganese are also in high concentration in comparison with that of other lakes. The lakes are often surrounded by *Phragmites communis* communities along the shore, and the bottom may be thickly covered with water mosses. Suzuki isolated only 5 species from a series of lakes of this inorganic acidic type. *Saprolegnia monoica* var. *acidamica* was a preponderant species and was distributed widely. *Achlya flagellata* and *A. racemosa* were relatively scarce. The genus *Aphanomyces* was limited only to weakly acidic lakes. In general, the weakly acidic lakes were somewhat more abundant in species. For example, four species were found in Lake Midoronuma, which has a pH of 5.8, and three in Lake Benten-numa, at a pH of 5.2.

One other special habitat ought to be mentioned here. Suzuki (1961j) studied the microorganisms in the water from 14 wells in Tokyo and its suburbs. Relatively high numbers of bacteria, aquatic phycomycetes, and filamentous fungi were found. *Mucor, Penicillium,* and an unidentified species were the dominant "filamentous fungi" whereas *Pythium* and *Saprolegnia* were the most common aquatic phycomycetes.

VII. HABITAT FACTORS

A. Turbidity of the Water

As H. E. Petersen (1910) pointed out, turbidity is a factor of considerable consequence for phycomycetes, for when there is silt in suspension it tends to settle on substrata and even on fungal growths. Undoubtedly zoospores are prevented from reaching a proper substratum when this is covered with silt.

B. Light

This was not considered either by Petersen or A. Lund (1934) to be a factor directly affecting the growth of fungi. Earlier, Maurizio (1899) showed in the laboratory that reduction of light had no effect on growth or reproduction of saprolegnians. Indirect effects of light on fungal growth are of course operative by way of effects on the temperature of the site. Furthermore, light promotes algal growth on possible substrata, and the competition for space on twigs and other such favorable substrata for fungi can be a real factor. Whether, as Petersen suggested, algae prevent renewal of water around the substratum to the detriment of fungal growth seems doubtful. Competition for space and the possible production of fungistatic or fungicidal substances by algae seem much more likely to be significant habitat factors. However, it is certainly true that twigs from a site in early spring when there are few algae have an abundance of fungi on them, whereas twigs from this same site collected later in the season are frequently covered by algae and have few fungi, and these are of the coarsest type. Such a condition was also noted by A. Lund (1934). Although light for most fungi growing in water does not seem an important factor, laboratory studies show otherwise in some instances (Chapter 23, Volume I; Chapter 10, Volume II). Thus, both Wemmer (1954) and Krause (1960) indicate light affects oogonial and oospore formation in *Saprolegnia ferax*. The latter has determined that blue and green spectral ranges suppress completely, and the red partially, the formation of oogonial rudiments.

In *Blastocladiella emersonii* and *B. brittanica,* Horenstein and Cantino (1961, 1962) and Cantino and Horenstein (1956) have shown by laboratory studies that white light has a profound effect upon growth and resting spore formation (see also Cantino, Chapter 10, Volume II). In the chytrid *Rhizophlyctis rosea,* Haskins and Weston (1950) found pigmentation of this fungus to be more intense when cultures were grown in the light. Greater growth occurred in light when glucose was used as a carbon source, but the reverse was true when cellobiose was substituted. More complete respiration of glucose appeared to be achieved in the dark.

The zoospores of *Polyphagus euglenae* (with pigmented globule) and *Rhizidium vorax* (uncolored globule), both parasites of algae, have been reported to exhibit tactic response to light (Strasburger, 1878; Wager, 1913). On the other hand S. Goldstein (1960a) found that light had no effect on the polycentric aquatic saprophytic chytrid *Cladochytrium replicatum,* which has a pigmented zoospore globule. Similarly, he found that light had no effect on growth, activity, etc., of two saprophytic monocentric chytrids (1960b) with colorless globules in their zoospores.

C. *Substratum*

Needless to say, substratum character and availability are critical factors for heterotrophic organisms. Whiffen (1941) in an early physiological investigation of certain chytrids separated them into cellulose-utilizers and nonutilizers, and these are recognizable in the field. Many, such as *Rhizophlyctis rosea,* can readily be caught on cellophane bait whereas others are never found on such substrata. Collections in nature frequently indicate clear preferences of fungi for certain substrata, even though they may later be cultivated in the laboratory on a wide variety of media. Thus, *Achlya, Blastocladia, Monoblepharis, Araiospora, Apodachyla,* and others are found on twigs. On the other hand, chytrids are rare on such substrata, perhaps because they are hard to observe, for they have been isolated on other cellulosic materials. Pine pollen supports a wide variety of epibiotic chytrids, as do moribund and dead green algae. Fruits harbor a flora somewhat similar to twigs, as von Minden (1916) showed. Empty insect integuments, as H. E. Petersen (1903) and Sparrow (1937) demonstrated, possess a unique chytrid flora. Dead animal carcasses of whatever size, invertebrate or vertebrate, as the early mycologists observed, will become covered in time with saprolegnian mycelium in ordinary aquatic habitats. As earlier stated, these nutritional preferences so apparent in nature may not be so well marked under laboratory conditions. Thus Karling (1947) and Ajello (1948) found that apparent chitinophilic fungi would grow on keratin, and, more strikingly still, Antikajian (1949) and Ajello (1948) grew the chitinophilic fungi *Asterophlyctis* and *Polychytrium* on peptone-yeast dextrose agar. Other such instances might be mentioned.

That huge amounts of chitin are produced in the aquatic environment has been stressed by Reisert and Fuller (1962). In a study of the decomposition of this material by *Chytriomyces* sp. they found exocellular chitinases hydrolyzing it to *N*-acetylglucosamine. Murray and Lovett (1966) have recently shown, however, that *Karlingiomyces asterocystis* is the only chytrid thus far described which is an obligate chitinophile. Unestam (1966b) investigated the enzymes of 7 phycomycetes, 3 of which were parasites of plants, 4 of animals. All showed chitinase activity in varying degrees. Only the 3 plant parasites showed cellulase as well as pectinase activity.

All these substrata no doubt originally are invaded in nature because of the "selective power" of the fungus zoospore. Chemotactism was long ago shown by Pfeffer (1884), Müller (1911), etc., to be a characteristic of aquatic phycomycete zoospores, and more recently this feature has been investigated by Fischer and Werner (1955, 1958a,b). The latter investigators attempted to identify the diffusing substances which lead saprolegnian zoospores toward a natural substrate, in this case a fly leg. They found chemotactic sensibility of zoospores was largely dependent upon their age and solutes in the medium. Alkali metal chlorides and alkaline earth metal chlorides such as $CaCl_2$ and $MgCl_2$ are positively chemotactic substances. Mixtures of these had different effects both qualitatively and quantitatively. Surprisingly, proteins freed of their dialyzable fractions had no tactic effect. Very small amounts of different amino acids function to increase the chemotactic activity of the aforementioned salts. Solutions containing primarily NaCl and KCl and traces of amino acid mixtures induce by their action both the chemotactic attraction of zoospores to natural substrata and their subsequent encystment. Machlis (1958) and Carlile and Machlis (1965) found male gametes of *Allomyces* positively chemotactic to a hormone secreted by the female gametangia whereas the zygotes, meiospores, and zoospores were not. The latter three did, however, respond to casein hydrolysate. Motile zygotes responded to the amino acids cysteine, proline, and serine but not to other amino acids tested. This area of investigation is greatly in need of much precise, definitive work on other zoosporic fungi. For example, we know that such fungi as *Blastocladia, Gonapodya,* and *Rhipidium* commonly colonize such diverse substrata as submerged apples and twigs. It does not seem likely that the same chemotactic degradation products attractive to the zoospores are produced by both twigs and apples, but this could be the case.

Just how important zoospore motility is as compared with water turbulence in disseminating propagules has been considered by J. W. G. Lund (1957). In the case of chytrid parasitism of planktonic algae such as the colonial *Asterionella,* he is more inclined to credit water turbulence as the chief means of dispersal. Other investigators too, have expressed doubt as to the large-scale effectiveness of zoospore motility. It undoubtedly plays an essential part, however, in substrate selection, once spores arrive in the vicinity of a substratum.

Hickman and Ho (1966) have reviewed the behavior of zoospores in plant-pathogenic phycomycetes, i.e., those of importance to the plant pathologist.

In recent years considerable use has been made of "baiting" techniques which probably had been employed for the first time on a large scale by von Minden (1916). Baiting has been extended to "capturing" chytrids with great success, and it is now a routine procedure. For large "macro-omycetes," split boiled hemp seed (*Cannabis sativa*), although of vegetable origin, gives cultures less fouled by bacteria and protozoa than flies, beetles, fish, etc., which were earlier employed. This bait also has been used extensively in the recovery of zoosporic soil phycomycetes. Pine pollen in particular has been in high favor among those primarily interested in monocentric fungi in both marine and fresh waters. Other pollen such as that of *Liquidambar* and *Typha* are effective but seem to be more subject to bacterial attack. Unwaterproofed cellophane, boiled onion skin, decalcified shrimp exoskeleton, hair, hoof parings, spider webs, human skin, snake skin casts, insect integuments, insect wings, porcupine quills, even plates of human fibrin film (Karling, 1964) have been employed with success as substrata. These have called forth from the environment fungi of varying physiological capacities and needs and have been of great value in the discovery of new forms in nature. There is emerging from this work a picture of various groups of fungi in water which are physiologically specialized for the destruction of substrata of radically different composition. The investigations of Paterson (1967) on benthic chytrids which were reviewed earlier also show that these organisms, of great nutritional dexterity, are present and active at considerable depths and in large bodies of water. High concentrations of food are not always necessary for support in nature of some fungi. Thus, Schade (1940) and Schade and Thimann (1940) were impressed by the high efficiency of the assimilative process in *Leptomitus lacteus,* a phycomycete not known to form resting spores. The ability to form cell and reserve material from simple substrata with such economy is of great service to the fungus whose food supply may be interrupted for varying periods without its being able to form resting spores, and "this economical oxidative assimilation probably helps to explain why *Leptomitus* grows well in the very dilute media in which it is often found in nature." Cantino (1955), Cantino and Turian (1959), and Murray and Lovett (1966) have reviewed the various nutritional studies of phycomycetes in the laboratory under exacting conditions and have given a critical evaluation of, for example, so-called "chitinophilic" fungi found in nature. Bhargava (1945, and other papers), Whiffen (1945), Reischer (1951), and many more have reported on nutritional work on members of the Saprolegniaceae, and recently Unestam (1966a) has given an account of similar studies on *Monoblepharis*. The whole area of baiting in nature, recovery of fungi, and subsequent establishment of pure cultures for critical physiological work is well covered by Emerson (1950).

Aquatic imperfects are found in nature on decaying leaves, twigs, bark, and so forth. For example, Ingold (1942, 1943) found that leaves just becoming skeletonized under aerobic conditions in the bottoms of clear streams are excellent substrata for these imperfects. Late autumn and winter are preferable, he reported, although we have obtained a variety in late summer in situations such as he mentions. Accumulations of foam and scum act as traps in such streams to hold the conidia. The spores do not float, being denser than water, but if they are brought to the surface by an eddy, they are readily caught by the foam or scum. Trapped in this manner they are easily collected. Inasmuch as these conidia are highly characteristic in shape, many being tetraradiate in the arrangement of their arms, they are readily recognizable. Decaying leaves which are brown colored and found in the bottom of flowing streams are most prolific sources. Those black leaves dredged up from the bottom of lakes on which the fungi have existed in mycelial form under more or less anaerobic conditions (Glen-Bott, 1951) have a different flora. Such leaves when placed in damp chambers (not submerged) develop conidia usually belonging to members of the Helicosporae (see page 63). These conidia are apparently unwettable, and air is trapped in the coils, so if submerged they will rise to the water surface. Hence, the helicosporous coil is evidently an adaptive mechanism for ensuring aerobic conditions for conidial germination. Thornton (1963) has examined the physiology and nutrition of members of the aquatic imperfects from running waters. He found, among other things, that the ease with which these hyphomycetes utilize inorganic nitrogen-sources gives them an advantage over the more fastidious water molds, such as the Saprolegniaceae. Hence, hyphomycetes may benefit more from nitrate and ammonium ions leached from soil into streams than do aquatic phycomycetes, which according to Thornton can use only organic sources of nitrogen (see however, Cantino and Turian, 1959). Thornton also found that imperfects use a wide range of simple and polymeric carbohydrates and again have a nutritive advantage over their competitors, the Saprolegniaceae, which are more restricted as to their carbon sources.

The tetraradiate arrangement of conidial arms, so prevalent in these fungi (Ingold, 1966) is a device which probably aids in anchoring the conidia. Webster (1959a) has shown experimentally that tetraradiate spores impact on cylinders with greater efficiency than do oval ones. Anchorage on a proper substratum in a flowing water habitat can be a problem for such fungi so that it is not surprising that the successful ones have emphasized this structural feature. This device is also found in the algae (for example, *Sphacelaria*).

Certain ascomycetes as earlier noted are common in cold running water on twigs (*Vibrissea,* etc.); others occur in bogs on submerged vegetable debris in association with *Sphagnum* (*Mitrula paludosa*). Those in open lakes, ponds, and so forth inhabit submerged twigs, particularly the old culms of herbaceous emergent angiosperms such as *Typha, Juncus, Scirpus.* Tubaki (1966) has reviewed the few instances where ascogenous and imperfect states of aquatic ascomycetes have been linked.

Cantino (1950, 1955), Cantino and Turian (1959), and Emerson (1950) have reviewed the nutritional aspects of the Chytridiomycetes and mycelial water molds, and the reader is referred to their papers for further details.

D. *Temperature*

Of the various factors operating at a site, temperature obviously is of great importance and is certainly the easiest to measure. It acts directly upon such processes as germination of overwintering structures, which in temperate latitudes is often the first step in the reestablishment of fungal growth in the spring, for vegetative growth, and for induction of asexual reproduction by means of zoospores. The zoospores possibly afford quick and widespread establishment of new growth in the habitat. It is well known that temperature affects all vital activities, and considerable laboratory work on many water fungi has revealed the limits and optima for these various processes. For example, Cotner (1930) gives some data as it applies to the reproductive processes of the genus *Blastocladia.* He found that in *B. pringsheimii* and *B. globosa* the minimum temperature for zoospore formation was 5–7°C. The optimum of *B. globosa* was between 11 and 13°C, whereas that of *B. pringsheimii* was approximately 12–14°C. The maxima of both species lay between 21 and 24°C. Sparrow (1933) noted that the temperature necessary for sporangial formation in *Monoblepharis* was between 8 and 11°C, whereas 21°C favored sexual reproduction. In this same genus, Unestam (1966a) found in the case of *M. macrandra* that the optimal growth temperature in culture was around

25°C. As he remarked, this is far higher than the temperature at which representatives of this genus are usually found in nature, and it suggests that other factors than the temperature favorable for growth (possibly competition) might be decisive for the occurrence of this slow-growing fungus in nature. Such data as these are found scattered in a great variety of papers and must be selected by those interested, for example see Springer (1945) and Suzuki (1960b,c).

In the various papers of Suzuki earlier mentioned, it is evident that under field conditions, too, temperature has a profound effect upon zoospore formation, and instances of lowered zoospore production due to unfavorable temperatures are cited. It has been noted that the seasonal occurrence (page 80) of fungi is likely in large part to be a function of temperature. Krause (1960), for example, found the optimum temperature for oogonial formation in *Saprolegnia ferax* was between 20–25°C. At 27°C only gemmae were found. It is to be hoped that more precise information on the effect of temperature on sex organ formation based on laboratory studies of many of these aquatic fungi will be forthcoming.

The relation of temperature to the induction of morphological structures of taxonomic importance presents a promising field of investigation. Thus, Reischer (1949), pointed out that at high temperatures (25°C) *Achlya colorata* formed nearly smooth-walled oogonia whereas at 15–20°C various degrees of papillation and roughness were found.

Mention has already been made of the fact that during warm weather the growth of phycomycetes is evidently cut down and the life cycle is restricted (Bock, 1956), and under some circumstances in summer they may be somewhat difficult to find. While water temperature seems important for some fungi, others appear more or less independent of it. Thus *Achlya* grows best in cold water and completes its life cycle, whereas at high temperatures in seasons of bright sunlight, it has difficulty in competing with algae and in forming sex organs. It is undoubtedly a matter of competition which hinders fungal growth under these circumstances. H. E. Petersen (1910) emphasized that oogonia in *Achlya* were formed primarily in cooler months, but A. Lund (1934) pointed out that in the laboratory, grown alone, they were formed at ordinary room temperatures.

Aquatic hyphomycetes when studied critically in the laboratory have been found by Thornton (1963) to have a somewhat low optimum temperature for growth and sporulation. This, as well as other factors mentioned elsewhere again give them a competitive advantage in the habitat they occupy.

E. Oxygen

Quite predictably oxygen has proved to be a major factor in determining which fungi will grow in water. For a variety of reasons natural habitats vary greatly in the amount of oxygen available (Welch, 1952). Dissolved oxygen in a lake, for example, comes principally from the atmosphere through the exposed surface of water, and from photosynthesis of green plants. Shallow lakes subject to wave action have ready access to abundant oxygen whereas small ponds rich in organic materials and with considerable bottom debris are deficient in it, the oxygen being used up in the respiration of the many microorganisms active in disintegration. At ordinary growing temperatures the bottoms of most aquatic sites are places of low oxygen content. Substrata near the surface but surrounded by great masses of bacterial-protozoal slime may also be limiting in oxygen. The close relationship of the oxygen content of water to parasitism of phytoplankton has been earlier considered (page 56) (Paterson, 1960). It will be recalled that Paterson found that the maxima of the parasite of *Anabaena planktonica* occurred within 6.4 to 8.0 ppm (77–82% saturation) of dissolved O_2, which seemed to be the limiting factor. The maximal percentage of saprophytism of the plankter *Ceratium hirundinella* by *Amphicypellus elegans* occurred, according to Paterson, during periods of drops in dissolved O_2, but this was not a limiting factor since it ranged from 5.2 to 10.3 ppm. (60–126% saturation). The importance of oxygen to common saprophytic aquatic fungi apparently varies. Some grow on substrata easily accessible to air. For example, they float on twigs, dead bodies of insects, etc., where they may be eventually submerged in relatively shallow water. Others occupy situations which are obviously quite poor in oxygen and rich in decaying materials, for example, the bottom of pools the surface of which may be covered by aquatic growths of duckweed which will shade other photosynthetic organisms, reduce free water surface, etc.

A. Lund (1934) pointed out that there were certain forms which typically required an abundance of oxygen. Members of the Saprolegniaceae and Leptomitaceae, for example, *Apodachlya* and *Sapromyces,* and probably many species of *Monoblepharis, Pythium,* and *Phytophthora* have such a requirement. Others such as *Rhipidium, Gonapodya, Blastocladia, Pythiogeton,* and *Macrochytrium* may grow under conditions of low oxygen content and generally foul environment. This was earlier pointed out by von Minden (1916). The reason for this capacity has been made clear in *Blastocladia* and *Pythiogeton* by the laboratory studies of Emerson and Cantino (1948) and Cantino (1949a,b). They showed that such fungi can occupy these habitats because they are capable of carrying on a fermentative type of metabolism. This must be a tremendous advantage since the number of competitors so equipped are probably few. On the other hand, as indicated, certain of the Leptomitales are characterized by an oxidative rather than a fermentative type of metabolism, according to

Golueke (1957), and this is the reason why these fungi are found in places of higher oxygen content than *Blastocladia* and *Pythiogeton. Aqualinderella* (Emerson and Weston, 1967) is an extreme case, for this fungus is almost a total anaerobe living in stagnant water. Suzuki's (1961a) account of the distribution of fungi in lake bottoms at times when the hypolimnion in some types of lakes becomes virtually exhausted of oxygen has already been mentioned. The diurnal migration of zoospores (Suzuki, 1961b) of aquatic fungi in a shallow (50 cm deep) lake was closely correlated with the distribution of the dissolved oxygen. During[4] the spring and fall on a clear day, at 7–8 A.M., the zoospores gather at the surface, where oxygen is abundant. As the oxygen concentration increases in the bottom with time, the zoospores move toward the bottom, and they became distributed uniformly from surface to bottom. By 4 P.M. most zoospores are at the bottom. Two to 3 hours after sunset the zoospores move upward because of a decrease in oxygen concentration below. On a cloudy day there is slightly more oxygen at the surface than on the bottom, therefore the zoospores are found mostly at the surface. There are very few or none in the middle layers or on the bottom. On a rainy day the oxygen is distributed nearly as on a cloudy day. The zoospores are scattered homogeneously as to depth throughout the day. Any lack of correlation between oxygen concentration and zoospore concentration could be due to the rain causing encysted zoospores to become motile. During summer and winter the oxygen concentration is most abundant at the surface and middle region of the lake. The zoospores are found in the surface layer throughout the daytime, apparently in an inactive state. When the temperature is unfavorable, as it is in this period, no vertical movement appears to take place. There are apparently no nighttime data, at least not after 8:00 P.M.

Congeneric species (*Pythium,* for example) evidently differ in their oxygen demands as a comparison of Suzuki's (1961a) and Lund's (1934) accounts seems to indicate.

F. Hydrogen-Ion Concentration

This factor of the environment has been most studied in connection with water fungi by A. Lund (1934) and more recently by Roberts (1963). Lund took careful notes on the occurrence of the water fungi at Danish sites with reference to pH. He divided the aquatic habitats examined by him into the following groups according to their pH: highly acid (pH 3.5–4.5), slightly acid (pH 5.5–6.8), neutrally acid (pH 5.3–7.5), neutrally alkaline (pH 6.5–7.7), constantly alkaline (pH 7.0–8.4).

[4] I wish to thank my colleague, Professor H. Ikuma, for this translation.

Lund found that a number of fungi were specific for highly acid waters, some being fairly common and some quite rare. He concluded that fresh water phycomycetes may occur in all types of waters so far as pH is concerned, *Achlya racemosa,* for example, being more or less constantly found. On the other hand, some species seem to be limited to, or at least prefer, certain types of habitats. For example, one group is peculiar to acid waters, other groups prefer neutrally alkaline or constantly alkaline waters. Lund listed seven species typical of highly acid waters and seven or eight others which seem to prefer alkaline waters. The slightly acid and neutrally acid waters did not seem to harbor any phycomycete flora peculiar to them. It has been our experience, as indicated earlier (page 63), that a group of water fungi exists which is highly characteristic of acid waters, as found in bogs. Among these might be mentioned the chytrids *Blyttiomyces helicus, Phlyctochytrium furcatum, Rhizidium verrucosum, Rhizidiomyces* sp. (near *bivellatus*), and such filamentous forms as *Pythium undulatum,* and *Achyla* (*Aplanes*) *treleaseana.* As A. Lund correctly pointed out, whether these fungi are dependent on the pH of the water alone for their occurrence, or whether other factors come into play, can be settled only experimentally. According to Hutchinson (1957), the presence of sulfuric acid is a characteristic of such environments and predilection for the sulfate ion as a source of sulfur is common but not universal in aquatic fungi. Indeed, reduction of sulfate and utilization of it as the sole source of sulfur for growth has been pointed to as evidence for the primitiveness of the chytrids. Lund felt that pH was not the decisive factor, primarily because many of the fungi which are obtained from acid habitats did well in water at pH 7.2–7.7. Other characteristics of his fungi, while under gross culture cultivation in the laboratory, also tend to reduce the significance of pH. Perhaps, as with certain other factors of the environment, the capacity to live and thrive under such low conditions of pH may be a definite competitive advantage to a fungus and this is the primary reason why we find them where they are. A great deal of work, particularly on bog chytrids, is needed in order to clear up in definitive fashion the real significance of pH as a factor in the distribution of these fungi in their environment.[5] Furthermore, just how much of a

[5] Dr. Willoughby has kindly added a welcome comment here which is reproduced *in toto*.

"In this connexion it is necessary to point out that in the aquatic environment pH cannot necessarily be considered in isolation because of its inter-relationship with dissolved carbon dioxide and bicarbonate. Already there is evidence from pure culture studies (Cantino and Lovett, 1964) that the concentration of the latter may be of importance to the growth of aquatic fungi in nature. Depletion of dissolved carbon dioxide by photosynthetic algae and higher plant activity can raise the pH considerably, particularly in water bodies with a low bicarbonate content; conversely

factor pH is in the formation of reproductive organs must be further investigated. Thus, Lilienstern (in A. Lund, 1934) found that a species of *Saprolegnia* studied by her developed sporangia most readily on acid substrata (pH 2.6 and 5.5) whereas oogonia were most readily produced at an alkaline reaction (pH 7.3, 8.0). As A. Lund, in noting Lilienstern's paper, pointed out, some species will thrive vegetatively on both acid and alkaline substrata, whereas the formation of reproductive organs seems to be conditioned by a specific range of pH. Lund himself found in his investigations that this same species of fungus used by Lilienstern (*Saprolegnia monoica*) occurred in all types of aquatic habitats. Krause (1960) found oogonia of *Saprolegnia ferax* formed only in a range of pH 5.2–7.2, pH 5.8–6.9 being optimal. The lack of agreement between the pH at which the organism apparently thrives in nature and the pH at which it grows under laboratory conditions is constantly repeated in other fungi which have been examined experimentally. Lund found that *Monoblepharis* species had a definite preference for alkaline waters. Perrott, however, observed (1960) that certain species of this genus were to be obtained only in neutrally acid waters (pH 5.3–7.5), whereas others such as *M. macrandra* occurred in waters ranging from constantly alkaline (pH 7.0–8.4) to neutrally acid. She suggested that this is probably the reason why this particular species is the commonest one recorded by investigators. It is also the one which Unestam (1966a) found under laboratory conditions assumed its optimal growth in shake culture at pH 6.0–6.5, whereas in an agar medium this value was about pH 7.0. Perrott states that the rarer *M. fasciculata, M. insignis,* etc., occurred primarily in neutrally acid waters (pH 5.2–7.5).

Roberts (1963) made a somewhat similar study to that of A. Lund concerning pH and the distribution of the Saprolegniales in 21 natural waters in the United Kingdom. An attempt was made to compare the

---

pH may fall if respiratory products accumulate. These effects may apply on a seasonal or even diurnal basis. Thus for Esthwaite Water (English Lake District) Talling (1966) has recorded pH values between 6.8 and 9.4 for surface water samples within a period of fourteen days, the fluctuation being ascribed to photosynthetic activity.

"Many other examples are known, for example Whitney (1942) has reported similarly for ponds. Megard (1961) has reported that a similar pH range may even occur in a series of samples taken in depth profile on a single day. Thus it is important that wide conclusions should not be drawn from a single pH determination in the field; and other related factors should be considered. Some possible general pH effects on water mould metabolism in the natural environment might be predicted from *in vitro* studies, e.g., increased solubility and availability of certain cations such as calcium and magnesium at low pH. More particular effects of pH on the formation of reproductive structures have been studied."

distribution of saprophytic species in waters of differing pH, ranging from acid bogs to constantly alkaline lakes. It was found they fell into three groups: (1) acid group in soft waters (pH below 5.2); (2) alkaline group in waters with pH above 7.8; (3) neutral group, i.e., species found over a wide range of pH (5.6–7.4) with the greatest number confined to pH 5.2–7.4. She also pointed out that the "ion" content of the water is not the only factor which determines distribution of these fungi. The type of decaying vegetation, i.e., substratum, found in acid waters as opposed to that in alkaline ones may be a more decisive factor. "Acid" species may be capable of breaking down debris unaided by bacteria which are scarce at low pH, whereas those in alkaline waters where bacteria abound, may only be able to utilize secondary degradation products.

Suzuki and Hatakeyama (1960) studied two lakes of contrasting types, that is, acid and neutral. *Pythium* was found only in neutral lakes, whereas *Saprolegnia diclina, Aplanes braunii,* and *Leptolegnia caudata* were recovered only from acid lake water.

Suzuki (1960d) observed in certain small, shallow lakes of volcanic origin in Japan (see also page 64) that the distribution of aquatic fungi was closely correlated to acidity and the amount of mineral components in the water. He stated that *Saprolegnia monoica* var. *acidamica* was found only in inorganic acidotrophic lakes, that is, those which varied in pH from 1.9 to 5.8 and were high in mineral acids. *Pythium,* on the other hand, was found in neutral lakes and never in acidic ones, a statement somewhat at variance with results recorded in a later paper (Suzuki, 1961d). In a more extensive study of acidotrophic lakes, Suzuki (1961d) indicated that fungi were very scarce or absent in the bottom mud of such lakes but he was able to isolate five from the water. In the lakes of lowest pH (1.9–2.75) no fungi were found. In the others, which varied from pH 2.9 to 5.8, one or more fungi were discovered. The greatest number (4) in any one lake was in that at pH 5.8.

Suzuki and Nimura (1961a,b) noted that aquatic hyphomycetes were abundant in harmonious lakes (pH 6.2–6.5) and scarce or lacking in acidotrophic ones. Few were found in dystrophic lakes. *Tricladium gracile* var. *oxyphilum* and *Anguillospora longissima* dominated in highly acidic waters. *Lemonniera aquatica* and *Anguillospora longissima* seem to adapt to acidotrophic lakes containing large amounts of mineral acids. They found that almost all the leaves which they tested for hyphomycetes in harmonious lakes yielded them, whereas fungi were infrequent or absent in acidotrophic and dystrophic lakes. Fungus production in acidotrophic lakes was correlated not only with pH but with the amount of mineral elements present. Of the 14 hyphomycetes recovered, five were obtained from acidotrophic lakes and nine from harmonious lakes. Only one from the former was not also found in harmonious lakes, namely, the *Tricladium* variety mentioned earlier. Laboratory experiments supported the data found in the field.

G. *Other Factors*

Several other habitat factors might be briefly mentioned. Harvey (1942) has suggested that altitude affects the distribution of water molds belonging to the Saprolegniaceae. In California at 1100 feet he found water samples from aquatic sites to be rich in water molds whereas at increased altitudes such fungi became fewer and fewer. In a lake at 4600 feet an asexual strain of *Aphanomyces* was found in abundance (presumably nothing else); in another at 6750 feet only one specimen, an asexual saprolegnian was found, while at several nearby lakes at this same altitude, no members of the group were found. Neither water nor soil samples taken at 6000 feet produced members of the Saprolegniales. Other factors in addition to altitude must have been at work at the above sites, for Gregory and Wentworth (1937) have reported a species of *Achlya* from a small lake at the summit of Mauna Kea on the island of Hawaii, at an altitude of 13,000 feet, and on Maui we (Sparrow, 1965b) isolated from soil the same zoosporic phycomycete (*Rhizophlyctis rosea*) at sea level, and at 10,000 feet elevation on Haleakala Volcano, and another (*Rhizophydium sphaerocarpum*) from the latter site.

The production of potent fungistatic and fungicidal substances by algae, fungi, or other members of the aquatic community will, no doubt, in the future be found to be habitat factors of influence in the ecology of aquatic fungi. Owing, however, to the nature of the medium, the effect of these may not be so evident as in soils.

Needless to say, the impact of the whole biotic environment on these organisms will someday have to be assessed.

VIII. PHENOLOGY (SEASONAL OCCURRENCE)

There is a fair body of information on this aspect of aquatic fungi. Coker (1923) followed the seasonal occurrence of a number of the Saprolegniaceae. He stated that for the great majority of species, spring is the most favorable season for growth. Little difference was found between winter and summer occurrence in North Carolina, ten fungi appearing more frequently in warm weather and nine in colder months. Suzuki (1960c) followed seasonal changes in aquatic fungi of Senshun-ike Pond through a period of one year. *Achlya flagellata* and *Pythium* spp. were seen throughout the year, whereas *A. racemosa* and *Apodachlya brachynema* were found only in winter. Zoospore production was influenced by temperature as well as "prosperity and decay of lacustrine bacteria" and took place in a "stepwise" manner with rise in temperature. Suzuki also followed the seasonal variation in numbers of zoospores in several lakes. However, his quantitative data, as earlier indicated, must be taken with reserve. He stated (1960b) that in one lake (Shinseiko) the number of zoospores increased in spring and autumn and decreased in summer and winter. *Saprolegnia monoica, S. diclina, Isoachlya eccentrica, Dictyuchus* sp., and *Aphanomyces* sp. were seen from autumn to early spring; *Achlya* was found mostly in summer; and *Pythium* throughout the year, with maxima in spring and autumn. The vertical distribution of the zoospores varied with the seasons. Two types of distribution were recognized (1) homogeneous, occurring during the circulation period and (2) stratified, taking place during stagnation (both summer and winter?). *Aphanomyces* and *Pythium* zoospores were in the surface layer during stagnation, but during circulation the former was mostly in the bottom layer. Further information of a similar nature is given by Suzuki (1960a, 1961e,g) on *Aphanomyces, Achlya,* and *Pythium.* In another lake the zoospore maximum appeared in early winter, with 65 zoospores per 10 ml of water. None was found in summer. *Saprolegnia monoica, S. ferax, Achlya flagellata,* and *Dictyuchus* sp. were found mostly in the winter, and *Aphanomyces* and *Pythium* occurred throughout the year with maxima in the winter time.

Waterhouse (1942) noted in the Hogsmill River study conducted over period of two years (page 48) that most fungi had a seasonal rhythm appearing in September or October, rising to a maximum in December to February and disappearing in summer. One species of *Pythium* was collected throughout the year. The autumnal renewal of growth was correlated with increased rainfall (flood water), the abundance of natural substratum (fruits, twigs, and so forth), declining temperature, and possibly change in pH. The disappearance in summer was attributed to higher temperatures, falling water level, and a decrease in pH. Since the river maintained a good flow throughout the year, lack of water could not be a contributory factor to cessation of growth in summer. Furthermore, extremes of high temperature are less likely in flowing than in the relatively still water of a pond. Aquatic phycomycetes, like some algae, are probably very sensitive to poisonous materials in effluent and hence are undoubtedly good biological indicators of pollution, which Waterhouse thought might also play a part in limiting certain fungi. Unhappily this probably holds true for many if not most flowing waters in these times. No specific physical-chemical data are provided in her study.

Dayal and Tandon (1962) explored certain aquatic sites in India near the junction of the Gauga and Jumna rivers at 25° 26″ N. latitude for the seasonal occurrence of 12 phycomycetes. They found that species collected during October and November showed vigorous growth and produced sex organs within 2–4 weeks, whereas those collected in March and April produced identifiable growth only after 4–5 months. They reasoned from this that the oospores of these fungi remained dormant during the months following April, i.e., the summer months, and did not usually germinate until August or September. Their data indicated that most species of the Saprolegniales (*Saprolegnia, Isoachlya, Achlya, Aphanomyces,* and *Dictyuchus*) become dormant with the approach of high temperatures and germinate following low temperature. *Pythium carolinianum* also showed a summer period of dormancy. *Allomyces* showed a longer period of dormancy commencing earlier in winter and ending later in summer than the Saprolegniales. Indeed, the chart of their seasonal occurrence indicates that members of this genus are recoverable only during August and part of September. *Aphanomyces* sp. was the most commonly occurring species and was recoverable from August to April. These workers concluded that their fungi were restricted in occurrence mainly to the winter months.

Forbes (1935a,b) found in a study of phycomycetes in several ponds that there was a winter maximum followed by a decline and eventual disappearance in summer. She also cited work by Allen with water molds of the Bristol area in which a similar pattern was observed, with a maximum in January. Milovtsova (1935, in Hughes, 1962) noted in the Kharkov region of the U.S.S.R. that *Saprolegnia* spp. were dominant in spring and *Achlya* in autumn, and, contrary to the instances just cited, the largest number was found in June or July. Naumov (1954, in Hughes, 1962) discovered two maxima, one in early spring and one in late autumn. In India, Chaudhuri *et al.* (1947, in Hughes, 1962) report that favorable growth periods are in October to mid-December and February to May. It is obvious that such data unaccompanied by measurement of seasonal temperatures, latitude, etc., are susceptible to only limited interpretation.

Hughes (1962) studied in the southern United States (Georgia) in water and soils, a somewhat different aspect of the seasonal occurrence of the Saprolegniaceae. He found in this area that these fungi could be placed in two groups of species with respect to seasonal periodicity. One, with centric and subcentric oospores, showed marked seasonal periodicity and variation in abundance, and the other with eccentric oospores had no such discernible pattern. The periodicity of the first group seemed associated with temperature, whereas in the eccentric-oospored group the effect of temperature was negligible. Keeping these two groups in mind, Hughes found it easy to clarify some of the conflicting periodicity patterns reported in the literature. Thus, the periodicity pattern described by Forbes

(1935b) in England differs radically from that noted by Coker (1923) in North Carolina. In the former, over 85% of the isolates were species forming centric or subcentric oospores, whereas in North Carolina numbers of the nonperiodic eccentric-oospore group were high enough throughout the year effectively to obscure the actual periodicity pattern of the centric oospore species. The latter pattern, in fact, was identical with the English one.

Roberts (1963), in connection with a study of the distribution of Saprolegniales in relation to pH, at various sites in the United Kingdom, noted a seasonal periodicity of occurrence. As shown by others, there was a pronounced drop in species recovered during summer. This occurred in both acid and alkaline habitats. It was found, however, that individual species had different types of periodicity throughout the year. Thus, it was possible to group the 27 different species recovered into three categories, (a) winter species (13), absent from May to November; (b) summer species (6), low frequency of occurrence in January to March; (c) constant species (8) which were isolated throughout the year. These were considered reflections of the seasonal variation in zoospore production due to differing temperature requirements. She was aware, however, that Salvin's (1941) work showed that zoospore germination factors, in addition to temperature, included oxygen and the nutrients present, and that all these should be considered. Roberts also noted the percentage frequencies of the oospore types, namely, centric 50%, subcentric 26.9%, and eccentric 23.1%, a pattern similar to that found by most others working in England.

Seasonal occurrence would certainly seem to be intimately associated with temperature and its effects. It is probable that this, perhaps more than any other factor, is operative in determining differences in the times of the year at which fungi are found. Temperature may also act indirectly to restrict competition for the substratum by other fungi or even by algae. This has been proved by common practice over many years when certain so-called "rare" groups of fungi have been induced to appear under laboratory conditions on natural substrata at low temperatures (3–5°C), where competition from coarser organisms, thriving at higher temperatures, is eliminated.

Twig- and fruit-inhabiting forms such as *Blastocladia* and *Rhipidium* have been reported by A. Lund (1934) and others (see, however, Waterhouse, 1942) to be present at all seasons of the year (except perhaps February and March) in temperate regions. Therefore these fungi seem to be little affected by temperature in water. Others appear to be highly seasonal, and this may be linked primarily again to water temperature as it affects growth, reproductive processes, and competition. Earlier reference has been made to Bock (1956), who emphasizes that there is a preponderance of the nonsexual stage of saprolegnian's in warmer months as compared with spring, when all phases of the life cycle undergo development.

The experienced collector of phycomycetes wishing to find unusual and rare mycelial forms has the best success in the spring, May being outstanding in temperate regions. Twigs and so forth at this time frequently support rich growths of such fungi as *Sapromyces, Araiospora, Monoblepharis,* etc., which are usually difficult to find or are absent in warmer weather, their place being then taken by commoner saprolegnians and algae.

IX. EVIDENCE FOR SUCCESSION

Evidence for the occurrence of ecological succession in aquatic fungi has not as yet been assembled although, from accounts in the literature and from common observation, it undoubtedly occurs. It is most strikingly seen when laboratory gross cultures of such things as sphagnum bog and pond water samples are baited with pine pollen. Within a period of as short as 48 hours there may be an "explosion" of a single species of chytrid on the pollen. As the days go on this population is succeeded by another or several others until, save for bacteria and flagellates, activity seems to be at a standstill. It is not unusual for several kinds of chytrids to establish the original population which as before, is then followed by mixtures of other types. If the grains lie close together in the water as they do in nature in the spring, dwarfed *Saprolegnia* and even appressorial species of *Pythium* will develop. Bacteria and occasional flagellates are, however, in our experience always the final inhabitants of the attacked pollen. Other instances of what is possible succession which are well known to aquatic mycologists might be cited. For example, newly notched corticated sticks left in submerged traps have the freshly exposed surfaces occupied by various fungi as well as by bacteria and protozoa and later imperfects. Similarly, sticks brought into the laboratory and left submerged at low temperature (for example 1°C) may at first yield interesting phycomycetes, such as *Monoblepharis, Apodachlya,* but their place is eventually taken by imperfects and mycelial fungi with clamp connections. The latter two groups persist and increase in variety over many years.

Kanouse (1926) and others describe sequences of fungi on rosaceous fruits in water which are suggestive of succession.

X. THE QUESTION OF COMMUNITIES

When we find several species invariably occurring together, we suspect that we are dealing with a community in the ecological sense of that term. Yet this may, in fact, be a mere aggregation of individuals which have selected the same habitat, and there is, in fact, no interdependence or mutual benefit involved. Thus, rosaceous fruits submerged for several weeks in water are commonly covered with whitish pustules. These, as von Minden (1916) first pointed out, and as has been our experience, are most frequently composed of representatives of two or three, sometimes more, genera of phycomycetes, notably, *Rhipidium, Blastocladia, Gonapodya,* and *Phytophthora.* Since the first three of these are also found commonly on submerged twigs they give the appearance, at least, of a community. Another striking aggregation on twigs is composed of various species of *Monoblepharis* (Sparrow, 1933, 1966; Perrott, 1955), or of these as well as *Apodachlya* and *Araiospora.* The fungi, primarily chytrids, inhabiting the evacuated larval cases (exuviae) of aquatic insects, such as mayflies, midges, caddisflies, might also be mentioned. Here, are rather constantly found, species of *Rhizoclosmatium, Siphonaria, Asterophlyctis, Aphanomyces,* etc. (H. E. Petersen, 1903; Sparrow, 1937). Only rarely in our experience are these substrata (twigs, apples, integuments) occupied by a single species of aquatic fungus. Just once, for example, have we found a submerged apple covered with pustules of a single species of arborescent phycomycete, in this case *Mindeniella spinospora.*

XI. GEOGRAPHIC DISTRIBUTION

Aquatic fungi have been found wherever they have been searched for except in extreme habitats, as for example, acidotrophic lakes (pH 1.9+) (Suzuki, 1961d). It was early realized from the work of Thaxter (1895a,b, 1896a,b, 1903) and others (e.g., von Minden, 1916) that the European and American floras were alike, and all subsequent work has confirmed this. Since soil is readily transportable, a great deal is known about the geographic distribution of terrestrial zoosporic phycomycetes, which, very often, are identical to those found in water. These as well as observations on aquatic hyphomycetes also confirm the ubiquity of most of the species. A glance, for example, at the papers of Karling (1944a–c), Beneke and Rogers (1962), Harder (1954), Höhnk (1962), Gaertner (1954), Persiel (1960), Harder and Gallwitz-Uebelmesser (1959), Crooks (1937), Jeffrey and Willoughby (1964), Das-Gupta and John (1953), Emerson (1941), Ingold (1958, 1959a), Tubaki (1957, 1958), Willoughby (1965b), Indoh (1940), Kobayashi and Ookubu (1954a), and Shen and Siang (1948) will show no appreciable differences between the aquatic fungus floras of the Hemispheres. Even such isolated land masses as those of the Hawaiian chain (Sparrow, 1965b), "Oceania" (Persiel *et al.,* 1966), and remote coral atolls (Sparrow, 1948) have fungi readily identifiable with continental species. Most striking in our experience was the recovery in a remote bog on the island of Kauai of the Hawaiian chain of several morphologically distinctive species on chitin, which have been regularly encountered on this substratum in a like habitat in Northern Michigan (Sparrow, 1965b). Harvey (1942) has suggested the possibility of endemism in a study of California saprolegnians but no well-defined instances are given. Nonetheless, it cannot be dismissed as unlikely for only intensive floristic work over the years will give the answer.

REFERENCES

Ajello, L. (1948). A cytological and nutritional study of *Polychytrium aggregatum* Part II. Nutrition. *Am. J. Botany* **35**: 135–140.

Anastasiou, C. J. (1963). Fungi from salt lakes, II. Ascomycetes and Fungi Imperfecti from the Salton Sea. *Nova Hedwigia* **6**: 243–276.

Antikajian, G. (1949). A developmental, morphological, and cytological study of *Asterophlyctis* with special reference to its sexuality, taxonomy, and relationships. *Am. J. Botany* **36**: 245–262.

Apinis, A. E. (1964). Concerning occurrence of Phycomycetes in alluvial soils of certain pastures, marshes and swamps. *Nova Hedwigia* **8**: 103–126.

Beneke, E. S., and A. L. Rogers. (1962). Aquatic Phycomycetes isolated in the states of Minas Gerais, São Paulo and Paraná, Brazil. *Rickia* (*São Paulo*) **1**: 181–193.

Beneke, E. S., and J. A. Schmitt. (1961). Aquatic fungi from South Bass and neighboring islands in Western Lake Erie. I. Uniflagellate and biflagellate Phycomycetes. *Ohio J. Sci.* **61**: 283–285.

Beneke, E. S., and J. A. Schmitt. (1962). Aquatic fungi from South Bass and neighboring islands in Western Lake Erie. II. Additional biflagellate and uniflagellate Phycomycetes. *Ohio J. Sci.* **62**: 11–12.

Bhargava, K. S. (1945). Physiological studies on some members of the family Saprolegniaceae. IV. Carbohydrate requirements. *Lloydia* **8**: 60–68.

Bock, K. J. (1956). Zur Ökologie und Systematik saprophytischer Wasserpilze aus dem Silbersee bei Bremerhaven. *Veroeffentl. Inst. Meeresforsch. Bremerhaven* **4**: 25–44.

Brock, T. D. (1966). "Principles of Microbial Ecology." Prentice-Hall, Englewood Cliffs, New Jersey.

Canter, H. M., and J. W. G. Lund. (1948). Studies on plankton parasites. I. Fluctuations in the numbers of *Asterionella formosa* Hass. in relation to fungal epidemics. *New Phytologist* **47**: 238–261.

Canter, H. M., and J. W. G. Lund. (1951). Studies on plankton parasites. III. Examples of the interaction between parasitism and other factors determining the growth of diatoms. *Ann. Botany* (*London*) [N.S.] **15**: 359–371.

Canter, H. M., and J. W. G. Lund. (1953). Studies on plankton parasites. II. The parasitism of diatoms with special reference to lakes in the English Lake District. *Brit. Mycol. Soc. Trans.* **36**: 13–37.

Cantino, E. C. (1948). The vitamin nutrition of an isolate of *Blastocladia pringsheimii*. *Am. J. Botany* **35**: 238–242.

Cantino, E. C. (1949a). The physiology of the aquatic phycomycete, *Blastocladia pringsheimii,* with emphasis on its nutrition and metabolism. *Am. J. Botany* **36:** 95–112.

Cantino, E. C. (1949b). The growth and nutrition of *Pythiogeton. Am. J. Botany* **36:** 747–756.

Cantino, E. C. (1950). Nutrition and phylogeny in the water molds. *Quart. Rev. Biol.* **25:** 269–277.

Cantino, E. C. (1955). Physiology and phylogeny in the water molds—a reevaluation. *Quart. Rev. Biol.* **30:** 138–149.

Cantino, E. C., and E. A. Horenstein. (1956). The stimulatory effect of light upon growth and CO_2 fixation in *Blastocladiella.* I. The S. K. I. cycle. *Mycologia* **48:** 777–779.

Cantino, E. C., and J. S. Lovett. (1964). Non-filamentous aquatic fungi: model systems for biochemical studies of morphological differentiation. *Advan. Morphogenesis* **3:** 33–93.

Cantino, E. C., and G. Turian. (1959). Physiology and development of lower fungi (Phycomycetes). *Ann. Rev. Microbiol.* **13:** 97–124.

Carlile, M. J., and L. Machlis. (1965). A comparative study of the chemotaxis of the motile phases of Allomyces. *Am. J. Botany* **52:** 484–486.

Cienkowski, L. (1861). Ueber parasitische Schlaüche auf Crustaceen. *Botan. Ztg.* **19:** 167–174.

Coker, W. C. (1923). "The Saprolegniaceae, With Notes on Other Water Molds." Univ. of North Carolina Press, Chapel Hill, North Carolina.

Collins, V. G., and L. G. Willoughby. (1962). The distribution of bacteria and fungal spores in Blelham Tarn with particular reference to an experimental overturn. *Arch. Mikrobiol.* **43:** 294–307.

Cooke, W. B. (1961). Pollution effects on the fungus population of a stream. *Ecology* **42:** 1–18.

Cooke, W. B. (1966). The occurrence of fungi in acid mine-drainage. *Proc. Ind. Waste Conf., Purdue Univ.* **21:** 258–274.

Cooke, W. B., and A. F. Bartsch. (1959). Aquatic fungi in water with high waste loads. *Sewage Ind. Wastes* **31:** 1316–1322.

Cooke, W. B., and A. F. Bartsch. (1960). Aquatic fungi in some Ohio streams. *Ohio J. Sci.* **60:** 144–148.

Cooke, W. B., and F. J. Ludzack. (1958). Predacious fungus behavior in activated sludge systems. *Sewage Ind. Wastes* **30:** 1490–1495.

Cooney, D. G., and R. Emerson. (1964). "Thermophilic Fungi." Freeman, San Francisco, California.

Cotner, F. B. (1930). Cytological study of the zoospores of *Blastocladia. Botan. Gaz.* **89:** 295–309.

Cowling, S. W., and J. S. Waid. (1963). Aquatic Hyphomycetes in Australia. *Australian J. Sci.* **26:** 122.

Crooks, K. M. (1937). Studies on Australian Phycomycetes. *Proc. Roy. Soc. Victoria* [N.S.] **49:** 206–233.

Cunnell, G. J. (1956). Some pycnidial fungi on *Carex. Brit. Mycol. Soc. Trans.* **39:** 21–47.

Cunnell, G. J. (1957). *Stagonospora* spp. on *Phragmites communis* Trin. *Brit. Mycol. Soc. Trans.* **40:** 443–455.

Cunnell, G. J. (1958). On *Robillardia phragmites* sp. nov. *Brit. Mycol. Soc. Trans.* **41:** 405–412.

Das-Gupta, S. N., and R. John. (1953). Studies in the Indian aquatic fungi. I. Some water moulds of Lucknow. *Proc. Indian Sci.* **B38**: 165–170.

Dayal, R., and R. N. Tandon. (1962). Ecological studies of some aquatic Phycomycetes. *Hydrobiologia* **20**: 121–127.

Dick, M. W. (1962). The occurrence and distribution of Saprolegniaceae in certain soils of south-east England. II. Distribution within defined areas. *J. Ecol.* **50**: 119–127.

Dick, M. W. (1963). The occurrence and distribution of Saprolegniaceae in certain soils of south-east England. III. Distribution in relation to pH and water content. *J. Ecol.* **51**: 75–81.

Dick, M. W. (1966). The Saprolegniaceae of the environs of Blelham Tarn: Sampling techniques and the estimation of propagule numbers. *J. Gen. Microbiol.* **42**: 257–282.

Dick, M. W., and H. V. Newby. (1961). The occurrence and distribution of Saprolegniaceae in certain soils of south-east England. I. Occurrence. *J. Ecol.* **49**: 403–419.

Emerson, R. (1941). An experimental study of the life cycles and taxonomy of *Allomyces. Lloydia* **4**: 77–144.

Emerson, R. (1950). Current trends of experimental research on the aquatic Phycomycetes. *Ann. Rev. Microbiol.* **4**: 169–200.

Emerson, R., and E. C. Cantino. (1948). The isolation, growth, and metabolism of *Blastocladia* in pure culture. *Am. J. Botany* **35**: 157–171.

Emerson, R., and W. H. Weston, Jr. (1967). *Aqualinderella fermentans* gen. et sp. nov., a Phycomycete adapted to stagnant waters. I. Morphology and occurrence in nature. *Am. J. Botany* **54**: 702–719.

Fischer, F. G., and G. Werner. (1955). Eine Analyse des Chemotropismus einiger Pilze, insbesondere der Saprolegniaceen. *Z. Physiol. Chem.* **300**: 211–236.

Fischer, F. G., and G. Werner. (1958a). Die chemotaxis der Schwärmsporen von Wasserpilzen (Saprolegniaceen). *Z. Physiol. Chem.* **310**: 65–91.

Fischer, F. G., and G. Werner. (1958b). Uber die Wirkungen von Nicotinsäureamid auf die Schwärmsporen wasserbewohnender Pilze. *Z. Physiol. Chem.* **310**: 92–96.

Forbes, E. J. (1935a). Observations on some British water moulds (Saprolegniales and Blastocladiales). *Brit. Mycol. Soc. Trans.* **19**: 221–239.

Forbes, E. J. (1935b). Water moulds of the Manchester District. *Mem. Proc. Manchester Lit. Phil. Soc.* **79**: 1–11 (separate).

Fuller, M. S., and R. O. Poyton. (1964). A new technique for the isolation of aquatic fungi. *BioScience* **14**: 45–46.

Gaertner, A. (1954). Über das Vorkommen niederer Erdphycomyceten in Afrika, Schweden und an einigen mitteleuropäischen Standorten. *Arch. Mikrobiol.* **21**: 4–56.

Glen-Bott, J. I. (1951). *Helicodendron giganteum* n. sp. and other aerial-sporing Hyphomycetes of submerged dead leaves. *Brit. Mycol. Soc. Trans.* **34**: 275–279.

Goldstein, S. (1960a). Factors affecting the growth and pigmentation of *Cladochytrium replicatum. Mycologia* **52**: 490–498.

Goldstein, S. (1960b). Physiology of aquatic fungi. I. Nutrition of two monocentric chytrids. *J. Bacteriol.* **80**: 701–707.

Golueke, C. G. (1957). Comparative studies of the physiology of *Sapromyces* and related genera. *J. Bacteriol.* **74**: 337–343.

Gregory, H. E., and C. K. Wentworth. (1937). General features and glacial geology of Mauna Kea, Hawaii. *Bull. Geol. Soc. Am.* **48**: 1719–1742.

Harder, R. (1948). Über das Vorkommen niederer Phycomyceten in deutschen Böden. *Nachr. Akad. Wiss. Goettingen, Math.-Physik. Kl., IIa. Math.-Physik.-Chem. Abt.* pp. 5–7.

Harder, R. (1954). Über die arktische Vegetation niederer Phycomyceten. *Nachr. Akad. Wiss. Goettingen, Math.-Physik. Kl., IIb. Biol.-Physiol.-Chem. Abt.* pp. 1–9.

Harder, R., and E. Gallwitz-Uebelmesser. (1959). Über niedere Erdphycomyceten Australiens. *Arch. Mikrobiol.* **32**: 115–126.

Harvey, J. V. (1925). A study of the water molds and pythiums occurring in the soils of Chapel Hill. *J. Elisha Mitchell Sci. Soc.* **41**: 151–164.

Harvey, J. V. (1927). A survey of the water molds and pythiums occurring in the soils of Wisconsin, as studied during the summer of 1926. *Trans. Wisconsin Acad. Sci.* **23**: 551–562.

Harvey, J. V. (1928). A survey of the water molds occurring in the soils of North Carolina, Wisconsin and Oklahoma. *Proc. Oklahoma Acad. Sci.* **7**: 135.

Harvey, J. V. (1942). A study of western watermolds. *J. Elisha Mitchell Sci. Soc.* **58**: 16–42.

Harvey, J. V. (1952). Relationship of aquatic fungi to water pollution. *Sewage Ind. Wastes* **24**: 1159–1164.

Haskins, R. H., and W. H. Weston, Jr. (1950). Studies in the lower Chytridiales. I. Factors affecting pigmentation, growth, and metabolism of a strain of *Karlingia* (*Rhizophlyctis*) *rosea*. *Am. J. Botany* **37**: 739–750.

Hickman, C. J., and H. H. Ho. (1966). Behavior of zoospores in plant-pathogenic Phycomycetes. *Ann. Rev. Phytopathol.* **4**: 195–220.

Höhnk, W. (1939). Ein Beitrag zur Kenntnis der Phycomyceten des Brackwassers. *Kiel. Meeresforsch.* **3**: 337–361.

Höhnk, W. (1952). Studien zur Brack- und Seewassermykologie. I. *Veroeffentl. Inst. Meeresforsch. Bremerhaven* **1**: 115–125.

Höhnk, W. (1953). Studien zur Brack- und Seewassermykologie. III. Oomycetes, 2. *Veroeffentl. Inst. Meeresforsch. Bremerhaven* **2**: 52–108.

Höhnk, W. (1962). Über die Phycomyceten der Insel Madeira. *Veroeffentl. Inst. Meeresforsch. Bremerhaven* **8**: 99–108.

Höhnk, W., and K. J. Bock. (1954). Ein Beitrag zur Ökologie der saprophytischen Wasserpilze. *Veroeffentl. Inst. Meeresforsch. Bremerhaven* **3**: 9–26.

Horenstein, E. A., and E. C. Cantino. (1961). Morphogenesis in and the effect of light on *Blastocladiella britannica* sp. nov. *Brit. Mycol. Soc. Trans.* **44**: 185–198.

Horenstein, E. A., and E. C. Cantino. (1962). Dark-induced morphogenesis in synchronized cultures of *Blastocladiella britannica*. *J. Bacteriol.* **84**: 37–45.

Hughes, G. C. (1962). Seasonal periodicity of the Saprolegniaceae in the south-eastern United States. *Brit. Mycol. Soc. Trans.* **45**: 519–531.

Hutchinson, G. E. (1957). "A Treatise on Limnology," Vol. I. Geography, Physics and Chemistry. Wiley, New York.

Indoh, H. (1940). Studies on Japanese aquatic fungi. II. The Blastocladiaceae. *Sci. Rept. Tokyo Bunrika Daigaku* **B4**: 237–284.

Ingold, C. T. (1942). Aquatic Hyphomycetes of decaying alder leaves. *Brit. Mycol. Soc. Trans.* **25**: 339–417.

Ingold, C. T. (1943). Further observations on aquatic Hyphomycetes of decaying leaves. *Brit. Mycol. Soc. Trans.* **26**: 104–114.

Ingold, C. T. (1951). Aquatic Ascomycetes: *Ceriospora caudae-suis* n. sp. and *Ophiobolus typhae. Brit. Mycol. Soc. Trans.* **34:** 210–215.
Ingold, C. T. (1954). Aquatic Ascomycetes: Discomycetes from lakes. *Brit. Mycol. Soc. Trans.* **37:** 1–18.
Ingold, C. T. (1955). Aquatic Ascomycetes: Further species from the English Lake District. *Brit. Mycol. Soc. Trans.* **38:** 157–168.
Ingold, C. T. (1958). Aquatic Hyphomycetes from Uganda and Rhodesia. *Brit. Mycol. Soc. Trans.* **41:** 109–114.
Ingold, C. T. (1959a). Aquatic spora of Omo Forest, Nigeria. *Brit. Mycol. Soc. Trans.* **42:** 479–485.
Ingold, C. T. (1959b). Submerged aquatic Hyphomycetes. *J. Quekett Microscop. Club* [4] **5:** 115–130.
Ingold, C. T. (1960). Aquatic Hyphomycetes in southern Rhodesia. *Rhodesia Sci. Assoc., Proc. Trans.* **48:** 49–53.
Ingold, C. T. (1961). Another aquatic spore-type with clamp connexions. *Brit. Mycol. Soc. Trans.* **44:** 27–30.
Ingold, C. T. (1966). The tetraradiate aquatic fungal spore. *Mycologia* **58:** 43–56.
Ingold, C. T., and B. Chapman. (1952). Aquatic Ascomycetes: *Loramyces juncicola* Weston and *L. macrospora* n. sp. *Brit. Mycol. Soc. Trans.* **35:** 268–272.
Jeffrey, J. M., and L. G. Willoughby. (1964). A note on the distribution of Allomyces in Australia. *Nova Hedwigia* **7:** 507–515.
Kanouse, B. B. (1926). On the distribution of the watermolds . . . *Papers Mich. Acad. Sci.* **5:** 105–114.
Karling, J. S. (1944a). Brazilian chytrids. I. Species of *Nowakowskiella. Bull. Torrey Botan. Club* **71:** 374–389.
Karling, J. S. (1944b). Brazilian chytrids. II. New species of *Rhizidium. Am. J. Botany* **31:** 254–261.
Karling, J. S. (1944c). Brazilian anisochytrids. *Am. J. Botany* **31:** 391–397.
Karling, J. S. (1947). Keratinophilic chytrids. II. *Phlyctorhiza variabilis* n. sp. *Am. J. Botany* **34:** 27–32.
Karling, J. S. (1964). Indian chytrids. I. Eucarpic monocentric species. *Sydowia* **17:** 285–296.
Kobayasi, Y., and M. Ookubo. (1952). Studies on the aquatic fungi of Ozegahara Moor. (2). *J. Japan. Botany* **27:** 181–188.
Kobayasi, Y., and M. Ookubo. (1954a). Studies on the aquatic fungi of the Ozegahara Moor. (3). *Gen. Sci. Survey Comm.* pp. 561–575.
Kobayasi, Y., and M. Ookubo. (1954b). On a new genus *Oedogoniomyces* of the Blastocladiaceae. *Bull. Natl. Sci. Museum (Tokyo)* [N.S.] **1:** 59–66.
Krause, R. (1960). Bildung der Oogonien bei *Saprolegnia ferax* (Gruith.) Thuret. *Arch. Mikrobiol.* **36:** 373–386.
Lackey, J. B. (1939). Aquatic life in waters polluted by acid mine waste. *Public Health Rept. (U.S.)* **54:** 740–746.
Lund, A. (1934). Studies on Danish freshwater Phycomycetes and notes on their occurrence particularly relative to the hydrogen ion concentration of the water. *Mem. Acad. Roy. Sci. Danemark, Sect. Sci.* [9] **6:** 1–97.
Lund, J. W. G. (1957). Fungal diseases of plankton algae. *In* "Biological Aspects of the Transmission of Disease" (C. Horton-Smith, ed.), pp. 19–23. Oliver & Boyd, Edinburgh and London.
Machlis, L. (1958). Evidence for a sexual hormone in *Allomyces. Physiol. Plantarum* **11:** 181–192.

Maurizio, A. (1899). Beiträge zur Biologie der Saprolegnieen. *Mitt. Deut. Fischerei-Verein* **7**: 1–66 (reprint).

Megard, R. O. (1961). The diel cycle of stratification and productivity in two lakes of the Chuska Mountains, New Mexico. *Am. Midland Naturalist* **66**: 110–127.

Miller, C. E. (1961). Some aquatic Phycomycetes from Lake Texoma. *J. Elisha Mitchell Sci. Soc.* **77**: 293–298.

Miller, C. E. (1965). Observations on some parasitic aquatic Phycomycetes. *J. Elisha Mitchell Sci. Soc.* **81**: 4–9.

Müller, F. (1911). Untersuchungen über die chemotaktische Reizbarkeit der Zoosporen von Chytridaceen und Saprolegniaceen. *Jahrb. Wiss. Botan.* **49**: 421–521.

Murray, C. L., and J. S. Lovett. (1966). Nutritional requirements of the chytrid *Karlingia asterocysta,* an obligate chitinophile. *Am. J. Botany* **53**: 469–476.

Nagai, M. (1931). Studies on the Japanese Saprolegniaceae. *J. Fac. Agr., Hokkaido Imp. Univ.* **32**: 1–43.

Nilsson, S. (1964). Freshwater Hyphomycetes. Taxonomy, morphology and ecology. *Symbolae Botan. Upsalienses* **18**: 1–130.

Nybelin, O. (1931). Undersökningar över kräftpestens orsak. *Ny Svensk Fiskeritidskr.* pp. 144–149.

Nybelin, O. (1934). Nya undersökningar över kräftpestens orsak. *Ny Svensk Fiskeritidskr.* pp. 110–114.

Nybelin, O. (1936). Untersuchungen über die Ursache der in Schweden gegenwärtig vorkommenden Krebpest. *Medd. Undersoeknanst. Soetvaltensfisk. (Stockholm)* p. 9.

Ookubo, M. (1954). Studies on the aquatic fungi collected in the moor and ponds of Hakkôda. *Nagaoa* **4**: 48–60.

Ookubo, M., and Y. Kobayasi. (1955). Studies on the water moulds on keratinized materials. *Nagaoa* **5**: 1–10.

Paterson, R. A. (1960). Infestation of chytridiaceous fungi on phytoplankton in relation to certain environmental factors. *Ecology* **41**: 416–424.

Paterson, R. A. (1966). Personal communication.

Paterson, R. A. (1967). Benthic and planktonic Phycomycetes from Northern Michigan. *Mycologia* **59**: 405–416.

Perrott, P. E. (1955). The genus *Monoblepharis, Brit. Mycol. Soc. Trans.* **38**: 247–282.

Perrott, P. E. (1960). The ecology of some aquatic Phycomycetes. *Brit. Mycol. Soc. Trans.* **43**: 19–30.

Persiel, I. (1960). Über die Verbreitung niederer Phycomyceten in Böden aus verschiedenen Höhenstufen der Alpen und an einigen Standorten subtropischer und tropischer Gebirge. *Arch. Mikrobiol.* **36**: 257–262.

Persiel, I., E. Scholz, and R. Harder. (1966). Chytridiales und einige andere niedere Phycomyceten aus Ozeanien. *Arch. Mikrobiol.* **53**: 173–177.

Petersen, H. E. (1903). Note sur les Phycomycètes observés dans les téguments vides der nymphes des Phryganeés avec description de trois espèces nouvelles des Chytridinées, *J. Botan. (Paris)* **17**: 214–222.

Petersen, H. E. (1910). An account of Danish freshwater-Phycomycetes, with biological and systematical remarks. *Ann. Mycologici* **8**: 494–560.

Petersen, R. H. (1962). Aquatic Hyphomycetes from North America. I. Aleuriosporae (Part I), and key to genera. *Mycologia* **54**: 117–151.

Petersen, R. H. (1963a). II. Aleuriosporae (Part 2) and Blastosporae. *Mycologia* **55**: 18–29.

Petersen, R. H. (1963b). III. Phialosporae and miscellaneous species. *Mycologia* **55**: 570–581.

Pfeffer, W. (1884). Lokmotorische Richtungsbewegungen durch chemische Reize. *Untersuch. Botan. Inst. Tubingen* **1**: 466–467.

Prowse, G. A. (1954). *Aphanomyces daphniae* sp. nov., parasitic on *Daphnia, hyalina. Brit. Mycol. Soc. Trans.* **37**: 22–28.

Ranzoni, F. V. (1953). The aquatic Hyphomycetes of California. *Farlowia* **4**: 353–398.

Reinboldt, B. (1951). Über die Verteilung einiger niederer Phycomyceten im Erdboden. *Arch. Mikrobiol.* **16**: 177–200.

Reischer (Vishniac), H. S. (1949). The effect of temperature on the papillation of oogonia of *Achlya colorata. Mycologia* **41**: 398–402.

Reischer (Vishniac), H. S. (1951). Growth of Saprolegniaceae in synthetic media. I. Inorganic nutrition. *Mycologia* **43**: 142–155.

Reisert, P. S., and M. S. Fuller. (1962). Decomposition of chitin by *Chytriomyces* species. *Mycologia* **54**: 647–657.

Rennerfelt, E. (1936). Untersuchungen über die Entwicklung und Biologie des Krebspestpilzes *Aphanomyces astaci* Schikora. *Mitt. Anstalt Binnenfischerei Drottningholm* 10. (In Unestam, 1965.)

Roberts, R. E. (1963). A study of the distribution of certain members of the Saprolegniales. *Brit. Mycol. Soc. Trans.* **46**: 213–224.

Salvin, S. B. (1941). Comparative studies on the primary and secondary zoospores of the Saprolegniaceae. I. Influence of temperature. *Mycologia* **33**: 592–600.

Sánchez, A., and R. P. Korf. (1966). The genus *Vibrissea,* and the generic names *Leptosporium, Apostemium, Apostemidium, Gorgoniceps* and *Ophiogloea. Mycologia* **58**: 722–737.

Schade, A. L. (1940). The nutrition of *Leptomitus. Am. J. Botany* **27**: 376–384.

Schade, A. L., and K. V. Thimann. (1940). The metabolism of the watermold, *Leptomitus lacteus. Am. J. Botany* **27**: 659–670.

Schäperclaus, W. (1935). Die Ursache der pestartigen Krebssterben. *Z. Fischerei* **33**: 343–366. (In Unestam, 1965.)

Schikora, F. (1903). Über die Krebpest und ihren Erreger. *Fischereiztg. (Neudamm)* **6**: 353–355.

Schikora, F. (1906). Die Krebpest. *Fischereiztg. (Neudamm)* **9**: 529–532, 549–555, 561–566, and 581–583.

Schikora, F. (1922). Über die Krebpest und ihrer Erreger *Aphanomyces magnusii* Schikora. *Verhandl. Botan. Ver. Brandenburg* **63**: 87–88.

Scholz, E. (1958). Über niedere Phycomyceten aus Salzböden und ihr Verhalten in Salzlösungen. *Arch. Mikrobiol.* **30**: 119–146.

Scott, W. W. (1961). A monograph of the genus *Aphanomyces. Virginia Agr. Expt. Sta. Tech. Bull.* **151**: 1–95.

Scott, W. W., and A. H. O'Bier. (1962). Aquatic fungi associated with diseased fish and fish eggs. *Progressive Fish-Culturist* **24**: 3–15.

Shen, S., and W. N. Siang. (1948). Studies in the aquatic Phycomycetes of China. *Sci. Rept. Natl. Tsing Hua Univ.* **B3**: 179–203.

Skuja, H. (1948). Taxonomie des Phytoplanktons einiger Seen in Uppland, Schweden. *Symbolae Botan. Upsalienses* **9**: 1–399.

Sparrow, F. K., Jr. (1933). The Monoblepharidales. *Ann. Botany* (*London*) **47:** 517–542.

Sparrow, F. K., Jr. (1937). Some chytridiaceous inhabitants of submerged insect exuviae. *Proc. Am. Phil. Soc.* **78:** 23–53.

Sparrow, F. K., Jr. (1948). Soil Phycomycetes from Bikini, Eniwetok, Rongerik and Rongelap atolls. *Mycologia* **40:** 445–453.

Sparrow, F. K., Jr. (1965a). A preliminary note on a population of *Monoblepharis. Brit. Mycol. Soc. Trans.* **48:** 55–58.

Sparrow, F. K., Jr. (1965b). The occurrence of *Physoderma* in Hawaii, with notes on other Hawaiian Phycomycetes. *Mycopathol. Mycol. Appl.* **25:** 119–143.

Sparrow, F. K., Jr. (1966). A new bog chytrid. *Arch. Mikrobiol.* **53:** 178–180.

Springer, M. (1945). A morphologic study of the genus *Monoblepharella. Am. J. Botany* **32:** 259–269.

Stjerna-Pooth, I. (1957). *Achlya prolifera* als Abwasserpilz in einem mittelschwedischen Wasserlauf. *Inst. Freshwater Res. Rept. Drottningholm* **38:** 247–266.

Strasburger, E. (1878). Wirkung des Lichtes und der Warme auf Schwärmsporen. *Jena. Z. Naturwiss.* **12:** 551–625.

Suzuki, S. (1960a). Ecological studies on the genus *Aphanomyces* (aquatic fungi) in Japanese lakes. *Japan. J. Limnol.* **21:** 17–24. (Since these Japanese papers are not generally known a rather complete list is included here.)

Suzuki, S. (1960b). Seasonal variation in the amount of zoospores of aquatic Phycomycetes in Lake Shinseiko. *Botan. Mag.* (*Tokyo*) **73:** 483–486.

Suzuki, S. (1960c). The seasonal variation of aquatic fungi in Senshunike pond. *Japan. J. Limnol.* **21:** 271–278.

Suzuki, S. (1960d). Microbiological studies on the lakes of Volcano Bandai. I. Ecological studies on aquatic Phycomycetes in the Goshikinuma Lake group. *Japan. J. Ecol.* **10:** 172–176.

Suzuki, S. (1960e). The seasonal variation of aquatic Phycomycetes in Lake Nakanuma. *Japan. J. Ecol.* **10:** 215–218.

Suzuki, S. (1960f). Ecological studies on the aquatic fungi in the Arakawa River. *Japan. J. Limnol.* **21:** 25–31.

Suzuki, S. (1960g). Distribution of aquatic Phycomycetes in a river polluted by municipal wastes. *J. Waterworks Sewerage Assoc.* (*Tokyo*) **35:** 51–54. (In Japanese.)

Suzuki, S. (1961a). The seasonal changes of aquatic fungi in the lake bottom of Lake Nakanuma. *Botan. Mag.* (*Tokyo*) **74:** 30–33.

Suzuki, S. (1961b). The diurnal migration of zoospores of aquatic fungi in a shallow lake. *Botan. Mag.* (*Tokyo*) **74:** 138–141.

Suzuki, S. (1961c). The vertical distribution of the zoospores of aquatic fungi during the circulation and stagnation period. *Botan. Mag.* (*Tokyo*) **74:** 254–258.

Suzuki, S. (1961d). Distribution of aquatic Phycomycetes in some inorganic acidotrophic lakes of Japan. *Botan. Mag.* (*Tokyo*) **74:** 317–320.

Suzuki, S. (1961e). Ecological specificity of *Achlya,* a genus of aquatic fungi in Japanese lakes. *J. Japan. Botany* **36:** 11–15.

Suzuki, S. (1961f). On the ecological specificity of *Saprolegnia monoica* var. *acidamica. J. Japan. Botany* **36:** 292–295.

Suzuki, S. (1961g). Ecological studies on the genus *Pythium* (aquatic fungi) in Japanese lakes. *Japan. J. Ecol.* **11:** 91–93.

Suzuki, S. (1961h). Some considerations on anaerobic life of aquatic fungi in lake bottom. *Japan. J. Ecol.* **11**: 219–221.
Suzuki, S. (1961i). Ecological studies on aquatic fungi in the lakes of Volcano Nikko. *Japan. J. Ecol.* **11**: 1–4.
Suzuki, S. (1961j). On microorganisms in well waters. *J. Waterworks Sewerage Assoc.* (*Tokyo*) **36**: 53–54. (In Japanese.)
Suzuki, S., and T. Hatakeyama. (1960). Ecological studies on the aquatic fungi in the Shiga Lake group. *Japan. J. Limnol.* **21**: 64–72.
Suzuki, S., and T. Hatakeyama. (1961). Ecological studies on the aquatic fungi in Lake Yamanakako. *Japan. J. Ecol.* **11**: 173–175.
Suzuki, S., and H. Nimura. (1960a). The microbiological studies of the lakes of Volcano Bandai. II. Ecological study on aquatic Hyphomycetes in the Goshikinuma and Akanuma Lake group. *Botan. Mag.* (*Tokyo*) **73**: 360–364.
Suzuki, S., and H. Nimura. (1960b). Microbiological studies in the lakes of Volcano Bandai. III. The microbial populations in the Sunuma Lake group. *Japan. J. Ecol.* **10**: 189–193.
Suzuki, S., and H. Nimura. (1961a). Relation between the distribution of aquatic Hyphomycetes in Japanese lakes and lake types. *Botan. Mag.* (*Tokyo*) **74**: 51–55.
Suzuki, S., and H. Nimura. (1961b). Aquatic Hyphomycetes in the lakes of Volcano Shiga. *J. Japan. Botany* **36**: 135–138.
Suzuki, S., and H. Nimura. (1961c). Microbiological studies of the lakes of Volcano Bandai. V. The microbial populations in the Sohara Lake group. *Japan. J. Limnol.* **22**: 15–23.
Suzuki, S., and H. Nimura. (1961d). The vertical distributions of fungi and bacteria in lake during the circulation and stagnation period. *Japan. Mycol. Soc. Trans.* **7**: 115–117.
Suzuki, S., and H. Nimura. (1961e). The microbiological studies of the lakes of Volcano Bandai. VI. The microbial populations in the Akanuma Lake group. *Japan. J. Ecol.* **11**: 59–62.
Suzuki, S., and H. Nimura. (1961f). The microbiological studies in the lakes of Volcano Bandai. VII. The microbial populations in the Onogawa Lake group. *Japan J. Ecol.* **11**: 140–142.
Talling, J. F. (1966). Personal communication with Willoughby. (See footnote p. 75.)
TeStrake, D. (1959). Estaurine distribution and saline tolerance of some Saprolegniaceae. *Phyton* (*Buenos Aires*) **12**: 147–152.
Thaxter, R. (1895a). New or peculiar aquatic fungi. 1. *Monoblepharis. Botan. Gaz.* **20**: 433–440.
Thaxter, R. (1895b). New or peculiar aquatic fungi. 2. *Gonapodya* Fischer and *Myrioblepharis,* nov. gen. *Botan. Gaz.* **20**: 477–485.
Thaxter, R. (1896a). New or peculiar aquatic fungi. 3. *Blastocladia. Botan. Gaz.* **21**: 45–52.
Thaxter, R. (1896b). New or peculiar aquatic fungi. 4. *Rhipidium, Sapromyces,* and *Araiospora,* nov. gen. *Botan. Gaz.* **21**: 317–330.
Thaxter, R. (1903). Mycological notes, 1–2. *Rhodora* **5**: 97–108.
Thornton, D. R. (1963). The physiology and nutrition of some aquatic Hyphomycetes. *J. Gen. Microbiol.* **33**: 23–31.
Tiffany, W. N. (1939a). The host range of *Saprolegnia parasitica.* Mycologia. **31**: 310–321, 2 figs.

Tiffany, W. N. (1939b). The identity of certain species of the Saprolegniaceae parasitic to fish. *J. Elisha Mitchell Sci. Soc.* **55:** 134–151.

Tubaki, K. (1957). Studies on the Japanese hyphomycetes. III. Aquatic group. *Bull. Nat. Sci. Museum (Tokyo)* **41:** 249–268.

Tubaki, K. (1958). Studies on Japanese hyphomycetes. *J. Hattori Botan. Lab.* **20:** 142–144.

Tubaki, K. (1966). An undescribed species of *Hymenoscyphus,* a perfect stage of *Varicosporum. Brit. Mycol. Soc. Trans.* **49:** 345–349.

Unestam, T. (1965). Studies on the crayfish plague fungus *Aphanomyces astaci.* I. Some factors affecting growth *in vitro. Physiol. Plantarum* **18:** 483–505.

Unestam, T. (1966a). Studies on the physiology of *Monoblepharis. Physiol. Plantarum* **19:** 1–14.

Unestam, T. (1966b). Chitinolytic, cellulolytic, and pectinolytic activity *in vitro* of some parasitic and saprophytic Oomycetes. *Physiol. Plantarum* **19:** 15–30.

Van Beverwijk, A. L. (1953). Helicosporous hyphomycetes. I. *Brit. Mycol. Soc. Trans.* **36:** 111–124.

Vishniac, H. S., and R. F. Nigrelli. (1957). The ability of the Saprolegniaceae to parasitize platyfish. *Zoologica* **42:** 131–134.

von Minden, M. (1916). Beiträge zur Biologie und Systematik einheimischer submerser Phycomyceten. *Falck, Mykol. Untersuch. Ber.* **2:** 146–255.

Wager, H. (1913). Life-history and cytology of *Polyphagus euglenae. Ann. Botany (London)* **27:** 173–202.

Waterhouse, G. M. (1942). Some water moulds of the Hogsmill River collected from 1937 to 1939. *Brit. Mycol. Soc. Trans.* **25:** 315–325.

Webster, J. (1959a). Experiments with spores of aquatic hyphomycetes. I. Sedimentation and impaction on smooth surfaces. *Ann. Botany (London)* [N.S.] **23:** 595–611.

Webster, J. (1959b). *Nectria lugdunensis* sp. nov., the perfect state of *Heliscus lugdunensis. Brit. Mycol. Soc. Trans.* **42:** 322–327.

Webster, J. (1961). The *Mollisia* perfect state of *Anguillospora crassa. Brit. Mycol. Soc. Trans.* **44:** 559–564.

Welch, P. S. (1952). "Limnology." McGraw-Hill, New York.

Wemmer, L. (1954). Über die Ruheperiode der Zygosporen von *Saprolegnia ferax. Arch. Mikrobiol.* **21:** 217–229.

Weston, W. H., Jr. (1929). Observations on *Loramyces,* an undescribed aquatic ascomycete. *Mycologia* **21:** 55–76.

Weston, W. H., Jr. (1941). The role of aquatic fungi in hydrobiology. *In* "A Symposium on Hydrobiology," pp. 129–151. Univ. of Wisconsin Press, Madison, Wisconsin.

Whiffen, A. J. (1941). Cellulose decomposition by the saprophytic chytrids. *J. Elisha Mitchell Sci. Soc.* **57:** 321–330.

Whiffen, A. J. (1945). Nutritional studies of representatives of five genera in the Saprolegniaceae. *J. Elisha Mitchell Sci. Soc.* **61:** 114–123.

Whitney, R. J. (1942). Diurnal fluctuations of oxygen and pH in two small ponds and a stream. *J. Exptl. Biol.* **19:** 92–99.

Whisler, H. C. (1962). Culture and nutrition of *Amoebidium parasiticum. Am. J. Botany* **49:** 193–199.

Willén, T. (1958). Conidia of aquatic hyphomycetes amongst plankton algae. *Botan. Notiser* **3:** 431–435.

Willoughby, L. G. (1961a). The ecology of some lower fungi at Esthwaite Water. *Brit. Mycol. Soc. Trans.* **44:** 305–332.

Willoughby, L. G. (1961b). Chitinophilic chytrids from lake muds. *Brit. Mycol. Soc. Trans.* **44:** 586–592.

Willoughby, L. G. (1962a). The ecology of some lower fungi in the English Lake District. *Brit. Mycol. Soc. Trans.* **45:** 121–136.

Willoughby, L. G. (1962b). The occurrence and distribution of reproductive spores of Saprolegniales in fresh water. *J. Ecol.* **50:** 733–759.

Willoughby, L. G. (1962c). New species of *Nephrochytrium* from the English Lake District. *Nova Hedwigia* **3:** 439–444.

Willoughby, L. G. (1965a). Some observations on the location of sites of fungal activity at Blelham Tarn. *Hydrobiologia* **25:** 352–356.

Willoughby, L. G. (1965b). A study of chytridiales from Victorian and other Australian Soils. *Arch. Mikrobiol.* **52:** 101–131.

Willoughby, L. G., and V. G. Collins. (1966). A study of the distribution of fungal spores and bacteria in Blelham Tarn and its associated streams. *Nova Hedwigia* **12:** 150–171.

Willoughby, L. G., and P. J. Townley. (1961a). Two new saprophytic chytrids from the Lake District. *Brit. Mycol. Soc. Trans.* **44:** 177–184.

Willoughby, L. G., and P. J. Townley. (1961b). A further contribution to our knowledge of *Phlyctochytrium unispinum* Paterson. *J. Roy. Microscop. Soc.* **80:** 131–136.

CHAPTER 3

Saprobic Marine Fungi

T. W. JOHNSON, JR.

Department of Botany
Duke University
Durham, North Carolina

I. INTRODUCTION

Convincing demonstration that so-called higher fungi existed in sea water came in the mid-1800's. The discovery of these organisms in maritime habitats did not stimulate more than sporadic investigation, a trend that held until about 1950 when a few investigators concentrated their efforts exclusively in this field. The resulting information, coupling the pioneer with the modern, is at once largely taxonomic, in part ecological, and to a very limited extent physiological in nature.

The approach to marine fungi through systematics has provided parallel accumulation of ecological data, primarily data relative to habitat and substratum. To a limited extent, representatives of every fungal group known to occur in maritime environments have been studied ecologically, from the simpler Chytridiomycetes, Plasmodiophoromycetes, and labyrinthulas, through the most common fungi known in sea water, the Ascomycetes. It is, of course, the free-living, saprobic forms, of whatever group, that lend themselves most readily to ecological study; hence these fungi are perhaps more fully understood than are their parasitic counterparts.

The accumulated information on ecology of marine, saprobic fungi falls conveniently into three categories, namely, occurrence and habitat (or substratum), geographical distribution, and ecological distribution. Since these are interrelated, none must be excluded. Aquatic taxa of the Phycomycetes (in the classical sense), Ascomycetes, Basidiomycetes, and Fungi Imperfecti all have saprobic representatives in marine waters and sediments. This chapter will single out some highlights of ecological information on specific groups of these major classes. At the same time, it will point to a bothersome paucity of data, and emphasize important avenues of future work. In the interest of brevity, publications of authors cited without date citations are to be found summarized in the 1961 compilation by Johnson and Sparrow.

II. THE HABITAT

Saprobic fungi occur both in the open ocean waters (pelagic) and in the bottom (benthic) zones. They are also distributed in comparable areas in estuaries. For the most part, more is known about those fungi occurring in various types of submerged materials in waters and sediments nearest to land masses, the neritic and littoral zones, than about those occurring in deeper waters and their subtending sediments.

The commonest habitat for marine fungi, or so studies seem to suggest, is submerged wood. Ascomycetes, often forming uniquely appendaged spores (Kohlmeyer, 1961), and dematiaceous Fungi Imperfecti predominate. Doguet (1962) found a hemibasidiomycete on submerged wood, the first record of a saprobic representative of the class in a strictly marine environment. Wood, either placed in sea water as panels (Johnson and Sparrow, 1961) or as structural material such as pilings, also becomes inhabited by fungi that are not normally considered part of the marine biota. Siepmann and Johnson isolated a number of terrestrial fungi (members of such genera as *Cladosporium* and *Trichoderma*) simply by culturing bits of wood that had been submerged for varying periods of time in estuarine and sea waters. Even a few water molds (Saprolegniaceae) occur on wood submerged in brackish water of very low salinity. Submerged cordage also harbors some saprobic myceloid fungi, such as various Ascomycetes, but these organisms are evidently not as abundant as those occurring on wood. A few species develop on submerged bark, and one, *Herpotrichiella ciliomaris,* seems to be limited to this substratum. The precise role of these lignicolous fungi in cellulosic decomposition remains to be explored in depth, but evidence suggests a high degree of cellulolytic activity in some. Regardless of whether wood is submerged in tropical, temperate, or colder waters, the fungal flora developing on it can be diverse and abundant. Even a predacious *Arthrobotrys* has been recovered from wood submerged in saline waters of an estuary (Johnson and Autery, 1962).

A surprising number of fungi have been described from calcareous or siliceous deposits or from accretions of marine animals. Species of *Corollospora* (Ascomycetes), for example, produce fructifications readily on calcareous deposits on wood, or even on sand grains. These fungi undoubtedly obtain nutrients from the woody material, but there are some species supposedly capable of existing directly on calcareous shell material. Several early accounts record observations on tubules or canals in such materials as mollusc shells and sponge spicules. Some observers treated these filamentous areas as fungi; others subsequently considered them to be lichens. From the scant descriptive matter available, it seems possible that a fungus might be associated with shell deformity of the common edible oyster, *Ostrea edulis*. Several genera and species of "fungi" assigned to the Cladochytriaceae (Chytridiomycetes) were described by Zebrowski from shell fragments. He illustrated filaments and tubules resembling sporangia and rhizoids. Whether these are true fungi or only artifacts remains to be discovered; none of them has yielded to culture. More recent is the report of an unidentified *Endogone* in the jingle shell, *Anomia simplex* (Johnson and Anderson, 1962).

Dead culm tissue of intertidal and salt marsh phanerogams, such as species of *Spartina* and *Juncus,* harbor abundant populations of fungi usually assignable to *Leptosphaeria, Sphaerulina,* or *Pleospora.* A few fungi, mainly Deuteromycetes, have been collected from marine algae cast on shorelines as drift.

Associations of marine, saprobic fungi with invertebrate animals have been reported, including several species of Trichomycetes. While these fungi are considered by some to be parasitic, there is no evidence whatever to favor this view. One trichomycete has been cultured (Whisler, 1962), and it is likely that methods and media will be devised to permit propagating marine representatives in culture. Marine Trichomycetes are known to occur primarily on intertidal animals, and are to be found in abundance attached to the chitinous lining of the hind gut of the mole crab (*Emerita talpoida*), mud crab (*Panopeus herbstii*), fiddler crabs (*Uca* spp.), shore crabs (*Hemigrapsus oregonensis* and *H. nudus*), and on various species of beach fleas (*Orchestia* spp.), among others. Reports indicate that Trichomycetes are to be found in a wider variety of marine animals than once was supposed. Lichtwardt (1961) describes a trichomycete in species of *Callianassa* (Decapoda). The startling exception to the usual habitat of marine Trichomycetes—intertidal animals— is that of *Alacrinella limnoriae* (Manier and Ormieres, 1961). This fungus occurs on the gut lining of the common isopod boring gribble, *Limnoria tripunctata.* A few Ascomycetes—species known to occur on submerged wood—have been found in the fruiting stage on sea squirts (tunicates), and these animals can even be used as an artificially inoculated substratum for certain lignicolous, marine fungi in the laboratory.

The most controversial relationship of saprobic marine fungi with marine animals is the so-called nutritive association of fungi with marine borers (*Limnoria* and *Teredo*). Investigators concerned with this problem segregated into three groups, those favoring the view that marine borers are directly dependent on fungi for nutrition, those admitting that such a dependency *could* exist, and the third group denying that there was any evidence whatever for the association. Proponents of the nutrition-dependency theory hold that fungi, through degradation of submerged wood, contribute such substances as proteins and amino acids that are necessary to the diet of the borers. While the nutrition-dependent idea has been criticized severely Kampf and his associates (Johnson and Sparrow, 1961) maintain that fungi are essential to settling by the borers. The experimental evidence for this theory is unconvincing, and for a settling (colonization) dependency is unconfirmed. Some data from studies on borers reared in the laboratory suggest that the animals live longer in fungus-infested wood than in fungus-free wood.

Saprobic fungi have been recovered from beach sands and from marine, salt marsh, and estuarine sediments, and the diversity and abundance of the fungal populations suggests that a very significant mycoflora exists in these habitats. The most extensive studies of beach sand mycoflora are those of Brown and Nicot. A number of the fungi recovered by Nicot are also known to occur on wood submerged in estuarine waters.

Elliott, who first attempted to culture fungi from salt marsh sediments, reported forty-eight species. Many of these are recognized as common terrestrial fungi and air-borne contaminants. Siepmann, in a study of the tidal mud flat of the Weser River basin, recovered many common soil-inhabiting fungi. There is little doubt that representatives of such genera as *Alternaria, Cladosporium, Fusarium, Trichoderma, Gliocladium, Gymnoascus, Aspergillus,* and *Penicillium* occur with remarkable frequency in marine and estuarine sediments.

Sparrow first demonstrated that fungi existed in sediments at considerable depths in the ocean. Species of *Trichoderma, Alternaria, Cephalosporium, Cladosporium, Chaetomium,* and *Penicillium* were recovered from sediments taken at depths of 18–1127 meters below the ocean's surface. Fungi Imperfecti have been isolated from sediment cores from a depth of 3425 meters, and imperfects have also been recovered from water samples taken as deep as 4610 meters.

Yeasts, yeastlike fungi, and Actinomycetes inhabit both marine waters and sediments (Johnson and Sparrow, 1961), but some have been found associated with a wide variety of materials submerged in sea water, as Siepmann and Höhnk (1962) have demonstrated. Frietas and Bhat point to yeasts associated with fish-net deterioration, while Nakazima, among others, reports saprobic yeasts isolated from the mid-gut gland in little-neck clams (*Venerupis*). Saprobic species have also been isolated from surfaces of shrimp, oysters, and marine plants. Roth and his associates (1962) concluded that the yeast flora associated with marine vegetation was not only numerically uniformly low, but was also consistent, in species composition, with that of adjacent waters and sediments. According to

Fell and Van Uden (1963), the majority of yeasts that they recovered from marine habitats were "transitory" terrestrial species, or forms adapted to existence in either environment.

III. DISTRIBUTION

A. Geographical

It would be premature to attempt a detailed analysis of the geographical distribution of saprobic marine fungi, for only at widely scattered sites have intensive searches been made, and vast oceanic and coastal regions, pelagic and benthic, have not been sampled. The available conclusion, from the meager data available, is that some ascomycetous and deuteromycetous species enjoy cosmopolitan distribution, which is not at all surprising in view of the continuity of marine waters, while other species seem restricted geographically. This statement is reflected only in compilations of published collection lists (see also Chapter 19).

Two investigations, at least, were designed in part to study the geographical distribution of saprobic marine fungi. Harder and Uebelmesser collected various aquatic Phycomycetes from ten coastal areas of the North Sea, the Baltic, the Mediterranean, and the Atlantic coast of Spain. Although fewer fungi occurred in the littoral zones than in the inundated beach soils or coastal soils above the high tide line, some species were found in only one or two of the areas sampled, while others were present in several of the coastal regions. The data suggest that there are no significant differences either in kinds or numbers of fungi among beach soils and littoral sediments in the three major maritime areas sampled.

The second investigation, that of Reynolds and Meyers, was an attempt to determine the geographical distribution of lignicolous marine fungi by direct examination of submerged wood panels from 63 coastal stations in North America. They reported that certain Deuteromycetes, e.g., *Piricauda pelagica* (*P. arcticoceanorum*) and *Humicola alopallonella,* are prominent in colder waters, whereas others, *Cirrenalia macrocephala,* for example, are reputedly rare in northerly, colder waters. Ascomycetes, including *Halosphaeria mediosetigera, Ceriosporopsis halima,* and species of *Lulworthia,* among others, are unmistakably cosmopolitan. Additional, more extensive collections are needed to confirm these distributional patterns.

B. Ecological-Field

The distribution of saprobic fungi relative to environmental factors of oceans and estuaries is largely unexplored. Exceptions to this statement are few, the data are scanty, and conclusions are largely unconfirmed.

1. Nonlignicolous Species

The most extensive analyses of fungal populations in sea water and subtending sediments are those by Höhnk (Johnson and Sparrow, 1961). His data show definite incidence patterns of nonlignicolous, saprobic fungi in relation to salinity. As salinity decreases, the percentage of Phycomycetes increases and, conversely, that of Ascomycetes and Fungi Imperfecti decreases. Thus, the frequency of uniflagellate Phycomycetes—members of *Olpidium, Chytridium,* and *Hyphochytrium,* for example—decreases with an increase in salinity. However, biflagellate Phycomycetes in such genera as *Lagenidium, Thraustochytrium,* and *Sirolpidium,* on the other hand, display a generally increasing tolerance to increasing salinities, and the same may be said for Phycomycetes inhabiting sediments below these waters. The observations by Harder and Uebelmesser do not bear out Höhnk's account, for their data show that the abundance of aquatic Phycomycetes, in littoral sediments of very restricted localities, is hardly less than that occurring in adjacent terrestrial soils. The lists of species given by Höhnk and by Harder and Uebelmesser make one point clear, namely, that numerous so-called freshwater or terrestrial Phycomycetes occur in abundance in bottom terrain below sea water.

According to Höhnk, fewer Ascomycetes and Deuteromycetes occur in sediments than in water. Borut and Johnson (1962), however, isolated a considerable number of species in these groups from sediments in a single estuary. I have had remarkably little success in isolating such fungi from estuarine waters of various salinities. Whether, as Höhnk's data indicate, Fungi Imperfecti dominate in the mycoflora of lower saline waters remains to be confirmed.

Other than the report by Brown that alkali dune beaches exhibit a greater frequency (threefold) of mycelium than do acid dunes, there are no substantial ecological data on fungi in beach areas. Saitô detected seasonal variation in the numbers of fungi recoverable from sand beaches on the Pacific side of Japan. To what this variation is due is unexplored.

Elliott concluded that fungi are more common in salt marsh sediments of high organic or humus content than in those of lower organic content. Saitô also noted essentially the same phenomenon. As would be expected, fewer fungi occur in "anaerobic" sediments than in surface "aerobic" sediments. A general up-shore increase in frequency of *Cercospora salina* is evident in a developing salt marsh, according to Pugh (1962a). He has also shown (Pugh, 1962b) that certain species, "salt marsh inhabitants," increase in frequency in an up-shore direction. Others, "salt marsh transients" such as species of *Penicillium, Aspergillus,* and *Mucor,* are increasingly abundant down-shore. None of the 142 species isolated by

Borut and Johnson (1962) from estuarine sediments (freshwater as well as seawater sectors) showed any distributional pattern in response to any single hydrographic factor or group of factors.

2. *Lignicolous Species*

The ecological distribution of lignicolous marine fungi has been studied almost exclusively in estuarine or near-shore littoral waters. By means of culture studies, Ritchie detected a temperature-salinity response, the "*Phoma* pattern," in certain fungi isolated from maritime habitats: as temperature is raised, tolerance to salinity is increased. Gold's data show that this same pattern can be detected in nature, in lignicolous fungi from estuarine waters. Certain species, he noted, occurred only in the lower salinity reaches of the estuary at low water temperatures, but were found in the high salinity regions when the temperature was high. Some species, however, were limited to fresh water, some to salt water, and others were distributed throughout the estuary irrespective of prevailing temperature-salinity regimes. The results of a somewhat more extensive but parallel study by Hughes, contradicted Gold's investigation with respect to certain individual species. *Ceriosporopsis halima,* for example, showed a *Phoma*-pattern response according to Gold, but Hughes' data suggest the distribution of this species to be influenced largely by salinity alone. Whereas Gold found *Lignincola laevis* to be distributed erratically, without detectable response to a given environmental factor, Hughes noted that it did distribute according to a "*Phoma* pattern." In one estuary at least, dissolved oxygen, pH, and the content of nitrate and phosphate in the water seemed not to be factors limiting the distribution of any common lignicolous fungi in those waters. Temperature appeared to influence the distribution of one species only, an unidentified *Mycosphaerella.*

3. *Yeasts and Yeastlike Fungi*

Ecological work on yeasts and yeastlike fungi in marine habitats has been fruitful only in providing tallies of occurrence and distribution without reference to hydrographic factors. Some general ecological data on yeasts comes from studies by Kriss and Novozhilova, notably, in waters of the Black Sea and northern Pacific. Their data bear on three aspects of yeast distribution. First, the number of yeasts is measurably greater in the upper strata of water and in the shallow, littoral zones than in pelagic waters. Temperature, salinity, and proximity to a land mass seem to be the principal factors accounting for this distribution. Second, yeasts occur at rather remarkable depths. Viable cells have been collected at 3300 meters, and, by direct observation (not culture), yeasts have been detected in waters from 4000 meters. The third aspect is microzonicity. Certain species, and variants of them, seem to occur in definite, restricted zones or "layers" in waters at various depths and distances from the shoreline. It remains to be seen whether these zones are relatively stable or are merely chance configurations resulting from, for instance, vagaries of water currents.

The greatest yeast populations occur in waters from zones directly influenced by terrestrial drift, whereas open ocean waters contain the smallest (Roth *et al.,* 1962). The yeasts found by Roth and his co-workers were oxidative, asporogenous forms with vitamin requirements. Temperature and salinity tolerances, at least for the most common species, were well within the ranges that could be expected in the natural marine environment. In areas of high plankton concentration, or of sea grass and alga beds, for example, there are larger populations of yeasts than in the open ocean (Fell and Van Uden, 1963). There is not, however, a significant yeast flora associated with surfaces of marine algae, judged from the study by Fell and van Uden.

C. *Ecological-Laboratory*

Prominent among reports of autecological studies of saprobic fungi from maritime habitats are those by Te Strake, Siepmann, Höhnk, Scholz, Ritchie, Hughes (Johnson and Sparrow, 1961) and Borut and Johnson (1962).

Höhnk has shown that while vegetative growth of filamentous, biflagellate Phycomycetes is not necessarily impaired by salinity, reproduction often is suppressed. Strains of the same species may express very different reactions to salinity stresses, as, for example, one strain not being capable of producing sporangia in salinities greater than 7 ‰ (parts per thousand), while another develops such structures in salinities up to 25 ‰. There is a general coincidence between salinity tolerance in culture of some fungi, and their occurrence in marine waters, according to Höhnk. Te Strake, on the other hand, found this not to be the case with representative Saprolegniaceae. She recovered water molds from the freshwater and low-salinity brackish water sectors of an estuary only (2.8 ‰ maximum), yet could propagate test species to reproductive maturity in salinities approaching a level three times greater than that of normal (35 ‰) sea water. She suggested that the nutrient level was partly responsible for this remarkable adjustment to saline waters. That terrestrial Ascomycetes and Fungi Imperfecti can tolerate far higher salinity stresses in culture than in the natural saline sediments is suggested by the results of several investigations. Surprisingly, however, some so-called marine fungi have a lesser tolerance for changing salinity stresses than do their terrestrial counterparts.

Scholz collected a number of Phycomycetes from saline areas and was able to categorize them on the basis of reproduction in relation to salinity by the use of culture techniques. One *Thraustochytrium* species reproduced only in sea water or in NaCl solution. Two species reproduced only in fresh water, six in fresh water or NaCl solution, and thirteen in either fresh water, natural sea water, or NaCl solutions.

The influence of temperature on salinity tolerance, the "*Phoma* pattern," is also characteristic of terrestrial fungi. Ritchie has shown the pattern to be manifested by a *Curvularia* (probably *C. interseminata*), as well as by a *Pestalotia* sp. Hughes observed that another presumably terrestrial fungus, oligohaline as far as its occurrence in an estuary was concerned, grew in culture in an inverse "*Phoma* pattern."

The vast majority of species isolated from estuarine sediments by Borut and Johnson (1962) were typical of terrestrial habitats, yet many occurred in sediments below saline waters. None of the test organisms, taken as representative of the collections as a whole, was inhibited completely by growth under salinity stresses. Spore germination of the same organisms, however, was clearly reduced or retarded by an unknown factor, particularly if sea water rather than NaCl was used to obtain a saline medium.

IV. EVALUATION AND SUMMARY

So far as existing data indicate, the most diverse and abundant populations of marine, saprobic fungi occur on materials submerged in littoral and estuarine temperate and subtropical waters. However, vast extents of coastal and pelagic waters have not been sampled, even superficially. The lignicolous species account for the greater numbers of these fungi, and may well be considered adapted to maritime habitats. The large numbers of fungi occurring in estuarine and oceanic sediments remain largely unstudied so far as their adaptability to and activities in the marine environment are concerned.

Some attention has been devoted to vertical and horizontal distribution of saprobic fungi in oceans, but largely without precise ecological correlation. Nothing is known of population stability, and decidedly little of the environmental factors responsible for establishing or perpetuating distributional patterns. While salinity and temperature have been tentatively explored as factors determining distribution and occurrence of saprobic fungi in salt water, other segments of the marine environment have been neglected both observationally and experimentally as to their influence, if any, on the mycoflora.

REFERENCES

Borut, S. Y., and T. W. Johnson, Jr. (1962). Some biological observations on fungi in estuarine sediments. *Mycologia* **54**: 181–193.

Doguet, G. (1962). *Digitatispora marina,* n.g., n.sp., Basidiomycete marin. *Compt. Rend.* **254**: 4336–4338.

Fell, J. W., and N. Van Uden. (1963). Yeasts in marine environments. *Symp. Marine Microbiol., Chicago, 1961* pp. 329–340. Thomas, Springfield, Illinois.

Johnson, T. W., Jr., and W. R. Anderson. (1962). A fungus in *Anomia simplex* shell. *J. Elisha Mitchell Sci. Soc.* **78**: 43–47.

Johnson, T. W., Jr., and C. Autery. (1962). An *Arthrobotrys* from brackish water. *Mycologia* **53**: 432–433.

Johnson, T. W., Jr., and F. K. Sparrow, Jr. (1961). "Fungi in Oceans and Estuaries," 668 pp. Cramer, Weinheim/Bergstr., Germany.

Kohlmeyer, J. (1961). Synoptic plates for quick determination of marine Deuteromycetes and Ascomycetes. *Nova Hedwigia* **3**: 383–398.

Lichtwardt, R. W. (1961). A stomach fungus in *Callianassa* spp. (Decapoda) from Chile. *Lunds Univ. Arsskr., Avd. 2* [N.S.] **57**: 1–10.

Manier, J.-F., and R. Ormieres. (1961). *Alacrinella limnoriae* n.g., n. sp., Trichomycete Eccrinidae parasite du rectum de *Limnoria tripunctata* Menzies (Isopode). *Vie et Milieu* **12**: 285–295.

Pugh, G. J. F. (1962a). Studies on fungi in coastal soils. I. *Cercospora salina* Sutherland. *Brit. Mycol. Soc. Trans.* **45**: 255–260.

Pugh, G. J. F. (1962b). Studies on fungi in coastal soils. II. Fungal ecology in a developing salt marsh. *Brit. Mycol. Soc. Trans.* **45**: 560–566.

Roth, F. J., Jr., D. G. Ahearn, J. W. Fell, S. P. Meyers, and S. A. Meyer. (1962). Ecology and taxonomy of yeasts isolated from various marine substrates. *Limnol. Oceanog.* **7**: 178–185.

Siepmann, R., and W. Höhnk. (1962). Über Hefen und einige Pilze (Fungi imp., Hyphales) aus dem Nordatlantik. *Veroeffentl. Inst. Meeresforsch. Bremerhaven* **8**: 79–98.

Whisler, H. C. (1962). Culture and nutrition of *Amoebidium parasiticum. Am. J. Botany* **49**: 193–199.

CHAPTER 4

Thermophiles

RALPH EMERSON

Department of Botany
University of California
Berkeley, California

I. INTRODUCTION

A. Fungal Thermophily Defined

As one of the basic, limiting, physical factors of the environment, temperature plays an immensely important and often decisive role in the distribution of living organisms over the face of the earth. The true fungi, like all other groups of microorganisms, have, during the millennia of their evolution, become adapted to occupy a wide series of temperature niches. They can be roughly categorized as psychrophiles, mesophiles, and thermophiles. By far the majority are mesophiles, thriving between about 10° and 40°C. The psychrophiles extend below this range and the thermophiles, literally heat-lovers, go well above it.

There is no natural or magic dividing line between mesophiles and thermophiles. If temperature characteristics (maxima, optima, minima) of a sufficient number of fungi are tabulated, they will be found to fall on a continuous cline. Thus the thermophilic species can conveniently be defined (Cooney and Emerson, 1964) as those with a minimum for growth at 20°C or above and a maximum for growth at 50°C or above. This definition is purely arbitrary, but it has the advantage that it excludes all fungi which grow readily at ordinary laboratory temperatures and are, therefore, likely to have been frequently seen and studied. A definition based upon optimum temperatures for growth at or above 40°C has also been used (Crisan, 1959, 1964). In the following account attention will be focused upon the small group of species—less than 20 described thus far—that become specially active at the very temperatures where competition from ordinary mesophiles is beginning to be eliminated by a level of heat to which they are not adapted. Without doubt the thermophilic fungi owe their ubiquity and common occurrence in large measure to this special capacity to occupy a temperature niche which most other fungi cannot penetrate.

Fungi are by no means the most thermophilic microorganisms. Bacteria, actinomycetes, and blue-green algae (Cyanophyceae) have maxima for growth extending 10–15°C higher than those of the fungi (Vouk, 1950; Kempner, 1963). Protozoa, on the other hand, are generally less thermophilic than fungi, as are higher animals and plants. Because of this difference in temperature characteristics of different groups of organisms, thermophily must be defined on a separate basis in each particular case if it is to be meaningful and useful. And, finally, it is important to recognize the difference between thermophily and thermodurism. The latter term refers to organisms that can withstand high temperatures in a dormant or inactive state. Thus, for example, some fungi, which grow vegetatively at ordinary temperatures, have spores that will withstand the heat used to pasteurize certain canned goods (Olliver and Rendle, 1934) (see also Chapter 17). Such fungi are thermoduric, not thermophilic, and they are not included in the present account.

B. Pioneering Studies

The first two thermophilic fungi to be recognized and cultured were turned up essentially as chance contaminants on organic substrata being incubated at somewhat elevated temperatures. Lindt (1886) found *Mucor pusillus* on bread in an incubator at 30°C, and Tsiklinskaya (1899) described *Humicola lanuginosa* growing on a potato that she had inoculated with crumbs of soil and then incubated. These two species are probably the commonest of all fungal thermophiles, and it is not surprising that they were the first to be observed.

With Hugo Miehe's (1907a) pioneering investigation of self-heating hay came the first really intensive and penetrating analysis of thermophily in the fungi. His book, *Die Selbsterhitzung des Heus,* was, until very recently, the sole treatment of the biology of thermophilic fungi, and it is sure to remain a distinguished landmark in the development of this subject. Working for the first time with naturally self-heated (see Section II, D) materials such as damp hay and leaf composts, Miehe (1907a,b) isolated and characterized several striking, thermophilic fungi, among them *Thermoascus aurantiacus* and *Malbranchea pulchella* var. *sulfurea.* We will have occasion to refer repeatedly hereafter to Miehe's contributions. A few years later Griffon and Maublanc (1911) accurately described *Talaromyces* (*Penicillium*) *dupontii,* which, until very recently, remained the only thermophilic member of the large and widespread genus *Penicillium. T. dupontii* was isolated that first time from self-heated manure; it was not seen again until it was cultured from retting guayule

(Cooney and Emerson, 1964) nearly thirty-five years later. In two comprehensive papers, Noack (1912, 1920) reported the results of his experiments and observations on the nature of thermophily in fungi. His work will be reviewed in Section II. Between 1912 and 1950 no new thermophilic fungi were reported, but La Touche's (1950) description of *Chaetomium thermophile* ushered in a new period of vigorous research in many parts of the world on numerous aspects of fungal thermophily. A comprehensive account of the systematics, morphology, and general biology of the thermophilic Eumycota has recently been given by Cooney and Emerson (1964), whose monograph has served as the major basis for preparation of the present chapter and should be consulted for further details.

II. PHYSIOLOGY

A. Temperature Ranges and Characteristics

The ranges of temperature for growth of each of the known species of thermophilic fungi are presented in Table I. They cannot be considered to be absolutely fixed because different isolates of the same species may have somewhat different characteristics, any one isolate may exhibit a different range depending upon its past history or the cultural conditions employed for determining its growth, and, in the final analysis, the exact end points for growth are subject to individual interpretation. Temperature optima are, likewise, difficult to establish with precision. Nevertheless, the data reveal clearly that some species (e.g., *Humicola lanuginosa* or *Talaromyces dupontii*) are more thermophilic than others (e.g., *H. stellata* or *Mucor pusillus*) and that there is no natural dividing line between the thermophiles and the mesophiles. Many investigators would include *Aspergillus fumigatus* in the thermophiles, but its growth at temperatures below 20°C places it among the mesophiles according to the definition adopted in Section I. Crisan (1959, 1964) and Cooney and Emerson (1964) have discussed temperature ranges and the definition of thermophily in considerable detail, and the latter authors have included an analysis of doubtful or excluded thermophiles.

Undoubtedly because the thermophilic fungi have remained generally unknown to microbiologists until recently, very few data relating temperature to amount of growth are yet available. The growth curves shown in Figs. 1 and 2 indicate the sort of information that is needed. As might be expected, dry weight production drops off more abruptly above the optimum than it builds up below; lag periods and rates of growth are markedly affected by temperature. Such data have long been available for the bacteria and will be essential if the basis and mechanism of thermophily in the fungi is to be explained.

TABLE I

APPROXIMATE MINIMUM AND MAXIMUM TEMPERATURES (IN °C) FOR GROWTH OF THE KNOWN THERMOPHILIC FUNGI[a]

Name	Minimum	Maximum
Phycomycetes		
Mucor miehei	25	57
Mucor pusillus	20	55
Ascomycetes		
Allescheria terrestris[b]	<28	>48
Chaetomium thermophile	27	58
Myriococcum albomyces	26	57
Talaromyces (Penicillium) dupontii	27	59
Talaromyces (Penicillium) emersonii[c]	30	60
Thermoascus aurantiacus	22	55
Deuteromycetes		
Humicola grisea var. *thermoidea*	24	56
Humicola insolens	23	55
Humicola lanuginosa	30	60
Humicola stellata	22	50
Malbranchea pulchella var. *sulfurea*	27	56
Paecilomyces sp.[d]	<30	55–60
Sporotrichum thermophile	24	55
Stilbella thermophila[e]	25	55
Torula thermophila	23	58

[a] Data from Cooney and Emerson (1964) except as noted.
[b] Data from Apinis (1963a).
[c] Data from Blom and Snider (1962).
[d] Data from Küster and Locci (1964). Possibly some of these may be included in *Paecilomyces variotii*.
[e] Data from Fergus (1964).

B. Isolation and Culture

The temperature characteristics of thermophilic fungi provide the key to their isolation and culture and reveal at the same time why thermophily has been so generally overlooked by mycologists. With little or no growth occurring at ordinary laboratory temperatures and good growth and vigorous competition in a mixed microbial population being ensured only at temperatures above the ordinary range, thermophilic fungi will not be encountered unless temperatures are artificially raised to a marked extent. Conversely, thermophilic fungi are sure to be revealed whenever appropriate materials (cf. Section III) are incubated at temperatures of 40–50°C. In nearly every instance where thermophilic fungi were found and studied prior to 1950, they were discovered pretty much by chance either because organic materials were kept at artificially high temperatures in the

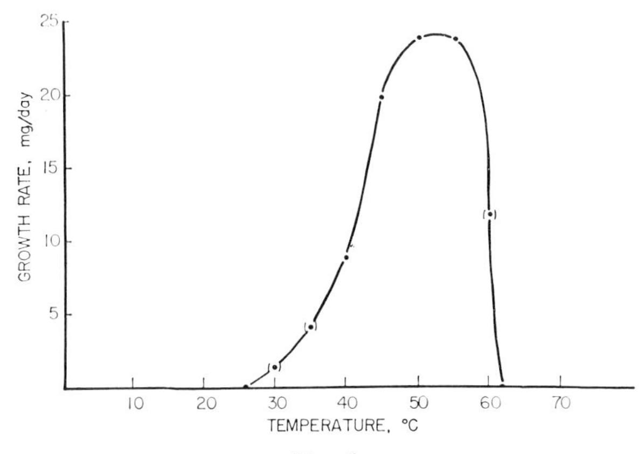

FIG. 1

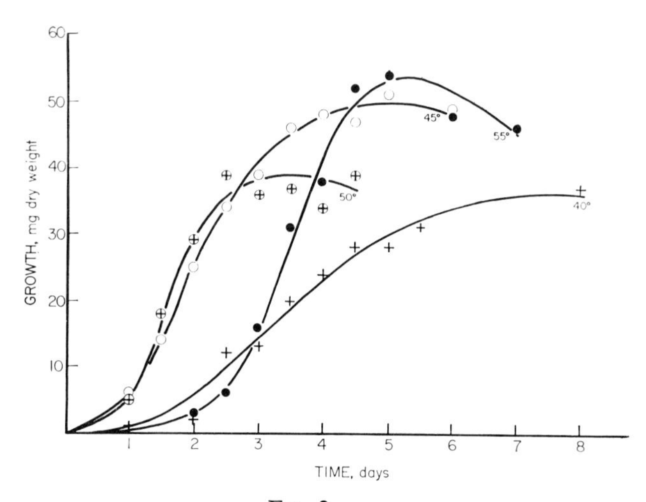

FIG. 2

FIGS. 1 and 2. Temperature-growth characteristics of *Humicola lanuginosa,* an isolate from garden compost, grown in standing broth cultures on a medium composed of glucose (3 gm), asparagine (2 gm), KH_2PO_4 (1 gm), K_2HPO_4 (1 gm), $MgSO_4 \cdot 7\ H_2O$ (0.5 gm), and water (1000 ml). Each point (except those in parentheses in Fig. 1) on the graphs represents the mean of six dry-weight determinations. Data were kindly provided by Byron D. Blom and Philip J. Snider. Fig. 1. Growth rate, measured as dry weight of mycelium produced per day, shows an optimum at about 50°C, with the minimum and maximum temperature for growth at about 30°C and 60°C, respectively. Fig. 2. Growth curves for four different temperatures show changes in growth rates, initial lag times, maximum growth, etc.

laboratory or because naturally self-heated materials such as dung, hay, peat, or compost were being explored. Cooney (1952), Crisan (1959, 1964), and Cooney and Emerson (1964) have stressed the primary incubation of substrata and secondary incubation of isolation cultures at elevated temperatures for the systematic enrichment and display of thermophilic mycofloras. In any microbiological investigation designed to reveal the occurrence and distribution of fungi, standard techniques to obtain the thermophiles should now be routinely employed.

Little need be said here about media. There is no evidence as yet of special substrate requirements and, given the proper temperature, thermophilic fungi can be isolated on a variety of standard mycological media, both natural and defined. Cooney and Emerson (1964) used yeast-starch, yeast-glucose, oatmeal, and Czapek's agars. Crisan (1959) favored peptone-glucose media with certain additives such as crystal violet or streptomycin. Fergus (1964) also used peptone-glucose, and Apinis (1963a) has discussed special methods for isolating thermophiles from soils.

C. *Nutrition and Carbon Dissimilation*

Like temperature characteristics, nutritional characteristics of the thermophilic fungi remain largely unexplored and are basic to any comprehensive physiological investigations. Several of the species (cf. Cooney and Emerson, 1964), including *Talaromyces dupontii, Thermoascus aurantiacus, Malbranchea pulchella* var. *sulfurea,* and *Humicola stellata,* have been grown on glucose-Czapek's agar. This suggests that they are autotrophic for all vitamins and can utilize nitrate and sulfate as sources of nitrogen and sulfur, respectively, but definite conclusions must await more precisely controlled experiments with liquid media. Rege (1927) and Crisan (1962), who worked with *H. lanuginosa,* and Reese (1946), who studied both *H. insolens* and *H. lanuginosa,* concluded that these species can use ammonium as a nitrogen source, and apparently both can use sulfate and require no exogenous vitamins.

Rege (1927) and Reese (1946) also made systematic surveys of the availability of various carbon sources to the species of *Humicola* they were investigating. *H. lanuginosa* utilized glucose, sucrose, maltose, mannose, galactose, xylose, starch, and lignin; *H. insolens* utilized glucose, maltose, xylose, and starch. Knowledge about the dissimilatory capacities of the various thermophilic fungi has been accumulated largely, however, because of the special interest in their composting and humifying action. Despite considerable early confusion over species identification (Cooney and Emerson, 1964), it is quite clear now that *H. lanuginosa* cannot attack cellulose (Rege, 1927; Norman, 1930; Reese, 1946; Henssen,

1957), whereas *H. insolens* is an active cellulose decomposer (Reese, 1946; Henssen, 1957). Indeed Reese (1946) has demonstrated cellulose breakdown by cell-free extracts of *H. insolens*. Henssen (1957) found that *Sporotrichum thermophile* is also a cellulose decomposer but will grow more vigorously on substrata containing pectin or glucose. It is likely that other thermophilic fungi can attack cellulose or related polysaccharides, but no positive information is yet available on this point. From the work of Allen *et al.* (1944), Allen and Emerson (1949), and Cooney and Emerson (1964) on retting guayule, we know that seven thermophiles (*Mucor pusillus, M. miehei, Talaromyces dupontii, Thermoascus aurantiacus, Humicola insolens, H. lanuginosa,* and *Malbranchea pulchella* var. *sulfurea*) have the capacity to decompose resinous compounds and cause clearing of resin-emulsion plates.

D. *Oxygen Relations and Thermogenesis*

Ever since the work of Cohn (1889, 1891) and Miehe (1905, 1907a) microbiologists have recognized that the spontaneous heating of insulated organic materials results from the metabolism of the microorganisms growing on the substrate. Both Cohn and Miehe, as well as many later investigators (cf. Niese, 1959; Gregory *et al.,* 1963; Rothbaum, 1963; Dye and Rothbaum, 1964; and literature citations in Cooney and Emerson, 1964), demonstrated that heating depends upon the presence of living microorganisms, that sufficient moisture, oxygen, and nutrients must be present to permit active metabolism, and that heat production will be cut down if conditions become too anaerobic. James *et al.* (1928), Norman (1930), Miehe (1930), and others have clearly demonstrated by means of pure culture studies that the fungi, along with bacteria and actinomycetes, make a significant and possibly major contribution to the overall heat production. Moreover, in elegant experiments comparing the maximum temperatures attained with fungi having different temperature maxima, Miehe (1930) was able to show how mesophiles, such as *Rhizopus stolonifer* could raise the temperature only to their maximum for growth, i.e., 35–40°C, whereas various thermophiles could take it to their own maximum of 60°C. It is evident that the composition of the active flora in a large naturally heating mass of material will shift from predominant mesophiles in the early stages of thermogenesis to predominant thermophiles at the peak of the heating cycle.

Whereas anaerobic matter will not heat appreciably and, conversely, a good supply of oxygen is essential for vigorous heating (James *et al.,* 1928; Allen and Emerson, 1949), it is certain that, in materials piled deeply enough and compacted enough to provide good self-insulation, some degree of anaerobiosis does in fact develop in the inner regions. The few observations that have been made on the oxygen requirements of thermophilic fungi are, therefore, of special interest. The first and only detailed study of oxygen relations was made by Noack (1920) during his pioneering investigations of the physiology of *Thermoascus aurantiacus*. He found, among other things, that although the rate of respiration was reduced in response to reduced oxygen supply, the respiratory quotient (CO_2/O_2) remained essentially the same, even at very low oxygen levels. Furthermore, vegetative mycelium of *T. aurantiacus* could withstand exposure to an essentially anaerobic environment for as long as 8 days. Henssen's (1957) remarks about the anaerobiosis of *Humicola insolens* are particularly interesting in this connection. At elevated temperatures, that species developed better under anaerobic than under aerobic conditions. Moreover, Cooney and Emerson (1964) have found that the ascocarpic stage of *Talaromyces dupontii* is dependent upon the advent of anaerobic conditions. Aerobic cultures generally form the imperfect conidial, penicillium stage only. These and other observations suggest that the thermophilic fungi may have evolved some unusual metabolic machinery in parallel with their striking temperature adaptations.

E. The Basis of Thermophily

The most fundamental queries about thermophilic fungi, indeed about any thermophiles, concern their temperature relations. Not only, (1) Why *can* they grow at such high temperatures, up to 60°C? but also, (2) Why *can't* they grow at the ordinary temperatures, 15–25°C, where so many of their close relatives thrive? These questions are as difficult to answer as they are basic, and, so far, even the start of an explanation remains to be provided for the fungi. In the bacteria (Ingraham, 1962) several theories have been proposed and some convincing evidence has been presented. Structural proteins as well as enzymes in thermophiles have been found to be more heat resistant than their counterparts in mesophilic species. Failure to grow at low temperatures may be due to heat labile inhibitors that block metabolism until they are destroyed as temperatures mount to a favorable range. Parallel observations need to be made with the fungi. Only a few points merit attention here.

In his second paper, Noack (1920) considered whether in becoming adapted to thermophily the high-temperature fungi have evolved a peculiarly rapid metabolism. He found, to be sure, that the respiratory rates of *Mucor pusillus* and *Thermoascus aurantiacus* were high at 45°, but not spectacularly so. In fact the rates were not even as high as might have been predicted from an analysis of metabolism-temperature relations in mesophilic species. Thus, an ordinary mesophile such as *Penicillium glaucum* formed CO_2 at a rate of 67% of the dry weight of the mycelium per 24 hours at 15°C and 133% at 25°. Could it have grown at 45°C, Noack argued, its CO_2 production would, by extrapolation, have been over 500%. That of *T. aurantiacus,* however, was only about 300%. Evidently thermophily involves something more significant than merely outdoing the competitor at its own game. The thermophilic fungi succeed not because of a high metabolic rate but because of a capacity to thrive in an environment that their nearest competitors cannot tolerate. Perhaps their survival depends, in fact, upon a metabolism that is *slower* than would have been predicted.

Noack (1912) had also considered whether, because the high temperatures they require would arise only sporadically under special circumstances, the thermophilic fungi might have spores that are exceptionally resistant to long periods of desiccation and low fluctuating temperatures. Here too he found that they showed no particular adaptations, for their spores were no more resistant than those of many mesophilic forms.

There have been only one or two other attempts thus far to explore the basis of thermophily in the true fungi. Believing that special pigments might provide some clue to the metabolism and the temperature relations, Crisan (1962) attempted to discover the chemical nature of pigments released into the medium by *Humicola lanuginosa.* In Russia, where there has been a long continuing interest in thermophilic microorganisms, Evreinova and Miroshnichenko (1962) found differences in the proportions of nucleotides in low temperature and high temperature strains of *Aspergillus fumigatus.* However, no direct connection has yet been established between pigments, nucleotide ratios, or other features of metabolism and the thermophilic properties of the fungi. The basis of their thermophily remains the most interesting and challenging feature of their physiology.

III. NATURAL OCCURRENCE

A. Geographical

The thermophilic fungi have thus far displayed no unusual features of geographical distribution (Cooney and Emerson, 1964). While collections are still too limited to allow much generalization, all indications are that, like most terrestrial microorganisms, and mesophilic microfungi in particular, the thermophilic species have a worldwide distribution. There is a possibility that some of them may be more common in the tropics owing to higher prevailing temperatures and insolation there, but no evidence on this point has yet been published. It seems more likely that a generally worldwide distribution is a result of the worldwide occurrence of self-heating masses of organic debris.

TABLE II

SOURCES OF THERMOPHILIC FUNGI[a]

Genera	Microbially self-heated materials				Soils		Herbivore dung	Miscellaneous plant material[d]
	Composts[b]	Hay and grass	Peat	Manure	General	Thermal[c]		
Mucor	+	+	+		+		+	+
Allescheria					+			
Chaetomium	+	+					+	+
Myriococcum	+							+
Talaromyces	+	+	+	+	+			+
Thermoascus	+	+	+		+			+
Humicola	+	+	+	+	+		+	+
Malbranchea	+	+		+			+	+
Paecilomyces			+					
Sporotrichum					+		+	
Stilbella	+							
Torula	+						+	+

[a] Data compiled from Cooney and Emerson (1964).

[b] Including guayule rets, garden compost, leaf mold, mushroom compost, municipal refuse, etc.

[c] No fungi from thermal soils have yet been identified by name.

[d] Including bird nests, cacao seeds and husks, straw, grain, cardboard, cordage, etc.

B. *Composts: Self-Heating Organic Materials*

A tabulation of the available collection data (Table II) amply demonstrates what we could now predict, namely that the thermophilic fungi are well represented in the microbial population of aerobic or semi-aerobic, self-heating, organic materials wherever these occur in sufficiently large masses to be reasonably well self-insulated. Extensive collections have come from hay (Miehe, 1907a) and garden compost or manure (Crisan, 1959), stored peat (Küster and Locci, 1964), retting guayule (Cooney and Emerson, 1964), stacked oil palm kernels (Eggins and Coursey, 1964), and mushroom composts (Fergus, 1964). Certainly these are the richest kinds of habitats and the ones deserving the most intensive future exploration. At the same time, one must recognize that most of the thermogenic environments just noted are man-made, and similar habitats, while they are certain to occur in nature, are not likely to represent such ideal conditions. Data should be accumulated on the temperatures reached and sustained in naturally occurring masses of decomposing plant debris in various parts of the world. A number of animals are known to incubate their eggs in the warmth from natural composts, and the carefully maintained mounds of the incubator birds (Megapodiidae) in Australia and the islands of the South Pacific (Frith, 1962) provide a marvelous example of microbial thermogenesis long antedating man's activities. Detailed temperature records are available for these mounds, but the microbial flora has not yet been examined.

C. *Other Sources: Nesting Materials, Dung, Diseased Animals, and Soils*

The heat from warm-blooded animals themselves may be involved in providing a favorable environment for thermophiles. Miehe (1907a) and Noack (1912) discussed the occurrence of thermophilic fungi growing on the nesting materials of birds or hibernating mammals, and Cooney (1952) made several successful isolations from such substrata. The dung of herbivorous animals has also been a good source of certain thermophiles (Cooney and Emerson, 1964) although the reason for their occurrence on this material is not clear. The heat of the dung when it is deposited is unlikely to be retained long enough to promote the growth of thermophiles, but viable spores might well be present in the dung in great numbers if self-heated fodder had been eaten previously. The likelihood that thermophilic fungi might be agents of disease in warm-blooded animals has frequently been considered (see Miehe, 1907a; Cooney and Emerson, 1964), but to date only the two species of *Mucor, M. pusillus* and *M. miehei,* have been definitely implicated. Mesophilic strains of *Malbranchea pulchella* have frequently been isolated from lesions in man and animals, but the thermophilic var. *sulfurea* does not seem to be involved.

Now that the simple requirements for enriching for thermophilic fungi are being recognized, soil microbiologists (Apinis, 1963a,b; Warcup, 1963) are beginning to report the widespread occurrence of thermophiles in soils. Whether, as first suggested long ago by Miehe (1907a) and Noak (1912), thermophiles are able to grow in the upper layers of soil as a result of insolation, or whether their presence in soil is simply a result of their wide distribution from foci of growth elsewhere in self-heated materials, is not known at present. Miehe (1907a) also noted that thermally heated soils of volcanic regions ought to harbor thermophilic microorganisms, and Loginova *et al.* (1962) have recently reported that there is indeed an extensive flora of obligate thermophiles in certain volcanic areas of the Ural Mountains. Detailed quantitative comparisons of the floras in thermally heated and nonthermally heated soils will provide some evidence of the effectiveness of insolation as a source of heat for thermophiles in ordinary soils. As yet, no thermophilic aquatic fungi have been found although Cooney (1952) made a preliminary effort to isolate some from the waters of hot springs.

IV. ECONOMIC IMPORTANCE

A. Beneficial Activities

From the very general occurrence of thermophilic fungi in self-heating composting materials such as garden composts and manure, one could infer that they themselves are involved in the complex breakdown reactions that are so important in humification, the production of leaf mold, and the conversion of waste materials into valuable fertilizer. No doubt this is true, but relatively little specific information that relates directly to the thermophiles is yet available. Nevertheless such studies as have been done (e.g., Rege, 1927; Stoller *et al.,* 1937; Waksman *et al.,* 1939; Kaila, 1952; Henssen, 1957) indicate that thermophilic fungi are indeed very active and that they constitute a particularly effective component of the total microbial flora. Kaila and Henssen both concluded that high temperature composting holds considerable promise for practical, large-scale use in agriculture. Moreover, for the disposal of municipal wastes and refuse, high temperature composts have received increasing attention and are being effectively employed in various parts of the world (Golueke and Gotaas, 1954; Gotaas, 1956; von Klopotek, 1962; Müller, 1964; Cooney and Emerson, 1964).

It is also interesting to discover how widespread are the industrial uses of thermogenic processes where microorganisms, including thermophilic fungi, play a major or contributory role (cf. Cooney and Emerson, 1964). Preparation of the compost for mushroom beds (Atkins, 1961) is dependent upon a large-scale self-heating process in which the ingredients are brought to a suitable degree of decomposition and simultaneously raised to a temperature at which various pests are killed. Cooney and Emerson (1964) and Fergus (1964) have identified many thermophilic true fungi from these mushroom composts. The processing of both chocolate (Chatt, 1953) and tobacco (Garner, 1946) may involve a thermogenic fermentation in which quality and flavor are dependent upon the microorganisms that develop and the conditions that are maintained. Penicillin has been produced (Rode *et al.,* 1947) from high-temperature cultures with *Malbranchea pulchella* var. *sulfurea,* and the industrial production of high-quality rubber from guayule by a thermogenic retting process has been investigated in detail (Allen and Emerson, 1949). Thermophilic fungi are active agents in the retting of guayule (Cooney and Emerson, 1964). Finally, while one would suppose that the molding of fodder for farm animals should be avoided, workers in Germany (Müller, 1961) have reported that the controlled self-heating and microbial treatment of various kinds of fodder converts it into better feed as judged by weight gains of the experimental animals. The basis for the improved quality resulting from "Futterverpilzung," as this process is called, has not been explained, but thermophilic fungi are undoubtedly involved.

B. Detrimental Activities

Ever since the dawn of agriculture, human society and security have depended upon the storage of food products in time of plenty for use in time of need. And ever since the first crude hay mow and grain bin were built, man has been struggling to protect his supplies of food and fodder from the inevitable attacks of pests of one sort or another. The ubiquitous fungi have always been, and remain today, an enemy capable of tremendous damage and destruction. Moldy corn and hay were well known to the ancients, and directions for the proper drying and curing of agricultural products are to be found among the earliest written records (Browne, 1929). Moreover, whenever organic materials are stored in masses large enough to be self-insulated, if they undergo microbial decomposition they will heat (see Section II, D), and the further hazards of damage from heat and possible ultimate destruction by fire are very real. Therefore, because of their growth at elevated temperatures and their role in microbial thermogenesis, the thermophilic fungi unquestionably contribute to annual losses of immense economic magnitude throughout the world.

It is not surprising that the first detailed information about thermophily in fungi was revealed when Miehe (1907a) undertook to explain the self-heating and spontaneous combustion of hay. Studies on all aspects of the problem followed and carry through to the present day with reports (e.g., Glathe, 1960a,b) on the actual financial losses and the use of microbiological evidence in litigation over fire insurance adjustments. Thermophilic fungi have been repeatedly found also in stacked peat (Isachenko and Mal'chevskaya, 1936; Mishustin, 1950; Küster and Locci, 1964) where the problems of self-heating and combustion are, likewise, serious and of long standing. In his book on "The Molds and Man," Christensen (1961) has given a lively account of the complex factors that enter into the microbial heating of stored grain. Spontaneous bin-burning is by no means a thing of the past.

Mention was made in Section III, C of thermophilic fungi being the causal agents of disease in domestic animals. This has been discussed by Ainsworth and Austwick (1955, 1959), who conclude that such diseases do not appear to have more than minor economic significance. Recently Gregory and Lacey (1963) and other workers have been investigating the possibility that thermophilic fungi are involved in certain inhalant allergic conditions. For example, the ailment known as "farmer's lung

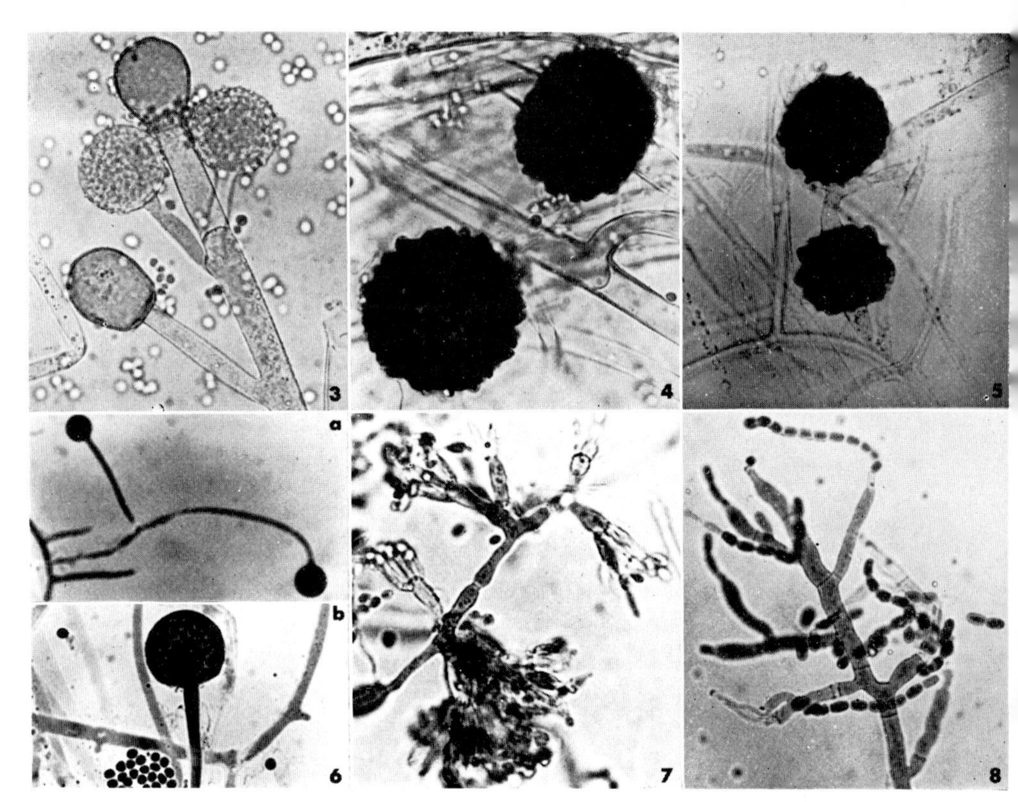

FIGS. 3–26. Representative photomicrographs of the thermophilic fungi, lighted by bright field and stained by aqueous, alkaline phloxine except where otherwise indicated. Slide preparations and photographs were made by Barbara M. Licht. All the organisms were grown at 37–40°C (except *Talaromyces dupontii,* which was grown at 45°C) on yeast-glucose (YG) or yeast-starch (YpSs) media as made up by Cooney and Emerson (1964) (except *Thermoascus aurantiacus,* which was grown on oat agar, and *Allescheria terrestris,* which was grown on 2% malt agar). All strains photographed were those of Cooney and Emerson (1964) except the *A. terrestris,* sent by the courtesy of A. E. Apinis, and the *Sporotrichum thermophile,* kindly provided by Aino Henssen.

FIGS. 3 and 4. *Mucor pusillus.* Fig. 3. Sporangiophore, sporangia, and sporangiospores. ×345. Two of the sporangia have shed their spores, revealing the large columella. Fig. 4. Mature zygospores. ×345.

FIGS. 5 and 6. *Mucor miehei.* Fig. 5. Mature zygospores. ×345. Fig. 6. Sporangiophore, sporangia, and sporangiospores. a, ×170; b, ×345.

FIG. 7. *Talaromyces* (*Penicillium*) *dupontii* conidiophores and conidia. ×550.

FIG. 8. *Thermoascus aurantiacus,* conidiophores and conidia. ×345.

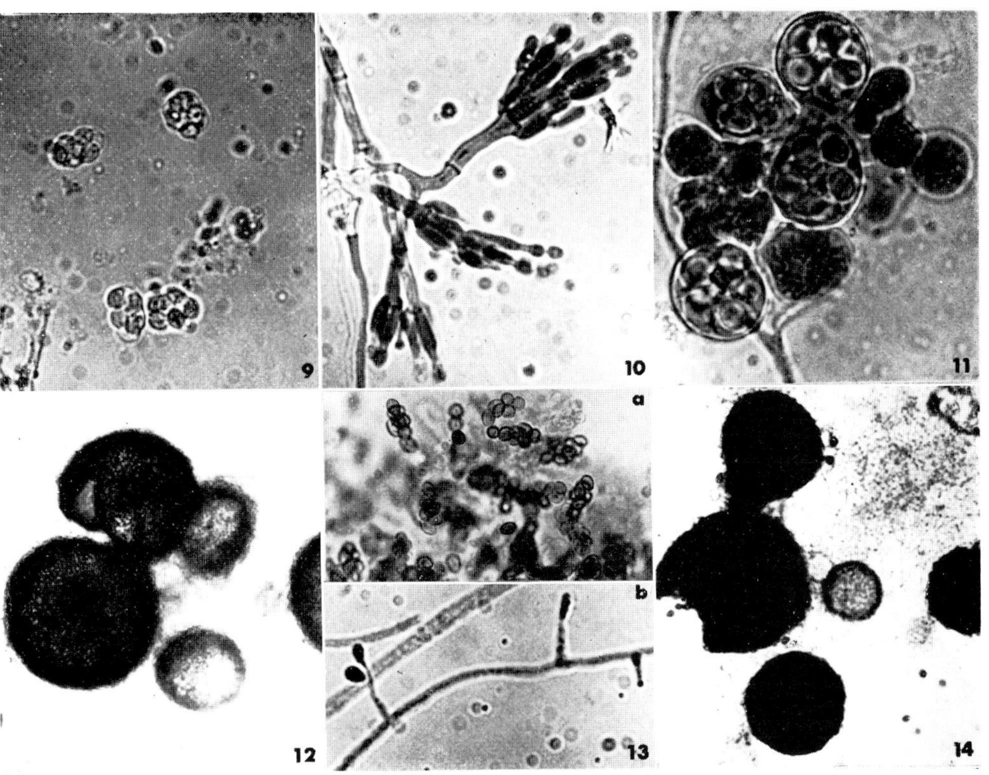

FIGS. 9 and 10. *Talaromyces* (*Penicillium*) *emersonii*. Fig. 9. Asci and ascospores. ×550. Fig. 10. Conidiophores and conidia. ×550.

FIG. 11. *Thermoascus aurantiacus,* a cluster of asci, ranging from young, without any indication of ascospores, to mature, with fully formed ascospores. ×550.

FIGS. 12 and 13. *Allescheria terrestris*. Fig. 12. Cleistothecia. ×75. Fig. 13a. Ascopores. ×345. Fig. 13b. Phialides and developing conidia. ×550.

FIG. 14. *Myriococcum albomyces* cleistothecia and ascospores. ×75.

disease" apparently results from an allergic reaction to the extensive inhalation of spores from moldy hay or compost. However, the medical implications of the thermophilic fungi appear very unimportant compared with their agricultural activities.

V. NOTES ON THE IDENTIFICATION OF THERMOPHILIC FUNGI

The thermophilic fungi are all included in the Phycomycetes, Ascomycetes, and Fungi Imperfecti. No myxomycete or basidiomycete has been recorded as thermophilic.

For purposes of positive identification, detailed descriptions of species and varieties should be consulted. A comprehensive systematic account,

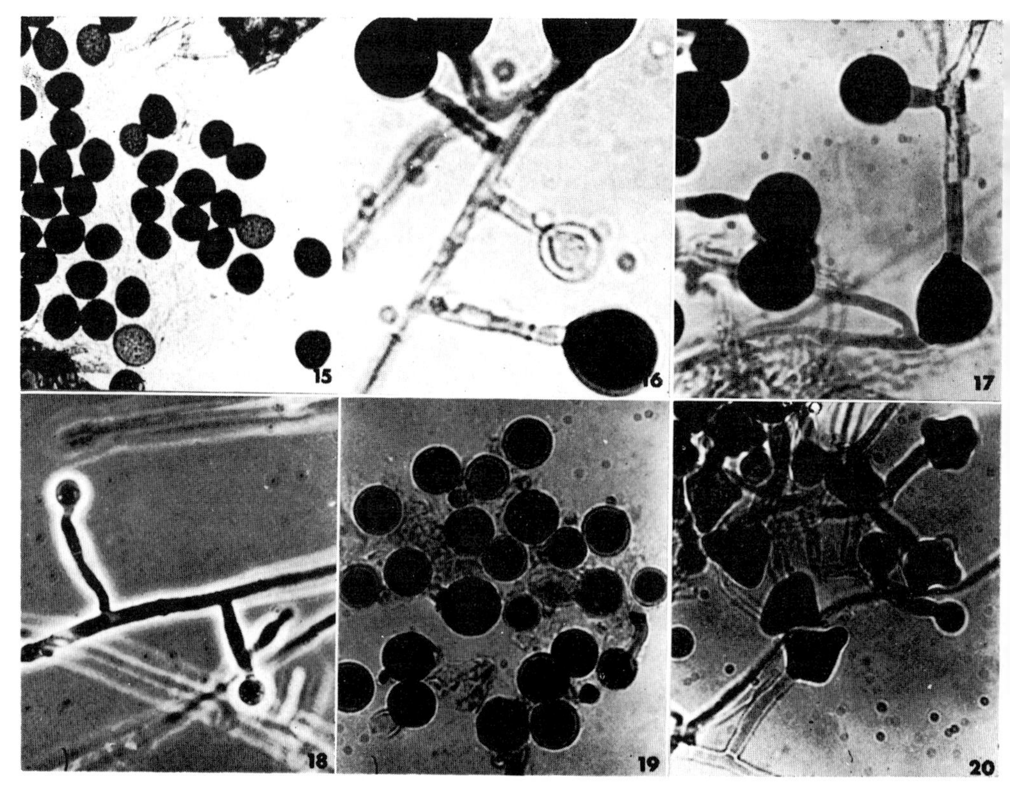

FIG. 15. *Myriococcum albomyces* detail of mature ascopores. ×345.

FIG. 16. *Humicola grisea* var. *thermoidea,* conidiophores and conidia. ×820.

FIG. 17. *H. insolens,* conidiophores and conidia. ×820.

FIGS. 18 and 19. *H. lanuginosa*. Fig. 18. Conidiophores and young conidia, phase contrast. ×820. Fig. 19. Mature conidia, several showing the characteristic attachment piece or pedicel. ×820.

FIG. 20. *H. stellata,* conidiophores and conidia. ×820.

including the synonymy, has been presented by Cooney and Emerson (1964). However, such a limited number of thermophilic Eumycota have been described that, *once established by its temperature characteristics as a bona fide thermophile* (Section I), any new isolate can be tentatively identified with little difficulty. The following brief notes are provided as a guide.

A. Mucor pusillus Lindt and Mucor miehei Cooney and Emerson

These are the only two thermophilic members of the Mucorales. They are readily recognizable by their compact, low, gray mycelium, their typical mucoraceous sporangia (Figs. 3 and 6) with very small (ca. 5 μ diameter), nearly spherical sporangiospores, and their warty black zygospores (Figs. 4 and 5). The two species are very similar but *M. miehei*

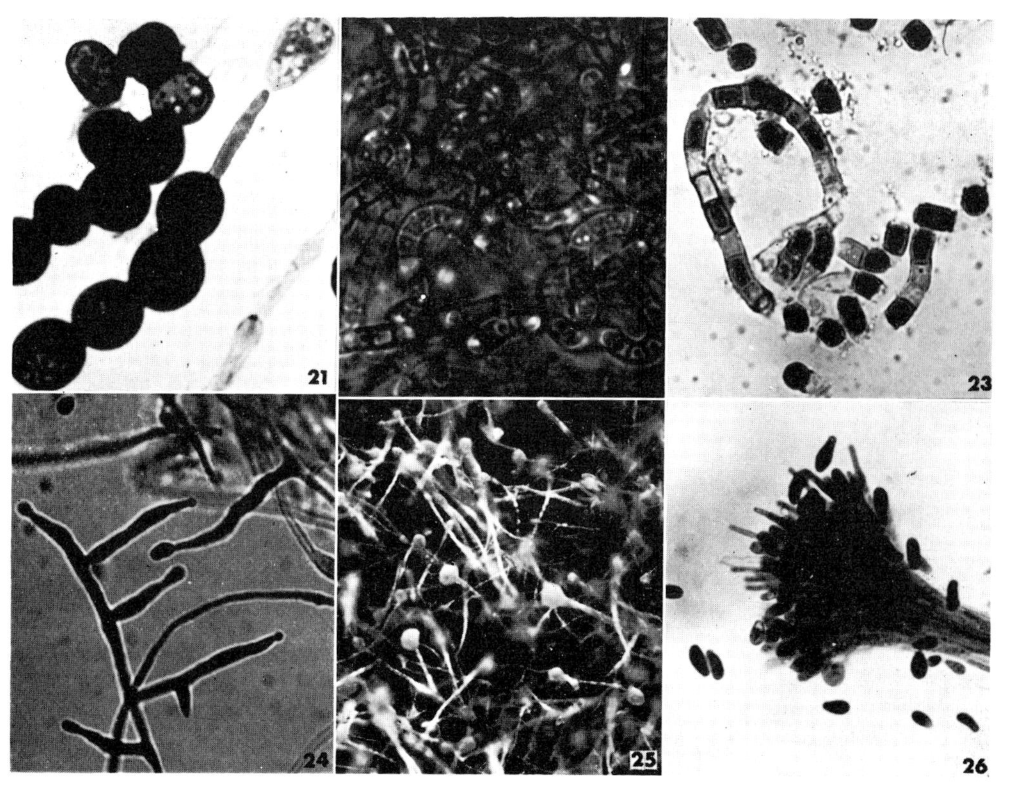

FIG. 21. *Torula thermophila,* conidia ×820.

FIGS. 22 and 23. *Malbranchea pulchella* var. *sulfurea.* Fig. 22. Young, spirally coiled (here flattened) conidiophore apices. ×820. Fig. 23. Mature conidia and alternating sterile cells. ×820.

FIG. 24. *Sporotrichum thermophile,* conidiophores and conidia. ×550.

FIGS. 25 and 26. *Stilbella thermophila.* Fig. 25. Habit of conidiophores and conidial heads. ×35. Fig. 26. Detail of coremioid apex of synnema showing conidiophores and conidia. ×240.

is homothallic and produces zygospores in abundance whereas *M. pusillus,* being heterothallic, forms them only in mixed or properly mated cultures. *M. miehei* also has slightly smaller dimensions of hyphae, sporangia, and zygospores.

B. *Talaromyces (Penicillium) dupontii (Griffon and Maublanc emend. Emerson) Apinis, Talaromyces (Penicillium) emersonii Stolk, and Thermoascus aurantiacus Miehe*

These three fungi are evident members of the Eurotiales, all having ascocarps typical of this order with scattered, globose asci. *Talaromyces dupontii* (Fig. 7) is distinguished by its lavender color at 40°C or above, its short conidiophores arranged laterally on trailing hyphae, and its small, somewhat irregular penicilli. The cleistothecia are rarely seen because they generally develop only under partially anaerobic conditions (Cooney and Emerson, 1964). They are pale tan, about 1 mm in diameter, subspherical, and with a delicate but well-developed plectenchymatous peridium. Photographic illustrations of these features can be found in Raper and Thom (1949, p. 576). Because Apinis (1963a) did not have *Penicillium dupontii* in hand when he proposed the new combination, *T. dupontii,* Stolk (1965) considers this name invalid and is proposing the name *T. thermophilus* for the perfect state of the long known *P. dupontii.*

The second thermophilic *Talaromyces, T.* (*Penicillium*) *emersonii* (Figs. 9 and 10) has recently been studied in several laboratories and has just now (Stolk, 1965) been fully described. Isolated from composting manure (Blom and Emerson, 1962), from slime in a pulp and paper mill (Eveleigh and Brewer, 1963), and from Italian compost as well as Nigerian palm oil kernels (Stolk, 1965), this fungus has been variously referred to *Byssochlamys* and to *Penicillium.* While the microscopic structure of its conidiophores is misleadingly similar to that of *P. dupontii,* it is clearly distinguished by its pale yellowish or greenish conidial phase and cottony, yellow or orange cleistothecial masses, which have no definite wall and hence resemble those of *P. luteum.* Stolk (1965) has concluded that this recent addition to the known thermophilic fungi can best be accommodated in the genus *Talaromyces.*

The third eurotialean species, *Thermoascus aurantiacus* (Figs. 8 and 11) is not to be confused with either of the two previous ones. It grows very much more rapidly; it has a creamy white, evanescent, conidial phase composed of very long (up to 1 mm) conidiophores with large, irregularly placed, paecilomyces-type phialides; and its cleistothecia, which are usually formed in abundance by fresh isolates, are bright orange or brick red, semi-confluent, irregular in shape, and covered by a distinct pseudoparenchymatous wall. Apinis and Chesters (1964) have used the name *Dactylomyces crustaceus* for some of these isolates, but Cooney and Emerson (1964) have presented detailed reasons for considering *Dactylomyces* a synonym of *Thermoascus.* While it is likely that there are several species in this *Thermoascus-Dactylomyces* complex, all seem clearly congeneric.

C. *Allescheria terrestris Apinis and Myriococcum albomyces Cooney and Emerson*

Besides the three eurotialean organisms just noted, two other thermophilic, cleistothecial ascomycetes have been described. Both are readily distinguishable from *Talaromyces* or *Thermoascus* because their ascocarps are black and very small, but they bear a resemblance to each other that is strong enough to suggest close relationship. *A. terrestris* (Figs. 12 and 13) has a *Cephalosporium* imperfect state and ascospores that are 4–6 $\times$ 3–4 μ in diameter, whereas *M. albomyces* (Figs. 14 and 15) appears to have no conidial state and its ascospores are 12–15 μ in diameter. In other respects, however, the similarities are very marked. Both have distinctly white mycelium, globose cleistothecia that open irregularly (compare Figs. 12 and 14), and smooth-walled, brown ascospores. Apinis (1963a) considers that his organism is a member of the Eurotiales, while Cooney and Emerson (1964) present evidence for a locular structure of the ascocarp and tentatively assign their *Myricoccum* to the Pseudosphaeriales.

D. *Chaetomium thermophile La Touche*

This member of the common genus *Chaetomium* is the only thermophilic pyrenomycete known thus far. Characteristic, dichotomously branched, stiff hairs cover the ostiolar region of its small (ca. 100 μ diameter), brownish perithecia, and the ascospores, which are brown and nearly globose, are about 8 μ in diameter. Varietal differences in this species are discussed by Cooney and Emerson (1964). Ames (1961) lists two other thermophilic species of *Chaetomium* but does not record their temperature characteristics fully.

E. *Humicola spp. and Torula thermophila Cooney and Emerson*

Five species of the Fungi Imperfecti constitute this group. They have often been confused in the literature because it is not easy to differentiate among them. All produce dark-colored chlamydospores singly and/or in chains. The spores of *Humicola lanuginosa* (Griff. and Maubl.) Bunce (Figs. 18 and 19) are always single and terminal on laterally placed short aleuriophores. When mature they have a wall that is irregularly sculptured or thickened, and they commonly show a portion of the conidiophore that remains attached to the spore when it is released. The spores of *H. stellata* Bunce (Fig. 20) are closely similar to those of *H. lanuginosa* in morphology and arrangement, but their wall thickening has a stellate form. In *H. grisea* Traaen var. *thermoidea* Cooney and Emerson (Fig. 16) chlamydospores are, again, borne singly on short lateral aleuriophores, but they are always smooth-walled and lack any attachment piece. Instead, the spore nearly always shows a flattened apiculus where it was attached to the aleuriophore. Only very rarely are intercalary chlamydospores to be found in this species. *H. insolens* Cooney and Emerson (Fig. 17), besides bearing single, terminal spores on short lateral aleuriophores, as in the three previous species, regularly produces intercalary chlamydospores singly, in pairs, or in short chains. Whether terminal or intercalary, the spores are smooth-walled and brown. Finally, in *Torula thermophila* Cooney and Emerson (Fig. 21), where the chlamydospores are again smooth and brown, virtually all spores are formed in longer or shorter chains which are usually intercalary but may be terminal. Obviously the species in this *Humicola–Torula* complex are quite similar and tend to intergrade, but clarification of their status and relationships must await monographic reviews of the genera involved.

F. Malbranchea pulchella Saccardo and Penzig var. sulfurea Cooney and Emerson

This thermophilic variety of *M. pulchella* (Figs. 22 and 23) is most likely to be noted because of its conspicuously sulfur-colored, somewhat mealy growth. Microscopically it is readily distinguished by the unusual, coiled, fertile tips of the conidiophores and the distinctive way in which the blocklike, thick-walled, yellow conidia are formed in chains and released by breakdown of the sterile, thin-walled cells that alternate with them in the chains.

G. Sporotrichum thermophile Apinis

S. thermophile (Fig. 24) is the only thermophilic fungus that produces its conidia singly on individual sterigmata, or phialides, which are borne on simple or irregularly branched conidiophores arising from the mycelium. The phialides range from very short, so that the spores are almost sessile on the sides of the hyphae, to quite long, as illustrated in Fig. 24. The original Apinis (1963a) isolate has relatively short phialides, whereas the Henssen (1957) isolate has generally long ones. Moreover, whereas the conidia of the Henssen isolate are smooth and Apinis described the conidia as smooth in his isolate, they are in fact distinctly rough-walled in his type culture. Quite possibly more than one thermophilic species will be recognized in this genus.

H. Stilbella thermophila Fergus

This is the only thermophile (Figs. 25 and 26) in which the conidiophores are grouped in synnemata. The synnemata are 0.3 mm or more in height and bear apically a conspicuous white or yellowish drop of mucus in which the colorless conidia are held.

I. Paecilomyces sp.

While they have not yet been formally named, isolates of *Paecilomyces* that are unquestionably thermophilic are now known (Küster and Locci,

1964). They have the sandy or olive color and irregularly arranged, acuminate phialides that characterize the genus (Brown and Smith, 1957). Since the spores are borne in chains on a penicillus, cultures of *Paecilomyces* must be examined carefully to differentiate them from the conidial phase of *Thermoascus* or *Talaromyces*.

ACKNOWLEDGMENTS

It is a pleasure to acknowledge the assistance of Barbara M. Licht, who prepared the photographic illustrations and helped with numerous other aspects of this study. Previously unpublished work in the review was supported by National Science Foundation Grant GB-1925.

REFERENCES

Ainsworth, G. C., and P. K. C. Austwick. (1955). A survey of animal mycoses in Britain: Mycological aspects. *Brit. Mycol. Soc. Trans.* **38**: 369–386.

Ainsworth, G. C., and P. K. C. Austwick. (1959). "Fungal Diseases of Animals," 148 pp. Commonwealth Agricultural Bureaux, Farnham Royal, Bucks., England.

Allen, P. J., and R. Emerson. (1949). Guayule rubber, microbiological improvement by shrub retting. *Ind. Eng. Chem.* **41**: 346–365.

Allen, P. J., J. Naghski, and S. R. Hoover. (1944). Decomposition of guayule resins by microorganisms. *J. Bacteriol.* **47**: 559–570.

Ames, L. M. (1963). "A Monograph of the Chaetomiaceae," 125 pp. Army Research Office [Durham, North Carolina]. (U.S. Army Res. Develop. Ser., No. 2. Title page shows 1961 but publication was 1963.)

Apinis, A. E. (1963a). Occurrence of thermophilous microfungi in certain alluvial soils near Nottingham. *Nova Hedwigia, Z. Kryptogamenk.* **5**: 57–78.

Apinis, A. E. (1963b). Thermophilous fungi of coastal grasslands. *Soil Organisms, Proc. Colloq., Oosterbeek, Neth., 1962,* North-Holland Publ., Amsterdam.

Apinis, A. E., and C. G. C. Chesters. (1964). Ascomycetes of some salt marshes and sand dunes. *Brit. Mycol. Soc. Trans.* **47**: 419–435.

Atkins, F. C. (1961). "Mushroom Growing To-day," 4th ed., 186 pp. Faber & Faber, London.

Blom, B. D., and R. Emerson. (1962). Studies on thermophily in fungi with particular reference to a new thermophilic *Penicillium*. *Am. J. Botany* **49**: 665 (abstr.).

Blom, B. D., and P. J. Snider. (1962). Personal communication.

Brown, A. H. S., and G. Smith. (1957). The genus *Paecilomyces* Bainier and its perfect stage Byssochlamys Westling. *Brit. Mycol. Soc. Trans.* **40**: 17–89.

Browne, C. A. (1929). The spontaneous combustion of hay. *U.S. Dept. Agr., Tech. Bull.* **141**: 1–38.

Chatt, E. M. (1953). "Cocoa, Cultivation Processing Analysis," 302 pp. Wiley (Interscience), New York.

Christensen, C. M. (1961). "The Molds and Man, an Introduction to the Fungi," 2nd ed., 238 pp. Univ. of Minnesota Press, Minneapolis, Minnesota.

Cohn, F. (1889). Über thermogene Wirkung von Pilzen. *Jahresber. Schles. Ges. Vaterl. Kultur* **66**: 150–156.

Cohn, F. (1891). Ueber Wärme-Erzeugung durch Schimmelpilze und Bakterien. *Jahresber. Schles. Ges. Vaterl. Kultur* **68**: 23–29.

Cooney, D. G. (1952). "Morphology and Taxonomy of the Thermophilic Fungi," 111 pp. Ph.D. Thesis, University of California, Berkeley, California.

Cooney, D. G., and R. Emerson. (1964). "Thermophilic Fungi, an Account of their Biology, Activities, and Classification," 188 pp. Freeman, San Francisco, California.

Crisan, E. V. (1959). "The Isolation and Identification of Thermophilic Fungi," 107 pp. M.S. Thesis, Purdue University, Lafayette, Indiana.

Crisan, E. V. (1962). "Growth and Pigmentation of Monotospora lanuginosa (Tsil.) Mason," 56 pp. Ph.D. Thesis, Purdue University, Lafayette, Indiana.

Crisan, E. V. (1964). Isolation and culture of thermophilic fungi. *Contrib. Boyce Thompson Inst.* **22**: 291–302.

Dye, M. H., and H. P. Rothbaum. (1964). Self-heating of damp wool. *New Zealand J. Sci.* **7**: 87–146.

Eggins, H. W. O., and D. G. Coursey. (1964). Thermophilic fungi associated with Nigerian oil palm produce. *Nature* **203**: 1083–1084.

Eveleigh, D. E., and D. Brewer. (1963). Studies on slime accumulations in pulp and paper mills. VI. Isolation of thermophilic and thermotolerant fungi from paper mills. *Can. J. Botany* **41**: 1377–1382.

Evreinova, T. N., and G. P. Miroshnichenko. (1962). Free nucleotides of the thermophilic and mesophilic variants of *Aspergillus fumigatus. Mikrobiologiya* **31**: 428–433; see *Microbiology* (*USSR*) (*English Transl.*) **31**: 350–354.

Fergus, C. L. (1964). Thermophilic and thermotolerant molds and Actinomycetes of mushroom compost during peak heating. *Mycologia* **56**: 267–284.

Frith, H. J. (1962). "The Mallee-fowl, the Bird that Builds an Incubator," 136 pp. Angus & Robertson, Sydney, Australia.

Garner, W. W. (1946). "The Production of Tobacco," 516 pp. Blakiston, Philadelphia, Pennsylvania.

Glathe, H. (1960a). Selbsterhitzung und Selbstentzündung von Erntestoffen und ihre Verhütung. *Ergeb. Landwirtsch. Forsch.* **3**: 83–98.

Glathe, H. (1960b). Die mikrobiologische Analyse im Dienste der Brandursachenermittlung. *Kriminalistik. Z. Ges. Kriminal. Wiss. Praxis* **14**: 121–123.

Golueke, C. G., and H. B. Gotaas. (1954). Public health aspects of waste disposal by composting. *Am. J. Public Health* **44**: 339–348.

Gotaas, H. B. (1956). "Composting. Sanitary Disposal and Reclamation of Organic Wastes," World Health Organ. Monograph Ser. No. 31, 205 pp. World Health Organ., Geneva.

Gregory, P. H., and M. E. Lacey. (1963). Mycological examination of dust from mouldy hay associated with Farmer's Lung disease. *J. Gen. Microbiol.* **30**: 75–88.

Gregory, P. H., M. E. Lacey, G. N. Festenstein, and F. A. Skinner. (1963). Microbial and biochemical changes during the moulding of hay. *J. Gen. Microbiol.* **33**: 147–174.

Griffon, E., and A. Maublanc. (1911). Deux moisissures thermophiles. *Bull. Soc. Mycol. France* **27**: 68–74.

Henssen, A. (1957). Über die Bedeutung der thermophilen Mikroorganismen für die Zersetzung des Stallmistes. *Arch. Mikrobiol.* **27**: 63–81.

Ingraham, J. L. (1962). Temperature relationships. *In* "The Bacteria" (I. C. Gunsalus and R. Y. Stanier, eds.), Vol. IV, pp. 265–296. Academic Press, New York.

Isachenko, B. L., and N. N. Mal'chevskaya. (1936). Biogenic spontaneous heating of peat. *Dokl. Akad. Nauk SSSR* **13**: 377–380. (In English, with German summary.)

James, L. H., L. F. Rettger, and C. Thom. (1928). Microbial thermogenesis. II.

Heat production in moist organic materials with special reference to the part played by microorganisms. *J. Bacteriol.* **15**: 117–141.

Kaila, A. (1952). Humification of straw at various temperatures. *Acta Agral. Fennica* **78**: 1–32.

Kempner, E. S. (1963). Upper temperature limit of life. *Science* **142**: 1318–1319.

Küster, E., and R. Locci. (1964). Studies on peat and peat microorganisms II. Occurrence of thermophilic fungi in peat. *Arch. Mikrobiol.* **48**: 319–324.

La Touche, C. J. (1950). On a thermophile species of Chaetomium. *Brit. Mycol. Soc. Trans.* **33**: 94–104.

Lindt, W. (1886). Mitteilungen über einige neue pathogene Schimmelpilze. *Arch. Exptl. Pathol. Pharmakol.* **21**: 269–298.

Loginova, L. G., A. E. Kosmachev, R. S. Golovacheva, and L. M. Seregina. (1962). A study of the thermophilic microflora of Mount Yangan-Tau in the southern Urals. *Microbiologiya* **31**: 1082–1086; see *Microbiology* (*USSR*) (*English Transl.*) **31**: 877–880.

Miehe, H. (1905). Über die Selbsterhitzung des Heues. *Arb. Deut. Landwirtschges.* **111**: 76–91.

Miehe, H. (1907a). "Die Selbsterhitzung des Heus. Eine biologische Studie," 127 pp. Fischer, Jena.

Miehe, H. (1907b). Thermoidium sulfureum n. g. n. sp., ein neuer Wärmepilz. *Ber. Deut. Botan. Ges.* **25**: 510–515.

Miehe, H. (1930). Die Wärmebildung von Reinkulturen im Hinblick auf die Ätiologie der Selbsterhitzung pflanzlicher Stoffe. *Arch. Mikrobiol.* **1**: 78–118.

Mishustin, E. N. (1950). "Thermophilic Microorganisms in Nature and Practice," 391 pp. Inst. Microbiol., Acad. Sci., Moscow. (In Russian.)

Müller, G. (1961). Mikrobiologische Untersuchungen über die "Futterverpilzung durch Selbsterhitzung." I. Mitteilung. Orientierende Untersuchung eines laboratoriumsmässig angesetzten Schimmelfutters. *Zentr. Bakteriol. Parasitenk., Abt. II,* **114**: 192–202.

Müller, G. (1964). Die praktische Bedeutung der thermophilen Mikroorganismen. *Biol. Rundschau* **1**: 155–164.

Niese, G. (1959). Mikrobiologische Untersuchungen zur Frage der Selbsterhitzung organischer Stoffe. *Arch. Mikrobiol.* **34**: 285–318.

Noack, K. (1912). Beiträge zur Biologie der thermophilen Organismen. *Jahrb. Wiss. Botan.* **51**: 593–648.

Noack, K. (1920). Der Betriebstoffwechsel der thermophilen Pilze. *Jahrb. Wiss. Botan.* **59**: 413–466.

Norman, A. G. (1930). The biological decomposition of plant materials. Part III. Physiological studies on some cellulose-decomposing fungi. *Ann. Appl. Biol.* **17**: 575–613.

Olliver, M., and T. Rendle. (1934). A new problem in fruit preservation. Studies on *Byssochlamys fulva* and its effect on the tissues of processed fruit. *J. Soc. Chem. Ind.* **53**: 166–172.

Raper, K. B., and C. Thom. (1949). "A Manual of the Penicillia," 875 pp. Williams & Wilkins, Baltimore, Maryland.

Reese, E. T. (1946). "Aerobic decomposition of Cellulose by Micro-organisms at Temperatures above 40°C," 100 pp. Ph.D. Thesis, Pennsylvania State College, State College, Pennsylvania.

Rege, R. D. (1927). Bio-chemical decomposition of cellulosic materials, with special reference to the action of fungi. *Ann. Appl. Biol.* **14**: 1–44.

Rode, L. J., J. W. Foster, and V. T. Schuhardt. (1947). Penicillin production by a thermophilic fungus. *J. Bacteriol.* **53**: 565–566.

Rothbaum, H. P. (1963). Spontaneous combustion of hay. *J. Appl. Chem.* **13**: 291–302.

Stolk, A. C. (1965). Thermophilic species of *Talaromyces* Benjamin and *Thermoascus* Miehe. *Antonie van Leeuwenhoek, J. Microbiol. Serol.* **31**: 262–276.

Stoller, B. B., F. B. Smith, and P. E. Brown. (1937). A mechanical apparatus for the rapid, high-temperature microbial decomposition of fibrous, cellulosic materials in the preparation of composts for mushroom cultures. *J. Am. Soc. Agron.* **29**: 717–723.

Tsiklinskaya, P. (1899). Sur les mucédinées thermophiles. *Ann. Inst. Pasteur* **13**: 500–505.

von Klopotek, A. (1962). Über das Vorkomen und Verhalten von Schimmelpilzen bei der Kompostierung städtischer Abfallstoffe. *Antonie van Leeuwenhoek, J. Microbiol. Serol.* **28**: 141–160.

Vouk, V. (1950). "Grundriss zu einer Balneobiologie der Thermen," 88 pp. Birkhäuser, Basel.

Waksman, S. A., W. W. Umbreit, and T. C. Cordon. (1939). Thermophilic Actinomycetes and fungi in soils and in composts. *Soil Sci.* **47**: 37–61.

Warcup, J. H. (1963). Personal communication.

CHAPTER 5

Psychrophiles

B. J. Deverall

Botany Department
Imperial College
London, England

I. INTRODUCTION

A psychrophile is a cold-loving organism which either grows best at low temperatures or is restricted to cold environments. Because most fungi have growth optima between 20°C and 30°C, and growth minima of 10°C, cold in this context is considered to be below 10°C. Therefore psychrophiles should be sought in environments in which temperatures rarely rise above 10°C. The suspected psychrophile should be shown to have a growth optimum near 10°C or below.

Reports of fungi growing in cold environments are grouped below according to their habitats.

II. POLAR FUNGI

Differences in physical features of northern and southern polar regions are likely to be reflected in differences between their respective mycofloras. The Arctic embraces several large islands, parts of the Siberian and American mainlands and large tracts of ocean. The Antarctic is an isolated plateau of 5 million square miles with an estimated average altitude of 8000 ft.

A. Arctic Fungi

The growth of fungi is dependent upon the availability of suitable substrata, and the only major sources of organic matter in areas affected by the Arctic climate are in the tundra. Tundra comprises a ground cover of herbaceous plants which decreases in density from the tree line to the area of permanent snow and ice. The climate of the tundra provides at least one month with an average temperature between 0°C and 10°C, although maximum temperatures may exceed 20°C on occasion. Thus fungi found in the tundra may grow under warm conditions, although they must be capable of survival at temperatures between —60°C and 0°C for much of the year.

Singer (1954) pointed out that, although some potential habitats for fungi had not been examined, the species of fungi found in the Arctic outweigh in number and diversity the flowering plants of the region. All four classes of fungi are represented, but some groups of Ascomycetes and Basidiomycetes appear to predominate. Certain Sphaeriales and other Ascomycetes are numerous on dead stems and leaves which persist for long periods probably because of the relatively low activity of soil bacteria and Fungi Imperfecti in breaking down organic matter. Many members of the Agaricaceae occur on mosses, and together with species of the Phycomycetes, Pezizales, and Helotiales on bird droppings and other dung. Mycorrhizal fungi, particularly species of Boletaceae and Agaricaceae associated with shrubby birches, are abundant. Plant pathogens appear to be fewer than farther south, and, although there are numerous rusts and smuts, there is evidence among the Uredinales of the omission of spore forms from the life cycle. One-third of the arctic rusts are microcyclic (Arthur, 1928).

There is a rich lichen flora (Dahl, 1954), and there are many fungi associated with the lichens both as symbionts and parasites.

Lind (1934) found 422 species of fungi on Arctic plants deposited throughout sixty years in the Copenhagen Botanical Museum. None of the fungi were strictly endemic, a high proportion were also known in alpine regions, and many had a worldwide distribution.

Numerous surveys by Polunin, Pady, and co-workers of the fungal spores in the air over the Arctic have been reviewed by Gregory (1961). On some occasions, spores may be found over the polar ice cap, but it is thought that the origin of air masses sampled is more important in deciding the origin of the spores than the locality of the sampling. Pady and Kelly (1953) found many nonviable spores over the Arctic, mostly of soil fungi but also of plant pathogens, particularly *Ustilago* spp. The air spora probably is derived mostly from agricultural regions farther south.

B. *Antarctic Fungi*

A small area of the Antarctic, which is free from a permanent covering of ice and snow, supports a sparse growth of mosses, lichens, fungi, and freshwater algae. No month has a mean temperature appreciably above 0°C.

There are great similarities between the Arctic and Antarctic mycofloras although the latter has numerous deficiencies, lacking species in the genera *Lactarius* and *Hebeloma,* for example, and having no members of the Boletaceae (Singer, 1954). Identical or nearly identical species of the Agaricaceae occur in both polar regions.

Dodge and Baker (1938) reviewed reports of surveys of lichens and fungal parasites of lichens from Marie Byrd Land and King Edward VII Land. They stated that members of the fungi imperfecti were common, fruiting lichens and mosses often being covered and apparently parasitized by fungi. Hyphae of *Hormiscium* sp. often covered the surface of small pebbles. *Scopulariopsis brevicaulis, Botrytis,* and *Penicillium* spp. developed on decomposed remains of a gull returned enclosed from Antarctica and then placed in sterile moist chambers at 10°C. Contamination was possible however.

Siple (1938) stated that, although air temperatures in Marie Byrd Land rarely exceeded freezing point, the rays of the sun had strong heating effects upon rocks. Brief growing periods occurred, but all plant life must have been adapted to withstand sudden return of freezing temperatures. Rocks sheltered from the wind and covered with bird droppings provided the best habitats for growth of lichens, mosses, and fungi.

Tubaki (1961) isolated 5 species of mycelial fungi and 3 species of yeast from soil samples obtained by the Japanese Antarctic Expedition. Only 2 species of *Rhacodium* and *Cryptococcus laurentii* var. *flavescens* were thought with certainty to be growing in the Antarctic. The other species may have been introduced by the expedition. Subsequently Di Menna (1966a,b) described isolates of yeasts from Antarctic soils, including several new species of *Candida.*

Although the polar regions support many fungi which must be able to tolerate extreme cold, there is little knowledge of the temperatures under which the organisms make significant growth. It is highly likely that growth minima are below freezing point, but the fungi may grow best at 20°C and above. The growth optima of polar fungi should be found in laboratory tests before they can be claimed to be truly psychrophilic.

III. ALPINE FUNGI

Cooke (1955) reviewed some reports of the growth of fungi at high altitudes, and stated that many fungi have been found near the snow line and that there are indications that some fruit bodies are produced before the seasonal melting of the snow. He described several habitats of macrofungi around snow-banks during summer months at altitudes between 3000 and 8000 ft in mountains of the north western states of the United States, and he measured ground and snow temperatures at known points near fruit bodies at specified times of day. Fruit bodies of *Lyophyllum* spp. were growing at temperatures between 1.5°C and 9°C, *Paxina nigrella* at 2.5°C, and *Hygrophorus vernalis* at temperatures of 2°C and above. Temperatures of 1–2°C were recorded beside fruit bodies at the melting edges of the snow. It is likely that the early development of the fructifications was under the snow at temperatures around the freezing point.

Common components of alpine microfloras include species of Uredinales. For example, Hiratsuka (1935) found 83 species of rusts in high mountains in Japan and noted a correlation between the occurrence of the microcyclic habit, high altitude, and low temperature. There are several similar records providing correlations between occurrence of fungi, altitude, and general climatic condition, but there is little experimental evidence that particular fungi have ability to grow at extremely low temperatures.

IV. PLANT PATHOGENIC FUNGI AT LOW TEMPERATURES

A number of fungal diseases of grasses, trees, and other plants are associated with snow cover. Because of their economic importance, more attention has been paid to the effects of temperature on growth of these fungi.

Dahl (1934) studied the behavior of *Fusarium nivale* [*Calonectria nivalis*], which causes a snowmold disease of turf grasses and cereals. Conditions which favor the disease are moisture, deep snow on unfrozen ground, and a prolonged cold and wet spring. The fungus in culture grew between 2°C and 32°C with an optimum at 20°C, but caused disease rapidly between 0°C and 5°C, and slowly between 15°C and 20°C. The important feature is its ability to grow at low temperatures, but success as a pathogen must depend upon interactions with the host at low temperatures involving factors other than rapid growth of hyphae.

Remsberg (1940) showed that *Typhula variabilis,* which destroys stored sugar beet and potatoes, grew *in vitro* between 0°C and 21°C with an optimum between 12°C and 15°C, and that *T. idahoensis,* which also causes a snowmold of grasses, grew at temperatures of 0–18°C, with an optimum at 9–12°C. These are among the lowest growth optima recorded for fungi.

Broadfoot and Cormack (1941) reported that in Alberta an unidentified basidiomycete killed grasses and legumes in early spring. The fungus was isolated more readily at 5°C than at 20°C, and it had cardinal temperatures of —4°C, 15°C, and 26°C (minimum, optimum, and maximum, respectively).

Pehrson (1948) found that the optimum temperature for the growth of *Phacidium infestans,* which causes a blight of pines in northern Sweden, was 15°C under several nutrient regimes. Although it grew poorly at 27°C, the fungus grew well at 5°C and produced slight growth at —21°C. Growth at —3°C was better if the fungus was kept at 0°C for a period before transfer to the lower temperature. Ability of the fungus to grow at the optimum was not impaired by keeping it for long periods at —21°C.

There are other reports of plant disease developing at low temperatures. Hedgcock (1914) noted that leaves and twigs of trees, which had been buried under snow, were smothered with mycelium of *Herpotricha nigra.* Baxter (1943) mentioned a damping-off disease caused by *Pythium* spp. in forest nurseries at high altitudes.

The evidence of the ability of fungi to grow, in addition to being able to survive, at low temperatures is rather better for these pathogenic fungi than it is for fungi of less economic importance. The species of *Typhula* with optima near 10°C must be considered to be psychrophilic, and it is a matter of opinion whether one includes the two pathogens which have optima of 15°C and ability to grow below freezing point.

V. FUNGI ON REFRIGERATED FOODS

Berry and Magoon (1934) reviewed reports since 1880 that fungi and bacteria grew below freezing point, particularly on frozen fruit and vegetables. They were unable to conclude that any of the organisms were truly psychrophilic because all grew more rapidly at temperatures well above freezing point. Therefore it was thought that they were mesophilic organisms able to grow relatively slowly at a lower temperature than the majority of organisms.

C. Brooks and Cooley (1917) found that, with two exceptions, all the apple-rot fungi tested by them grew in apples at 0°C but the optimum for rotting was between 20°C and 30°C, which was the same as the optimum for growth *in vitro.* They found that the process of infection was more susceptible to inhibition by low temperature than the later rotting, and they advised on the importance of immediate rather than delayed low temperature storage.

Smart (1934) reported on a survey of over 3000 samples of frozen packed fruits and vegetables. Many organisms including *Aspergillus, Penicillium, Rhizopus, Mucor,* and *Cladosporium* spp. survived over a year at —10°C in packed fruit and vegetables. Destruction of the food would be serious if the closed packs were allowed to thaw and stand before use.

F. T. Brooks and Hansford (1923) stated that black spot of chilled and frozen meat was caused by *Cladosporium herbarum,* which could be isolated from diseased meat together with species of *Thamnidium, Mucor,* and *Penicillium. C. herbarum* grew and infected meat between —6°C and 0°C, but produced profuse growth at 2°C.

Wright (1923) found that *Mucor mucedo, Rhizopus* sp., and *Penicillium glaucum* were associated with black spot of frozen mutton. Only once was *Cladosporium herbarum* isolated. Black spot was claimed to develop when *M. mucedo* was established on meat between —2°C and —1°C before transfer to —12°C to —15°C. The starting temperature necessary for *P. glaucum* was higher, being 4°C.

Sporotrichum carnis occurred frequently on lean stored meat kept for 8–10 weeks at —10°C to 0°C, according to Haines (1930). The growth optimum for the fungus in culture was 25°C, but slow growth occurred at —5°C, at which temperature germ tubes were thick and curled. Some growth was detectable at —10°C.

The habit of low temperature storage of food may select a group of invading organisms which can tolerate and grow slowly below freezing point. Hygienic procedures before refrigeration and avoidance of long periods of standing after thawing are sensible rules to apply to avoid losses caused by cold storage fungi. Negligible growth of fungi may occur if the temperature is kept constantly below —6°C.

VI. CONCLUSIONS

There is ample evidence that fungi are present in environments which provide long periods with temperatures below freezing point and where the air temperature rarely rises above 10°C. The temperatures of the substrata in which the fungi make most of their growth is less well documented, but Cooke (1955) recorded temperatures between 1°C and 2.5°C around growing fruit bodies near snowbanks. There is also the evidence that some plant diseases develop under snow cover, and that some fungi grow on frozen foods. All the fungi which grow at the freezing point might be considered to be psychrophiles, although some authorities distinguish between cold-tolerant mesophiles and true psychrophiles. The range of temperatures over which the plant pathogenic fungi (discussed in Section IV) grow indicates that these fungi at least should be claimed as psychrophiles. Evidence on the behavior of polar fungi at different temperatures is lacking.

REFERENCES

Arthur, J. C. (1928). Notes on arctic Uredinales. *Mycologia* **20**: 41–43.
Baxter, D. V. (1943). "Pathology in Forest Practice," 618 pp. Wiley, New York.

Berry, J. A., and C. A. Magoon. (1934). Growth of microorganisms at and below 0°C. *Phytopathology* **24**: 780–796.

Broadfoot, W. C., and M. W. Cormack. (1941). A low-temperature Basidiomycete causing early spring killing of grasses and legumes in Alberta. *Phytopathology* **31**: 1058–1059.

Brooks, C., and J. S. Cooley. (1917). Temperature relations of apple-rot fungi. *J. Agr. Res.* **8**: 139–163.

Brooks, F. T., and C. G. Hansford. (1923). Mould growth upon cold-store meat. *Brit. Mycol. Soc. Trans.* **8**: 113–141.

Cooke, W. B. (1955). Subalpine fungi and snowbanks. *Ecology* **36**: 124–130.

Dahl, A. S. (1934). Snowmold of turf grasses as caused by *Fusarium nivale*. *Phytopathology* **24**: 197–214.

Dahl, E. (1954). The cryptogamic flora of the Arctic. VII. Lichens. *Botan. Rev.* **20**: 463–476.

Di Menna, M. E. (1966a). Three new yeasts from Antarctic soils: *Candida nivalis, Candida gelida* and *Candida frigida* spp. n. *Antonie van Leeuwenhoek, J. Microbiol. Serol.* **32**: 25–28.

Di Menna, M. E. (1966b). Yeasts in Antarctic soils. *Antonie van Leeuwenhoek, J. Microbiol. Serol.* **32**: 29–38.

Dodge, C. W., and G. E. Baker. (1938). The Second Byrd Antarctic Expedition—Botany II. Lichens and lichen parasites. *Ann. Missouri Botan. Garden* **25**: 515–718.

Gregory, P. H. (1961). "The Microbiology of the Atmosphere," 251 pp. Leonard Hill, London.

Haines, R. B. (1930). The influence of temperature on the rate of growth of *Sporotrichum carnis,* from −10°C to +30°C. *J. Exptl. Biol.* **8**: 379–388.

Hedgcock, G. G. (1914). Notes on some diseases in our national forests. IV. *Phytopathology* **4**: 181–188.

Hiratsuka, N. (1935). A contribution to the knowledge of the rust-flora in the alpine regions of high mountains in Japan. (Contribution to the rust flora of Eastern Asia I.) *Mem. Tottori Agr. Coll.* **3**: 125–247.

Lind, J. (1934). Studies on the geographical distribution of arctic circumpolar micromycetes. *Kgl. Danske Videnskab. Selskab, Biol. Medd.* **9**: 1–152.

Pady, S. M., and C. D. Kelly. (1953). Studies on microorganisms in Arctic air during 1949 and 1950. *Can. J. Botany* **31**: 107–122.

Pehrson, S. O. (1948). Studies of the growth physiology of *Phacidium infestans* Karst. *Physiol. Plantarum* **1**: 38–56.

Remsberg, R. E. (1940). Studies in the genus *Typhula*. *Mycologia* **32**: 52–96.

Singer, R. (1954). The cryptogamic flora of the Arctic. VI. Fungi. *Botan. Rev.* **20**: 451–462.

Siple, P. A. (1938). The Second Byrd Antarctic Expedition—Botany. I. Ecology and geographical distribution. *Ann. Missouri Botan. Garden* **25**: 467–514.

Smart, H. F. (1934). Microorganisms surviving the storage period of frozen-pack fruit and vegetables. *Phytopathology* **24**: 1319–1331.

Tubaki, K. (1961). Notes on some fungi and yeasts from Antarctica. *Antarctic Record* **11**: 161–162.

Wright, A. M. (1923). Moulds on frozen meats. *New Zealand J. Sci. Technol.* **6**: 208–211.

Ecology

SYMBIOTIC FUNGI AND THEIR ASSOCIATES

CHAPTER 6

Mycorrhiza

J. L. HARLEY

Department of Botany
University of Sheffield
Sheffield, England

I. INTRODUCTION

More than a century of observation and experiment with root systems of plants from natural habitats has shown that very often particular kinds of mycelium are normally associated with healthy roots of particular species of higher plants. Hyphae and cellular tissue in association form definite composite organs, called mycorrhizas, which vary in structure and composition according to the species of host and fungus and to the conditions of the habitat. Extensive and comprehensive accounts of these mycorrhizas have been written by Rayner (1927), Kelley (1950), and Harley (1959). Here we are especially concerned with mycorrhizal organs as resultants of the activities of fungi in the special habitat of the subterranean organs of higher plants.

Certain general aspects of the association of fungi with roots have been discussed in previous chapters. Roots provide in their immediate environs, on their surfaces and in their tissues, specialized habitats where some fungi may find all or some of their essential requirements for growth. The continual movement of substances into and out of the living tissues, the loss of senescent cells and other results of growth and metabolism combine to make subterranean organs of higher plants habitats with special properties. Their surfaces and outer tissues become in consequence not only sites of active mycelial development, but also of populations of fungi which differ in specific constitution and activity from the fungal populations of other soil habitats. There are, moreover, considerable differences between the fungal populations of the root regions of different plant species. The proximity of members of these fungal populations to the absorbing organs of the higher plant endows them with the ability to influence the growth and activity of their hosts more directly and more fundamentally than other soil denizens.

Some of the fungal species in the root region are relatively unselective in their requirements and occur far and wide in other habitats, but many are more restricted. Among the latter are organisms, the root-inhabiting specialized parasites of Garrett (1956), which have direct effects upon the host by causing parasitic lesions. Others enter into close association with the root without causing any structural disorganization of the tissues but causing reactions that result in the development of morphologically and histologically differentiated dual organs of fungus and host—the mycorrhizas. Garrett views the mycorrhizal fungi as the end term of specialization and evolution of the parasites, and there is much to be said for this way of viewing them. It has, indeed, the peculiar advantage of stressing a very important point. For just as the interaction of pathogen and host give rise, owing to variations of their specific nature and of their environment, to different kinds of diseased organs having different morphological and histological patterns and different physiological consequences, so different combinations of organisms and environment produce different mycorrhizal structures. Indeed, one can no more generalize about mycorrhizal conditions than one can about diseases of roots. It is first necessary to classify mycorrhizas into clear-cut kinds about which generalization can be made before propounding hypotheses concerning their significance.

Although a great deal has been learned about the fungal populations of root systems, there is yet still more to learn. Accounts, even such as those of Garrett (1944, 1956) which have led to valuable generalizations about root disease fungi, suffer from the lack of fuller information. Our appreciation of the nature and importance of rhizosphere organisms and their interaction with one another and their hosts is even more deficient. Again, of the many thousands of described examples of mycorrhizal organs only a few have been subjected to detailed observation and experiment, hence only the most striking and obvious aspects of all these subjects are well understood. There is in addition a kind of association of fungus and host which does not fall squarely into any of the three types mentioned, for it has become more and more apparent that the surface of living roots provides a habitat for specialized, often sterile mycelia, sometimes referred to form genera such as *Rhizoctonia,* which may behave as innocuous associates, may form minor lesions or other disease symptoms, or may at times produce histological and morphological conditions reminiscent of the well-known mycorrhizal types. For instance, Peyronel (1923, 1924) in his work on phycomycetous mycorrhiza of a large number of species of plants, described the presence of two endophytes, one a phycomycete now known to be the true mycorrhiza former, the other a species of *Rhizoctonia.* So frequent was the occurrence of the *Rhizoctonia* that Peyronel put forward the theory that the mycorrhizas in question were formed by the joint action of two fungal species on the roots of their hosts. McLuckie and Burges (1932) observed a similar kind of double infection in *Eriostemon crowei,* and Lihnell (1939) an even more complicated case of multiple infection in *Juniperus communis.*

In 1923 Melin isolated fungi, referred to *Rhizoctonia sylvestris* and *Mycelium radicis atrovirens,* from conifer roots, in addition to basidiomycetes that formed true mycorrhizas. Similar fungi were later isolated by Robertson (1954) from *Pinus* and by Harley and Waid (1955) from *Fagus.* This kind of fungus has been shown to form weakly parasitic associations resembling mycorrhizal organs with many kinds of forest tree, and these have been called pseudomycorrhizas. Rayner and Levisohn (1941) and Levisohn (1954) made a special study of them.

On the other hand, rather similar organisms have been definitely implicated as mycorrhiza formers in Ericaceae, as Doak (1928), Freisleben (1933, 1936), Bain (1937), and Burgeff (1961) have shown. Burgeff classified them under *Cladosporium* on observing the spore type. Sterile imperfect sclerotial fungi, referable also to *Rhizoctonia,* are the authenticated mycorrhizal fungi of many orchids (Bernard, 1909; Burgeff, 1936).

The former group of apparently obligate root associates, whose taxonomic position is uncertain, have been responsible for a great deal of confusion in mycorrhizal studies. Some observers (e.g., Demeter, 1923; Mostafa, 1938; Bouwens, 1937) misinterpreted them as the true mycorrhiza formers in plants whose endophytes are certainly of phycomycetous affinity. Others (e.g., Hildebrand, 1934; Truscott, 1934; Hildebrand and West, 1941; Katznelson and Richardson, 1948), have isolated them from diseased roots of crop plants. In many respects the incomplete "pseudomycorrhizal" associations that they sometimes form, especially with trees, may be compared with similar incomplete states encountered in lichens. The "lichenized covers" or "Halbflechten" bear a somewhat similar relationship to fully formed lichen thalli as do pseudomycorrhizas to fully formed mycorrhizas. These problems will be touched upon again during the consideration of more easily recognizable fully developed mycorrhizal states but consideration will be primarily given to root-fungus associations which are most common in natural communities in normal habitats. These are associations in which there is not only an absence of destructive disorganization of the host tissue and a prolonged condition of associated healthy physiological activity but also often clear evidence of mutual interdependence between host and fungus.

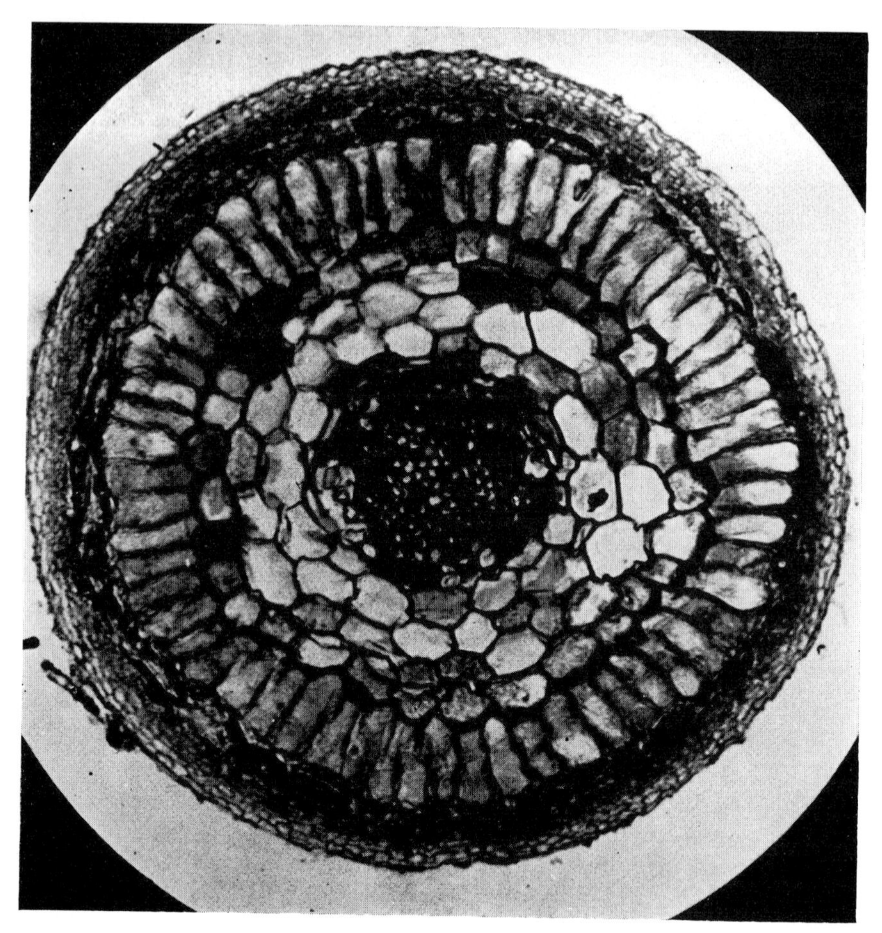

FIG. 1A. Ectotrophic mycorrhiza of *Fagus sylvatica*. Transverse section showing fungal sheath and Hartig net between the radially expanded external cortical cells. Inside the latter a suberized cell layer is visible. Photograph by Dr. F. A. L. Clowes. Magnification: ×280.

II. TYPES OF MYCORRHIZA AND THEIR FUNGI

A. *Ectotrophic Mycorrhiza*

Frank (1885) observed the composite organs of European Amentaceae such as *Fagus;* later he found the same kind of structure on the roots of *Pinus* and its allies and gave them the name "mycorrhiza." These are by far the most conspicuous and easily recognized of mycorrhizal organs, for the host tissue is enclosed in a tight pseudoparenchyma of fungal tissue which sends branches inward between the cortical cells of the root and

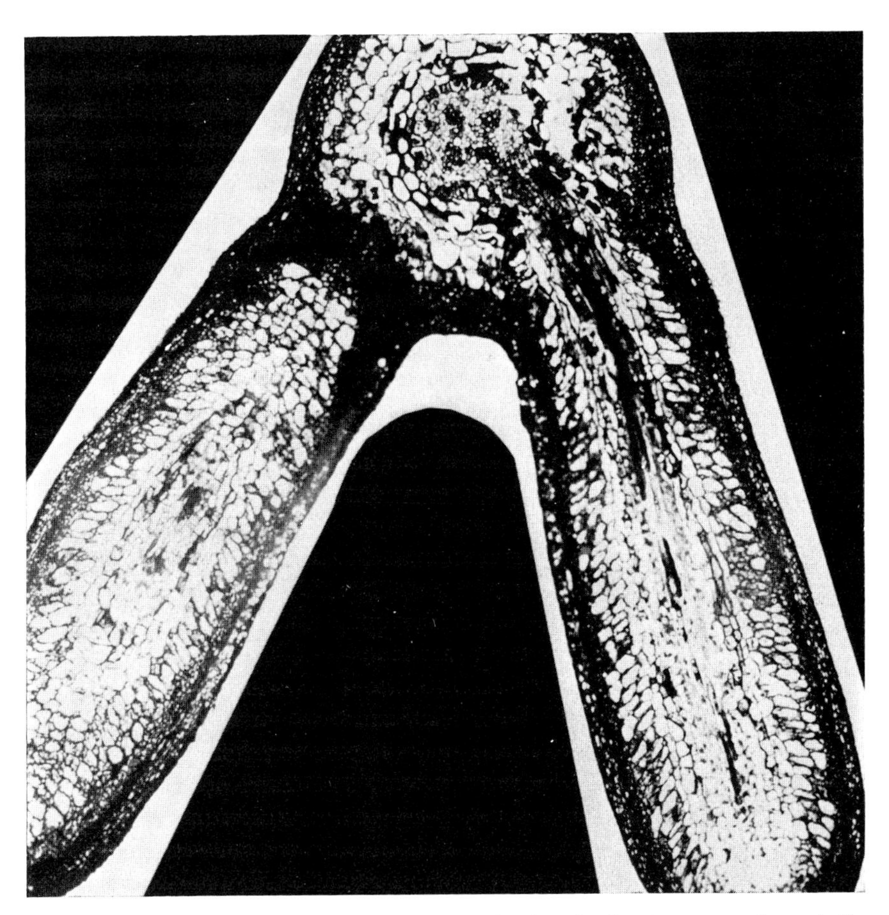

FIG. 1B. Ectotrophic mycorrhiza of *Fagus sylvatica.* Section transverse through the main axis and longitudinal through the branches, showing continuity of the fungal sheath. Photograph by Dr. F. A. L. Clowes. Magnification: $\times 130$.

outward into the soil. The pseudoparenchymatous layer (Fig. 1) which isolates the root from the soil comprises a considerable part of the total weight and volume of the whole organ. In *Fagus sylvatica,* for instance, it may be 40% of the dry weight and 40 μ in thickness in mycorrhizas 0.5–1.0 mm in diameter. The hyphae which penetrate the cortex form a network, often called the "Hartig net," in the middle lamella of the cell walls and the intercellular spaces of the external cortex. Hyphae pass outward into the soil and ramify among the soil particles. These may be scarce or abundant in different kinds of mycorrhiza, or on some kinds the mycorrhizal apices may be smooth although outgoing hyphae exist further back.

FIG. 1C. Ectotrophic mycorrhiza of *Fagus sylvatica*. Longitudinal section showing branch initials which cause the sheath to bulge but not break as they grow. Photograph by Dr. F. A. L. Clowes. Magnification: ×94.

Roots infected in this way are characteristically the feeding rootlets of the root system and become repeatedly and closely branched to form systems of branches which seem to exploit intensively the humus and litter layers of the soil. The form of the branching is usually racemose, but in *Pinus* it is dichotomous. The main mother roots by which the root system spreads, are not usually completely infected. In some species an internal Hartig net only is present in the cortex (e.g., *P. sylvestris:* Robertson, 1954), in others only an external sheath is found (*Fagus sylvatica:* Clowes, 1951, and *Eucalyptus:* Chilvers and Pryor, 1965). Nevertheless, as new lateral rootlets are produced from the mother roots, they become infected during their passage through the cortex or sheath so that a permanent state of mycorrhizal infection persists after initial infection in the seedling stage.

This kind of mycorrhiza, with its conspicuous external sheath of fungal tissue, was called "ectotrophic" by Frank. It is somewhat reminescent of stages of infection in certain specialized root parasites. *Ganoderma pseudoferrum* and *G. lucidum* are described as spreading ectotrophically over the host root forming a coherent tissue, the edge of which advances ahead of penetration and parasitic attack. Ectotrophic mycorrhiza is common in temperate trees, and many of the forest dominants of the deciduous and northern coniferous formations are normally infected in this way, as are the eucalypts and beeches of the southern hemisphere. Members of the genera *Pinus, Picea, Cedrus, Abies, Fagus, Quercus, Corylus, Castanea, Alnus, Betula, Populus, Eucalyptus,* and many others are infected naturally and are encountered uninfected only under exceptional circumstances. The ectotrophic mycorrhizal condition also occurs in regions other than temperate; Fassi and Fontana (1962) have, for instance, described it in tropical legumes such as *Brachystegia* and *Afzelia.*

A fairly wide knowledge of the fungi of these mycorrhizas has been obtained. It has been long inferred that many basidiomycetes, especially belonging to Agaricaceae, Boletaceae, and families of Gastromycetes, and possibly certain genera of the larger ascomycetes, e.g., *Tuber* and *Elaphomyces,* are involved in ectotrophic mycorrhiza formation. Full confirmation by the production of mycorrhizas by inoculation under controlled condition has been achieved with 50–100 species. Melin (1959), who has performed much of the experimental work, lists some of these with detailed references. Other lists are given by Hacskaylo (1961) and Moser (1963). In addition, fungi isolated from surface-sterilized mycorrhizas have been successfully back-inoculated onto their host. The taxonomic positions of some of the latter have been determined by hyphal anastomosis with cultures of known provenance, using the method of Buller (1933), Modess (1941), and others. There are available in addition long lists of basidiomycetes, the fruit bodies of which are so consistently associated with certain trees that they have been supposed to be mycorrhiza formers (e.g., Peyronel, 1921, 1924; Trappe, 1962). It cannot be too strongly emphasized that information of this kind provides only a basis of knowing which fungi are worth testing as putative mycorrhiza formers by inoculation experiments. However, the acutest ecological observers have produced extremely reliable suggestions.

The ectotrophic mycorrhizal condition here briefly described is normal in a very large number of species of trees. The hosts are actively photosynthetic and self-dependent throughout life for carbon compounds. Their seeds are well equipped with food materials and germinate readily in suitable conditions, and their seedlings may be grown in the uninfected condition with suitable manurial treatment. Nevertheless, in forest soils the root system is so infected that the great majority of the feeding roots are ensheathed by hyphal tissue and are therefore dependent upon the fungus for nutrient supply. The mycorrhizal condition is not obligate but ecologically inevitable and when present must be, by virtue of its structure at least, nutritionally significant.

In certain circumstances, when plants grow outside their usual ecological ambit, such as on agricultural soils or in deep shade, other kinds of infection are found upon their feeding roots. These are caused by imperfect fungi which, although they commonly occur on the roots, achieve dominance only in certain conditions and cause imperfect or pseudomycorrhizal infections. These are an extreme variety of ectotrophic infection between which and the common central types of mycorrhiza there is a range of forms which depend upon the association of various fungi with any given host in a variety of soils and habitats. Classifications of ectotrophic mycorrhizas into subtypes differing from one another in structure have been made by several observers for specific purposes (Melin, 1927; Björkman, 1941; Dominik, 1955). Some consideration of this variation will be made below, but in the main, its ecological and physiological significance has not yet been studied in very great detail.

B. *Endotrophic Mycorrhiza*

Quite early in the study of mycorrhiza it was shown that in addition to ectotrophic mycorrhiza other types of mycorrhizal infection were even more common in the plant kingdom. In most of these the composite organs are less conspicuously different from uninfected roots in appearance. No coherent sheath is usually formed by the fungus outside the roots although there may be a loose weft of hyphae in the soil around them. Hyphae penetrate into the cortex of the host passing between and into the cells. Within the cells, after a period of active development, the hyphae usually undergo destructive disorganization or digestion brought about by the activities of the host cell, the nucleus of which often becomes enlarged and active as digestion proceeds. These "endotrophic" infections are clearly not destructively parasitic because they are either always present on a given host or normally occur at certain times as part of the normal processes of root development. It has been found, moreover, that endotrophic mycorrhizal infection occurs in one or other of its forms in all partial or completely saprophytic higher plants, and it has been therefore judged to be implicated in nutrient absorption by these hosts at least.

Two main types of endotrophic infection have been clearly distinguished. There is that caused by fungi with septate hyphae, e.g., in Ericales, Orchidaceae, Gentianaceae, and in a number of other angiosperm families and a few Pteridophyta and Bryophyta. Secondly, there is that caused by aseptate phycomycetous fungi which is very common indeed in angiosperms, gymnosperms other than Pinaceae, pteridophytes and bryophytes.

1. *Endotrophic Mycorrhiza with Septate Endophytes*

Endotrophic mycorrhizas with septate endophytes are best illustrated by the Orchidaceae, a family in which all the members so far adequately studied are mycorrhizal. In these the roots are internally infected and attacked by hyphae which pass through hairs or surface cells into the cortical cells. They form coils in the cells of the outer cortex and develop in a healthy manner for some time. Later the hyphae undergo a breakdown by digestion, swell, lose their integrity, and much of their content passes into the host cell. A knot of disorganized hyphal wall material is left in the cell (Fig. 2). As the root grows, the fungus colonizes the cells behind the growing region so that exploitation and digestion go on throughout the life of the root. In some instances fungal exploitation and digestion seem to recur in the same cell more than once. There are several variants of the digestion process; for instance, in some hosts the tips of the hyphae are eroded away rather than a whole coil being digested. In adult orchids the fungal colonization is restricted to the subterranean absorbing organs, whether root or rhizome, and is especially evident where these are in contact with the substratum. The fungal hyphae do not exploit green tissues, nor do they attack storage organs such as tubers.

In Orchidaceae, and in some other plants having this type of infection, the seeds are minute in size and depend upon infection for successful germination in natural conditions. The facts have been well described (see Burgeff, 1932, 1936). The absorption of water and the rupture of the seed coat are followed by the penetration of the fungus into the suspensor end of the seed. The hyphae pass into the large central cells

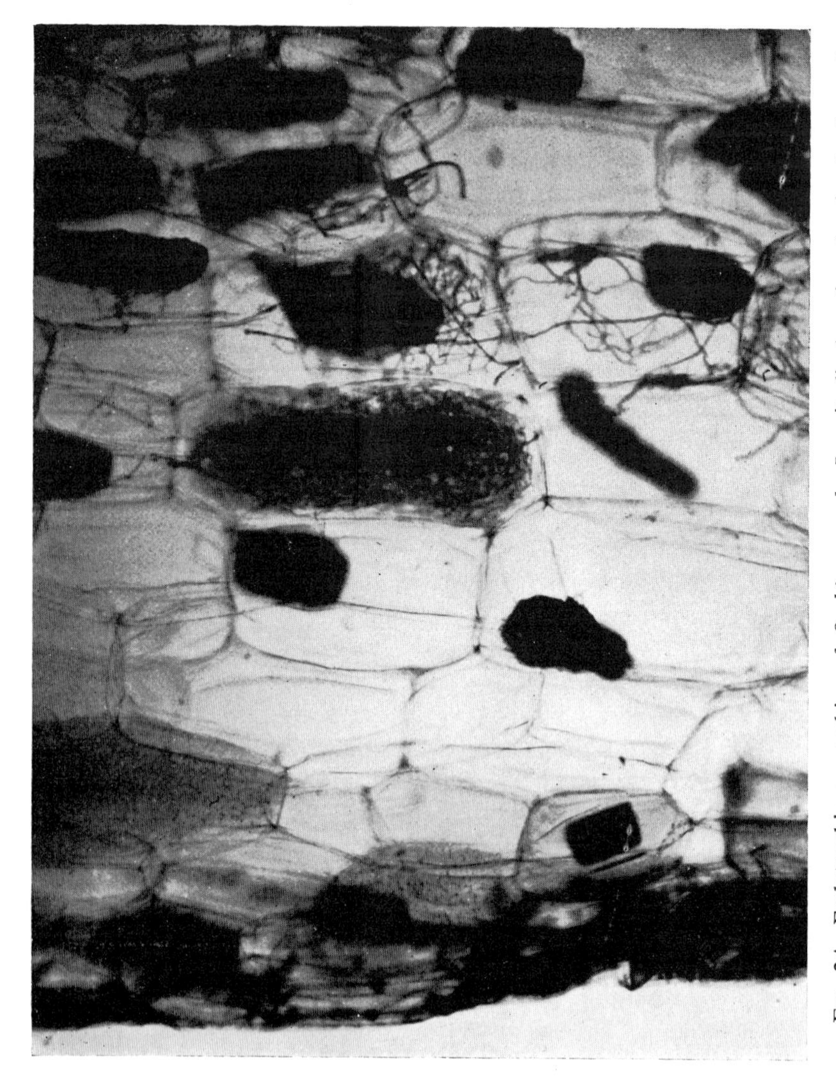

FIG. 2A. Endotrophic mycorrhiza of *Orchis mascula*. Longitudinal section showing hyphae colonizing the cortical cells, and stages of their digestion. Photograph by Mr. G. Wood from preparations by Dr. J. Webster. Magnification: ×100.

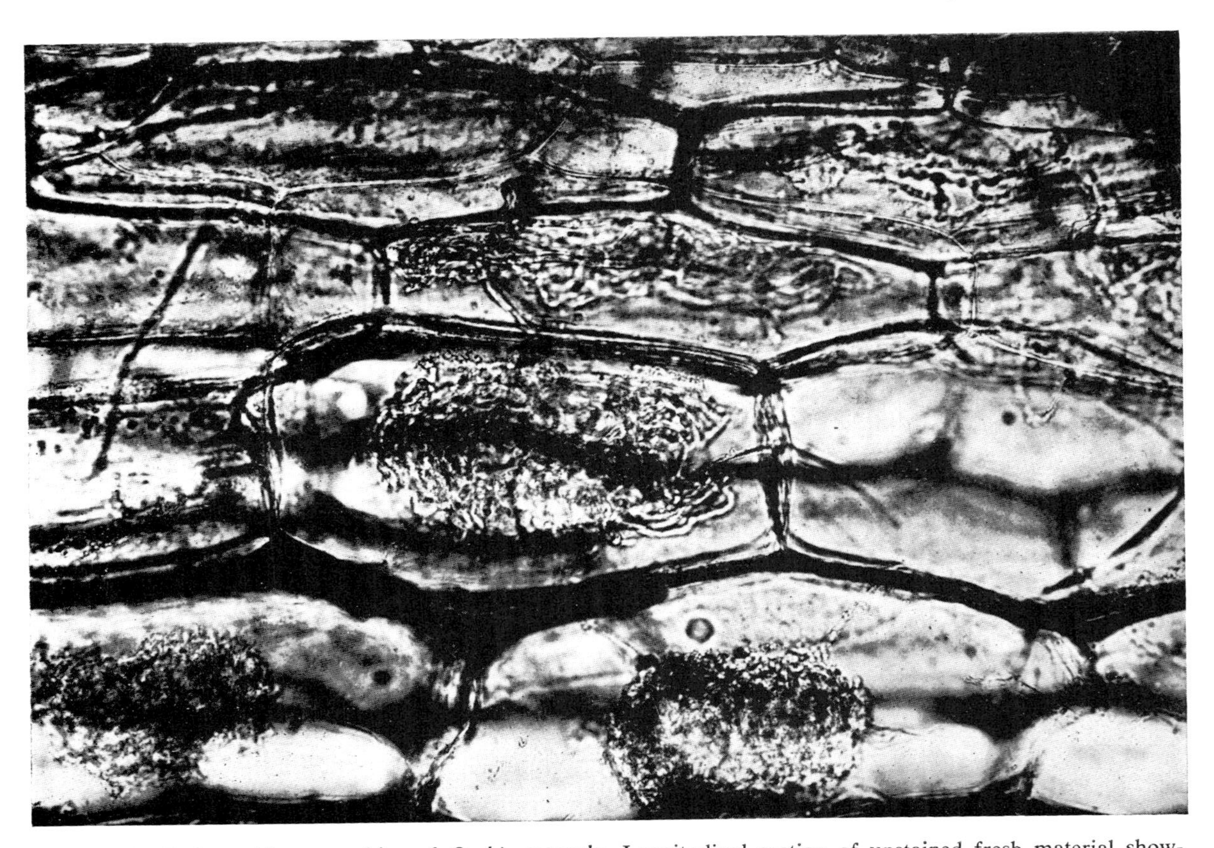

FIG. 2B. Endotrophic mycorrhiza of *Orchis mascula*. Longitudinal section of unstained fresh material showing digestion stages. Photograph by Mr. G. Wood from preparations by Dr. J. Webster. Magnification: ×340.

of the embryo and a pattern of exploitation and digestion is established. Following this the small uninfected cells of the apex divide and growth of the young protocorm follows. Growth is dependent on an external source of carbohydrate material for a long period, and this may be supplied either as insoluble carbon compounds in the presence of the fungus or artificially as soluble sugars together with other essential organic accessories in the absence of the fungus (see Knudson, 1922, 1924, 1925, 1927, 1930; Schafferstein, 1938, 1941). In nature germination seems to be always dependent on fungal infection.

The fungal endophytes of orchids are probably all basidiomycetous, either imperfect or perfect. A large number of species or strains of *Rhizoctonia,* some of which have been shown to produce *Corticium* fruit bodies, are endophytes of those orchids which become green as adults. Clamp-bearing mycelia have proved to be mycorrhizic with others, especially with the complete saprophytes. Certain of the saprophytic orchids harbor species of well-known wood- and litter-destroying genera as endophytes, e.g., *Fomes, Xerotus, Hymenochaete,* and *Armillaria.* It appears to be a general rule in the Orchidaceae, which are all saprophytes as seedlings and in some species also as adults, that the fungi not only stimulate germination and growth by providing accessory growth factors, but are also essential in carbon nutrition. They belong to species capable of digesting and utilizing complex organic substances and resistant carbon sources such as cellulose and lignin, and in this they contrast with the fungal associations of the ectotrophic mycorrhiza of forest trees. The same appears to be true, although experimental evidence is far from complete, of other plants, e.g., Gentianaceae, which possess *Rhizoctonia* endophytes. The Ericaceae and related Epacridaceae, Pyrolaceae, and Monotopaceae also have imperfect fungi or species of basidiomycetes as endophytes (Doak, 1928; Freisleben, 1933, 1936; Bain, 1937; Francke, 1934; Schmucker, 1959; Burgeff, 1961). The tendency to saprophytism shown in these families and in certain bryophytes, e.g., *Aneura* and its saprophytic relative *Cryptothallus*, together with the similarity of the pattern of infection to that in Orchidaceae lead to the conclusion that infection has the same significance.

The extensive researches on certain Ericaceae in which some evidence was obtained that species of *Phoma* might be mycorrhizal have been heavily criticized. An analysis of the position is given by Harley (1959). The possibility that these species of *Phoma* fix atmospheric nitrogen was built into a hypothesis that the importance of mycorrhiza to Ericaceae was to be found in a dependence of the host plant upon atmospheric nitrogen fixed by the endophyte. The potential of *Phoma* in this regard is at most very slight and in any event could not explain the saprophytic tendency in Ericales. It seems now probable that the mycorrhiza of

Ericaceae is in some ways intermediate between ectotrophic mycorrhiza and that of Orchidaceae (Burgeff, 1961).

2. *Endotrophic Mycorrhiza with Aseptate Endophytes*

Mycorrhizas containing aseptate phycomycetous fungi as endophytes are found in some members of all the phyla of land plants, Bryophyta (especially Hepaticae), Pteridophyta, Gymnospermae, and Angiospermae. An excellent recent description of this kind of infection is given by Mosse (1963) and in a monograph on pteridophytes by Boullard (1957). In the infected organs the hyphae penetrate the cortex forming either main hyphae in the intercellular spaces and short lateral haustoria in the cells, or penetrate directly from cell to cell. Two characteristic organs are commonly present (Fig. 3). Dichotomously branched haustoria, called *arbuscules,* are formed in many cells; these remain healthy for a time but later undergo digestion. At first the tips become eroded away, and later they are completely broken down and disintegrated. This seems to be the result of an active reaction on the part of the host cell, the nucleus of which enlarges and becomes active as digestion proceeds. The second characteristic organ of the fungus is the *vesicle.* Vesicles are swellings of the hyphae, usually terminally placed and formed in or between the host cells. They become thick walled and furnished with many fat globules. These endophytic fungi also form a considerable amount of extramatrical mycelium outstide the root in the soil, which is differentiated into long permanent hyphae, short, much-branched hyphae of shorter life-span (perhaps the homologue of the arbuscules), and also vesicles of a similar pattern to those within the tissues. There is some variation in the distribution of arbuscules and vesicles and in the stage of infection at which these are produced, but it can be safely concluded that this is a group of similar mycorrhizal infections which have been called the phycomycetous or vesicular-arbuscular mycorrhiza.

These fungi have posed considerable problems in isolation and identification. Indeed, many workers not only failed to isolate aseptate colonies, but misinterpreted septate isolates as the mycorrhiza-formers. This has resulted in considerable confusion in the literature (see Harley, 1950, for a review). In 1946 Magrou, who had spent great effort at isolating the fungi, and who had not been led to such false assumptions, succeeded in extending his early results by causing the endophyte of *Arum* to grow across an agar bridge from an infected root of *A. maculatum* to infect a root of *A. italicum.* The hyphae were aseptate. Stahl (1949) repeated this type of experiment with numerous infected liverworts and obtained cross-inoculations in a similar way. In the meantime, Barrett (1947) isolated eleven strains of phycomycetous endophytes from a variety of plants onto hemp seed, but his work was not widely appreciated because full details

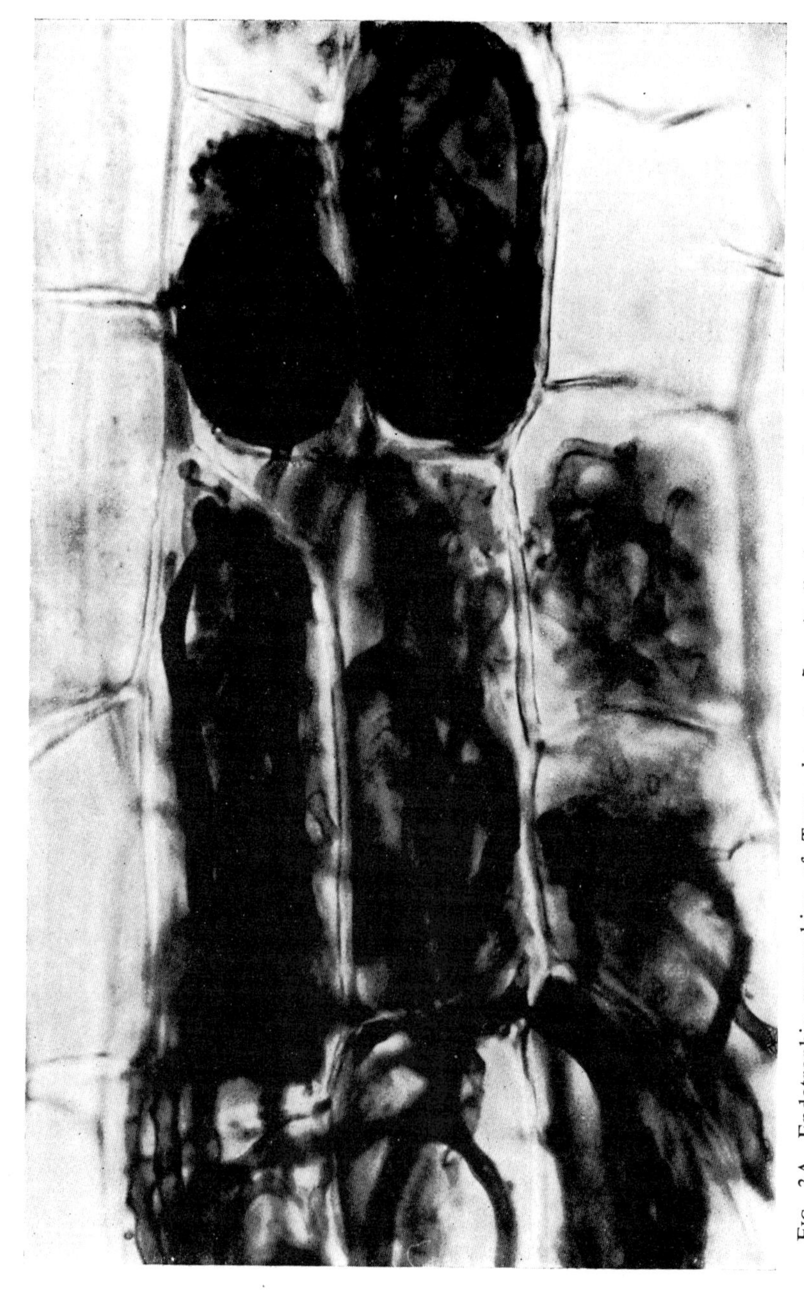

FIG. 3A. Endotrophic mycorrhiza of *Taxus baccata*. Longitudinal section through cortex showing colonizing hyphae and vesicle. Photograph by Mr. G. Wood from preparations by Dr. J. Webster. Magnification: ×630.

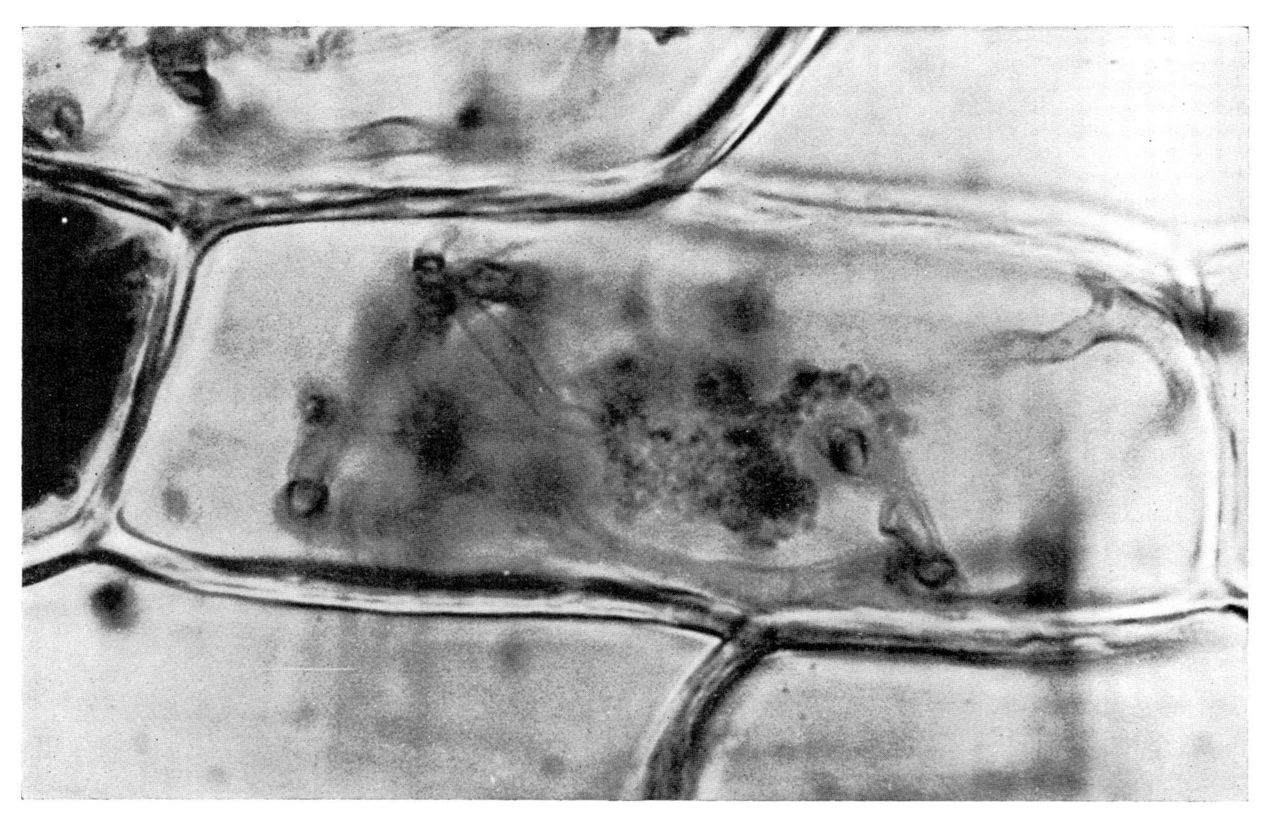

FIG. 3B. Endotrophic mycorrhiza of *Taxus bacata*. Longitudinal section of cell containing an arbuscule. Photograph by Mr. G. Wood from preparations by Dr. J. Webster. Magnification: ×1750.

of his techniques were not then published. Later, however, others successfully repeated his procedures. The fungi so isolated Barrett referred to the genus *Rhizophagus,* Dangeard's name for the endophyte of *Populus* which had been described in 1900. Barrett (1961) has offered the opinion that they may be imperfect conditions of species of *Endogone.* The genus *Endogone* was first implicated seriously as containing endophytes of this kind of mycorrhiza by Peyronel (1923) on the grounds that he observed hyphal connections between fruit bodies and mycorrhizas. This suggestion was confirmed by Mosse (1953, 1956), who has used sporocarps and resting spores as sources of inocula. Others (e.g., Gerdeman, 1961) have provided further confirmation by similar means.

In addition to the *Rhizophagus-Endogone* complex, a species of *Pythium,* somewhat resembling *P. ultimum,* has been isolated repeatedly by Hawker and her colleagues (see Hawker, 1962, for references), from *Allium* and some other plants with vesicular-arbuscular mycorrhiza. Some of the isolates have been shown to form mycorrhizal infection in selected conditions with some hosts, particularly species of *Allium* and some ferns (Hawker *et al.,* 1957; Ham, 1962; Hepden, 1960).

Vesicular-arbuscular mycorrhiza has therefore been reasonably well characterized and shown to be exceedingly common and widespread in the plant kingdom. Most of the host plants have seeds which germinate easily and seedlings and adult phases capable of photosynthesis and the absorption of nutrients in the uninfected state at least on well-fertilized soils. Host species include members of many of the largest and economically important angiosperm families, such as Gramineae, Palmae, Leguminosae, Compositae. The fact that mycorrhizal infection does not have to be considered with respect to the growth of agricultural crops has thrown doubt upon its significance in host physiology. The effects of mycorrhizal infection upon growth in natural or nutrient-deficient habitats have only recently been properly investigated and will be considered later. Certain complete saprophytes, e.g., some Burmaniacaceae and some lycopod prothalli, have infections of the vesicular-arbuscular type, and these plants have been considered, without other evidence except analogy with Orchidaceae, to be dependent on their fungi for carbon nutrition.

III. THE PHYSIOLOGY OF MYCORRHIZAL FUNGI

Mycorrhizal fungi may be divided into two groups: septate fungi which are mostly basidiomycetes or imperfect fungi of possible or probable basidiomycetous affinity; and aseptate phycomycetous fungi including species of *Endogone,* the imperfect *Rhizophagus* (probably congeneric with *Endogone*), and species of *Pythium.* Here a comparative treatment of the mycorrhizal fungi within each of these groups will be made.

A. *Basidiomycetes and Septate Mycorrhizal Fungi*

The septate mycorrhizal fungi may be arranged from a comparative point of view, in a series showing a gradation from great selectivity in nutrition to relative absence of selectivity. This series follows approximately a series from ectotrophic mycorrhizal fungi through pseudo-mycorrhizal fungi and fungi endotrophic in autotrophic plants to those in partial and complete saprophytes.

We owe to Melin and his colleagues (see Melin, 1953, 1963, for references) most of our knowledge of the physiology of ectotrophic mycorrhizal fungi and to Burgeff (1936) that of the septate endotrophic fungi of orchids. A review of these subjects is given by Harley (1959).

The basidiomycetes of ectotrophic mycorrhiza are physiologically specialized in their dependence upon simple carbohydrates for growth. Most of those studied utilize glucose and fructose, some also mannose and sucrose. Others can hydrolyze starch, but few are able to utilize cellulose even when supplied with a starting quantity of glucose. Lignin is very rarely or perhaps never utilized. Most grow best on organic or inorganic compounds of ammonia as nitrogen source. Amides, simple amino acids, and other soluble organic sources of nitrogen may be utilized, but the faculty of nitrate reduction appears to be limited.

For some species or strains, specific amino acids or casein hydrolyzate are necessary or stimulatory for growth. Most require thiamine and may also require other vitamins, such as biotin, pantothenic acid, or nicotinic acid. Over and above the requirement for known substances, Melin (1963) has shown that root exudates and extracts of certain plants, some mycorrhizal and some nonmycorrhizal, contain substances that stimulate fungi. Some of these fungi, e.g., *Cortinarius lagopus, Pholiota caperata,* and *Russula xerampelina* make little growth in culture solutions without these root derivatives. Melin (1963) has called the active substances "M-Factors," and has found those from pine roots to be complex and probably to contain at least two components. A diffusible substance is readily released into the medium, and a second, relatively indiffusible, substance tends to be retained by the living roots. In addition, inhibitory substances may also be present in root exudates and extracts.

The ectotrophic mycorrhizal fungi in culture are ineffective in competition with other organisms and moreover are readily inhibited by some extracts of leaf litter and humus (Melin, 1946; Handley, 1963).

All these properties together show most of the fungi of ectotrophic mycorrhiza to be probably restricted in their natural distribution to roots or their environs. Robertson (1954) showed that spore germination occurs readily in the environs of the root surface but not at large in the soil. Moreover, infection spreads more readily from the root system of infected seedlings to uninfected seedlings than from chopped mycorrhizal material added to the soil. Romell (1938) produced evidence from trenching experiments that many mycorrhizal basidiomycetes do not produce fruit bodies except when attached to host plants. All these observations agree with the ecological observation that the fruit bodies of many of these fungi are only found near certain species of host (e.g., *Lactarius rufus* near birch, *Boletus elegans* near larch). It is indeed this kind of evidence which lends credence to lists of putative mycorrhiza formers (e.g., Trappe, 1962).

In any ecological grouping exceptions are met, and this is true of the ectotrophic mycorrhizal fungi. Some seem to have a wider ambit of existence than the surfaces of susceptible roots. For instance, Romell (1938) observed that *Boletus subtomentosus,* a mycorrhizal fungus of *Pinus montana* (Modess, 1941), fruited in locations where its connections with its host had probably been severed. *B. bovinus,* mycorrhizal with *P. sylvestris, P. nigra,* and *P. strobus* (Rayner and Levisohn, 1941; Hatch and Hatch, 1933), has been reported to exist as rhizomorphs in heath soil in the absence or rare occurrence of host trees. There is some possibility also that *B. scaber* (*Betula verrucosa* and *Populus tremula*) can exist away from living hosts (Dimbleby, 1953). Certain species appear, moreover, to have some limited ability to use cellulose and possibly lignin. *Boletus subtomentosus* was observed by Lindeberg (1948) to produce extracellular polyphenolase, a property usually restricted to lignin-destroying fungi, and to be able to cause decay of litter. *B. scaber* was found by Handley (1963) to be more resistant to inhibitors extracted from *Calluna* humus than other mycorrhizal fungi. Norkrans (1950) pointed out that among the mycorrhizal species of *Tricholoma,* one, *T. fumosum* (*Pinus sylvestris*) has some power of cellulose utilization. The formation of ectendotrophic mycorrhiza on certain trees has been ascribed to the presence of mycorrhizal fungi of those types which have greater capabilities of hydrolysis and hence are able to penetrate the cell walls of their hosts. The pseudomycorrhizal fungi, e.g., *Mycelium radicis sylvestris,* also seem to lie at this point in our series, for they are able to utilize a wider range of carbon substrates (Schelling, 1950) and to inhabit a wider range of soil habitats than most typical ectotrophs. It is of interest in this connection that Lyr (1963) has made a study of exoenzyme production of a few mycorrhizal fungi in culture, viz. *Boletus subtomentosus, B. varigatus, B. badius,* and *B. luteus, Amanita citrina,* and *A. muscaria.* He was able to demonstrate cellulase, xylanase, amylase, and proteinase in the filtrate of each, but not pectinase. The production of amylase and xylanase was significant in all types, but the quantities produced of these and all other enzymes observed were distinctly smaller than in litter- or wood-destroying fungi. It would appear very doubtful whether any could grow successfully on cellulose although some might upon starch or hemicellulose.

The mycorrhizal fungi of orchids (both rhizoctonias and basidiomycetes) constitute a further extension of this series. Most of them may be grown in ordinary culture media without amendments and actively utilize many complex organic substances as sources of carbon. On simple sugars they typically grow much faster than ectotrophs; starch is rapidly hydrolyzed, and glycogen, proteins, glycosides, and humic acid are all utilized. Many produce extracellular polyphenolase, oxidize tannins, utilize cellulose and lignin, and can therefore be cultured upon natural fiber or wood (Burgeff, 1936). Certain of them indeed belong to well-known brown-rot or white-rot genera such as *Fomes, Armillaria, Xerotus,* and *Corticium.*

These orchid fungi seem to have no close dependence on their hosts in ecological distribution. Indeed some appear to be very much more widely distributed. *Rhizoctonia solani* (*Corticium solani*), a mycorrhiza former with *Orchis purpurella* (Downie, 1957), is also common as a pathogen of crop plants. *Armillaria mellea,* mycorrhizal with species of the saprophytic genera *Galeola* and *Gastrodia,* is well known as a wood-destroying and disease organism. It has been shown by Kusano (1911) and Hamada (1940a,b) that this fungus can be simultaneously mycorrhizal with an orchid whose growth it stimulates, and parasitic on standing trees. The recent work of Ruinen (1953) on epiphytic orchids, and the older observations of de Cordenoy (1904) on *Vanilla,* that hyphae pass from orchids to penetrate other hosts lead to similar conclusions.

Not enough is yet known of the endophytes of Ericales to give a satisfying account of their physiology. It seems clear that the view that nitrogen fixation was brought about by the species of *Phoma* isolated from Ericad tissues and believed to be mycorrhizal is unfounded. Burgeff's observations (1961) confirm this and also show that the mycorrhizal fungi of the species autotrophic for carbon do not occur except in the environs of the roots of their hosts. It seems likely that, since in the Ericales there is a transition from carbon-autotrophic to purely saprophytic species such as *Monotropa,* with various Pyrolaceae as intermediate forms, a series of fungi from nutritionally selective to active wood- and litter-destroying forms will be found to be their symbionts.

B. Phycomycetous Mycorrhizal Fungi

Two kinds of fungi are included here: first, *Rhizophagus* strains isolated by Barrett (1947, 1958, 1961), together with species of *Endogone* observed by Mosse (1953, 1956, 1959a) and Gerdeman (1955, 1961);

second, the strains of *Pythium* spp. cultured by Hawker and her colleagues (1957; Hawker, 1962). These will be separately considered.

Rhizophagus and the species of *Endogone* seem to be obligate associates of roots. *Rhizophagus* has been cultured, after a period of adaptation upon hemp seed, but *Endogone* has not been obtained in permanent culture. These fungi are even more specialized than the most nutritionally selective fungi of ectotrophic mycorrhiza. In culture media their hyphae may spread to a limited degree (approximately 1 cm) from spores. Growth occurs only so long as the hyphae are attached to the spore; excised hyphal tips cease growth. Mosse (1959a,b, 1963), working with the short hyphal systems produced on spore germination, showed that the hyphae frequently anastomosed and thereafter grew a little more actively. Growth was limited to pH in the range 6.2–6.6, and was stimulated by tartaric acid and other organic acids and by sterile soil.

In and about the root, mycelial growth is more active. Thus, Magrou (1946) and Stahl (1949) both succeeded in causing hyphae to cross a bridge of agar from one infected root to another. Indeed, in soil the fungus may produce a fairly dense mycelium bearing vesicles, spores, and sporocarps around a root. If the host root is removed, infective particles persist in the soil but there is no evidence of infectivity increasing with time, but rather of a decrease (Koch, 1961; Meloh, 1961). Thus, although these fungi seem to be extremely widely distributed in soil (Butler, 1939; Dowding, 1959), they seem to be dependent for physiological activity on living roots. In soil, the mycelium which is attached to roots seems to be more versatile metabolically than expected from its behavior in culture. It permeates extensively and colonizes humus particles and appears to accelerate their breakdown. Indeed it is possible that by virtue of substances obtained from the host, perhaps of the nature of vitamins, it is enabled to exploit and absorb nutrients from the soil (see also below).

The strains of *Pythium* isolated by Hawker and her colleagues differ from the aseptate mycorrhizal fungi described above in their ready growth in culture and also in the fact that they form mycorrhiza only in a very narrow range of conditions, outside which they may become parasitic. They were isolated first on water agar and grown upon a variety of media. Growth occurred most profusely in synthetic media where glucose or fructose were supplied as sources of carbon. Sucrose, starch and inulin were also utilized. Substances such as asparagine or peptone were better sources of nitrogen than nitrate or ammonium compounds. For purposes of inoculating hosts, mycelia were grown in quantity on oatmeal and sand media. Growth in culture was inhibited or reduced by dilute extracts of bulbs or roots of *Allium ursinum* (a known host) obtained by freezing the living tissue. This may be important in the control of the extent of the exploitation of *Allium* tissues, for it is in this genus that mycorrhizal infection rather than parasitic attack has most readily been brought about by inoculation with these *Pythium* strains.

IV. SUSCEPTIBILITY AND RESISTANCE OF HOSTS TO MYCORRHIZAL FUNGI

Although most mycotrophic plants are infected in their natural habitats, some variation in intensity of mycorrhizal development is observed. Part of this variation is related to the growth cycle of the host and to the season of the year, and part is due to habitat variations. Cyclic and seasonal variations are shown in many tree species. Seedlings remain uninfected until active photosynthesis begins; later in each season there is a period of extensive ectotrophic mycorrhizal development after the cessation of rapid root growth in spring. In endotrophic mycorrhizas each root initially is usually fungus free and becomes infected from the soil after a period of growth. Habitat variations, especially those arising from human activity, as in arable land, and well manured or disturbed soil, provide localities where infection may be scarce or sporadic.

Hatch (1937) showed in field and laboratory experiments that, given the presence of ectotrophic mycorrhizal fungi species of *Pinus* developed mycorrhizas most readily and completely in soils of moderate nutrient deficiency or of unbalanced nutrient supply. In extreme starvation conditions the growth of both young plants and their mycorrhizal partner was poor, but in the low ranges of soil nutrient supply mycorrhizal development was at its greatest. A moderate deficiency of available nitrogen, phosphorus, or potassium was a prerequisite for intense mycorrhizal infection. Hatch's findings have since been found to apply to other ectotrophic species and have been confirmed and extended especially by Björkman, who showed that light intensity was an important factor also. Björkman (1942) found that mycorrhizas were not formed as prolifically in low light intensity as in high. Indeed both light intensity and nutrient supply were important in determining the degree of mycorrhizal development. The higher the nutrient supply, especially of nitrogen, the greater the light intensity required, on the whole, to promote infection. These findings have been confirmed by some observers, but others have failed, so their explanation has been a cause of discussion. Björkman himself connected the needs of the ectotrophic mycorrhizal fungi for simple carbohydrates, photosynthesis, and the presence of free sugars in the roots to formulate an explanatory hypothesis. In high light and low nutrient supply, excess sugar would be available and encourage infection by the sugar-dependent fungi. It does not seem, however, likely that a fungal spore or other propagule in the soil could perceive directly available carbohydrate in a neighboring root. It also seems improbable that so unspecific an event as the excretion of sugar from a root into the soil would stimulate mycorrhizal fungus to invade, in view of their sensitivity to competition. It seems more likely that the internal nutritional condition within the root might affect the release of root secretions, such as the M-factors of Melin, which might exert a more specific stimulation of mycorrhizal fungi.

Björkman's hypothesis has stimulated much investigation and the correlation of mycorrhizal infection with light supply and with conditions in which photosynthesis might be rapid has been confirmed by a number of observers. However some modification of the hypothesis has been suggested because some of the results of carbohydrate analysis do not fit well with it. Meyer (1962, 1964) working with beech and pine obtained a general correlation between mycorrhizal frequency and the content of simple sugars of the roots in three soils. However, fertilization with nitrogen and phosphorus compounds did not bring about the expected reduction in mycorrhizal frequency, especially on eutrophic brown earth soils. Meyer found on further examination, an inverse correlation of sugars in the whole plant and mycorrhizal development. He also observed, using beech seedlings, that when one set of branch roots was more infected and another set of branch roots on the same plant less infected, the latter had less simple sugar. For instance a root with 86% mycorrhizal frequency had a soluble sugar content of 2.22% dry weight whereas a root with 60% mycorrhizal frequency had 2.01% of sugar. Meyer pointed out that Moser and Slankis had shown that mycorrhizal fungi produce auxins and that auxins are reported to stimulate starch hydrolysis and increased permeability of protoplasts. Hence the inverse correlation of the sugar content of the whole plant to mycorrhizal frequency and the mode of perception of internal sugar by the fungus could be explained. Handley and Sanders (1962) carried out analysis in exactly the same manner as Björkman with similar manurial treatments, but in the absence of mycorrhizal fungi, and concluded as Meyer had done, that the easily soluble reducing sugar content of the roots of mycotrophic plants was the result of infection, not its cause. Richards (1965) and Richards and Wilson (1963) on the other hand, had obtained an inverse relationship between mycorrhizal development and nitrogen content of seedling roots of *Pinus caribaea* and *P. taeda*. Richards pointed out that a good positive correlation existed between mycorrhizal development and reducing sugar to nitrogen ratio in their own and Björkman's experiments.

It must at this point be emphasized that the analytical methods used in much of this work are open to criticism. The analysis of internal carbohydrates in both infected and uninfected roots is not so simple a process as has been assumed. Lewis and Harley (1965) have pointed out some of the problems. First, much of the easily soluble reducing power in the tissues is not due to sugar at all but to non-sugar reducing compounds. Secondly any procedure involving drying of the tissue at 80°C before extraction does not necessarily destroy hydrolytic enzymes. Hence considerable hydrolysis of starch, sucrose, and trehalose, for instance, could occur in the extraction procedures. Third, where disaccharides are being taken into account, trehalose, the common disaccharide of basidiomycetes would not be hydrolyzed by the hydrolytic procedures used by most workers. Last, substances like the polyol mannitol, common in beech mycorrhiza and in many fungi, would not be estimated by the procedures adopted. The whole subject of detailed analysis of photosynthetic products in the roots of mycotrophic plants needs reexamination. In the meantime a correlation of degree of infection with light supply is not to be doubted (see Boullard, 1961, for a summary).

The absence of any considerable degree of intracellular penetration of the host in ectotrophic mycorrhiza together with the prolific development of fungus as a sheath around the root surface suggest that the host stimulates the fungus. There is no evidence that the fungus is per se aggressive. There are, moreover, few signs of host activities that might be interpreted as defense mechanisms. Exceptions to this occur, such as the cutinized zone described by Clowes (1951) in the cortex of *Fagus* mycorrhiza. There is, by contrast, a selective stimulation of the mycorrhizal fungus, which is enabled to grow within the walls of the cortical cells and form an external sheath. Those, less usual, extreme variants of ectotrophic mycorrhizas called ectendotrophic have been ascribed, as mentioned above, to fungi having exceptionally developed powers of hydrolysis of cell-wall materials and therefore enabled to be more aggressive.

The only available observations on the susceptibility of ericalean hosts to mycorrhizal fungi upon which adequate credence can be placed are those of Brook (1952), Baylis (1954), and Morrison (1957) on *Pernettya macrostigma*. These observers found that factors arising out of nutrient deficiency in the soil promoted most intense infection in a manner essentially like the ectotrophs and Baylis showed that shading depressed infection. A difference lies, however, in the apparently aggressive penetration of the cells of the root which is controlled by digestion of the hyphae by host activity.

Infection in Orchidaceae, whether it is a primary infection of the embryo at germination or the infection of a newly formed root of an adult, usually takes place from the soil. In both these cases attack by the fungus is aggressive and active defense by digestion of the hyphae comes into play. In the seedling a successful symbiotic union, followed by growth of the protocorm and root and leaf development, occurs when the attack is contained by digestion. A proportion of infections fail due to elimination of the fungus, and others succeed too well and result in complete parasitic degradation of the embryo.

Certain parts of the orchid, the growing region, the green tissues and the tubers, are resistant to fungal invasion which becomes, in adults, restricted to the roots or other subterranean absorbing organs. The resistance of the tubers to invasion was investigated by Bernard (1911), Nobécourt (1923), Magrou (1924), and Burges (1939), all of whom showed the presence of toxins to fungal growth in the tissues. Opinions differed as to whether this toxin was or was not present before the initial incipient fungal invasion. This subject has been further examined by Gäumann and his colleagues (1950, 1960; Gäumann and Hohl, 1960; Gäumann and Kern, 1959a,b). The tissues of the tubers of some orchids have been shown to develop a potential to inhibit fungal growth when they have been kept in contact with active fungal hyphae. It is, moreover, unnecessary for every cell to be contacted, for the stimulus to produce the toxin appears to be passed from cell to cell. The antifungal property of the tubers was found to be due to substances which appeared to be synthesized only after the stimulation of incipient invasion. Two substances in particular, hydroxybenzyl alcohol and a phenolic compound, orchinol, present in fresh tissue in traces, increased greatly in quantity. A number of fungi other than the mycorrhizal endophytes were found to stimulate the production of the toxins, nor were these specific in their inhibitory action to mycorrhizal fungi. The toxins are therefore more antifungal substances resisting general invasion than peculiar to the mycorrhizal habit. Slight production of these toxins occurred in the roots of orchids. Gäumann and his colleagues therefore view them as an active chemical resistance mechanism by means of which there develops a differential invasion of roots and tubers. The root remains susceptible of attack by certain fungi which are resisted and exploited by digestion.

The investigation of Mosse (1963) on the conditions necessary for mycorrhizal infection by *Endogone* have yielded especially interesting results which show that biological soil factors are involved in the process. In soil cultures successful inoculations were obtained with ease using spores or sporocarps provided that conditions of light and temperature favored vigorous growth of the host. Adequate light has also been stressed by other observers (Boullard, 1959, 1961). Heavy manurial supplies under field conditions tend to decrease the intensity of infection but may, in some instances, increase arbuscule formation. In some respects there is therefore a similarity with ectotrophic infection, but this requires further investigation. In contrast to the ease with which infection was brought about in soil, great difficulty was experienced in producing mycorrhizal infection in aseptic, two-membered cultures of host and spores on agar. The spores germinated but their germ-tubes failed to grow toward the host. If contact was made by chance, no appressoria and no penetration were observed. When certain bacteria, especially of a strain of *Pseudomonas,* were present in the culture, infection preceded by development of appressoria occurred, the more so if the medium was deficient in nitrogen. In high nitrogen supply, infection was delayed until absorption by the host had reduced its quantity. Cell-free filtrates of the bacterial cultures, dilute pectinase solutions, and the chelating agent EDTA had slight stimulatory effects upon mycorrhizal infection. It seems likely therefore that changes in the membranes of the cells of the host, resulting in the release of substances, are necessary to stimulate invasion. These may be caused by bacterial activity, slight enzymatic digestion or by chelation of calcium. Such changes in membranes may be expected to occur readily in unsterile soil by activity of microorganisms or maybe by abrasion by soil particles.

Once a pure two-membered culture of host and fungus has been set up and invasion brought about aseptically, the infection of further hosts readily occurs. Mosse has shown that even the residual extramatrical mycelium left in a culture after removal of a host has a greater invasive potential than the spores. The conclusion is therefore inescapable that the host has a definite effect on the activity and virulence of the fungus.

Ham (1962) examined the conditions under which *Pythium* may cause mycorrhizal infection in *Allium.* She used both an isolate of *Pythium* obtained from the roots of *Allium ursinum* and a virulent pathogenic strain of *P. ultimum* from damped-off lettuce. In various experiments both types of *Pythium* caused a variety of symptoms ranging from destructive parasitism to failure to invade. In general it was found that factors which tended to increase the vigor of the fungus such as the presence of glucose and nitrate in the medium of the cultures tended to increase pathogenicity. In the same sense, factors tending to depress the vigor of the host also predisposed it to pathogenic attack. Mycorrhizal development of a normal phycomycetous type developed in some cases where the host grew well, both with the *Pythium* isolated from mycorrhizal roots of *Allium,* and with *P. ultimum.* It appears, therefore, that in certain very restricted conditions species of *Pythium* can produce a mycorrhizal infected condition of *Allium* but that they are, unlike *Endogone,* potentially virulent parasites under most circumstances in which they have been observed in experiments.

V. PHYSIOLOGICAL INTERACTION OF HOST AND FUNGUS

A. *Ectotrophic Mycorrhiza*

The interdependence of the host and fungus is better understood for ectotrophic mycorrhiza than other types. Outline explanations at least of the mechanisms of interaction can be suggested. Interaction takes place at several levels. The two component organisms have been found to be mutually dependent at a nutritional level for each provides some of the materials of which the body of the other is built. There may be in addition an exchange of accessory substances, such as vitamins. Furthermore, the forms of their associated tissues, the root axis and the fungal body, differ when associated and free, hence morphogenic stimuli or factors must be exchanged.

It has already been described how the fungi are nutritionally demanding, and the work of Melin upon the release by the root of substances such as the M-factors gives a partial explanation of their selection of the root-surface as a site for growth. The release of vitamins such as thiamine and biotin and of amino acids and other substances by root tissues is well known (see Rovira, 1965) and provides further evidence that this kind of explanation is valid. These basidiomycetes are also dependent on simple carbon compounds which have been assumed to be provided by their hosts. Melin and Nilsson (1957) provided the first confirmation of this by allowing seedlings of *Pinus sylvestris,* grown in aseptic two-membered culture with *Boletus variegatus* or *Rhizopogon roseolus,* to assimilate $^{14}CO_2$ in the light. The analysis of the plant material showed considerable accumulation of ^{14}C-labeled compounds in the fungal sheaths of mycorrhizas. Decapitated seedlings, used as controls, contained far less ^{14}C in their fungal sheaths. The presence of significant small amounts of radioactive carbon compounds in the sheath of decapitated seedlings may be due to dark fixation of $^{14}C_2$ by the mycorrhizas which has been shown by Harley (1964) to occur in beech mycorrhizas. However, the high labeling of the sheath of intact photosynthesizing seedlings indicates that there is a supply of labeled photosynthetic products in addition to the fungus. Shiroya *et al.* (1962) examined the translocation of ^{14}C-labeled photosynthates in *P. resinosa* and *P. strobus*. The rate of translocation to the roots of mycorrhizal seedlings greatly exceeds that in uninfected seedlings. Lewis and Harley (1965) carried out detailed analyses of carbohydrate metabolism in the mycorrhizas of *Fagus sylvatica* which confirm and amplify these results. The main carbohydrate stores in the fungal sheath were of glycogen, trehalose, and mannitol, whereas those of the host tissue were sucrose and to a very minor extent insoluble carbohydrate.

By applying ^{14}C-sucrose in agar blocks to the host tissue of the axis of mycorrhizas, it was shown that the labeled sugars were translocated rapidly through the host tissue. In the tips of the mycorrhiza the partition of radioactivity between fungal sheath and host tissue showed that as much as 60–75% had passed to the fungus. It was present in the fungus in the expected components, glycogen, trehalose, and mannitol. Further experiments confirmed that the host tissue was not able to absorb any of these three carbohydrates at all rapidly whereas the fungus could do so. Hence they seem to act as a sink within the sheath encouraging translocation to it. Indeed, there is little doubt of the correctness of the hypothesis that the fungus depends on carbon supplies from the host in ectotrophic mycorrhiza.

There is as yet little understanding of the morphogenic stimuli arising from the host and affecting the fungus. The remarkable pseudoparenchymatous structure of the sheath indicates that morphogenic factors must be operative, but none of the known root exudates or extracts have such effects on mycelia in culture. Work on this problem awaits advances in the study of the factors involved in the development by basidiomycetes of bulky organs such as rhizomorphs, sclerotia, and fruit bodies.

The majority of the feeding roots of ectotrophically mycorrhizal hosts are covered by a layer of fungal sheath. This simple fact alone shows that the host is dependent upon the fungal partner for materials absorbed from the soil. The analysis of this dependence has proved complex. Many lines of experiment aimed at comparing rates of growth and rates of nutrient absorption of mycorrhizal and uninfected ectotrophs, all lead to similar conclusions (see Hatch, 1937; Mitchell *et al.*, 1937; McComb, 1938; Finn, 1942). Mycorrhizal plants when growing on nutrient-deficient soils produce greater dry weight and absorb disproportionately larger amounts of nutrients from the soil than uninfected plants. In particular, absorption of phosphorus, nitrogen, and potassium are usually enhanced. There are two suggested explanations which are not mutually exclusive: (1) infection may increase the total and relative absorbing area of the root system; and (2) infected roots may have an increased ability to accumulate nutrients per unit area. Both these explanations have been examined and have been found to apply.

Hatch (1937) put forward the view, based upon the observed behavior of the rootlets of pine, that mycorrhizal infection caused an effective increase of root surface. This arose not only because of increased diameter, the presence of the sheath of fungus and the presence of emanating hyphae in mycorrhiza, but also by virtue of effects on growth and branching. The roots formed by pines, for instance, are of three kinds apart from the main mother and pioneer axes. Some develop into mycorrhizas which are relatively long lived, some grow slowly and are relatively less long lived, and some soon abort either of themselves or after attack by pseudo-mycorrhizal fungi. Mycorrhizal infection not only increases the life span of the subsidiary roots, but also encourages their branching. Other observers have described similar features, and Wilson (1951) made an especial study of the matter by sampling seedling root-systems of beech during their first year. He was able to demonstrate the sequence of infection and the probable increase of longevity of infected roots. He observed that short rootlets went through a sequence of histological changes irrespective of fungal infection so that the tissues became progressively fully differentiated closer to the tip and the growing region became reduced in extent. It was at a late stage in this sequence that mycorrhizal infection took place. Early in the first season of the seedling the ultimate rootlets all showed well-developed apical growing regions. As the season advanced an increasing proportion showed differentiation of cortical and stelar tissues close to the apex and reduced meristems. Later still, mycorrhizal infection developed on the latter rootlets and increased in quantity until almost all surviving rootlets were mycorrhizal. This sequence has been observed in *Eucalyptus* by Chilvers and Pryor (1965) in essentials. Clowes and Harley (see Harley, 1959) showed, by observing marked beech roots in natural soil throughout the growing season, that mycorrhizas of beech had a life of some nine months. Many observers agree that mycorrhizal short roots last about one growing season as physiologically active organs, but others (e.g., Lobanow, 1960) have shown that some can function for several years. In any event although they are not permanent structures they have a life-span far exceeding that of uninfected roots.

There is little doubt, from these and similar studies, that mycorrhizal infection has a morphogenic effect leading to prolonged life, growth, and branching of the rootlets. The mechanism is not understood. Slankis (1948, 1951), Moser (1959), and Ulrich (1962) have shown that many mycorrhizal fungi produce indolyl or other compounds in their culture media which have properties similar to auxins. These affect growth, root-hair production, and branching. Further work on similar lines will no doubt provide more complete explanations of the structure and development of mycorrhizal organs.

Work on the absorption of nutrients by ectotrophic mycorrhizas has not shown that they increase the availability of nutrients in the soil by bringing insoluble compounds into solution. They have, however, been demonstrated to possess great powers of accumulation of soluble nutrients, and in this respect as well as in others they may be compared with lichens (D. C. Smith, 1962). Excised mycorrhizas accumulate ions, e.g., phosphate and potassium, at rates greatly in excess of accumulation into similar areas of uninfected root, by mechanisms that are dependent on metabolic activity and are sensitive to oxygen, temperature, and inhibitors. Work on this subject has been extensively reviewed by Harley (1959). In certain cases, as with phosphate, primary accumulation is into the fungal sheath. Harley and his colleagues in a series of experiments have been able to show that phosphate so accumulated may be secondarily translocated to the host tissue by mechanisms sensitive to oxygen and temperature, and inversely dependent in rate upon the rate of absorption from the external solution. This process has been further examined by Morrison (1962) and Clode (1956) using pine seedlings. They found greater rates of accumulation of phosphate into the roots of mycorrhizal than of non-mycorrhizal seedlings. Using ^{32}P-labeled phosphate they were able to show that the materials accumulated passed into the host during a period of phosphate deficiency in the external solution. Harley and Wilson (1959) have found that mycorrhizas exert, as might be expected, a similar selectivity in absorption of ions as do roots. Beech mycorrhizas vigorously select, for instance, potassium from a mixture of sodium and potassium salts.

Melin and Nilsson (1950, 1952, 1953, 1955) examined the ability of the extramatrical mycelia of ectotrophic mycorrhizas to absorb nutrients and to conduct them to the sheath and into the host. This was done in culture by feeding the mycelia with tracer at some distance from the host. Phosphate, nitrogenous substances, and calcium were shown to be absorbed and translocated. It is of interest that these observations not only confirm Hatch's view (1937) that part of the effective absorbing surface of mycorrhizal root systems was comprised of outgoing hyphae, but also agree with workers on translocation in fungi who have found that basidiomycetes especially have this property.

The interdependence of host and fungus in ectotrophic mycorrhizas is therefore seen to involve the supply of major and minor nutrients as well as morphogenic factors to both partners and demonstrates how closely integrated are the two components, fungus and host, which form these nutrient absorbing organs.

B. *Endotrophic Mycorrhiza in Orchids*

The fungi of orchids have been seen to be aggressive and to be controlled by digestive activities of their hosts. There is, however, little evidence available of other effects of the hosts upon the fungi, except that a few have been shown to be heterotrophic for vitamins [e.g., *Rhizoctonia repens* is vitamin B-dependent (Vermuelen, 1946)], but this does not seem to be general. By contrast, much information is available on the effects of the fungi upon growth and nutrition of their hosts.

The seeds of orchids require special conditions for germination. This occurs in natural substrates and is stimulated by fungal infection. Examination of conditions which allow aseptic germination in culture has explained much of the stimulating effects of invasion. Bernard (1909), Knudson (1922, 1924, 1925, 1927, 1930) and Burgeff (1909, 1936) showed that the seeds of a few species germinated readily in aseptic conditions if simple soluble carbohydrates were available. Others required in addition plant extracts before aseptic growth was possible. There seemed therefore to be two factors, a major nutritive factor of carbohydrate, not unexpected considering the minute stores present in the seeds, and a supply of minor or accessory nutrients. The subsequent investigation of the accessory factors present in plant extracts by Burgeff (1934, 1936), Schafferstein (1938, 1941), Noggle and Wynd (1943), and others, showed that these were vitamins. In particular, many orchids require nicotinic acid or nicotinamide, pyrodoxin, and riboflavine for germination. In the adult condition, the green orchids are usually self-supporting in this regard, but in the saprophytic seedling condition the utilization of absorbed carbohydrates and the normal metabolic reactions are dependent on external supplies of vitamins. During the prolonged saprophytic phase, which may be of several years' duration even in green orchids, supplies both of carbohydrates and of accessories are required and are made available by the fungi, which have considerable powers of utilization of resistant substrates such as wood and cellulose.

In some of Knudson's experiments germination of some orchids was brought about on starch media by the activities of nonmycorrhizal fungi which hydrolyzed the starch to produce soluble carbohydrates free in the substrate. This is not a general explanation of the effect of the fungi upon carbohydrate nutrition, as was shown by Burgeff. There may indeed be no external increase of soluble carbohydrate in the medium, and one is led to suppose that carbon compounds are absorbed and translocated within the hyphae, to be released in part by digestion in the seedling cells.

S. E. Smith (1965, 1966) has examined translocation of nutrients in the mycelia of orchid endophytes. She utilized several strains including some belonging to *Rhizoctonia* (*Corticium*) *solani*. With ^{14}C- and ^{32}P-labeled compounds she observed translocation from a food base through mature hyphal systems. Using an experimental arrangement in which *Rhizoctonia* growing on a food-base was connected to distant orchid seedlings by mycelium, it was observed not only that cellulose was utilized, but also that its products were translocated to the seedlings. When the food base contained ^{14}C-labeled glucose or ^{32}P labeled phosphate, radioactivity appeared in the seedling. In later experiments (S. E. Smith, 1967) a chromatographic analysis was made of the ^{14}C-labeled compounds in the seedlings after different times of translocation from a glucose source.

Most of the radioactivity was at first in sugars, but later amino acids and other compounds became labeled. Among the sugars, trehalose was at first most strongly labeled and later the radioactivity of sucrose exceeded that of trehalose. This clearly indicates that there has been a transfer of carbohydrate to the seedling from the fungus.

Thus in sharp contrast with ectotrophic mycorrhiza there seems to be in Orchidaceae a situation where the apparently aggressive attack of the fungus upon the orchid results in setting up of a system where the fungus is essentially parasitized by the host, in an interaction that is sometimes complex. The cases mentioned above of *Gastrodia, Galeola,* and some epiphytes described by Kusano (1911), Hamada (1940a,b), and Ruinen (1953) have suggested that essentially parasitic fungi derive nutrient from one host and lose some of it to chlorophyll-free orchids which are parasitic on them.

It still remains to be determined to what extent orchids in their saprophytic or green phases are dependent upon their fungi for nitrogenous and other essential nutrients.

C. *Mycorrhiza in the Ericales*

Very diverse views have been current about the relationship between host and fungus in the mycorrhizas of Ericales. The idea that species of *Phoma* were the endophytes and that among other activities they fixed atmospheric nitrogen for the mycorrhizal system may be discounted. An analysis of the older views is given by Harley (1959).

It is now quite clear that the seeds of most host plants germinate and grow without fungal infection in suitable artificial surroundings, but that in peat substrata aseptic germination and growth may be inhibited. The inhibition is offset by the presence of the endophytic fungi and to a lesser extent by others (Freisleben, 1936; Bain, 1937; Burgeff, 1961). Burgeff found that the inhibition did not occur when aseptically grown plants are able to grow in substrates that inhibit germination.

The sequence of infection, recently redescribed by Burgeff involves the penetration of the root cortex by the fungus, which utilizes the tannin substances in the epidermis. The formation of hyphal systems in the cells and the onset of digestion follows. Many hyphal connections between root and substrate are formed.

Brook (1952) and Morrison (1957) have examined the effect of infection upon the growth of *Pernettya macrostigma* and have shown that on nutrient-deficient substrata infected plants grow and develop where uninfected plants fail. There seems to be no doubt of the truth of Burgeff's suggestion that the fungi operate in a fashion analogous to those of ectotrophs in the absorption of nutrients in the carbon-autotrophic ericads.

This is perhaps rendered even more likely when one considers that the structure of the mycorrhizas of *Arbutus* and *Arctostaphylos* are described as having an external sheath like ectotrophs as opposed to the external weft of hyphae of most ericads.

In the Ericales saprophytic plants occur in the Monotropaceae and the Pyrolaceae. In these it is reasonable to assume that the fungi must be capable of utiltizing organic compounds of soil origin and passing their products on to the host plant, but verification is required. Recently Björkman (1960) has shown that *Monotropa hypopitys* is epiparasitic on tree roots. It appears that one and the same mycelium forms mycorrhiza with both the tree and the saprophyte. He was able to show that ^{14}C-labeled sugars injected into a specimen of *Picea* were passed into the *Monotropa,* presumably through the mycelium.

D. *Vesicular-Arbuscular Mycorrhizas*

Those species of *Endogone* (including *Rhizophagus*) which are endophytic in vesicular-arbuscular mycorrhizas are even more selective in nutrition than the most selective of ectotrophic mycorrhizal fungi. They appear to be totally dependent on association with plant roots for growth. Clearly, in the initial stages of infection they require the stimulation of exudation from the host for the determination of the direction of growth of the hyphae, for the production of appressoria, and for penetration of the host tissues. The actual stimuli involved are as yet unknown.

The properties of the mycelium connecting infected roots to the substrate seem to be somewhat changed. Not only is growth over artificial substrates and through the soil possible but exploitation of uninfected roots and of humus particles seems to occur. Mosse (1963) showed that residual extramatrical mycelium left in a culture after removal of the host had a positive infective potential and also (1959b) that it ramifies plentifully in organic matter giving the impression of causing breakdown. This important matter requires further investigation but in any event there is already strong evidence that factors arising from association with the host enhance the physiological activity of the fungus.

Such an influence is clearly necessary if the results of recent experiments upon nutrient uptake by this kind of mycorrhiza are to be fully explained. Positive effects of infection upon growth and nutrient uptake have been published with increasing frequency in recent years. Baylis (1962) and Mosse (1963) review the subject. Mosse herself (1957) showed that there occurred significantly greater growth rate in mycorrhizal than nonmycorrihizal apples grown in autoclaved soil. This was correlated with increased uptake per unit plant weight of potassium, calcium, copper and iron and a decrease per unit weight of magnesium and manganese. Baylis (1959, 1961) obtained increased growth coupled with increased phosphate uptake in *Griselinia*. Baylis *et al.* (1963) showed that *Podocarpus totara* and *P. dacrydioides* were greatly stimulated in growth by mycorrhizal infection in nutrient-deficient soils. The dry weights of seedlings of the former was seven times as great when infected as when uninfected during the first year of life. Somewhat similar results have been obtained with other species, both woody and herbaceous. Clark (1964) used *Liriodendron;* Peuss (1958) tobacco; Winter and Meloh (1958) maize; Holevas (1966) strawberry; Daft and Nicolson (1966) tobacco, tomato, and maize; and Gerdemann (1964) maize. Gerdemann infected his maize plants with sporocarp material of *Endogone*. Not only had the infected plants greater weights of root and shoot, but also intensity of infection and weight were positively correlated. Analysis of the plant material showed that their phosphate contents were increased by infection but their potassium, magnesium, boron, and manganese contents decreased. Similarly Daft and Nicolson and Holevas also observed greatly increased phosphate uptake from deficient soils by infected plants.

It is clear from these recent results that under ecologically natural conditions as opposed to rich agricultural conditions infection may greatly stimulate growth.

VI. CONCLUSIONS

Mycorrhizal infection defined as an association of fungus and host in which destructive disintegration of the host does not occur, and which is a prevalent and usual condition of the host plant in natural habitats, is very common and widespread. Indeed, in this respect, roots provide an important habitat for certain special ecological groups of fungi. Mycorrhizal association takes many physiological and morphological forms. Any given kind or form can be analyzed in respect of the effect of each partner upon the major and minor nutritional supplies of the other and in respect of the morphogenic effect of one upon the other. This analysis has been attempted but not completed in certain well-known examples of mycorrhiza, and it has provided many results of interest in connection with other kinds of interactions especially with pathogenesis.

In this essay information has been reviewed only from the special aspect of roots as a habitat of fungi, emphasizing the effect of the fungi on their habitat and vice versa. Ecological implications of mycorrhiza, its importance in forestry, agriculture, and horticultural practice are clearly beyond our scope here.

REFERENCES

Bain, H. F. (1937). Production of synthetic mycorrhiza in the cultivated cranberry. *J. Agr. Res.* **55**: 811–835.

Barrett, J. T. (1947). Observations on the root endophyte *Rhizophagus* in culture. *Phytopathology* **37**: 359–360.

Barrett, J. T. (1958). Synthesis of mycorrhiza with pure cultures of *Rhizophagus*. *Phytopathology* **48**: 391.

Barrett, J. T. (1961). Isolation, culture and host relation of the phycomycetoid vesicular-arbuscular mycorrhizal endophyte *Rhizophagus*. *In* "Recent Advances in Botany," Vol. 2, p. 1725. Univ. of Toronto Press, Toronto, Canada.

Baylis, G. T. S. (1954). Experiments with Mycorrhizas of some New Zealand plants. *8th Congr. Intern. Botan., Paris, 1954, Rappt. Commun.* Sect. 13, pp. 135–136. Lab. Physiol. Vegetale Sorbonne, Paris.

Baylis, G. T. S. (1959). Effect of vesicular-arbuscular mycorrhiza on the growth of *Griselinia littoralis* (Cornaceae). *New Phytologist* **58**: 274–280.

Baylis, G. T. S. (1961). The significance of mycorrhizas and root nodules in New Zealand vegetation. *Proc. Roy. Soc. New Zealand* **89**: 45–50.

Baylis, G. T. S. (1962). *Rhizophagus*. The Catholic Symbiont. *Australian J. Sci.* **25**: 195–200.

Baylis, G. T. S., R. F. R. McNabb, and T. H. Morrison. (1963). The Mycorrhizal nodules of Podocarps. *Brit. Mycol. Soc. Trans.* **46**: 378–384.

Bernard, N. (1909). L'évolution dans la symbiose. Les orchidées et leurs champignons commenseaux. *Ann. Sci. Nat. Botan. Biol. Vegetale* **9**: 1–96.

Bernard, N. (1911). Sur la fonction fungicide des bulbes d'ophrydées. *Ann. Sci. Nat. Botan. Biol. Vegetale* [9] **14**: 223–234.

Björkman, E. (1941). Die Ausbildung und Frequenz der Mykorrhizen in mit Asche gedüngten und ungedüngten Teilen von entwassertem Moor. *Medd. Skogsforsøksanst.* **32**: 255–296.

Björkman, E. (1942). Über die Bedingungen der Mykorrhiza-bildung bei Kiefer und Fichte. *Symbolae Botan. Upsalienses* **6**: 1–191.

Björkman, E. (1960). *Monotropa hypopitys* L. epiparasitic on tree roots. *Physiol. Plantarum* **13**: 308–327.

Boullard, B. (1957). La Mycotrophie chez les Ptéridophytes. *Botaniste* **41**: 1–4.

Boullard, B. (1959). Relations entre la photopériode et l'abondance des Mycorrhizas chez l'*Aster* tripolium L. *Bull. Soc. Botan. France* **106**: 131–134.

Boullard, B. (1961). Influence du Photopériodisme sur la mycorrhization de jeunes conifères. *Bull. Soc. Linneenne Normandie* [10] **2**: 30–40.

Bouwens, H. (1937). Investigations about the mycorrhiza of fruit trees, especially of Quince (*Cydonia vulgaris*) and of strawberry plants (*Fragaria vesca*). *Zentr. Bakteriol., Parasitenk., Abt. I. Orig.* **97**: 34–49.

Brook, P. J. (1952). Mycorrhiza of *Pernettya macrostigma*. *New Phytologist* **51**: 388–397.

Buller, A. H. R. (1933). "Researches on Fungi," Vol. V. Longmans, Green, New York.

Burgeff, H. (1909). "Die Wurzepilze der Orchideen ihre Kultur und ihr Leben in der Pflanze." Fischer, Jena.

Burgeff, H. (1932). "Saprophytism und Symbiose. Studien an tropischen Orchideen." Fischer, Jena.

Burgeff, H. (1934). Pflanzliche Avitaminose und ihre Behebung durch vitaminzufuhr. *Ber. Deut. Botan. Ges.* **52**: 384–390.

Burgeff, H. (1936). "Samenkeimung der Orchideen." Fischer, Jena.

Burgeff, H. (1961). "Mikrobiologie des Hochmoores." Fischer, Stuttgart.

Burges, N. A. (1939). The defensive mechanism in orchid mycorrhiza. *New Phytologist* **38**: 273–283.

Butler, E. J. (1939). The occurrences and systematic position of the vesicular-arbuscular type of mycorrhizal fungi. *Brit. Mycol. Soc. Trans.* **22**: 274–301.

Chilvers, J. A., and L. D. Pryor. (1965). The structure of eucalypt mycorrhizas. *Australian J. Botany* **13**: 245–259.

Clark, F. (1964). Micro-organisms and soil structure affect yellow-poplar growth. *U.S. Forest Serv. Res. Paper* **CS-9**.

Clode, J. J. E. (1956). As micorrizas na migracao de fosforo. Estudo como. ^{32}P. *Publ. Serv. Flor. aquic. Portugal* **32**: 167–206.

Clowes, F. A. L. (1951). The structure of mycorrhizal roots of *Fagus sylvatica*. *New Phytologist* **50**: 1–16.

Daft, M. J., and T. H. Nicolson. (1966). The effect of *Endogone* mycorrhiza on plant growth. *New Phytologist* **65**: 343–350.

de Cordenoy, H. J. (1904). Sur une fonction spéciale des mycorrhizas des racines latérales de la vanille. *Compt. Rend.* **138**: 391–393.

Demeter, K. (1923). Ueber Plasmoptysenmycorrhiza. *Flora (Jena)* **116**: 405–456.

Dimbleby, G. W. (1953). Natural regeneration of pine and birch on heather moors of north-east Yorkshire. *Forestry* **26**: 41–52.

Doak, K. D. (1928). The mycorrhizal fungus of *Vaccinium*. *Phytopathology* **18**: 148.

Dominik, T. (1955). Vorschlag eine neuer Klassifikation der ektotrophen Mykorrhizen auf morphologisch-anatomischen Merkmalen begrundet. *Roczniki Nauk Rolniczych* **14**: 223–245. [Polish with German summary.]

Dowding, E. S. (1959). Ecology of *Endogone*. *Brit. Mycol. Soc. Trans.* **42**: 449–457.

Downie, D. G. (1957). *Corticium solani* as an orchid endophyte. *Nature* **179**: 160.

Fassi, B., and A. Fontana. (1962). Micorrhize ectotrofiche di alcune altre Çesalpinacce minori del Congo. *Allionia (Turin)* **8**: 121–131.

Finn, R. F. (1942). Mycorrhizal inoculation of soil of low fertility. *Black Rock Forest Papers* **1**: 116–117.

Francke, H. L. (1934). Beitrage zur Kenntnis der Mykorrhiza von *Monotropa hypopytis* L. Analyse und Synthese der Symbiose. *Flora (Jena)* **129**: 1–52.

Frank, B. (1885). Ueber die auf Wurzelsymbiose beruhende Ernährung gewisser Bäume durch unterirdische Pilze. *Ber. Deut. Botan. Ges.* **3**: 128–145.

Freisleben, R. (1933). Über experimentelle Mykorrhiza-Bildung bei den Ericaceen. *Ber. Deut. Botan. Ges.* **51**: 351–356.

Freisleben, R. (1936). Weitere Untersuchungen über die Mycotrophie der Ericaceen. *Jahrb. Wiss. Botan.* **82**: 413–459.

Garrett, S. D. (1944). Soil conditions and take-all disease of wheat. VIII. Further experiments on the survival of *Ophiobolus graminis* in infected wheat stubble. *Ann. Appl. Biol.* **31**: 186–191.

Garrett, S. D. (1956). "Biology of Root-infecting Fungi." Cambridge Univ. Press, London and New York.

Gäumann, E. A., and H. R. Hohl. (1960). Weitere Untersuchungen über die chemische abwehrreaktionen der Orchideen. *Phytopathol. Z.* **38**: 93–104.

Gäumann, E. A., and H. Kern. (1959a). Über chemische Abwehrreaktionen der Orchideen. *Phytopathol. Z.* **36**: 1–26.

Gäumann, E. A., and H. Kern. (1959a). Über die Isoliering und der chemischen Nachweis des Orchinols. *Phytotpathol. Z.* **36**: 347–356.

Gäumann, E. A., R. Braun, and G. Bazzigher. (1950). Über induzierte Abwehrreaktionen bei Orchideen. *Phytopathol. Z.* **17**: 36–62.

Gäumann, E. A., J. Nuesch, and R. H. Rimpau. (1960). Weitere untersuchungen über die chemischen Abwehrreaktionen der Orchideen. *Phytopathol. Z.* **38**: 274–308.

Gerdemann, J. W. (1955). Relation of a large soil-borne spore to phycomycetous mycorrhizal infections. *Mycologia* **47**: 619–632.
Gerdemann, J. W. (1961). A species of *Endogone* from corn causing vesicular-arbuscular mycorrhiza. *Mycologia* **53**: 254–261.
Gerdemann, J. W. (1964). The effect of mycorrhiza on the growth of maize. *Mycologia* **56**: 342–349.
Hacskaylo, E. (1961). Mycorrhizal Fungi on *Pinus virginiana. Mycologia* **53**: 538–539.
Ham, A. M. (1962). Studies on vesicular-arbuscular endophytets. IV. Inoculation of species of *Allium* and of *Lactuca sativa* with *Pythium* isolates. *Brit. Mycol. Soc. Trans.* **45**: 179–189.
Hamada, M. (1940a). Studien über die Mykorrhiza von *Galeola septentrionalis* Reichb. Ein neuer Fall der Mykorrhizabildung durch intraradikale Rhizomorphen. *Japan. J. Botany* **10**: 151–212.
Hamada, M. (1940b). Physiologische–morphologische Studien über *Armillaria mellea* (Vahl) Quèl. mit besondere Rücksicht auf die Oxalsäuerbildung. *Japan. J. Botany* **10**: 387–464.
Handley, W. R. C. (1963). Mycorrhizal associations and *Calluna* heathland afforestation. *Forestry Comm. Bull.* **36**.
Handley, W. R. C., and C. J. Sanders. (1962). The concentration of easily soluble reducing substances in roots and the formation of ectotrophic mycorrhizal associations. A re-examination of Björkman's hypothesis. *Plant Soil* **16**: 42–61.
Harley, J. L. (1950). Recent progress in the study of endotrophic mycorrhiza. *New Phytologist* **49**: 213–247.
Harley, J. L. (1959). "The Biology of Mycorrhizas." Leonard Hill, London.
Harley, J. L. (1964). Incorporation of carbon dioxide into excised beech mycorrhizas in the presence and absence of ammonia. *New Phytologist* **63**: 203–208.
Harley, J. L., and J. S. Waid. (1955). The effect of light upon the roots of beech and its surface population. *Plant Soil* **7**: 96–112.
Harley, J. L., and J. M. Wilson. (1959). Absorption of potassium by beech mycorrhiza. *New Phytologist* **58**: 281–298.
Hatch, A. B. (1937). The physical basis of mycotrophy in the genus *Pinus. Black Rock Forest Bull.* **6**: 1–168.
Hatch, A. B., and C. T. Hatch. (1933). Some hymenomycetes forming ectotrophic mycorrhizas with *Pinus strobus,* L. *J. Arnold Arboretum* (*Harvard Univ.*) **14**: 324–334.
Hawker, L. E. (1962). Studies on vesicular-arbuscular endophytes. V. A review of the evidence relating to identity of the causal fungi. *Brit. Mycol. Soc. Trans.* **45**: 190–199.
Hawker, L. E., R. W. Harrison, V. O. Nicholls, and A. M. Ham. (1957). Studies on vesicular-arbuscular endophytes. I. A strain of *Pythium ultimum* Trow in roots of *Allium ursinum* L. and other plants. *Brit. Mycol. Soc. Trans.* **40**: 375–390.
Hepden, P. M. (1960). Studies in vesicular-arbuscular endophytes. II. Endophytes in the Pteridophyta with special reference to Leptosporangiate ferns. *Brit. Mycol. Soc. Trans.* **43**: 559–510.
Hildebrand, A. A. (1934). Recent observations on the strawberry root-rot on the Niagara peninsula. *Can. J. Res.* **11**: 18–31.
Hildebrand, A. A., and P. M. West. (1941). Strawberry root-rot in relation to

microbiological changes induced in root-rot soil by the incorporation of certain cover crops. *Can. J. Res.* **19:** 183–198.

Holevas, C. D. (1966). The effect of a vesicular-arbuscular mycorrhiza on uptake of soil phosphorus by Strawberry (*Fragaria* sp. var. Cambridge Favourite). *J. Hort. Sci.* **41:** 57–64.

Katznelson, H., and L. T. Richardson. (1948). Rhizosphere studies and associated microbiological phenomena in relation to strawberry root-rot. *Sci. Agr.* **28:** 293–308.

Kelley, A. P. (1950). "Mycotrophy in Plants." Chronica Botanica, Waltham, Massachusetts.

Knudson, L. (1922). Non symbiotic germination of orchid seeds. *Botan. Gaz.* **75:** 1–25.

Knudson, L. (1924). Further observations on non-symbiotic germination of orchid seeds. *Botan. Gaz.* **77:** 212–219.

Knudson, L. (1925). Physiological study of the germination of orchid seeds. *Botan. Gaz.* **79:** 345–379.

Knudson, L. (1927). Symbiosis and asymbiosis relative to orchids. *New Phytologist* **26:** 328–336.

Knudson, L. (1930). Flower production by orchid grown non-symbiotically. *New Phytologist* **32:** 192–199.

Koch, H. (1961). Untersuchungen über die Mykorrhiza der Kulturpflanzen unter besondere Berücksichtigung von *Althea officinalis* L., *Atropa belladonna* L., *Helianthus annuus* L., und *Solanum lycopersicum* L. *Gartenbauwissenschaft* **26:** 5.

Kusano, S. (1911). *Gastrodia elata* and its symbiotic association with *Armillaria mellea. J. Agr. Tokio* **4:** 1–66.

Levisohn, I. (1954). Aberrant root infections of pine and spruce seedlings. *New Phytologist* **53:** 284–290.

Lewis, D. H., and J. L. Harley. (1965). Carbohydrate physiology of mycorrhizal roots of beech. (1) Identity of endogenous sugars and utilization of exogenous sugars. (2) Utilization of exogenous sugars by uninfected and mycorrhizal roots. (3) Movement of sugars between host and fungus. *New Phytologist* **64:** 224–269.

Lihnell, D. (1939). Untersuchungen über die Mykorrhizen und die wurzelpilze von *Juniperus communis. Symbolae Botan. Upsalienses* **3:** 1–141.

Lindeberg, G. (1948). On the occurrence of polyphenol oxidase in soil inhabiting basidiomycetes. *Physiol. Plantarum* **1:** 196–205.

Lobanow, N. W. (1960). "Mykotrophie der Holzpflanzen." Deut. Verlag. Wiss., Berlin.

Lyr, H. (1963). "Zur Frage des Streuabbaues durch ektotrophe Mykorrhizapilze. Mykorrhiza Internationales Mykorrhiza Symposium, Weimar 1960." Fischer, Jena.

McComb, A. L. (1938). The relation between mycorrhizae and the development and nutrient absorption of pine seedlings in a prairie nursery. *J. Forestry* **36:** 1148–1154.

McLuckie, J., and N. A. Burges. (1932). Mycotrophism in the Rutaceae I. Mycorrhiza of *Eriostemon Crowei* F. v M. *Proc. Linnean Soc. N. S. Wales* **57:** 291–312.

Magrou, J. (1924). A propos du pouvoir fungicide des tubercles d'Ophrydées. *Ann. Sci. Nat. Botan. Biol. Vegetale* [10] **6:** 265–270.

Magrou, J. (1946) Sur la culture de quelques champignons de mycorrhizes à arbuscules et à vésicules. *Rev. Gen. Botan.* **53**: 49–77.

Melin, E. (1923). Experimentelle untersuchungen über die Konstitution und Ökologie der Mykorrhizen von *Pinus sylvestris* L. und *Picea abies* (L.) Karst. *Mykol. Untersuch.* **2**: 173–331.

Melin, E. (1927). Studier över Barrtrdsplantans utreckling råhumus (German summary). *Medd. Skogsforsoksanst.* **23**: 433–484.

Melin, E. (1946). Die einfluss von Waldstrueextrakten auf das Wachstum von Bodenpilzen mit besonderen Berückssichtigung der Wurzelpilze von Baumen. *Symbolae Botan. Upsalienses* **8**: 1–116.

Melin, E. (1953). Physiology of mycorrhizal relations in plants. *Ann. Rev. Plant Physiol.* **4**: 325–346.

Melin, E. (1959). *In* "Handbuch der Pflanzenphysiologie" (W. Ruhland, ed.), Vol. 11, pp. 605–633. Springer, Berlin.

Melin, E. (1963). Some effects of forest tree roots on mycorrhizal basidiomycetes. *In* "Symbiotic Associations" (P. S. Nutman and B. Mosse, eds.), pp. 125–145. Cambridge Univ. Press, London and New York.

Melin, E., and H. Nilsson. (1950). Transfer of radioactive phosphorus to pine seedlings by means of mycorrhizal hyphae. *Physiol. Plantarum* **3**: 88–92.

Melin, E., and H. Nilsson. (1952). Transfer of labelled nitrogen from an ammonium source to pine seedlings through mycorrhizal mycelium. *Svensk Botan. Tidsk.* **46**: 281–285.

Melin, E., and H. Nilsson. (1953). Transport of labelled phosphorus to pine seedlings through the mycelium of *Cortinarius glaucopus* (Schaeff ex. Fr.) Fr. *Svensk Botan. Tidskr.* **48**: 555–558.

Melin, E., and H. Nilsson. (1955). Ca^{45} used as an indicator of transport of cations to pine seedlings by means of mycorrhizal mycelia. *Svensk Botan. Tidskr.* **51**: 166–186.

Melin, E., and H. Nilsson. (1957). Transport of C^{14} labelled photosynthate to the fungal associate of Pine mycorrhiza. *Svensk Botan. Tidskr.* **51**: 166–186.

Meloh, K. A. (1961). "Untersuchungen zur Biologie und Bedeutung der endotrophen Mycorrhiza bei *Zea Mays* L. und *Avena sativa* L." Dissertation, Universität Köln.

Meyer, F. H. (1962). Die Buchen—und Fichten Mykorrhiza in verschiedenen Bodentypen, ihre Beeinflussung durch Mineraldungung sowie für die Mykorrhizabildung wichtige Faktoren. *Mitt. Bundeforschungsanstalt Forst-Holzwirtsch* **54**: 1–73.

Meyer, F. H. (1964). Neue Erkenntrnisse über das Zusammenleben von Pilze und Baum. *Umschau* **11**: 325–328.

Mitchell, H. L., R. F. Finn, and R. O. Rosendahl. (1937). The relation between mycorrhiza and the growth and nutrient absorption of coniferous seedlings in nursery beds. *Black Rock Forest Papers* **1**: 58–73.

Modess, O. (1941). Zur Kenntnis der Mykorrizabildner von Kiefer und Fichte. *Symbolae Botan. Upsalienses* **5**: 1–147.

Morrison, T. M. (1957). Host-endophyte relationship in mycorrhiza of *Pernettya macrostigma. New Phytologist* **56**: 247–257.

Morrison, T. M. (1962). Absorption of phosphorus from soil by mycorrhizal plants. *New Phytologist* **61**: 10–20.

Moser, M. (1959). Beiträge zur Kenntnis der Wuchsstoffbeziehungen in Bereich ektotropher Mykorrhizen. *Arch. Mikrobiol.* **34**: 251–269.

Moser, M. (1963). Förderung der Mykorrhizabildung in der forstlichen Praxis. *Mitt. Forst. Bundes-Versuchsanstalt Mariabrunn* (Wein) **60**: 693–720.
Mosse, B. (1953). Fructifications associated with mycorrhizal strawberry roots. *Nature* **171**: 974.
Mosse, B. (1956). Fructification of an *Endogone* species causing endotrophic mycorrhiza in fruit plants. *Ann. Botany (London)* [N.S.] **20**: 349–362.
Mosse, B. (1957). Growth and chemical composition of mycorrhizal and non-mycorrhizal apples. *Nature* **179**: 922.
Mosse, B. (1959a). The regular germination of resting spores and some observations on the growth requirements of an *Endogone* sp. causing vesicular-arbuscular mycorrhiza. *Brit. Mycol. Soc. Trans.* **42**: 273.
Mosse, E. (1959b). Observations on the extra-matrical mycelium of a vesicular-arbuscular endophyte. *Brit. Mycol. Soc. Trans.* **42**: 439.
Mosse, B. (1963). Vesicular arbuscular mycorrhiza: An extreme form of fungal adaptation. *In* "Symbiotic Associations" (P. S. Nutman and B. Mosse, eds.), pp. 146–170. Cambridge Univ. Press, London and New York.
Mostafa, M. A. (1938). Mycorrhiza in *Tropaeolum majus* and *Phlox drummondi* Hook. *Ann. Botany (London)* [N.S.] **2**: 481.
Nobécourt, P. (1923). Sur la production d' anticorps par les tubercules des Ophrydées. *Compt. Rend.* **177**: 1055–1057.
Noggle, C. R., and F. L. Wynd. (1943). Effect of vitamins on germination and growth of orchids. *Botan. Gaz.* **104**: 455–459.
Norkrans, B. (1950). Studies in growth and cellulolytic enzymes of *Tricholoma* with special reference to mycorrhiza formation. *Symbolae Botan. Upsalienses* **11**: 1–26.
Peuss, H. (1958). Untersuchungen zur Ökologie und Bedeutung der Tabakmykorrhiza. *Arch. Mikrobiol.* **29**: 112–142.
Peyronel, B. (1921). Nouveaux cas de rapports mycorrhiziques entre phanérogames et basidiomycetes. *Bull. Soc. Mycol. France* **37**: 143–148.
Peyronel, B. (1923). Fructification de l'endophyte à arbuscules et à vésicules des mycorrhizes endotrophes. *Bull. Soc. Mycol. France* **39**: 119–126.
Peyronel, B. (1924). Prime recherche sulle micorize endotrofiche et sulla microflora radiciola normala della fanerogame. *Riv. Biol. (Perugia)* **5**: 463–485; **6**: 17–53.
Rayner, M. C. (1927). "Mycorrhiza." *New Phytologist* Reprint 15. Cambridge Univ. Press, London and New York.
Rayner, M. C., and I. Levisohn. (1941). The mycorrhizal habit in relation to forestry. IV. Studies on mycorrhizal response in Pinus and other conifers. *Forestry* **15**: 1–36.
Richards, B. N. (1965). Mycorrhizal development of loblolly pine seedlings in relation to supply of nitrate. *Plant Soil* **22**: 187–199.
Richards, B. N., and G. L. Wilson. (1963). Nutritional supply and mycorrhizal development in Carribean pine. *Forest Sci.* **9**: 405–412.
Robertson, N. F. (1954). Studies of the mycorrhiza of *Pinus sylvestris*. I. *New Phytologist* **53**: 253–283.
Romell, L. G. (1938). A trenching experiment in spruce forest and its bearing on problems of mycotrophy. *Svensk Botan. Tidskr.* **32**: 89–99.
Rovira, A. D. (1965). Plant root exudates and their influence on soil microorganisms. *In* "Ecology of Soil-borne Plant Pathogens—Prelude to Biological Control" (K. F. Baker and W. C. Snyder, eds.), pp. 170–186. Univ. of California Press, Berkeley, California.

Ruinen, J. (1953). Epiphytosis. A second view on epiphytism. *Ann. Bogor.* **1**: 101–157.

Schafferstein, G. (1938). Untersuchungen über die Avitaminose der orchideen Keimlinge. *Jahrb. Wiss. Botan.* **86**: 720–752.

Schafferstein, G. (1941). Die Avitaminose der orchideen Keimlinge. *Jahrb. Wiss. Botan.* **90**: 141–198.

Schelling, C. L. (1950). Die Verwertbarkeit verschiedener Kohlenstoffquellen durch *Mycelium radicis atrovirens. Schweiz. Z. Allgem. Pathol. Bakteriol.* **13**: 570–574.

Schmucker, T. (1959). Saprophytismus bei Kormophyten. *In* "Handbuch der Pflanzenphysiologie" (W. Ruhland, ed.), Vol. 11, pp. 386–426. Springer, Berlin.

Shiroya, T., G. R. Lister, V. Slankis, G. Krotkov, and C. P. Nelson. (1962). Translocation of the products of photosynthesis to the roots of pine seedlings. *Can. J. Botany* **40**: 1125–1136.

Slankis, V. (1948). Einfluss der Exudaten von *Boletus variegatus* auf die dichotomische verzweigung isolierter Kiefernwurzeln. *Physiol. Plantarum* **1**: 390–400.

Slankis, V. (1951). Über den Einfluss von β-indolylessigsäure und andere Wirksstoffen auf das Wachstum von Kieferwurzeln. *Symbolae Botan. Upsalienses* **11**: 1–63.

Smith, D. C. (1962). The biology of lichen thalli. *Biol. Rev.* **37**: 537–579.

Smith, S. E. (1965). The ecology of orchid mycorrhizal fungi. Ph.D. Thesis, Cambridge University.

Smith, S. E. (1966). Physiology and ecology of orchid mycorrhizal fungi with reference to seedling nutrition. *New Phytologist* **65**: 488.

Smith, S. E. (1967). Carbohydrate translocation in orchid mycorrhiza. *New Phytologist* **66**: 371–378.

Stahl, M. (1949). Die Mykorrhiza der Lebermoose mit besonderen Berucksichtigung der thallosen Formen. *Planta* **37**: 103–148.

Trappe, J. M. (1962). Fungus association of ectotrophic mycorrhizae. *Botan. Rev.* **28**: 538–606.

Truscott, J. A. L. (1934). Fungus roots of the strawberry. *Can. J. Res.* **11**: 1–17.

Ulrich, J. M. (1962). Cultural requirements for the growth of excised Ponderosa Pine roots. *Physiol. Plantarum* **15**: 59–71.

Vermuelen, P. (1946). "Studies on *Dactylorchia.*" Utrecht.

Wilson, J. W. (1951). Microorganisms in the rhizosphere of Beech. D.Phil. Thesis, Oxford University.

Winter, A. G., and K. A. Meloh. (1958). Untersuchungen über den Einfluss der endotrophen Mycorrhiza auf die Entwicklung von *Zea mays. Naturwissenschaften* **45**: 319.

Ecology

PARASITIC FUNGI AND THEIR HOSTS

CHAPTER 7

Fungal Parasites of Plants

B. E. J. WHEELER

Imperial College Field Station
Silwood Park, Sunninghill, Berks, England

I. INTRODUCTION

Many fungi parasitize living plants, in the sense that they derive from these plants the food materials necessary for growth but confer no benefits in return. For some fungi the association is obligatory: they may exist outside their hosts in some dormant form such as a spore, but their growth under natural conditions is confined to their appropriate host or hosts. Other fungi have the ability to parasitize plants given suitable conditions, but otherwise live saprophytically on materials derived from the breakdown of plant and animal remains. Although the terms "obligate parasite" and "facultative parasite" are commonly used to denote these two types, they are in one respect misleading, for they suggest that parasitic fungi can be divided neatly into two groups. On the contrary, in nature fungi may be found whose parasitism is, in varying degrees, between these two extremes. In this chapter the term "obligate parasite" is used in the sense stated above and "nonobligate parasite" for any other fungus capable of parasitizing plants, accepting that this term covers diverse types of parasitic activity.

Whatever the capabilities of the fungus outside the plant, its parasitism inevitably involves an interference with the host physiology, and frequently changes occur which are detrimental to the plant. The net result is a deviation from the normal functioning of these physiological processes which is called disease (Anonymous, 1950). In this respect a parasite is also a pathogen. There are thus two ways in which these fungi can be considered, one concerned with their ability to obtain food and grow within a living plant, the other with their ability to induce disease. It is in the former context that they are considered here. One point, however, requires emphasis. The plant itself is not inert, but reacts, often in a highly characteristic way, to the activities of the parasite and by doing so frequently limits these activities. To confine attention to the fungi involved is therefore to present only one aspect of the parasite–host relationship. It is within these limits that the chapter is written.

II. ENTRY INTO THE PLANT

Before a fungus can parasitize plant tissues, the physical and chemical barriers associated with the plant surface must be passed. In general, fungi enter plants in one or more of three ways—through wounds, through natural openings, and by direct penetration of intact surfaces.

A. *Entry through Wounds*

In two groups of fungi entry through wounds is particularly common, those parasitizing trees and those causing rots of fruits and other storage organs. Since many of the fungi concerned cause serious crop losses, most attention has been directed to the type of wound through which they invade and how such wounds can be avoided. There is now a vast amount of literature dealing with these aspects as they relate to particular fungi and their hosts. Some examples of types of wounds and the fungi which exploit them are given in Table I.

TABLE I
ENTRY OF PARASITIC FUNGI THROUGH WOUNDS

Type of wound	Examples
(1) Wounds caused by nonliving agencies, e.g., fire, weather conditions	Species of *Fomes*, *Polyporus*, *Poria*, and *Ustulina*, causing heartrots of standing timber (Wagener and Davidson, 1954)
(2) Wounds that arise as the result of specific agricultural practices, e.g., pruning, grading of produce	*Nectria galligena* via pruning cuts on apple shoots (Marsh, 1939); *Fusarium caeruleum* through abrasions on potato tubers caused by grading (Foister *et al.*, 1952)
(3) Wounds caused by insects	*Ceratocystis ulmi* through the cavities of bark-boring beetles on elm (Peace, 1962); *Sclerotinia fructigena* through wounds caused by codling moth on apples (Wormald, 1954)
(4) Wounds caused by other pathogenic fungi, by actinomycetes or bacteria	*Nectria galligena* via the lesions of *Venturia inaequalis* on apple (Wiltshire, 1922); *Phytophthora infestans* through lesions of *Spongospora subterranea* on potato tubers (Schultz, 1952)
(5) Leaf scars	*Nectria galligena* on apple (Wiltshire, 1921); *Glomerella cingulata* on camellias (Baxter and Plakidas, 1944)

Old wounds are generally less favorable entry sites for parasitic fungi than those freshly made because barriers such as wound wood, cork, gum, and tyloses are formed during the natural healing processes. In experiments with *Nectria galligena* and apple shoots Marsh (1939), found that there was no period between October and March when mycelium failed to infect freshly made pruning cuts but inoculations of 2-month-old cuts resulted in very few cankers. Similarly, Crowdy (1952), found that this fungus was only able to infect the leaf scars for a limited time after leaf fall. The susceptibility of cut potato seed pieces to invasion by *Fusarium* species also decreases rapidly with time. This results from the formation of wound cork, which these fungi cannot penetrate, below the cut area (Cunningham and Reinking, 1946).

At certain times of the year healing of wounds may proceed more rapidly than at others, and this indirectly affects the entry of parasitic fungi. For example, infection of plum by *Stereum purpureum* does not occur readily during June, July, and August in Britain; this is related to the rapid blocking of wounds during these months (Swarbrick, 1927).

The restriction of many parasites of trees to entry through wounds can be attributed to the deposits of lignin and suberin in the outer tissues of the hosts. These present barriers of great physical strength and of a chemical composition resistant to most parasitic fungi. Why the entry of certain fruit-rotting fungi is limited to wounds is less readily explained. There have been comparatively few investigations on the nature of the resistance of the host surface in relation to the physiology of the fungus concerned, or what might be called the physiology of wound parasitism.

In a study of the infection of stone fruits by brown rot fungi, Curtis (1928) concluded that the cuticle played an important part in determining resistance. In none of the varieties examined was the fungus unable to pierce the cuticle, but this process was slow and of no practical significance, presumably because under natural conditions the germ tube dried out before it could gain access to the tissues. Curtis attributed the susceptibility of one variety (Yellow Cherry plum), with no stomata and lenticels on the fruit, to the possession of areas of thin cuticle, the inference being that the thickness of the cuticle is the critical factor. Unfortunately no investigations were carried out on the ability of this fungus to penetrate artificial membranes of graded thickness to determine whether this was purely a mechanical effect.

Investigations of a similar type with *Penicillium digitatum* and *P. italicum* on orange fruit suggest that it is the so-called "flavedo" layer of the skin which inhibits the penetration of these fungi (Green, 1932; Bates, 1936). Both species readily infect via deep wounds which penetrate to the inner "albedo" layer, or indeed, through the oil vesicles (Bates,

1933), but they do not readily penetrate shallow wounds which do not go beyond the "flavedo" layer. However, the apparent resistance of such shallow wounds, or of unbroken skin, can be broken down if the spore inoculum is suspended in juice or essential oil. Recent work (see Wood, 1960) suggests that this is an effect on the ability of the fungus to produce certain pectolytic enzymes.

Wound parasites frequently derive advantages from their mode of entry other than bypassing the surface barriers and the resistance associated with them. The spores of *Stereum purpureum,* for example, are sucked into the ends of the cut vessels of plum wood; as a result not only are the germ tubes protected during periods of desiccation, but they arise in the cells which are the main channels of invasion for this parasite (Brooks and Moore, 1923). Active suction of spores into the vessels may also be an important factor in the entry of *Nectria galligena* through leaf scars (Crowdy, 1952).

That wounding of plant tissues results in dead cells may or may not be an advantage to the parasite. Where a build-up of inoculum is essential to further penetration it probably is. In many instances, however, this material must be utilized in competition with saprophytic fungi which often grow more rapidly. Ultimately it is only those special properties with which the parasitic fungus is endowed, its ability to colonize living tissue of a particular plant and grow away from the area of wounding, which gives it a particular advantage in this situation.

B. *Entry through Natural Openings*

A number of parasitic fungi use the natural openings in the plant surface, the stomata, lenticels, and hydathodes, to gain access to the tissues.

Entry through stomata has received most attention probably as a result of the early discovery that the aecidial and uredial germ tubes of many rust fungi enter in this way. The actual process of penetration has been studied by many workers for particular parasite–host associations, e.g., *Puccinia graminis* and wheat (Pole-Evans, 1907), *Plasmopara viticola* and vine (Arens, 1929), *Cladosporium fulvum* and tomato (Bond, 1938). These examples illustrate three ways in which entry through stomata is accomplished.

The motile zoospore of *P. viticola* swims in the water film on the leaf surface. When it approaches a stoma its movements appear subject to some stimulus, and the spore comes to rest over the stomatal pore. From this now nonmotile spore, a slender hypha emerges which passes through the pore into the substomatal cavity.

The spores of *C. fulvum* germinate on the leaf surface either in a water film or in moist air. The orientation of the germ tubes is apparently haphazard, and frequently these grow over stomata. When penetration occurs, either the germ tube itself or a lateral branch from it grows directly through the stomatal pore into the substomatal cavity.

The germ tube from a uredospore of *Puccinia graminis* grows over the shoot surface, frequently forming V-shaped enlargements in the slight depressions between the epidermal cells. On reaching a stoma the tip of the germ tube enlarges and becomes closely appressed to the surface of the guard cells. From the structure so formed, the appressorium, a very fine penetration hypha emerges and enters the substomatal cavity. There it swells, forming a vesicle, from which hyphae develop under suitable conditions.

Two aspects of stomatal entry have attracted particular attention. These are the nature of the stimuli involved and the influence of stomatal movement on the process. There is a good deal of conflicting experimental evidence and opinion in both spheres of investigation: that concerned with the nature of the stimuli will be considered first

Entry of a fungus through a stoma involves two phases, movement or growth to the stoma and growth through the stomatal pore. It is not necessary, as Brown (1936) points out, to postulate a directive stimulus for the first phase, and the behavior of the germ tubes of *C. fulvum* suggests that none exists for this parasite–host combination. The same is true of *Alternaria longipes* on tobacco leaves (von Ramm, 1962), and *Physalospora obtusa* on apple leaves (Foster, 1937). On the other hand, the zoospores of *Plasmopara viticola* on vine aggregate around stomata in a manner which suggests that they are stimulated to do so. In contrast, the processes associated with the second phase can hardly be considered accidental, particularly for those fungi which form appressoria and penetration hyphae. Even where these structures are not formed, a change in the direction of germ-tube growth is involved. The idea that these events are influenced by chemical stimuli has not generally found favor. One reason for this is that the substomatal cavity is filled with air, and any chemical, to be effective, would have to be in the gaseous state. Growth responses to water (hydrotropism) or to contact with the plant surface (haptotropism or thigmotropism) are generally considered most likely to determine stomatal entry.

A response to water vapor was suggested in some early work by Balls (1905) with *Puccinia glumarum* [*P. striiformis*]. He used thin membranes of india rubber, perforated with holes comparable in size to stomata. These membranes were arranged with one side exposed to air saturated with water vapor, the other exposed to air in the laboratory. This latter side was seeded with unredospores. When the membranes were examined 2 days later, many germ tubes were found entering the holes, but once within the saturated atmosphere none grew back into the drier air.

There is also evidence that water droplets, rather than water vapor in the substomatal cavity, influences the entry of fungi through stomata. Bald (1952) observed that under certain conditions drops of water were exuded through the stomata of gladiolus leaves: these droplets apparently induced the spores of a *Pleospora* sp. to enter the stomata. He also stated that the germ tubes of *Botrytis gladiolorum* are induced to enter stomata when gladiolus leaves are alternately wetted and dried. Similar conditions were previously found by Bond (1938) to favor the entry of *Cladosporium fulvum* into tomato leaves. He suggested that penetration was controlled largely by a stimulus dependent on evaporation from the leaf.

Growth along a gradient of increasing relative humidity as indicated by these investigations does not, however, explain the formation of appressoria and the subsequent development of penetration hyphae. It is significant that in the experiments of Balls there was no marked vesicle formation by the germ tubes of *Puccinia striiformis.* In this respect penetration of the india rubber membrane differed from that observed on the host. There is now evidence which suggests that growth responses due to contact stimuli lead to the formation of these structures and that the nature of the plant surface itself may be an important factor. For example, Dickinson (1949b) found that when uredospores of *Puccinia triticina* [*P. recondita*], *P. graminis,* and *P. striiformis* germinated on paraffin-wax-collodion membranes, the germ tubes frequently produced small side branches giving a characteristic "gnarled" appearance. He concluded that the initiation of nuclear division associated with this branching formed part of a contact reaction. When cell-wall fragments were incorporated into such membranes, structures corresponding to appressoria, infection hyphae, and substomatal vesicles were formed by the germinating spores. Hurd-Karrer and Rodenhiser (1947) reported the formation of similar structures corresponding to appressoria and substomatal vesicles, when uredospores of *P. graminis* f. sp. *tritici, P. recondita, P. coronata, P. anomala* [*P. hordei*], and *P. maydis* were germinated on a nutrient solution agar. These were formed on the surface of the medium, but only by a few of the germinating spores. Spores germinated on water agar, however, did not produce these vesicles. In this instance, therefore, the possibility that chemical stimuli influenced vesicle formation cannot be discounted.

The influence of stomatal size and behavior on penetration by parasitic fungi has received comparatively little attention in recent years. That a closed stoma might prevent the entry of the fungal germ tube is a plausible hypothesis, but one not always supported by experimental results. Certainly, in their studies of *Cercospora beticola* on beet leaves, Pool and McKay (1916) found that under conditions resulting in closed stomata the conidia germinated on the leaf but did not penetrate. Similarly, the results obtained by Hart (1929) using *Puccinia graminis* and wheat suggested that the germ tubes did not force their way through closed stomata but entered only when the stomata were open. On the other hand, Caldwell and Stone (1932) found that closed stomata offered no barrier to the penetration of *P. recondita* on wheat leaves. Their studies indicated that the formation of an appressorium over an open stoma often caused it to close. Hirt (1938) also concluded that stomatal activity was of little significance in the infection of *Pinus strobus* by *Cronartium ribicola.*

In assessing conflicting results of this type, it is well to bear in mind that conditions vary with each parasite–host combination. A closed stoma on one plant may be a barrier of greater strength than a closed stoma on another. Where entry is normally made directly by the germ tube, a closed stoma may well constitute a barrier which this type of growth cannot pass. The type of stomatal entry shown by rust uredospores is more likely to be effective in this situation.

Entry through lenticels is confined mainly to fungi parasitic on fruit or other storage organs such as *Neofabraea malicorticis, Gloeosporium perennans,* and *Penicillium expansum* on apple (Kidd and Beaumont, 1925; K. F. Baker and Heald, 1932), and *Oospora pustulans* on potato (J. D. Allen, 1957). *Cylindrocarpon ehrenbergii* does, however, enter the roots of alfalfa and clover in this way (Cormack, 1937). Typically either the germ tubes or hyphae derived from them enter lenticels by growing between the loosely packed surface cells. On apples, lenticels may be closed by processes which favor dehydration of the outer tissues (Clements, 1935), and this could conceivably affect penetration by fungal hyphae, but there is little information on this point.

Penetration of hydathodes may occur particularly where guttation drops provide water necessary for germination (Stakman and Harrar, 1957), but generally this mode of entry appears comparatively unimportant as far as parasitic fungi are concerned.

C. *Penetration of Continuous Plant Surfaces*

There are many parasitic fungi which do not make use of either wounds or natural openings but penetrate the unbroken plant surface, in particular the cuticle which covers the shoot. The way in which they do so has been studied for many parasite–host combinations, e.g., *Phytophthora infestans* and potato (Pristou and Gallegly, 1954); *Venturia inaequalis* and *V. pirina* on apple and pear, respectively (Wiltshire, 1915; Nusbaum and

Keitt, 1938); *Erysiphe graminis* and wheat (Corner, 1935); *Puccinia graminis* and *Berberis* (Waterhouse, 1921); and *Stigmina carpophila* and almond (Samuel, 1927). The process of penetration, in its essential features, follows a similar pattern in the examples investigated. The germ tube, on contacting the cuticle, becomes flattened, often with the formation of an appressorium. From this area of contact, a fine penetration hypha emerges which grows through the cuticle and outer epidermal wall. Subsequently the penetration hypha increases in diameter forming either a hypha of normal size or a haustorium.

Many of the problems connected with direct penetration of plant surfaces have recently been discussed by Wood (1960) and by Dickinson (1960), and it is therefore proposed only to consider these briefly. Two aspects are of particular interest, the relative importance of chemical and physical factors in penetration, and the nature of the stimuli involved.

The evidence at present available suggests that penetration is predominantly mechanical. Many of these fungi can penetrate artificial membranes, e.g., collodion-paraffin-wax, gold leaf, which they are most unlikely to affect chemically. There is, however, no penetration if the thickness or hardness of these membranes is substantially increased. Similarly, the ability of certain fungi to infect is directly related to the resistance of the outer tissues to mechanical puncture, e.g., *Puccinia graminis* on barberry (Melander and Craigie, 1927), and *Macrosporium* on tomato (Rosenbaum and Sando, 1920). In addition to positive evidence of this type, no one has yet shown that parasitic fungi can degrade plant cuticle. On the other hand, certain cytological evidence suggests that chemical degradation may play a part in penetration by some fungi, e.g., *Venturia inaequalis* on apple (Wiltshire, 1915).

The relative roles of chemical and physical factors in penetration may well be determined not only by the intrinsic abilities of the fungus concerned, but also by the nature of the surface barrier. In this respect its permeability to substances produced either by the parasite or host is of particular importance. Several observers have noted that changes occur in the underlying cells before actual penetration of the surface barrier is achieved (G. Smith, 1900; Thomas, 1934; Chadhuri, 1935; Paddock, 1953). It is possible that the passage of substances alters the strength of the surface barrier and facilitates penetration in a similar way that plasmolyzing leaves of *Eucharis* spp. permits penetration by *Botrytis cinerea* (Brown and Harvey, 1927).

The penetration of artificial membranes also suggests that chemical factors play little part in stimulating fungi to penetrate plant surfaces. Experiments by Dickinson (1949a,b) and by van Burgh (1950) indicate that contact stimuli are more likely to be responsible. Substances diffusing through plant surfaces may, however, influence the process in a general way. Brown (1922) showed that when drops of water were placed on some plant surfaces the conductivity was raised, presumably by the passage of electrolytes through the cuticle, and that spore germination of *Botrytis cinerea* in these drops was enhanced. Kerr and Flentje (1957) also showed that the formation of infection cushions by *Rhizoctonia solani* [*Corticium solani*] on radish roots was stimulated by substances diffusing from the underlying cells.

III. GROWTH IN THE PLANT

Entry of a fungus into a plant is not necessarily an indication of its parasitic ability. C. M. Gibson (1904) found that the germ tubes of rust aecidiospores and uredospores would enter the stomata of many plants which were not their hosts. Similar observations have been made with powdery mildews (Salmon, 1905; Corner, 1935), and with a wide range of nonobligate parasites (Young, 1926; B. Johnson, 1932). In these instances, death of the fungus followed after entry had been achieved. Under appropriate conditions, however, a series of events takes place after entry by which the fungus establishes itself as a parasite within the host tissues. This involves two interrelated processes, growth of the fungus leading to certain spatial relationships between its mycelium and the plant tissues, and the absorption of food materials from the tissues to support this growth.

A. Spatial Relationships with the Host Tissues

Parasitic fungi show great diversity in the way they colonize plants. The variations which occur can be considered at three different levels, those of the whole plant, its organs and tissues, and its cells.

Some fungi develop mainly on the surface of the plant and colonize little of the internal tissues. The Erysiphaceae provides some of the best examples. The mycelium of *Erysiphe* spp., e.g., *E. graminis, E. polygoni,* and *E. cichoracearum,* remains as a superficial layer on the host. Colonization of the host tissue is restricted to the epidermal cells which are penetrated at intervals by haustoria. A few powdery mildews show a greater development of internal mycelium. Much of the mycelium of *Leveillula taurica* is intercellular, and haustoria are formed in the mesophyll cells (Salmon, 1906). Similarly, in the genus *Phyllactinia* special hyphae enter the stomata and penetrate the intercellular spaces of the leaf, forming a limited internal mycelium (Palla, 1899).

Many of the tropical, leaf-inhabiting ascomycetes develop on their hosts in a way comparable to the powdery mildews. In the genus *Meliola,* the black mycelium is attached to the leaf by short branches (hyphopodia) from which haustoria penetrate the epidermal cells. In some species, e.g., *Paradiopsis perae,* the stomata may be penetrated by specialized hyphae (stomatopodia) from which an internal mycelium develops with haustoria in the mesophyll cells as in *Phyllactinia* (Hansford, 1946).

A marked development of mycelium on the surface also occurs during the colonization of roots by certain fungi, but this is usually followed by extensive invasion of the tissues. For example, the hyphae of *Ophiobolus graminis,* which parasitizes the roots of cereals and various grasses, grow along the root surfaces and cover these with a mycelial mat. These hyphae are of two kinds, fairly thick, brown runner hyphae and finer, colorless infection hyphae. Penetration of the root by the latter occurs behind the limit of spread of the runner hyphae. The fungus then rapidly colonizes the root cortex. Later the endodermis may be passed and the stele also colonized. Under suitable conditions, all root tissues except the lignified xylem may be disintegrated (Davis, 1925; Fellows, 1928). A similar initial development of surface mycelium (or "ectotrophic growth habit") occurs during the colonization of tree roots by *Fomes lignosus* and *Armillaria mellea.* With *F. lignosus,* growth of the rhizomorphs may be some 15 ft ahead of actual penetration (Garrett, 1956).

A special type of superficial development of mycelium occurs during the initial colonization of apple leaves by *Venturia inaequalis.* A slender penetration hypha, arising from the germinated spore, enters the cuticle and, on contacting the outer cellulose wall of the epidermal cells, swells to form a 2–3-celled primary hypha. From this, lateral branches arise, and by continued growth a stroma, 2–4 cells thick, is formed within the cuticle from which conidiophores are subsequently produced. Host cells show no evidence of injury until some 10–14 days after the initial penetration when a sequence of events leads to the collapse of the epidermal cells (Nusbaum and Keitt, 1938). Not until the leaf becomes senescent, i.e., just before leaf fall, does the mycelium of the conidial stroma extend into the mesophyll and there form the perithecial primordia. *Venturia pirina* colonizes pear leaves in a similar way (Wiltshire, 1915), and *Diplocarpon rosae* also forms a comparable subcuticular stroma in rose leaves (Wolf, 1913).

Most other parasitic fungi show varying degrees of internal colonization of their hosts. They can be divided into two broad groups, one in which the mycelium is localized, in the sense that it is confined to a particular plant organ or tissue, and the other in which the mycelium is generally distributed within the host.

Fungi which colonize the roots of plants provide examples of the first group. Some, such as *Pythium debaryanum, P. ultimum,* and *Phytophthora cryptogea* attack particularly the roots and undergound parts of seedlings. On very young seedlings, they rapidly invade the cortical tissue, causing the cells to lose turgidity and shrink. As a result the seedlings collapse, a condition referred to as "damping off." Older seedlings may also be attacked. The tissues involved are chiefly the root cortex and pith, but when rotting is well advanced the wood vessels may also be invaded. There is generally no colonization of the stem, at least above soil level. Many other parasites operate in a simliar manner, rotting the tissues as they progress along the roots.

The relationship between parasite and host tissue which results from the invasion of cruciferous plants by *Plasmodiophora brassicae* is very different. This, in part, stems from the fact that the parasite does not form hyphae but exists only as masses of naked protoplasm (myxamoebae or plasmodia), or as spores. It also results from the effect this parasite has on the host cells. *P. brassicae* typically enters the root by way of the root hairs, migrating from these cells to those of the primary cortex. The multinucleate plasmodium of the parasite is developed within these cells, and at first it is often difficult to distinguish parasite plasmodium and host cytoplasm. The presence of the parasite causes both the invaded cell and those adjacent to it to divide. When the cambial cells, in particular, are invaded considerable disorganization and displacement of the root tissues results, and this leads to the formation of the "club-root" (Colhoun, 1958).

These fungi begin their parasitic activities on roots largely because they are present in the soil. In roots they obviously obtain the food material they require, and it may be that these are not readily available elsewhere in the plant. On the other hand, the cells of the stem may possess defense mechanisms which preclude further spread. Thus the penetration of stems by *Ophiobolus graminis* is prevented by a thickening of cell walls and gum formation, apparently in response to the presence of the fungus (Fellows, 1928).

Comparable host reactions limit many leaf parasites to small areas of tissue so that well defined "leaf-spots" result. The mechanisms involved are discussed by Akai (1959). In some instances the area of leaf tissue colonized by the fungus is abscissed, e.g., on peach leaves attacked by *Stigmina carpophila* (Samuel, 1927).

Certain smut fungi provide striking examples of restricted colonization. Of these *Ustilago maydis,* the common smut of maize, is probably the most familiar. This fungus can penetrate any young, meristematic tissue but commonly infects the axillary buds or floral organs. Development of the mycelium is, however, restricted to the organ invaded, and each smut gall which is produced is the result of a separate infection (G. W.

Fischer and Holton, 1957). The same is true of *Neovissia horrida* [*Tilletia barclayana*] on rice (Chowdhury, 1946), and *N.* [*T.*] *indica* on wheat (Mundkur, 1943; Bedi *et al.,* 1949), each "bunted" grain being derived from an infected ovary. Among ascomycetes, *Claviceps purpurea* is similarly restricted to the ovaries of cereals and grasses.

There are some fungi which appear to be restricted to a particular tissue. Outstanding among them are the vascular wilt fungi, such as the parasitic forms of *Fusarium oxysporum* (*sensu* Snyder and Hansen), *Verticillium alboatrum* and *V. dahliae*. These typically enter through the roots of their hosts, pass into the vascular system, and are confined to this throughout most of their parasitic life. When the hosts become moribund, however, these fungi frequently grow out into the cortical tissues. This growth can be induced artificially by cutting portions from infected plants and placing them in damp chambers (Keyworth, 1951). This suggests that the cortical tissues normally offer some resistance to infection, and this is hardly surprising because these are living cells whereas the vessels are not. It was originally thought that these fungi actively colonized vascular tissue only in the roots and lower portions of the plant, and the effects which these produced in the shoots were variously attributed to toxins or mechanical plugging of the vessels. It is now known that many are more widely distributed throughout the vascular system. *Verticillium alboatrum* and *V. dahliae,* for example, can be isolated from all parts of lucerne except the seed (Isaac, 1957). *Ceratocystis ulmi* also develops mainly in the vascular system; this gains access to these tissues through insect wounds in the bark. The distribution of these parasites is, in many instances, facilitated by the movement of spores within the vascular stream (Banfield, 1941; Scheffer and Walker, 1953).

There are certain fungi that do not invade every tissue but become generally distributed throughout their hosts in a manner very different from those so far described. These fungi are best considered in two groups: parasites on annual plants and parasites on perennials.

Tilletia caries is an example of the first group: the way this infects and colonizes wheat has recently been studied by Swinburne (1963). Colonization begins at a very early stage in the development of the seedling. The fungus penetrates the coleoptile and passes through the tissue into the first leaf base. From there it enters the young ear either by passing through successive leaf bases directly into the growing point or by passing from the older leaf bases into the tissues immediately beneath the growing point. The fungus also grows into tiller buds which arise adjacent to infected leaf bases. This early colonization of the growing points within the crown node region, which at this stage possesses all the tissues to be found in the mature plant, determines the subsequent distribution of the fungus. For, as the plant extends its growth by elongation of the internodes, the fungus is carried passively within these growing points. This also appears to be the way in which *Ustilago nuda* becomes distributed within wheat and barley (Batts and Jeater, 1958; Malik and Batts, 1960). Here, however, the fungus is within the embryo of the seed at sowing as a result of flower infection in the previous season.

Other than smuts of this type, few parasitic fungi become generally distributed within an annual plant. *Uromyces euphorbiae* does so on *Chamaecyse* (Arthur, 1929) and *Helminthosporium gramineum* on barley (N. Smith, 1929). The latter fungus achieves this by penetrating each leaf in succession as it emerges and ultimately the young ear. External mycelium on the inner surface of one leaf serves as inoculum for the next to emerge. In this respect, *H. gramineum* differs from the other fungi considered here which colonize their hosts by an internal movement of mycelium.

There is a greater variety of fungi which become generally distributed throughout perennial hosts. Notable examples are *Ustilago violacea* on *Melandrium album* (G. W. Fischer and Holton, 1957), *Uromyces pisi* on *Euphorbia cyparissias* (Tischler, 1911), *Epichloë typhina* on various grasses (Sampson, 1933), and *Pseudoperonospora humuli* on hops (Ware, 1926). Further examples are to be found particularly among the rusts (Arthur, 1929), smuts (G. W. Fischer and Holton, 1957), and downy mildews (Melhus, 1915). In grasses infected with *E. typhina,* narrow unbranched hyphae can be detected throughout considerable lengths of the host tissue; this observation suggests that the fungus colonizes the host by mycelial growth. It is assumed that many of the other fungi colonize their hosts in a similar manner. In hops, however, attacked by *P. humuli* there is apparently no continuity of mycelium between an infected rootstock and infected apical and lateral spikes.

In the final analysis it is the relationship which fungal hyphae have with their host cells which is most important, for by close contact with these cells the fungi absorb the food materials necessary for growth. Some fungi pass between the host cells (intercellular), others penetrate these cells (intracellular), yet others invade tissues both inter- and intracellularly. For example, *Botrytis cinerea* moves intercellularly at first by breaking down the middle lamellae of the host cells; *Colletotrichum lindemuthianum* on *Phaseolus* spp. passes initially into the cells of the leaf. *Tilletia caries* develops both inter- and intracellularly within the developing wheat seedling; *Plasmodiophora brassicae* is completely intracellular within the roots of its cruciferous hosts.

Few generalizations can be made as to the actual method used by different parasites, but the effects on the host cells divide these into groups. The nonobligate parasites, of which *B. cinerea* and *C. lindemuthianum* are examples, rapidly kill the cells they contact or invade, whereas the obligate parasites, e.g., *T. caries* and *P. brassicae* do not. The production of a haustorium within the host cell is one of the few physical differences between these two types of fungi. Only a few nonobligate parasites form these structures—*Diplocarpon rosae* is one—whereas they are commonly formed by rusts (Rice, 1927), powdery mildews (G. Smith, 1900), downy mildews (Fraymouth, 1956), and some smuts (G. W. Fischer and Holton, 1957).

B. *Nutrition of the Parasite within the Host*

Our knowledge of the ways in which fungi obtain the food materials they require during the colonization of plants is not extensive, and what is known concerns chiefly the nonobligate parasites. The concept has arisen that these fungi kill the host cells and then live saprophytically on the cell materials. This is an oversimplification of the situation, but it emphasizes that there are two aspects to be considered.

Several mechanisms may be involved in the death of cells. With fungi such as *Botrytis cinerea* that rot the tissues, it has not proved possible to separate from the pectolytic enzymes which degrade the middle lamella, any substance which specifically kills the protoplasts. It is inferred, therefore, that these substances are responsible for both processes (Brown, 1955). Death of the host cells may also result from the action of particular chemicals or toxins produced by the parasitic fungus. The presence of many materials has been demonstrated in fungal cultures, but in relatively few instances has it been shown that they occur in infected plants or reproduce in plants the effects associated with the parasitic activity of the fungus. There is, however, substantial evidence that some of the effects of *Alternaria solani* on the cells of its hosts result from the production of alternaric acid by this fungus. Similarly, with *Pyricularia oryzae* on rice and *Helminthosporium victoriae* on oats, specific chemicals may be involved in this way (Ludwig, 1960). In these instances, the materials isolated are fairly complex chemicals. It has been suggested that death of cells results from the production of oxalic acid by fungi. This may be so in particular parasite–host combinations, e.g., *Aspergillus niger* and groundnuts (I. A. S. Gibson, 1953), but the idea that this acid is involved in a wide range of diseases where rotting occurs is not now generally accepted (Brown, 1936).

These considerations apart, how do nonobligate parasites utilize the materials present in their hosts? Studies of these fungi in pure culture indicate they require a supply of carbohydrate and nitrogen, both in simple form, together with various mineral nutrients and sometimes additional growth substances such as biotin and thiamine (Hawker, 1950; Lilly and Barnett, 1951). Many of these materials are to be found in the cell sap—for example, nitrates, amino acids, and mineral compounds—and it is reasonable to assume that these are readily available to the invading parasite. Much of the plant carbohydrate, however, is in the form of sucrose, starch, and cellulose, and the nitrogen as proteins. To be able to use these materials the fungus must possess the enzymes which break these down into simple, readily assimilated compounds. That they do form these enzymes can often be demonstrated in pure culture where, for example, the carbohydrates can be supplied solely in the form of sucrose, starch, or cellulose. The ability to degrade these compounds, however, is one possessed by many fungi, including some that have no parasitic ability. What needs to be demonstrated, in addition is that similar conversions occur within infected plants.

With infected fruits and storage organs, changes in sucrose and starch content can be determined by chemical analyses (Hawkins, 1915; Hawkins and Harvey, 1919). Disappearance of starch grains, following the invasion of parasitic fungi also provides evidence that this material is degraded. In some instances, colonization of the tissues is governed by the distribution of this material. This can be seen in the roots of tea seedlings parasitized by *Armillaria mellea*. The fungal hyphae accumulate in the pith where starch is abundant, but not in the cortical tissues which are devoid of starch (Leach, 1937). Similarly, *Phymatotrichum omnivorum* colonizes seedling roots as soon as these accumulate starch, but not earlier (Blank, 1940).

Utilization of cellulose in plants can also be deduced from cytological preparations of infected tissues, and from evidence of cellulolytic activity by the fungus in culture. A particular difficulty occurs here in that the structure of the cellulose supplied in culture is not comparable to that found in the plant. Soluble salts of carboxymethylcellulose are frequently used whereas unchanged plant cellulose is insoluble. The basic unit of plant cellulose is a long chain of D-glucose residues in β-1,4 linkage. These chains are arranged in definite patterns, and in aggregates form the cellulose fibrils. Within spaces in these units other materials, e.g., lignin, pectic substances, are deposited. This complex pattern undoubtedly affects the action of cellulolytic enzymes *in vivo*. Generally, cellulose decomposition is associated with the later stages of colonization by fungi. This may be because some of the substances associated with the cellulose fibrils must first be removed. Also there is evidence from studies *in vitro* that glucose and other sugars can lower the production and activity of cellulolytic enzymes. Where lignin infiltration of the fibrils occurs, decomposition is more difficult. There are, however, some basidiomycetes, the so-called "white-rot fungi" which produce enzymes capable of decomposing lignin. Also some fungi, e.g., *Fusarium nivale* [*Calonectria nivalis*], causing "foot-rots" of monocotyledons which have a relatively high lignin content decompose this material (Husain and Kelman, 1959).

With obligate parasites, there are few visual signs which indicate the nature of the food materials utilized. With many of these parasites it is assumed that absorption of food materials occurs through haustoria, although this view has been questioned (Yarwood, 1956). The nature of these materials is not known, but it has been suggested that complex nitrogenous compounds, such as proteins, may be absorbed from the host in this way.

Diversion of materials to the parasite may be inferred, however, as in maize infected with *Puccinia maydis*. In healthy maize plants, excess carbohydrate is temporarily deposited as starch in the cells surrounding the vascular bundles: in infected plants these cells contain no starch, although seldom penetrated by haustoria (Rice, 1927). In this instance, the soluble carbohydrates formed during photosynthesis are presumably intercepted before they reach the cells of the bundle sheath.

There is evidence that the metabolic activities of the host cells are stimulated by these fungi. For example, Yarwood and Childs (1938) found with a number of rusts that the dry weight of plant tissue around the lesions was greater than portions cut from comparable areas of uninfected leaves. Recent work using radioactive materials has confirmed that the lesions of many obligate parasites become surrounded by zones of high metabolic activity. Yarwood and Jacobsen (1950) found that when bean leaves were exposed to the vapor of sodium sulfide, labeled with ^{35}S, there was an accumulation of radioactive material in areas infected with *Uromyces appendiculatus* and *Erysiphe polygoni*. Similar results were obtained by Shaw *et al.* (1954) and Shaw and Samborski (1956) using a wide range of radioactive materials and leaves of wheat and barley infected with *Puccinia graminis* and *Erysiphe graminis*. From 3 to 4 days after inoculation there was a rapid accumulation of radioactivity especially in the host mesophyll cells beneath the mycelium. The radioactive tracers did not accumulate in dead areas resulting from wounds, or within lesions caused by fungi which kill the host cells such as *Botrytis* sp. on broad bean (*Vicia faba*). Experiments using ^{14}C (supplied as CO_2) showed an accumulation of this material in starch deposited around the lesions. Young rust uredosori were closely surrounded by rings of starch but older pustules were separated from them by starch-free zones. This possibly reflects the more extensive demands made on the host by the parasite during sporulation. Thus in the gall tissue of *Gymnosporangium juniperi-virginianae* on red cedar (*Juniperus virgin-*

iana), starch is abundant until the teleutospores begin to form, when it rapidly disappears (Reed and Crabhill, 1915).

With obligate parasites, sporulation often marks the end of a "balanced" relationship in which the fungus, while not conferring any benefits on the plant, does not cause any visible damage. This is particularly true of many smuts which during sporulation utilize the ovary tissues. Even with the downy mildews, sporulation may cause reductions in plant growth. Quantitative studies indicated that the sporulation of *Peronospora destructor* caused a 55% reduction in the green weight of onion leaves. The corresponding figures for *Pseudoperonospora humuli* on hops, and *Peronospora effusa* on spinach were 17% and 48%, respectively. On onions, the dry matter content of sporangiophores and sporangia produced during the night of sporulation amounted to 5% of the dry weight of infected leaves (Yarwood, 1941). Although in this instance the effect of water loss could not be satisfactorily estimated, it is evident that there is a considerable transfer of nutrients from host to parasite at this time.

IV. LIFE CYCLE IN RELATION TO THAT OF THE HOST

So far the parasitic activities of fungi have been considered. Plants, however, have a limited existence, many less than a year. How these fungi survive from season to season or from one host generation to the next is one of the most interesting aspects of their life cycles. In general there are two ways in which they do so, within the host tissues and outside the living host. For fungi which have an existence independent of their living hosts there is an additional aspect to be considered, that of establishing contact with the host.

A. Survival and Growth within Living Host Tissues

Fungi which parasitize perennial plants are in a particularly advantageous position, for once established the nature of their hosts ensures their survival. Those infecting herbaceous perennials frequently become dormant in the perennating organs, such as *Transzchelia discolor* within the corms of *Anemone coronaria, Peronospora destructor* in the bulbs of *Allium* spp., and *Epichloë typhina* in the rhizomes of various grasses. They then colonize the new tissues which are formed in the following year (Butler and Jones, 1955).

Some fungi on woody perennials remain within local areas of tissue they have colonized, particularly those which cause galls and witches' brooms, such as *Gymnosporangium juniperi-virginianae* on red cedar (*Juniperus virginiana*), (Reed and Crabhill, 1915) and *Marasmius perniciosus* on cacao (R. E. D. Baker and Holliday, 1957). In the following year there is little, if any, mycelial extension within the host, but fruiting bodies are produced on the hypertrophied tissues and the fungi concerned thus complete their life cycles. Survival in this way varies from a few years as in *Gymnococonia interstitialis* on *Rubus* (Dodge, 1923), to as many as sixty years, reported by Gäumann (1950) for *Melampsorella caryophyllacearum* on *Abies*. Other fungi, in addition to producing spores, continue to grow within the host tissue. *Cronartium ribicola* does so on *Pinus strobus* (Spaulding, 1922), and *Nectria galligena* on apple (Crowdy, 1949). In these instances, successive periods of mycelial extension lead to canker formation.

Many of the Erysiphaceae overwinter in the buds of their perennial hosts. The mycelium of *Podosphaera leucotricha* becomes established within the young apple buds in the spring, and there remains protected by the bud scales until the next season (Woodward, 1927). *Microsphaera alphitoides* overwinters in the buds of oak in a similar manner (Woodward *et al.,* 1929), and there is evidence that *Uncinula necator* also does so on the vine (Arnaud, 1940).

While fungi which parasitize annual plants cannot overwinter in the ways described above, many achieve the same result by infecting the seeds of their hosts (M. Noble *et al.,* 1958). Infection of wheat and barley by *Ustilago nuda* occurs at anthesis, and the fungus passes into the scutellum and growing points of the embryo (Batts, 1955). Development of the grain is not impaired nor apparently its capacity to germinate. There are comparatively few fungi which enter the embryo in this way, but many invade the seed or fruit coat. They survive there either as resting mycelium, e.g., *Ustilago avenae* on oats (G. W. Fischer and Holton, 1957), or as fruiting bodies such as pycnidia, e.g., *Septoria apii-graveolentis* [*S. apiicola*] on celery (Taylor and Dillon Weston, 1948). Some fungi may also penetrate the cotyledons; *Ascochyta pisi* does so on *Vicia villosa* (Crosier, 1939) and *Colletotrichum lindemuthianum* on *Phaseolus* (Barrus, 1921).

B. *Survival and Growth outside the Host*

Many parasitic fungi form spores capable of surviving for long periods, often under conditions not tolerated by the fungus mycelium or its host. These spores are produced particularly though not exclusively by obligate parasites.

In the Uredinales and Ustilaginales, the teleutospores and chlamydospores commonly have this function. Those which do so often germinate only after a period of dormancy, frequently coinciding with the winter season. Much attention has been directed to ways of breaking this dormancy. With many species this has been achieved by chilling or by alternately wetting and drying the spores. In other instances, treating the spores with various chemicals has proved effective (Cochrane, 1960) (see also Chapter 23 of Volume II). Occasionally in the rust fungi other spore forms overwinter, particularly the modified uredospores with thickened walls (amphispores) formed by some species, e.g., *Puccinia vexans* (Carleton, 1904). The aecidiospores of a few species may also do so, e.g., *Cronartium ribicola* (Dosdall, 1918).

Many of the Peronosporales overwinter as oospores. These, too, often have a period of enforced dormancy; with *Peronospora destructor* this may extend over several years (McKay, 1957). During some of this time the spore may mature in the sense that cytological processes initiated during its formation are completed. The remainder of the period appears to be a physiological dormancy which, as in the rust and smut fungi, can often be broken by various treatments (Blackwell, 1943).

Whereas with these fungi specific spores serve to tide the fungi over adverse conditions, in many parasitic ascomycetes this function is carried out by the ascocarp itself. In the Erysiphales, the cleistocarps normally appear in late summer within the mycelial felt which covers the plant surface, but formation of ascospores within these cleistothecia may not occur until some time later. Typically the cleistothecia remain dormant throughout the winter months, and not until the following spring are the ascospores ejected. This mode of overwintering is particularly important in the life cycles of certain *Sphaerotheca* spp., e.g., *S. humuli* on hops, *S. mors-uvae* on gooseberry, and *S. pannosa* on rose (Butler and Jones, 1955). Certain members of the Sphaeriales such as *Guignardia bidwellii* on the grape vine, *Mycosphaerella sentina* and *Venturia pirina* on pears, *V. inaequalis* on apple and *Gnomonia veneta* on *Platanus* can overwinter in a similar manner. The perithecia are formed in the fallen leaves, or with *G. bidwellii* in the fallen fruit, the ascospores being liberated in the spring when the new foliage appears (Brooks, 1953).

The spores described have a special significance in the life cycles of the fungi concerned, apart from survival, because they are associated with various nuclear or sexual phenomena (cf. Chapter 23 in Volume II). In other fungi, resting spores are produced asexually. For example, the plasmodia of *Plasmodiophora brassicae* become divided into numerous spherical spores which are liberated into the soil when the host tissue decays. There they can remain viable for periods up to seven years. Similarly, thick-walled resting spores (or chlamydospores) may be formed from the hyphae of many *Fusarium* spp.

In contrast some fungi are able to survive for long periods as sclerotia (Garrett, 1956). These germinate in two ways: those of *Phymatotrichum omnivorum, Rhizoctonia* [*Corticium*] *solani, Sclerotium rolfsii* typically produce a new mycelium; those of various *Sclerotinia* spp. and *Claviceps purpurea* give rise to fruiting bodies in which asci are produced.

Not all fungi which survive apart from their living hosts do so by means of the special "resting" structures described. Some, particularly root-infecting fungi, remain as mycelia within plant residues. The factors influencing survival of such fungi have been investigated by Garrett and his associates, using *Ophiobolus graminis*. In general they concluded that survival of the fungus is determined largely by its ability to exploit the available food materials in the face of increasing activity by other micro-organisms, some of which may be antagonistic (Garrett, 1956). Initially parasites of this type have the advantage over saprophytic competitors because they are already in part of the root system. In addition, there may still be living cells within the root which saprophytes are unable to penetrate but the parasite can. In woody plants the period when excised roots contain living cells is likely to be very much longer than in herbaceous plants. In this respect, a parasite such as *Fomes annosus* has a much greater advantage in the colonization of pine stumps than *O. graminis* on wheat roots.

Under certain conditions, some leaf and stem parasites also survive in crop debris, e.g., *Alternaria longipes* on tobacco stalks (Wheeler, 1958). Other fungi such as species of *Pythium* and *Fusarium* remain as mycelia in the soil. Their existence there involves not simply survival but active saprophytic growth, and in this connection are discussed in Chapter 1. A fuller discussion of longevity and survival of fungi may be found in Chapter 17.

C. *Establishing Contact with the Host*

Fungi infecting seeds or perennating organs gain not only a means of survival, but also the advantage of maintaining contact with their hosts. Some fungi which form resting spores or sclerotia also remain in close association with their hosts by lodging on the outer surface of these organs. Wheat seeds, for example, become contaminated with spores of *Tilletia caries* at harvesting and the latter remain on the seed coat until the seed germinates, when infection occurs. The sclerotia of *Corticium solani* similarly adhere to potato tubers, and those of *Botrytis tulipae* to tulip bulbs. These fungi then infect the new shoots as they emerge.

Most other fungi, however, are separated from their hosts. The stem and leaf parasites rely mainly on particular mechanisms of spore release and dispersal to establish contact. These are discussed in Chapters 21 and 22 of volume II. With root parasites, contact is achieved in a variety of ways. Fungi which form rhizomorphs, such as *Armillaria mellea* and *Fomes lignosus,* are able to grow through the soil, using the decaying roots they have colonized as food bases. This gives them at least the opportunity of contacting fresh roots within the range of their rhizomorph extension. There is evidence, however, that the ability of rhizomorphs to infect decreases with distance from the food base so that the radius of rhizomorph spread is not necessarily the same as for infection (Garrett, 1956). In contrast, the hyphae of *Ophiobolus graminis* do not appear capable of growing much beyond the wheat roots so that, in this instance, the fungus depends almost entirely on the host root making contact with the decaying substrate it has colonized. This may apply also to those fungi existing in soil as mycelia, although these have the added advantage of a prolonged saprophytic life. While contact in a general way may be by chance certain evidence suggests that the host may influence the final stages. The formation of infection cushions by *Corticium solani,* for example, appears to be stimulated by substances diffusing from the root (Kerr and Flentje, 1957).

The germination of resting spores and sclerotia may also be stimulated by root excretions. When cabbage seedlings are planted in soil containing the spores of *Plasmodiophora brassicae* the roots become infected with the fungus in about 7 days; this suggests the plants influence spore germination in some way. Work by Hooker *et al.* (1945) indicated that mustard oils, which are present as glucosides in the roots of certain brassicas, stimulate spore germination if supplied at low concentrations. At higher concentrations, however, they have an inhibitory effect (MacFarlane, 1952).

Coley-Smith (1960) also found that the presence of the appropriate host plants (*Allium* spp.) stimulated germination of the sclerotia of *Sclerotium cepivorum.* This effect did not depend on contact between roots and sclerotia for it could be induced by root extracts. The nature of the chemical involved was not determined. In these experiments, little or no germination of sclerotia occurred in soil alone or in the presence of nonhost plants such as carrot, barley, and white clover.

In other instances there is not this host specificity. R. J. Noble (1924) found spore germination of *Urocystis tritici* [*U. agropyri*] stimulated by the roots of a number of plants which are not hosts for this fungus. MacFarlane (1952) obtained similar results in tests with *Plasmodiophora brassicae.* The root hairs of plants such as *Matthiola incana, Lolium perenne,* and *Dactylis glomerata* became invaded with zoosporangia, but there was no further colonization of the plant. The observations of Webb (1949) indicate that nonhosts are invaded by *P. brassicae* in this way under natural conditions. The disadvantage of this lack of specificity is that the population of resting spores is reduced with no corresponding increase in parasitic activity. None the less, any mechanism of this type, however imperfect, which increases the chances of contact between the fungus and its host is of obvious value.

V. HOST RANGES

In the preceding sections fungal parasites have been considered in relation to the individual plants which they parasitize. The relationships which exist between fungal parasites and plant populations are none the less interesting. These fungi can be considered in relation to a plant population of diverse species, in effect their host range, or in relation to a population of one species which concerns primarily the colonization of a crop by a fungal parasite. Since the latter has been discussed fully elsewhere (van der Plank, 1960), it will not be dealt with here.

A. *Parasites with One or Many Hosts*

Some fungi are able to parasitize a wide range of plants. *Phymatotrichum omnivorum,* for example, can attack at least 1300 plant species (Taubenhaus and Ezekiel, 1936). Others, though relatively few, are restricted to a single host, e.g., *Puccinia buxi* on *Buxus sempervirens* (Grove, 1913). Between these two extremes varying degrees of host specialization may be found. There are some fungi which attack only closely related plant species. *Urophylictis* [*Physoderma*] *alfalfae* is one; only *Medicago sativa* and *M. falcata* are hosts for this fungus (Butler and Jones, 1955). Similarly, *Septoria apiicola* occurs only on celery (*Apium dulce*) and celeriac (*Apium rapaceum*). Other fungi have a somewhat wider host range but remain confined to a single genus. *Puccinia violae* parasitizes only plants of the genus *Viola:* in Britain these are *V. canina, V. hirta, V. odorata, V. reichenbachiana, V. riviniana,* and *V. tricolor* (Wilson and Bisby, 1954). Yet others are confined to particular families of plants: *Puccinia malvacearum* infects only species within the Malvaceae (Grove, 1913) and under natural conditions *Phytophthora infestans* is similarly restricted to the Solanaceae (Hickman, 1958). In addition there are genera of fungi which are confined to certain host families, for example the rust genus *Phragmidium* to members of the Rosaceae (Cummins, 1959) and the smut genus *Farysia* to members of the Cyperaceae (G. W. Fischer and Holton, 1957).

These are the limitations which occur in nature. Under experimental conditions the host range of a particular fungus can apparently be widened. *Colletotrichum circinans* under natural conditions is found only on onion (*Allium cepa*), shallot (*A. ascalonium*), and leek (*A. porrum*). B. Johnson (1932) induced a limited parasitism by this fungus in a wide range of plants by inoculating these with spores suspended in prune juice and keeping them under conditions of high humidity.

Host ranges cannot always be stated in simple terms such as fungus *A* infects hosts *X, Y, Z*. Among fungi capable of infecting a wide range of plants there are many which have developed distinct forms or races, morphologically similar to each other but restricted in their host range. *Erysiphe graminis,* for example, considered as one morphological species, infects about 100 different plant species in 34 genera of the Gramineae (Blumer, 1933; Hardison, 1944). Marchal (1902) showed, however, that conidia of this fungus occurring on wheat would infect other species of *Triticum* but not barley. Similarly, conidia of *E. graminis* from barley would infect other *Hordeum* species but not wheat. Minor differences in the morphology of these forms do exist, but it is generally accepted that they are best separated on their ability to attack specific host plants. Further research has shown that it is possible to subdivide these forms into physiologic races. In this connection it is important to note that differential varieties of the host plant are used and frequently the degree of infection is recorded: it is not simply a question of infection or no infection of a particular plant species by a fungus.

Host specialization of this type is now known to occur in a wide range of parasitic fungi. The earliest report for a nonobligate parasite is that of Barrus (1918). He distinguished two races of *Colletotricum lindemuthianum* which he designated α and β. A third, or γ, race was subsequently discovered by Burkholder (1923). Other workers have distinguished a greater number of these races. Schreiber (1932), by testing 53 isolates of the fungus on 57 bean varieties differentiated 34 races, but these could be divided into three groups corresponding to the α, β, and γ races of Barrus and Burkholder.

Work of this type indicates that to determine host range, the fungal species must first be defined. Some of the criteria used for this purpose are discussed in Chapter 20. A consideration of the mechanisms which limit fungi to particular hosts is beyond the scope of this chapter. Particular aspects of this subject are reviewed by P. J. Allen (1959), Müller (1959), Buxton (1960), T. Johnson (1960), and in Chapter 15 of this volume.

B. *Heteroecism*

Although some fungi can infect a number of different plant species, it is not necessary that they should do so to complete their life cycles. They simply have a number of alternative hosts on which their development is similar. There are a limited number of fungi, however, which require two (alternate) hosts: such fungi are said to be heteroecious.

It is among rust fungi that most examples are to be found. In many there is a regular sequence related to the haploid and diploid phases of the life cycle, the pycnidial and aecidial stages occurring on one host and the uredo- and teleuto-spore stage on the other. Thus *Puccinia graminis* alternates between species of *Berberis* or *Mahonia* (O, I), and cereals (II, III); *Cronartium ribicola* between species of five-needle pine such as *Pinus strobus* (O, I) and *Ribes* (II, III).

Outside the rust fungi, heteroecism appears to be limited to three species. Two of them are species of *Sclerotinia*. *S. rhododendri* alternates between the leaves of *Vaccinium myrtillus* and the fruits of *Rhododendron ferrugineum* and *R. hirsutum* (E. Fischer, 1925); *S. heteroica* between the leaves of *Vaccinium uliginosum* and the fruits of *Ledum palustre* (Woronin and Nawaschin, 1896). The life cycle is similar for both species. Conidia are produced on the *Vaccinium* spp., and these infect the ovaries of the *Rhododendron* and *Ledum* spp. Mummified fruits (or sclerotia) result which fall to the ground and overwinter. In Spring these give rise to apothecia, and ascospores produced within these apothecia, complete the life cycle by infecting the young leaves of *Vaccinium*.

A type of heteroecism is reported by Stäger (1905) for the form of *Claviceps purpurea* occurring on *Brachypodium sylvaticum*. The sclerotia formed on this host overwinter and germinate in spring. The ascospores produced infect the flowers of *Milium effusum,* and on this host the conidia of the *Sphacelia* stage are formed but no sclerotia. Later in the year, the flowers of *B. sylvaticum* emerge, these become infected by conidia from *M. effusum,* and the life cycle is completed.

Heteroecism is thus a particular form of host specialization. Its origin, especially among the rust fungi, has been the subject of much speculation, and the general theories proposed are ably summarized by Arthur (1929). In the heteroecious rusts, there may be a further host specialization, of the type described for *E. graminis* and *C. lindemuthianum,* within the sporophytic generation. Thus several hundred physiologic races of *Puccinia graminis* have been recorded on wheat.

VI. DISCUSSION

Fungi which parasitize plants would appear to gain two main advantages by doing so: they avoid competition for food from less specialized, saprophytic fungi, and to a certain extent they are protected from those changes in environmental conditions which are adverse to their mycelial growth. Success in parasitism may be judged by the extent to which these advantages are enjoyed. A fungus such as *Pythium ultimum,* which causes a necrosis of seedling roots leading to rapid death of the young plants, is obviously a less successful parasite than *Tilletia caries* which enters its host at a similar stage and lives within the plant until flowering.

In this instance successful parasitism is equated with specialization of parasitism. There are in fact a number of individual characters by which parasites may be judged primitive or specialized. The most important of these are listed in Table II. Not all characters are of equal significance,

TABLE II

CHARACTERS ASSOCIATED WITH PRIMITIVE AND SPECIALIZED FUNGAL PARASITES

Character	Primitive	Specialized
Entry into the plant	Through wounds	Through stomata, and by direct penetration of intact surfaces
Growth in the plant		
Type of tissue invaded	Confined to immature or senescent tissues	Not so confined
Mycelium	Inter- and intracellular	Intracellular, intercellular, or intercellular with haustoria
Effect on host cells	Necrosis	No necrosis
Existence outside the plant	Saprobic	"Resting" stage only
Host range	Wide	Limited

and some are only so in conjunction with others. Thus the position of the mycelium in relation to the host cells is less important than the effect on these cells. When the mycelium is both inter- and intracellular because the fungus kills the host cells, as does *Botrytis cinerea,* the condition may justifiably be considered primitive. Where this condition is achieved without necrosis, as in the growth of *Tilletia caries,* in the young wheat seedling it has no such implication. Similarly, a fungus which does not live saprobically, either independently or on the plant remains, is not likely to enter its host through wounds since this involves some saprobic ability.

Omitting those factors which are related in this way, the characteristics of a primitive parasite are that (1) it is limited to immature or senescent tissues, (2) it causes necrosis of the host cells, (3) it is capable of saprobic growth under natural conditions, and (4) it has a wide host range. Any departure from these features can be regarded as a measure of specialization, a fungus with none of these features being most specialized. Table III illustrates the range which exists. Clearly there is no direct relationship here between parasitic ability and pathogenicity. Indeed, as McNew (1960) points out, specialization for one attribute may often be made at the expense of the other. A plant infected by *Botrytis cinerea,* for example, soon appears diseased and the fungus may be judged an effective pathogen although as a parasite it is relatively unspecialized.

TABLE III
SPECIALIZATION OF PARASITISM AMONG FUNGI

Number of primitive characters (see text)	Examples	
4	Many soil-inhabiting species of *Pythium* and *Fusarium*	Primitive parasites
3	*Ophiobolus graminis*, *Corticium solani*	↓
2	*Venturia inaequalis*, *Diplocarpon rosae*	
1	*Phytophthora infestans*, *Taphrina deformans*	
0	Most rusts, smuts, powdery and downy mildews, *Plasmodiophora brassicae*	Specialized parasites

It is also apparent that there is little relationship between specialization and the taxonomic position of the parasite. It must be assumed that parasitism has arisen independently, and probably at different times, within several groups of fungi. The general consensus of opinion is that obligate parasites have evolved from nonobligate forms (Yarwood, 1956), but with the possible exception of the Peronosporales there are few groups where intermediate types are found which lend weight to this opinion. Indeed, while much is known about the parasitism of plants by fungi, its origins remain a matter of speculation.

REFERENCES

Akai, S. (1959). Histology of defense in plants. *Plant Pathol.* **1**: 391–434.

Allen, J. D. (1957). The development of potato skin-spot disease. *Ann. Appl. Biol.* **45**: 293–298.

Allen, P. J. (1959). Physiology and biochemistry of defense. *Plant Pathol.* **1**: 435–467.

Anonymous. (1950). Definitions of some terms used in plant pathology. *Brit. Mycol. Soc. Trans.* **33**: 154–160.

Arens, K. (1929). Physiologishe Untersuchungen an *Plasmopora viticola,* unter besonderer Berücksichtigung der Infektionsbedingungen. *Jahrb. Wiss. Botan.* **70**: 93–157.

Arnaud, G. (1940). Développement des maladies de la vigne dans la région parisienne. *Ann. Epiphyties* **6**: 37–66.

Arthur, J. C. (1929). "The Plant Rusts," 446 pp. Wiley, New York.

Baker, K. F., and F. D. Heald. (1932). The importance of lenticel infection of apples by *Penicillium expansum. Wash. State Univ., Agr. Expt. Sta., Bull.* **264**: 1–15.

Baker, R. E. D., and P. Holliday. (1957). Witches' Broom disease of cacao (*Marasmius perniciosus* Stahel). *Phytopathol. Paper* **2**: 1–42.

Bald, J. G. (1952). Stomatal droplets and the penetration of leaves by plant pathogens. *Am. J. Botany* **39**: 97–99.

Balls, W. L. (1905). Infection of plants by rust fungi. *New Phytologist* **4**: 18–19.
Banfield, W. M. (1941). Distribution by the sap stream of spores of three fungi that induce vascular wilt diseases of elm. *J. Agr. Res.* **62**: 637–681.
Barrus, M. F. (1918). Varietal susceptibility of beans to strains of *Colletotrichum lindemuthianum* (Sacc. & Magn.) B. & C. *Phytopathology* **8**: 589–614.
Barrus, M. F. (1921). Bean anthracnose. *Cornell Univ., Agr. Expt. Sta. Mem.* **42**: 101–215.
Bates, G. R. (1933). Oil glands of citrus fruits as an avenue of infection. *Nature* **132**: 751.
Bates, G. R. (1936). Studies on the infection of citrus fruits. I. Some methods of infection of citrus by the green mould, *Penicillium digitatum. Brit. S. Africa Co., Publ., Mazoe Citrus Exptl. Sta.* **4b**: 87–101.
Batts, C. C. V. (1955). Observations on the infection of wheat by loose smut (*Ustilago tritici* (Pers.) Rostr.). *Brit. Mycol. Soc. Trans.* **38**: 465–475.
Batts, C. C. V., and A. Jeater. (1958). The development of loose smut (*Ustilago tritici*) in susceptible varieties of wheat, and some observations on field infection. *Brit. Mycol. Soc. Trans.* **41**: 115–125.
Baxter, L. W., and A. G. Plakidas. (1944). Dieback and canker of camellias caused by *Glomerella cingulata. Phytopathology* **44**: 129–133.
Bedi, S. K. S., M. R. Sikka, and B. B. Mundkur. (1949). Transmission of wheat bunt due to *Neovissia indica* (Mitra) Mundkur. *Indian Phytopathol.* **2**: 20–26.
Blackwell, E. (1943). On germinating the oöspores of *Phytophthora cactorum. Brit. Mycol. Soc. Trans.* **26**: 93–103.
Blank, L. M. (1940). The susceptibility of cotton seedlings to *Phymatotrichum omnivorum. Phytopathology* **30**: 1033–1041.
Blumer, S. (1933). Die Erysiphaceen Mitteleuropas mit besonderer Berücksichtigung der Schweiz. *Beitr. Kryptogamenflora Schweiz* **7**: 1–483.
Bond, T. E. T. (1938). Infection experiments with *Cladosporium fulvum* Cooke and related species. *Ann. Appl. Biol.* **25**: 277–307.
Brooks, F. T. (1953). "Plant Diseases," 457 pp. Oxford Univ. Press, London and New York.
Brooks, F. T., and W. C. Moore. (1923). The invasion of woody tissue by wound parasites. *Proc. Cambridge Phil. Soc.* **1**: 56–58.
Brown, W. (1922). Studies in the physiology of parasitism. VIII. On the exosmosis of nutrient substances from host tissue into the infection drop. *Ann. Botany (London)* **36**: 101–119.
Brown, W. (1936). The physiology of host parasite relations. *Botan. Rev.* **2**: 236–281.
Brown, W. (1955). On the physiology of parasitism in plants. *Ann. Appl. Biol.* **43**: 325–341.
Brown, W., and C. C. Harvey. (1927). Studies in the physiology of parasitism. X. On the entrance of parasitic fungi into the host plant. *Ann. Botany (London)* **41**: 643–662.
Burkholder, W. H. (1923). The gamma strain of *Colletotrichum lindenmuthianum* (Sacc. and Magn.) B. and C. *Phytopathology* **13**: 316–323.
Butler, E. J., and S. G. Jones. (1955). "Plant Pathology," 979 pp. Macmillan, New York.
Buxton, E. W. (1960). Heterokaryosis, saltation, and adaptation. *Plant Pathol.* **2**: 359–405.
Caldwell, R. M., and G. M. Stone. (1932). Appressorium formation and penetra-

tion by leaf rust of wheat, *Puccinia triticina,* in relation to stomatal aperture. *Phytopathology* **22:** 5–6.

Carleton, M. A. (1904). Investigation of rusts. *Bull. Bur. Plant. Ind. U.S. Dept. Agr.* **63:** 32.

Chadhuri, H. (1935). Infection by *Colletotrichum gloeosporiodes,* Penz. *Proc. Natl. Inst. Sci. India* **1:** 71–75.

Chowdhury, S. (1946). Mode of transmission of the bunt of rice. *Current Sci. (India)* **15:** 111.

Clements, H. F. (1935). Morphology and physiology of the pome lenticels of *Pyrus malus. Botan. Gaz.* **97:** 101–117.

Cochrane, V. W. (1960). Spore germination. *Plant Pathol.* **2:** 167–202.

Coley-Smith, J. R. (1960). Studies of the biology of *Sclerotium cepivorum* Berk. IV. Germination of sclerotia. *Ann. Appl. Biol.* **48:** 8–18.

Colhoun, J. (1958). Club root disease of crucifers caused by *Plasmodiophora brassicae* Woron. *Phytopathol. Paper* **3:** 1–108.

Cormack, M. W. (1937). *Cylindrocarpon ehrenbergi* Wr. and other species, as root parasites of alfalfa and sweet clover in Alberta. *Can. J. Res.* **C15:** 403–424.

Corner, E. J. H. (1935). Observations on resistance to powdery mildews. *New Phytologist* **34:** 180–200.

Crosier, W. (1939). Occurrence and longevity of *Ascochyta pisi* in seeds of hairy vetch. *J. Agr. Res.* **59:** 683–697.

Crowdy, S. H. (1949). Observations on apple canker III. The anatomy of the stem canker. *Ann. Appl. Biol.* **36:** 483–495.

Crowdy, S. H. (1952). Observations on apple canker. IV. The infection of leaf scars. *Ann. Appl. Biol.* **39:** 569–580.

Cummins, G. B. (1959). "Ilustrated Genera of Rust Fungi," 131 pp. Burgess, Minneapolis, Minnesota.

Cunningham, H. S., and O. A. Reinking. (1946). Fusarium seed piece decay of potato on Long Island and its control. *N.Y. State Agr. Expt. Sta. (Geneva, N.Y.) Bull.* **721:** 1–32.

Curtis, K. M. (1928). The morphological aspect of resistance to brown rot in stone fruit. *Ann. Botany (London)* **42:** 39–68.

Davis, R. J. (1925). Studies on *Ophiobolus graminis* Sacc. and the take-all disease of wheat. *J. Agr. Res.* **31:** 801–825.

Dickinson, S. (1949a). Studies in the physiology of obligate parasitism. I. The stimuli determining the direction of growth of the germ-tubes of rust and mildew spores. *Ann. Botany (London)* [n.s.] **13:** 89–104.

Dickinson, S. (1949b). Studies in the physiology of obligate parasitism. II. The behaviour of the germ tubes of certain rusts in contact with various membranes. *Ann. Botany (London)* [n.s.] **13:** 219–236.

Dickinson, S. (1960). The mechanical ability to breach the host barriers. *Plant Pathol.* **2:** 203–232.

Dodge, B. O. (1923). Systemic infections of *Rubus* with the orange rusts. *J. Agr. Res.* **25:** 209–242.

Dosdall, L. (1918). Overwintering of the aeciospores of *Cronartium ribicola* Fischer. *Phytopathology* **8:** 619.

Fellows, H. (1928). Some chemical and morphological phenomena attending infection of the wheat plant by *Ophiobolus graminis. J. Agr. Res.* **37:** 647–661.

Fischer, E. (1925). Mykologische Beiträge. 31. Der Wirtswechsel der *Sclerotinia rhododendri* nebst Bemerkungen zur Frage der Entstchung der Heteroecie. *Mitt. Naturforsch. Ges. Bern* **4:** 1–14.

Fischer, G. W., and C. S. Holton. (1957). "Biology and Control of the Smut Fungi," 622 pp. Ronald Press, New York.

Foister, C. E., A. R. Wilson, and A. E. W. Boyd. (1952). Dry-rot disease of the potato I. Effect of commercial handling methods on the incidence of the disease. *Ann. Appl. Biol.* **39:** 29–37.

Foster, H. H. (1937). Studies of the pathogenicity of *Physalospora obtusa. Phytopathology* **27:** 803–823.

Fraymouth, J. (1956). Haustoria of the Peronosporales. *Brit. Mycol. Soc. Trans.* **39:** 79–107.

Garrett, S. D. (1956). "Biology of Root-infecting Fungi," 293 pp. Cambridge Univ. Press, London and New York.

Gäumann, E. A. (1950). *In* "Principles of Plant Infection" (W. B. Brierley, ed.), p. 367. Crosby Lockwood, London.

Gibson, C. M. (1904). Notes on infection experiments with various Uredinae. *New Phytologist* **3:** 184–191.

Gibson, I. A. S. (1953). Crown rot, a seedling disease of groundnuts caused by *Aspergillus niger. Brit. Mycol. Soc. Trans.* **36:** 198–209.

Green, F. M. (1932). The infection of oranges by *Penicillium. J. Pomol. Hort. Sci.* **10:** 184–215.

Grove, W. B. (1913). "The British Rust Fungi," 412 pp. Cambridge Univ. Press, London and New York.

Hansford, C. G. (1946). The follicolous Ascomycetes, their parasites and associated fungi. *Mycol. Papers* **15:** 1–240.

Hardison, J. R. (1944). Specialization of pathogenicity in *Erysiphe graminis* on wild and cultivated grasses. *Phytopathology* **34:** 1–20.

Hart, H. (1929). Relation of stomatal behaviour to stem rust resistance in wheat. *J. Agr. Res.* **39:** 929–948.

Hawker, L. E. (1950). "Physiology of Fungi," 360 pp. Univ. of London Press, London.

Hawkins, L. A. (1915). Some effects of the brown-rot fungus upon the composition of the peach. *Am. J. Botany* **2:** 71–81.

Hawkins, L. A. and R. B. Harvey. (1919). Physiological study of the parasitism of *Pytrium debaryanum* on the potato tuber. *J. Agr. Res.* **18:** 275–297.

Hickman, C. J. (1958). *Phytophthora*—plant destroyer. *Brit. Mycol. Soc. Trans.* **41:** 1–13.

Hirt, R. R. (1938). Relation of stomata to infection of *Pinus strobus* by *Cronartium ribicola. Phytopathology* **28:** 180–190.

Hooker, W. J., J. C. Walker, and K. P. Link. (1945). Effects of two mustard oils on *Plasmodiophora brassicae* and their relation to resistance to clubroot. *J. Agr. Res.* **70:** 63–78.

Hurd-Karrer, A. M., and H. A. Rodenhiser. (1947). Structures corresponding to appressoria and substomatal vesicles produced on nutrient-solution agar by cereal rusts. *Am. J. Botany* **34:** 377–384.

Husain, A., and A. Kelman. (1959). Tissue is disintegrated. *Plant Pathol.* **1:** 132–188.

Isaac, I. (1957). Wilt of lucerne caused by species of *Verticillium. Ann. Appl. Biol.* **45:** 550–558.

Johnson, B. (1932). Specificity to penetration of the epidermis of a plant by the hyphae of a pathogenic fungus. *Am. J. Botany* **19**: 12–31.

Johnson, T. (1960). Genetics of pathogenicity. *Plant Pathol.* **2**: 407–459.

Kerr, A., and N. T. Flentje. (1957). Host infection in *Pellicularia filamentosa* controlled by chemical stimuli. *Nature* **179**: 204–205.

Keyworth, W. G. (1951). A petri-dish moist chamber. *Brit. Mycol. Soc. Trans.* **34**: 291–292.

Kidd, M. N., and A. Beaumont. (1925). An experimental study of the fungal invasion of apples in storage, with particular reference to invasion through the lenticel. *Ann. Appl. Biol.* **12**: 14–33.

Leach, R. (1937). Observations on the parasitism and control of *Armillaria mellea. Proc. Roy. Soc.* **B121**: 561–573.

Lilly, V. G., and H. L. Barnett. (1951). "Physiology of the Fungi," 464 pp. McGraw-Hill, New York.

Ludwig, R. A. (1960). Toxins. *Plant Pathol.* **2**: 315–357.

MacFarlane, I. (1952). Factors affecting the survival of *Plasmodiophora brassicae* Wor. in the soil and its assessment by a host test. *Ann. Appl. Biol.* **39**: 239–256.

McKay, R. (1957). The longevity of the oöspores of the onion downy mildew, *Peronospora destructor* (Berk.) Casp. *Sci. Proc. Roy. Dublin Soc.* [n.s.] **27**: 295–307.

McNew, G. L. (1960). The nature, origin, and evolution of parasitism. *Plant Pathol.* **2**: 19–69.

Malik, M. M. S., and C. C. V. Batts. (1960). The development of loose smut (*Ustilago nuda*) in the barley plant, with observations on spore formation in nature and culture. *Brit. Mycol. Soc. Trans.* **43**: 126–131.

Marchal, E. (1902). De la spécialisation du parasitisme chez *l'Erysiphe graminis. Compt. Rend.* **136**: 210–212.

Marsh, R. W. (1939). Observations on apple canker. II. Experiments on the incidence and control of shoot infections. *Ann. Appl. Biol.* **26**: 458–469.

Melander, L. W., and J. H. Craigie. (1927). The nature of resistance of *Berberis* spp. to *Puccinia graminis. Phytopathology* **17**: 45–114.

Melhus, I. E. (1915). Perennial mycelium in species of Peronosporaceae related to *Phytophthora infestans. J. Agr. Res.* **5**: 59–69.

Müller, K. O. (1959). Hypersensitivity. *Plant Pathol.* **1**: 469–519.

Mundkur, B. B. (1943). Karnal bunt, an air-borne disease. *Current Sci. (India)* **12**: 230–231.

Noble, M., J. de Tempe, and P. Neergaard. (1958). "An Annotated List of Seed-borne Diseases," 159 pp. Commonwealth Mycol. Inst., Kew.

Noble, R. J. (1924). Studies on the parasitism of *Urocystis tritici,* the organism causing flag smut of wheat. *J. Agr. Res.* **27**: 451–489.

Nusbaum, C. J., and G. W. Keitt. (1938). A cytological study of host-parasite relations of *Venturia inaequalis* on apple leaves. *J. Agr. Res.* **56**: 595–618.

Paddock, W. C. (1953). Histological study of suscept-pathogen relationships between *Helminthosporium victoriae* and seedling oat leaves. *Cornell Univ., Agr. Expt. Sta. Mem.* **315**: 1–63.

Palla, E. (1899). Über die gattung *Phyllactinia. Ber. Deut. Botan. Ges.* **17**: 64–72.

Peace, T. R. (1962). "Pathology of Trees and Shrubs," 753 pp. Oxford Univ. Press (Clarendon), London and New York.

Pole-Evans, I. B. (1907). The cereal rusts. I. Development of their uredo mycelia. *Ann. Botany (London)* **21**: 441–466.
Pool, V. W., and M. B. McKay. (1916). Relation of stomatal movement to infection by *Cercospora beticola. J. Agr. Res.* **22**: 1011–1038.
Pristou, R., and M. E. Gallegly. (1954). Leaf penetration by *Phytophthora infestans. Phytopathology* **44**: 81–86.
Reed, H. S., and C. H. Crabhill. (1915). The cedar rust disease of apples caused by *Gymnosporangium juniperi-virginianae* Schw. *Virginia Agr. Expt. Sta., Tech. Bull.* **9**: 1–106.
Rice, M. A. (1927). The haustoria of certain rusts and the relation between host and pathogenes. *Bull. Torrey Botan. Club.* **54**: 63–153.
Rosenbaum, J., and C. E. Sando. (1920). Correlation between the resistance of the skin to puncture, and its relation to infection with *Macrosporium* on tomato. *Am. J. Botany* **7**: 78–82.
Salmon, E. S. (1905). On the stages of development reached by certain biologic forms of *Erysiphe* in cases of noninfection. *New Phytologist* **4**: 217–222.
Salmon, E. S. (1906). On *Oidiopsis taurica,* an endophytic member of the Erysiphaceae. *Ann. Botany (London)* **20**: 187–200.
Sampson, K. (1933). The systemic infection of grasses by *Epichloë typhina* (Pers.) Tul. *Brit. Mycol. Soc. Trans.* **28**: 30–47.
Samuel, G. (1927). On the shot-hole disease caused by *Clasterosporium carpophilum* and on the 'shot-hole' effect. *Ann. Botany (London)* **41**: 375–404.
Scheffer, R. P., and J. C. Walker. (1953). The physiology of Fusarium wilt of tomato. *Phytopathology* **43**: 116–125.
Schreiber, F. (1932). Resistenzzüchtung bei *Phaseolus vulgaris. Phytopathol. Z.* **4**: 415–454.
Schultz, E. S. (1952). Powdery scab, a precursor for the late blight infection of blight-immune potato tubers. *Phytopathology* **42**: 343.
Shaw, M., and D. J. Samborski. (1956). The physiology of host-parasite relations. I. The accumulation of radioactive substances at infections of facultative and obligate parasites including tobacco mosaic virus. *Can. J. Botany* **34**: 389–405.
Shaw, M., S. A. Brown, and D. Rudd Jones. (1954). Uptake of radioactive carbon and phosphorus by parasitized leaves. *Nature* **173**: 768–769.
Smith, G. (1900). The haustoria of the Erysipheae. *Botan. Gaz.* **29**: 153–184.
Smith, N. J. G. (1929). Observations of the *Helminthosporium* diseases of cereals in Britain. I. The behavior of *Helminthosporium gramineum* in a common barley disease. *Ann. Appl. Biol.* **16**: 236–260.
Spaulding, P. (1922). Investigations of the white-pine blister rust. *U.S. Dept. Agr., Bull.* **957**: 1–100.
Stäger, R. (1905). Weitere Beiträge zur Biologie des Mutterkorns. *Centr. Bakteriol., Parasitenk., Abt II* **14**: 25–32.
Stakman, E. C., and J. G. Harrar. (1957). "Principles of Plant Pathology," 581 pp. Ronald Press, New York.
Swarbrick, T. (1927). The healing of wounds in woody stems. *J. Pomol. Hort. Sci.* **5**: 98–114.
Swinburne, T. R. (1963). Infection of wheat by *Tilletia caries* (DC.) Tul., the causal organism of bunt. *Brit. Mycol. Soc. Trans.* **46**: 145–156.
Taubenhaus, J. J., and W. N. Ezekiel. (1936). A rating of plants with reference to their relative resistance or susceptibility to Phymatotrichum root rot. *Texas Agr. Expt. Sta., Bull.* **527**: 1–52.

Taylor, R. E., and W. A. R. Dillon Weston. (1948). Celery "blight." The need for clean celery. *Agriculture (London)* **55**: 201–203.

Thomas, H. E. (1934). Studies on *Armillaria mellea* (Vahl) Quèl., infection, parasitism and host resistance. *J. Agr. Res.* **48**: 187–218.

Tischler, G. (1911). Untersuchungen über die Beeinflussung der *Euphorbia cyparissias* durch *Uromyces pisi. Flora (Jena)* **104**: 1–64.

van Burgh, P. (1950). Some factors affecting appressorium formation and penetrability of *Colletotrichum phomoides. Phytopathology* **40**: 29.

van der Plank, J. E. (1960). Analysis of epidemics. *Plant Pathol.* **3**: 229–289.

von Ramm, C. (1962). Histological studies of infection by *Alternaria longipes* on Tobacco. *Phytopathol. Z.* **45**: 391–398.

Wagener, W. W., and R. W. Davidson. (1954). Heart rots in living trees. *Botan. Rev.* **20**: 61–134.

Ware, W. M. (1926). *Pseudoperonospora humuli* and its mycelial invasion of the host plant. *Brit. Mycol. Soc. Trans.* **11**: 91–107.

Waterhouse, W. L. (1921). Studies in the physiology of parasitism. VII. Infection of *Berberis vulgaris* by sporidia of *Puccinia graminis. Ann. Botany (London)* **35**: 557–564.

Webb, P. C. R. (1949). Zoosporangia, believed to be those of *Plasmodiophora brassicae* in the root hairs of noncruciferous plants. *Nature* **163**: 608.

Wheeler, B. E. J. (1958). Investigations on Alternaria leaf-spot of flue-cured tobacco in Nyasaland. *Commonwealth Mycol. Inst. Misc. Publ.* **15**: 1–32.

Wilson, M., and G. R. Bisby. (1954). List of British Uredinales. *Brit. Mycol. Soc. Trans.* **37**: 61–86.

Wiltshire, S. P. (1915). Infection and immunity studies on the apple and pear scab fungi (*Venturia inaequalis* and *V. pirina*). *Ann. Appl. Biol.* **1**: 335–350.

Wiltshire, S. P. (1921). Studies on the apple canker fungus. I. Leaf scar infections. *Ann. Appl. Biol.* **8**: 182–192.

Wiltshire, S. P. (1922). Studies on the apple canker fungus. II. Canker infection of apple trees through scab wounds. *Ann. Appl. Biol.* **9**: 275–281.

Wolf, F. A. (1913). Black spot of roses. *Alabama Agr. Expt. Sta., Bull.* **172**: 113–118.

Wood, R. K. S. (1960). Chemical ability to breach the host barriers. *Plant Pathol.* **2**: 233–272.

Woodward, R. C. (1927). Studies on *Podosphaera leucotricha.* I. The mode of perennation. *Brit. Mycol. Soc. Trans.* **7**: 173–204.

Woodward, R. C., J. S. L. Waldie, and H. N. Steven. (1929). Oak mildew and its control in forest nurseries. *Forestry* **3**: 38–56.

Wormald, H. (1954). The brown rot diseases of fruit trees. *Ministry Agr. (Engl.), Tech. Bull.* **3**: 1–113.

Woronin, M., and S. Nawaschin. (1896). *Sclerotinia heteroica Z. Pflanzenkrankh. Pflanzenschutz* **6**: 129–140.

Yarwood, C. E. (1941). Sporulation injury associated with downy mildew infections. *Phytopathology* **31**: 741–748.

Yarwood, C. E. (1956). Obligate parasitism. *Ann. Rev. Plant Physiol.* **7**: 115–142.

Yarwood, C. E., and J. F. L. Childs. (1938). Some effects of rust infection on the dry weight of host tissues. *Phytopathology* **28**: 723–733.

Yarwood, C. E., and L. Jacobsen. (1950). Selective absorption of sulphur-35 by fungus infected leaves. *Nature* **165**: 973–974.

Young, P. A. (1926). Penetration phenomena and facultative parasitism in *Alternaria, Diplodia* and other fungi. *Botan. Gaz.* **81**: 258–279.

CHAPTER 8

Fungal Parasites of Vertebrates

G. C. AINSWORTH

Commonwealth Mycological Institute
Kew, Surrey, England

I. INTRODUCTION

There are still several widespread misconceptions regarding fungi which parasitize man and higher animals. It is generally held that few fungi parasitize vertebrates and that such fungi, the so-called "medical fungi," are a special group of which the taxonomy is difficult and the nomenclature confused.

Before commenting on these beliefs it is first necessary to recall that in everyday use at least a distinction can be made between a parasite and a pathogen, a parasite which induces disease in its host. Maybe all parasites are to some extent pathogenic, but most of the fungi parasitic on man have been recognized and named because of their marked pathogenicity, because they have proved to be the agents of more or less serious disease. It is also necessary to recall that in addition to parasitizing vertebrates fungi can affect man and higher animals in two other ways. When ingested they can act as poisons, and on coming in contact with a suitably sensitized individual they are able to induce an allergic response. In this chapter attention will be concentrated on a number of the fungi commonly found as human and animal pathogens.

But to return to the misconceptions. An examination of the index to Volume 4 of the *Review of Medical and Veterinary Mycology,* which covers the years 1961–1963, shows 205 species of fungi to have been recorded as pathogenic for man and 89 animals (all but one, a shrimp, are vertebrates); in other words there was an average of 2.3 species of fungi per host. The comparable figures for plant pathogenic fungi derived from an annual index to the *Review of Applied Mycology* (in which the literature on plant diseases is surveyed) was 1288 fungi from 659 hosts, an incidence of approximately 2 species per host (Ainsworth, 1961, 1966). These statistics suggest that as diverse a range of fungi attack animals as plants. They do not, of course, affect the generalization that fungal diseases of plants are of greater economic and social importance than fungal diseases of man and animals. No parallel is found among mycotic diseases of man to black stem rust of wheat and potato blight, which are the equivalents of such major human diseases as tuberculosis and malaria.

As regards confusion in taxonomy and nomenclature, evidence will be presented in this review to show that most of the fungi pathogenic for vertebrates are merely members of diverse groups of saprobic fungi which are able, given the opportunity, to play a pathogenic role; although their taxonomy was confused, the deployment of mycologists in the medical and veterinary fields has, during the past twenty-five years, quite changed the situation. The taxonomy of fungi pathogenic for man and animals is in as good order as that for most fungi, which is still far from final. The nomenclature in the best writing in this field is also now satisfactory, but a number of workers, particularly medical men who study fungi, pay scant attention to the International Code of Botanical Nomenclature, which regulates fungal names. Medical mycologists, like their nonmedical mycological colleagues, also do not always show an adequate knowledge of the provisions of the Code and, unlike phanerogamists, do not fully appreciate the great advantages that accrue from strict adherence to a Code.

II. TAXONOMIC DISTRIBUTION

In Table I a sample of fungi pathogenic for vertebrates is analyzed by classes and compared with a rather larger sample of plant pathogenic fungi. For both types, most pathogens are deuteromycetes (imperfect

TABLE I

TAXONOMIC DISTRIBUTION OF FUNGI PATHOGENIC FOR VERTEBRATES COMPARED WITH THAT OF PLANT PATHOGENIC FUNGI

	Vertebrates[a]		Plants[b]
Fungi	Pathogenic	Poisonous	Pathogenic
Phycomycetes	26 (12.7%)	0	91 (7.1%)
Ascomycetes	28 (13.6%)	4	289 (23.3%)
Basidiomycetes	0 (0.0%)	23	274 (21.3%)
Deuteromycetes	151 (73.7%)	13	634 (49.3%)
	205	30	1288

[a] For 1961–1963; data from Ainsworth (1966).
[b] For 1958; data from Ainsworth (1961).

fungi), and ascomycetes take second place. One striking contrast is the large number of basidiomycetes recorded as plant pathogens as against none in the animal sample. The plant pathogenic basidiomycetes include the many, and economically important, rusts (Uredinales) which are obligate parasites of plants and also many wood-destroying fungi, and, at least for man, it is the larger basidiomycetes which are the typical poisonous fungi. There was, however, a claim by Kligman (1950) that *Schizophyllum commune* (a widely distributed agaric) isolated from a human finger nail was pathogenic, and there are a number of records of other basidiomycetes being found in association, probably usually saprobic, with various disorders of man and animals.

Mycotic infections of man and animals, *mycoses,* may be classified according to the part affected into "cutaneous," "subcutaneous," and "deep-seated" or "systemic," etc. Such a classification, which is frequently exemplified by medical mycological texts, is most helpful for exposition to clinicians and for aiding diagnosis. It shows little correlation with the types of fungi implicated, and an exposition of mycoses within a frame work of mycological taxonomy is equally unsatisfactory. Here an ecological approach will first be made by a consideration of some examples of endogenous and exogenous mycotic infection, mycoses which result from infection by pathogens originating within and outside the host, respectively.

III. ENDOGENOUS MYCOSES

A. Candidiasis

Candidiasis, the complex of diseases caused by *Candida albicans* and a few other species of *Candida,* provides a typical example of an endogenous mycosis. The asporogenous yeast *C. albicans,* long known as the cause of thrush in infants, is a notorious fungus of worldwide distribution which has, according to Lodder and Kreger-van Rij (1952), been given some hundred names in a dozen genera. Occasionally recorded from soil (Di Menna, 1955; Ajello, 1956; Marples, 1961) and even more rarely from plants—e.g., Van Uden *et al.* (1956) from *Ulex* and *Myrtus;* Keymer and Austwick (1961) and Di Menna (1958) from grass—*C. albicans* is typically found in the alimentary tract of man and certain animals. At this site, and in the human vagina, *C. albicans* is normally harbored as a saprobe. There have been many surveys of the incidence of *C. albicans* in man, and the results show much variation. According to the tabulated summaries given by Winner and Hurley (1964), the incidence ranged from 6 to 54% in the mouth, 0.6 to 77% in sputum, 10 to 70% in feces, and to 35.9% in the vagina in surveys covering many thousand normal children and adults, hospital patients suffering from a variety of disorders, and pregnant and nonpregnant women. It is difficult to make any hard and fast generalizations, but it is common experience to find a higher incidence of *C. albicans* in children than in adults, in hospital patients than in healthy subjects, and in pregnant than nonpregnant women.

Surveys have also been made of the incidence of yeasts in domesticated animals (Van Uden *et al.,* 1958), exotic animals in zoological gardens and in animals in the wild. *C. albicans* is a common inhabitant of the alimentary tract of poultry (Ainsworth and Austwick, 1955), and although Van Uden (1962) and Van Uden and Branco (1963) recorded yeasts from grain-eating and omnivorous wild birds, e.g., house sparrows and gulls, they found such fish-eating species as cormorants (and also sea lions) to be free from yeasts. In an earlier survey (Van Uden and Do Carmo Sousa, 1957), *C. albicans* was not isolated from the bovine intestinal tract, a finding which may explain the rareness of oral and intestinal candidiasis in cattle.

It is abundantly clear that *C. albicans* is frequently carried by apparently normal individuals, both human and animal, and it seems certain that while infection is on occasion contracted from the environment, and then probably usually an environment contaminated by infected subjects the normal method of infection is from one individual to another. What determines pathogenicity is much less clear.

Van Uden (1962) was able to influence the yeast numbers in mice by adjustments in the starch:protein ratio in the diet. Presumably an increase in the numbers of yeasts could, by increasing the inoculation potential, tip the balance in favor of pathogenicity. This is a possible explanation of the increase in candidiasis, sometimes fatal, associated with broad spectrum antibiotic therapy. Normally *C. albicans* is in competition with bacteria the removal of which allows the yeast to multiply unchecked. On the other hand, the evidence is often inconclusive, and it could be that the antibiotics reduce host resistance, because it is also clear that changes in host physiology are often associated with candidiasis. Generalized candidiasis of the skin is, for example, frequently associated with diabetes mellitus. Yet again there may be environmental factors operating. Paronychia, infection of the nail fold, caused by *C. albicans* is often considered to be an occupational hazard of housewives, whose hands are frequently wet and who self-infect themselves following manicure or other injury to the skin. Finally disease may result from an increase in virulence of the fungus. At times this seems likely, but there is little supporting experimental evidence, most isolates of *C. albicans* being equally pathogenic to rabbits. In conclusion it must be emphasized that while *C. albicans* can be the primary cause of serious disease, it is so frequently carried by apparently healthy people that finding *Candida* in association with any disorder can rarely be taken as presumptive evidence that it is present in a pathogenic role. All the features of the case must be taken into consideration.

1. *Literature*

Candida and candidiasis currently account for nearly 20% of all publications on medical and veterinary mycology. The comprehensive review by Winner and Hurley (1964) may be supplemented by Winner and Hurley (1966). Lodder and Kreger-van Rij (1952) deal authoritatively with the mycology of *Candida*.

IV. EXOGENOUS MYCOSES

A. *Coccidioidomycosis*

Coccidioidomycosis caused by *Coccidioides immitis* was first incriminated about the turn of the century as a relatively rare and frequently fatal disease of man in arid regions of North and South America. The symptoms of this generalized form of the disease are very complex, the lungs, bones, skin, and subcutaneous tissues and the central nervous system being variously involved. In 1937, however, it was recognized that a mild respiratory disease, known as San Joaquin Valley fever, after the locality in California where the disease is prevalent, is the primary form of coccidioidomycosis and that very few primary infections become generalized. It was aso discovered that infection induces an immunological response in the infected individual, who in addition to acquiring immunity to subsequent infection gives a local skin reaction to an injection of antigens (coccidioidin) derived from cultures of *C. immitis*. The coccidioidin test gave a great impetus to epidemiological studies, and it quickly became apparent that most persons living in endemic areas have been infected and that the percentage of positive reactors increases with age and with period of residence in the region. It was also found that domestic and farm animals are also susceptible to the disease and that curves for the incidence of positive reactions to coccidioidin among cattle of increasing age groups are similar to those for man.

Another aspect of the coccidioidomycosis problem was the study by Emmons of the soil-burrowing desert rodents, many of which he found to be infected, but apparently not fatally, by coccidioidomycosis, and he was able to demonstrate regularly the fungus in their lungs. At first Emmons inclined to the view that the rodents were the reservoir of infection, but it is now apparent that *C. immitis*, a fungus of unspecialized nutritional requirements, is a common soil fungus, and it is from soil that the rodents are infected in the same way that man and domesticated animals contract infection from air-borne soil dust.

1. *Literature*

Coccidioidomycosis has been monographed by Fiese (1958), who covers all aspects of the disease and gives a detailed bibliography up to about 1957. This mycosis has attracted so much attention that workers on coccidioidomycosis have held two major symposia at Phoenix, Arizona, the first in 1957, the second in 1965; the published proceedings (Ferguson, 1957; L. Ajello, 1967), especially that of the second symposium, at which there was a registered attendance of 458, should be consulted.

B. *Adiaspiromycosis*

In passing it may be noted that Emmons discovered another mycotic infection of soil-inhabiting mammals of which the pathogen shows certain superficial resemblances to *Coccidioides immitis*. The infection, caused by several species of *Emmonsia,* has since been shown to have a worldwide distribution on many different hosts. It is characterized by the presence in the lungs of spherical bodies (10–70 μ in diameter for *E. parva;* 200–480 μ in diameter for *E. crescens:* Emmons and Jellison, 1960). Each of these spherules is developed from a single spore, which on lodging in lung tissue merely increases in size until it becomes macroscopically visible as a white spot. (It is these enlarged spores, *adiaspores,* which have given the name to the mycosis.) If transferred to culture medium, germ tubes develop and give rise to a mycelial colony bearing aleuriospores 2–4 $\times$ 2.5–4.5 μ in size.

C. *Histoplasmosis*

Histoplasmosis caused by *Histoplasma capsulatum* [the imperfect state of *Gymnoascus demonbreunii* according to Ajello and Cheng (1967)] shows certain parallels with coccidioidomycosis. It was first recognized in the early years of the century (when like coccidioidomycosis it was first thought to be caused by a protozoan) as a serious and often fatal infection of the reticuloendothelial system characterized by fever, emaciation, anemia, and leukopenia, frequently accompanied by enlargement of the spleen. It was subsequently found to be localized to certain more humid regions of the United States, where large numbers of both men and farm animals were found to give a positive skin reaction to histoplasmin (*H. capsulatum* antigen), and it soon became apparent that the usual manifestations of histoplasmosis are mild to subclinical. In endemic areas *H. capsulatum* has been isolated from soil and water, but the pathogen has also been found to be associated with the excreta of various animals. Small epidemic outbreaks have been traced to chicken manure, which frequently harbors the fungus, as do the droppings of starlings (Dodge *et al.,* 1965). In Venezuela and Tanzania an illness attacking speleologists after visiting certain caves containing large amounts of bat guano has been shown to be histoplasmosis, and *H. capsulatum* has also been found in bats and bat droppings in North America (Emmons *et al.,* 1966).

There is a variant form of histoplasmosis known in Africa (caused by *H. duboisii*), and an epizootic lymphangitis, a serious disease of horses and mules, is caused by another species of *Histoplasma* (*H. farciminosum*), but less is known about the origin of infection in these cases.

1. *Literature*

Histoplasmosis still needs comprehensive treatment. It has been monographed with special relation to Argentina by Negroni (1960), there is the multiauthor book edited by Sweaney (1960), and the proceedings of the conference on histoplasmosis held at Excelsior Springs, Missouri, in 1952 (Willis, 1952) is still useful.

D. *Other Exogenous Systemic Mycoses*

Among a number of other exogenous systemic mycoses, mention must be made of cryptococcosis caused by (*Cryptococcus neoformans*), a serious infection of the lungs and the central nervous system of man and various animals, which is of low incidence, sporadic, and worldwide in distribution. From the present point of view the interest of this mycosis is the widespread association of the causal agent, an asporogenous yeast, with pigeon droppings, to which the infection in a number of cases has been traced. Pigeon excreta in New York, London, India, and elsewhere have been shown to harbor *C. neoformans.* The pigeons themselves do not appear ever to be infected, it is rather that the droppings provide a suitable substrate for the growth of the yeast which is able to assimilate uric acid and creatinine as the sole source of nitrogen (Staib, 1962a,b).

Outbreaks of avian aspergillosis, in which the air sacs of affected birds may become coated by a growth of *Aspergillus fumigatus,* have frequently been associated with moldy straw or compost, and sporotrichosis (caused by *Sporothrix schenckii*) is characteristically a subcutaneous infection of horticulturalists and agricultural workers. However, some years ago there was a serious epidemic of sporotrichosis among workers in warm humid gold mines of the Witwatersrand where infection was contracted from the fungus growing on mine timbers. Sporotrichosis is also exceptional in that the pathogen isolated from man has been successfully inoculated into a plant, carnation buds (Benham and Kesten, 1932), and it is of interest to note that Mackinnon has attempted to forecast outbreaks of sporotrichosis from meteorological data. He defined "sporotrichosis weather" as having a relative humidity of 90% or higher, a mean temperature of 16–20°C with no low values at night, and abundant and repeated rainfall during a week or more; such weather is considered to favor the saprobic growth of the pathogen and thus to increase the likelihood of human infection. He claimed success in forecasting one small outbreak in Uruguay (Mackinnon, 1949).

1. Literature

Cryptococcosis has been comprehensively monographed by Littman and Zimmerman (1956), and aspergillosis is reviewed by Austwick (1965). The classical account of sporotrichosis is by Beurmann and Gougerot (1912), which may be supplemented by Nordén (1951), Mackinnon (1949), and "Sporotrichosis infection on mines of the Witwatersrand," 67 pp., 1947 published by the Transvaal Chamber of Mines, Johannesburg.

E. Ringworm

Ringworm has long been known. The causal fungi—the dermatophytes—were among the first pathogenic fungi to be recognized, and during the latter half of the nineteenth century and the first few decades of the twentieth ringworm and medical mycology were widely thought of as being synonymous. Until recently, dermatophytes were isolated only from man and animals and their taxonomic affinities were obscure. All this is changed. Dermatophytes and dermatophyte-like fungi are now known to be widely distributed in soil, and they are securely classified as gymnoascaceous fungi. These modern developments stem from two sources. First, the introduction by Vanbreuseghem (1952) of a "hair-baiting" technique by which sterilized hair is laid on the surface of a moistened soil sample spread in a petri dish; dermatophytes and other keratin-attacking fungi differentially invade the hairs, from which they can be obtained in pure culture. Second, the discovery by Stockdale (1961) and Dawson and Gentles (1961) that dermatophytes are heterothallic and that perfect states can be obtained by mating appropriate isolates.

As is usual for pathogenic fungi, the perfect states of dermatophytes are not associated with the pathogenic phase. Even the sporulation of the imperfect state on the host is limited to arthrospores, but in culture growth is more diverse and luxuriant. The imperfect states of dermatophytes can be accommodated in three genera differentiated by characteristic macroconidia which are typically thick-walled and rough in *Microsporum,* thin-walled and smooth in *Trichophyton,* and thick-walled and smooth in the monotypic *Epidermophyton* (Emmons, 1934). The first two, but not *Epidermophyton,* also produce microconidia (aleuriospores). The perfect states of *Microsporum* are species of *Nannizzia* while those of *Trichophyton* are typically species of *Arthroderma.*

That man can contract ringworm from infected animals has long been known although this knowledge was put to little use. In the early 1950's, however, La Touche achieved some success in Leeds, England, in reducing the incidence of human infections by the cat and dog ringworm fungus (*Microsporum canis*) by tracing animal contacts of patients seen at the dermatological clinic. *Microsporum canis* attacks both skin and hair, and infected hairs become surrounded by a sheath of arthrospores and frequently break off leaving the root still in position. Though often very difficult to locate in ordinary light, infected hairs are easily picked out by inspection in a darkened room when irradiated by "Wood's light" (filtered ultraviolet light) under which infected but not normal hairs give a characteristic greenish fluorescence. The procedure was to examine the patients' pet cats and dogs under Wood's light, and those found to be infected were either destroyed or attempts made to cure them. Elimination of these infected animals was correlated with a reduction in human infections (La Touche, 1952). Marples (1961) in New Zealand also traced human infection by *M. canis* in towns to cats, but there the situation was complicated because the cats frequently breed in the wild in lairs permanently infested with the pathogen so that the stray kittens adopted as pets bring the infection with them.

Another interesting elucidation of the epidemiology of a ringworm infection is the recent study by English (English, 1967; English and Southern 1967) on *Trichophyton persicolor* [which as Stockdale (1967) has shown has a *Nannizzia* perfect state and slightly roughened macroconidia, both features characteristic of the genus *Microsporum*]. This fungus has been regularly but infrequently recorded in England and elsewhere in western Europe since the beginning of the century and doubt has been cast on its specific status. The source of the human infections was unknown until the association of one case in the Bristol area with a vole induced Miss English to examine the population of voles and other small mammals which were the subject of an ecological study in a wood near Oxford. On several occasions when these animals have been trapped for examination they were sampled for ringworm fungi by being brushed with sterile toothbrushes (an adaption of the hairbrush technique devised by Mackenzie (1963) when making an epidemiological study of an outbreak of ringworm in a girl's school). The bristles of the toothbrushes were subsequently pressed onto a suitable agar culture medium, and *T. persicolor* was isolated from 53% of 127 bank voles (*Clethrionomys glareolus*) and 25% of 113 field voles (*Microtus agrestis*). In another series of 65 bank voles, 46% were infected but clinical lesions were present in only one. Voles clearly could provide the reservoir from which man has been infected but whether or not *T. persicolor* occurs as a saprobe in soil has not yet been established.

Microsporum gypseum has been isolated from soil in many different parts of the world and *M. gypseum* infections of man (C. Ajello, 1953) have been recorded from all continents. A characteristic of such outbreaks is that they are small, sporadic, and short-lived. This is in marked contrast with the classical head ringworm in children caused by *M. audouinii,* which may affect hundreds of children and persist both as individual infections and as an epidemic for a long period. There has, so far at least, been no record of the association of *M. audouinii* with the soil or with an animal reservoir, and it seems that this species has become well adapted to parasitize man. Similarly some species of *Trichophyton* responsible for scalp and body ringworm (e.g., *T. tonsurans*) and foot ringworm (e.g., *T. rubrum*) appear to be specialized for man.

1. Literature

The classical account of ringworm fungi is the monograph by Sabouraud (1910), "Les Teignes," now a rare book but one which students of the dermatophytes still find it essential to consult. The modern taxonomic treatment of the group dates from Emmons (1934), and of the many current accounts of dermatophytes and dermatophytoses available, those by Conant *et al.* (1954), Lewis *et al.* (1958), and Hildick-Smith *et al.* (1964) for man and by Ainsworth and Austwick (1959) and Georg (1959) for animals may be recommended.

V. HOST-PATHOGEN INTERACTIONS

Sufficient evidence has been offered in the last two sections to make the currently fashionable point that most fungal infections of man and higher animals, whether endogenous or exogenous, are opportunistic. Attention must now be turned to aspects of the host-pathogen interaction and to some effects of the environment on pathogenicity.

A. Environmental Effects

The environment has already been mentioned in connection with sources of infection, with environmental effects which increase the inoculum potential and hence the chance of infection. What is known about the effect of the environment on the host/pathogen interaction? Very little. One of the best-known generalizations about medical mycology is that mycoses are more serious in tropical than temperate countries, usually with the implication that the incidence of mycoses is highest in the tropics. There is little evidence for the last view. In fact the incidence of recognized mycotic infection is probably highest in the United States, but there, it must be remembered, the incidence of medical mycologists is also highest. On the other hand, there is evidence that warmth and humidity—whether in the tropics or in coal mines—can aggravate certain infections. Foot ringworm may be considered an occupational disease of coal miners and professional soldiers. Communal baths lead to the spread of infection, by infected skin scales on the floors, from diseased to healthy feet, and the infections are aggravated by heavy boots and hard work under humid conditions. While fungi are more diverse in the tropics, and some fungi pathogenic for man are typically tropical, tropical conditions may merely intensify an infection contracted in a temperate country. For example, examination of troops before they left England showed the incidence of foot ringworm to be as high though much milder than the incidence in the same troops when stationed in the Far East, where frequently the body also was affected (Sanderson and Sloper, 1953). Moreover, the dermatophytes involved were found to be the same as those detected at the first examination, and not those endemic to the region.

Mackinnon and his colleagues have studied the effect of temperature on the course of infection in laboratory animals of both South American blastomycosis paracoccidioidomycosis and sporotrichosis. In studies on the former it was found that when the yeast form of *Paracoccidioides brasiliensis* (for which the optimum temperature for growth was 35°C and which did not grow *in vitro* at 39°) was inoculated into guinea pigs (the internal temperature of which is 39.5–40°C) at an ambient temperature of 37°, no lesions developed. Lesions were formed, however, at 5–9°, particularly on the eyelids, muzzle, and testicles and on some skeletal muscles, especially those of the lumbar region. Between 14 and 30° no skeletal muscles showed lesions, and skin lesions developed at 14–20° healed rapidly when the animals were transferred to a room temperature of 37°. It was thus concluded that the pathogen induced lesions only in those tissues sufficiently cooled by the ambient temperature (Mackinnon *et al.*, 1960). In a subsequent study of sporotrichosis (*Sporothrix schenckii*) in young male rats, Mackinnon and Conti-Díaz (1962) found that after intraperitoneal or intracardiac inoculation lesions appeared in animals kept at low ambient temperature (5–20°) but that no lesions occurred at 31° On the basis of these results they successfully treated a human case of sporotrichosis with lesions localized in the right hand, and which had not responded to potassium iodide therapy, by the application of hot wet dressings for 30–40 minutes 2 or 3 times a day for 3 months.

B. *Effects of the Host on the Pathogen*

In the simplest cases of host effect on the pathogen, it is the structure of the host or the host physiology which limits the infection. The dermatophytes, for example, have the ability to attack keratinized tissue in which, as already noted, growth is mycelial and sporulation limited to arthrospores. In an infected human hair the growth of the mycelium of the dermatophyte is downward, but this growth is checked at the base of the hair, where keratinization is taking place. In other words, the downward growth of the dermatophyte keeps pace with the growth and keratinization of the hair with the result that the hair shaft becomes tunneled by the hyphae but the dermatophyte is unable to invade the unkeratinized tissue. Such an infection of a child's hair by *Microsporum audouinii* may persist for many years, fresh hairs constantly becoming infected by spores from infected hairs. At puberty, however, the infection spontaneously clears due to changes in the fatty acids secreted by the scalp, which renders them fungistatic if not fungicidal.

A host factor is almost certainly involved in determining whether coccidioidomycosis is subclinical and self-limiting, for the frequency of generalized infection is 3.5% in negroes but only 0.3% in white males. Also, although climatic factors may be involved, it is likely that peculiarities in host physiology play a part in preventing the classical tinea capitis of children caused by *M. audouinii* (which is a European export to North America) from becoming established among native children in tropical regions into which it is introduced. Conversely, host factors may contribute to preventing such tropical dermatophytes as *Trichophyton concentricum* (the cause of tinea imbricata) and *Microsporum ferrugineum* from becoming endemic in the temperate regions into which they are periodically introduced.

In other, and possibly more complicated, cases it is a host reaction induced by the infection that affects the pathogen. Such a reaction is thought to be involved in mycetomas of aspergillosis. *Aspergillus fumigatus* in avian or mammalian lungs may take the form of a spherical mycelial mass or colony with the peripheral hyphal tips more or less distinctly swollen or clubbed, and it has been claimed that the limitation in growth of the pathogen coincides with the development in the host of a sensitivity to the pathogen. The "grains" associated with mycetoma of the foot caused by *Madurella mycetomi* and other pathogens presumably are the result of a host/pathogen interaction. Such structures are discussed by Austwick in Chapter 17.

1. Dimorphism

Some fungi pathogenic for men and higher animals are mycelial in both the pathogenic and the saprobic states, as are dermatophytes. In others, *Cryptococcus neoformans* for example, both phases are yeastlike whereas for some the pathogenic state is yeastlike and the *in vitro* growth, mycelial.

This last phenomenon, termed *dimorphism,* which is characteristic of the agents of such deep-seated mycoses as North and South American blastomycosis, histoplasmosis, coccidioidomycosis, and sporotrichosis, has been dealt with in detail by Romano in Volume II, Chapter 7. Here it is only necessary to recall that the mycelial-yeast transformation is sometimes determined by temperature only, as in *Blastomyces dermatitidis* which is mycelial at 25°C, yeastlike at 37° and the conversion may be effected *in vitro* at will. For most dimorphic fungi, however, the mycelial-yeast transformation is dependent on a complex of factors. For *Sporothrix schenckii* at 37° an atmosphere of 5% CO_2 is a requirement, *Histoplasma capsulatum* needs a complex cystine- or cysteine-containing medium, and for *H. farciminosum* (the cause of epizootic lymphangitis) a complex medium must be supplemented with CO_2. It does seem that the ability to cause systemic infection is frequently determined by the ability to effect the mycelial-yeast transformation, and it is even possible to generalize by noting that growth of the pathogenic phase is always less luxuriant than that of the saprobic.

C. *Effects of the Pathogen on the Host*

The effects of the pathogen on the host are primarily the diverse clinical signs and symptoms by which mycoses are distinguished. They vary from the small superficial nodules on the surface of hairs which characterize black piedra (*Piedraia hortai*), a tropical disorder which is merely unsightly, to disturbances of sufficient magnitude to be fatal. This is not the place even to catalogue the main effects. The reader is referred to such texts as Emmons *et al.* (1963) and Hildick-Smith *et al.* (1964) for both macroscopic and microscopic details. A few points should, however, be noted.

First, to return again to the dermatophytes, it is interesting to note that zoophilic species such as *Microsporum canis* from cats and dogs and *Trichophyton verrucosum,* the principal cause of cattle ringworm, and *M. gypseum* from soil, cause more inflammatory lesions, but lesions of shorter duration, than do corresponding anthrophilic species such as *M. audouinii* and *T. tonsurans.* This suggests that the latter have become specialized for man, who is more tolerant of the infection than he is of less highly specialized forms. This phenomenon is certainly not a general principle, for the effects on the host of such a nutritionally unspecialized pathogen as *Coccidioides immitis* are very mild, but it is possible that the mildness of the general reaction is because at the cellular level the host response is rapid and thus generalized infection is prevented. An immunological response by the host is certainly a characteristic feature of mycoses, and one by which mycotic infections of man and animals are differentiated from fungal diseases of plants.

As is usual in infectious disease, the pathogen acts as an antigen to which the host responds by producing antibodies. In such mycoses as coccidioidomycosis and histoplasmosis, as already noted, infection marks an individual serologically for life in the same way that infection by the tubercle bacillus leaves an individual tuberculin positive, and this feature has been much used in epidemiological studies and for diagnosis. Unfortunately the diagnostic antigens, being usually derived from culture filtrates, are not always specific and cross-reactions can occur between the antigens of different pathogens; but refinements of technique are allowing the production of antigens of increased specificity. The immunological response not only is a basis for the diagnosis of mycotic infection but also is used for the converse, the identification of fungi and the assessment of taxonomic relationships. These latter aspects are treated in detail in Chapter 24 by Seeliger.

As already indicated, infection can confer permanent immunity. For dermatophytes, to return to them for the last time, immunity is only temporary, and after an interval a second infection can occur. That such superficial infection as that of ringworm does in fact induce an immunological response is perhaps surprising. Some dermatophyte infections induce an allergic response at a distance from the site of infection. A ringworm infection of the feet or groin, for example, may lead to the development of small sterile lesions, *mycids,* on the hands, face, or other part of the body.

REFERENCES

Ainsworth, G. C. (1961). The Review of Applied Mycology. *Rept. Commonwealth Mycol. Conf.* **6**: 17–22.

Ainsworth, G. C. (1966). The pattern of medical and veterinary mycological information. *Sabouraudia* **5**: 81–86.

Ainsworth, G. C., and P. K. C. Austwick. (1955). A survey of animal mycoses in Britain: Mycological aspects. *Brit. Mycol. Soc. Trans.* **38**: 369–386.

Ainsworth, G. C., and P. K. C. Austwick. (1959). "Fungal Diseases of Animals." Commonwealth Agricultural Bureaux, Farnham Royal, Bucks, England.

Ajello, L. (1953). The dermatophyte, *Microsporum gypseum,* as a saprophyte and parasite. *J. Invest. Dermatol.* **21**: 157–171.

Ajello, L. (1956). Soil as natural reservoir for human pathogenic fungi. *Science* **123**: 876–879.

Ajello, L., ed. (1967). "Coccidioidomycosis." Univ. of Arizona Press, Tucson, Arizona.

Ajello, L., and S.-L. Cheng. (1967). Sexual reproduction in *Histoplasma capsulatum. Mycologia* **59**: 689–697.

Austwick, P. K. C. (1965). Pathogenicity. *In* "The Genus *Aspergillus*" (K. B. Raper and D. I. Fennell, eds.), Chapter 8. Williams & Wilkins, Baltimore, Maryland.

Benham, R. W., and B. Kesten. (1932). Sporotrichosis; its transmission to plants and animals. *J. Infect. Diseases* **50**: 437.

Beurmann, D. C., and [H.] Gougerot. (1912). "Les Sporotrichoses." Libraire Felix Alcan, Paris.

Conant, N. F., D. T. Smith, R. D. Baker, J. C. Callaway, and D. S. Martin. (1954). "Manual of Clinical Mycology," 2nd ed. Saunders, Philadelphia, Pennsylvania.

Dawson, C. O., and J. C. Gentles. (1961). The perfect states of *Trichophyton terrestre* Durie & Frey and *Microsporum nanum* Fuentes. *Sabouraudia* **1**: 49–57.

Di Menna, M. E. (1955). A search for pathogenic species of yeasts in New Zealand soils. *J. Gen. Microbiol.* **12**: 54–62.

Di Menna, M. E. (1958). *Candida albicans* from grass leaves. *Nature* **181**: 1287–1288.

Dodge, H. J., L. Ajello, and O. K. Engelke. (1965). The association of a bird-roosting site with infection of school children by *Histoplasma capsulatum*. *Am. J. Public Health* **55**: 1203–1211.

Emmons, C. W. (1934). Dermatophytes. Natural grouping based on the form of the spores and accessory organs. *Arch. Dermatol. Syphilol., Chicago* **30**: 337–362.

Emmons, C. W., and W. L. Jellison. (1960). *Emmonsia crescens* sp. n. and adiaspiromycosis (haplomycosis) in mammals. *Ann. N.Y. Acad. Sci.* **89**: Art. 1, 91–101.

Emmons, C. W., C. H. Binford, and J. P. Utz. (1963). "Medical Mycology." Lea & Febiger, Philadelphia, Pennsylvania.

Emmons, C. W., P. D. Klite, G. M. Baer, and W. B. Hill, Jr. (1966). Isolation of *Histoplasma capsulatum* from bats in the United States. *Am. J. Epidemiol.* **84**: 103–109.

English, M. P. (1967). The nature of *Trichophyton persicolor* infection in the bank vole and the interpretation of the results of sampling techniques. *Sabouraudia* **5**: 295–301.

English, M. P., and H. N. Southern. (1967). *Trichophyton persicolor* infection in a population of small wild animals. *Sabouraudia* **5**: 302–309.

Ferguson, M. S. (1957). *U.S., Public Health Serv., Publ.* **575**.

Fiese, M. J. (1958). "Coccidioidomycosis," 253 pp. Thomas, Springfield, Illinois.

Georg, L. (1959). "Animal Ringworm in Public Health." U.S. Dept. of Health, Education, and Welfare, Public Health Service, Washington, D.C.

Hildick-Smith, G., H. Blank, and I. Sarkany. (1964). "Fungus Diseases and their Treatment." Little, Brown, Boston, Massachusetts.

Keymer, I. F., and P. K. C. Austwick. (1961). Moniliasis in partridges (*Perdix perdix*). *Sabouraudia* **1**: 22–29.

Kligman, A. M. (1950). A basidiomycete probably causing onychomycosis. *J. Invest. Dermatol.* **14**: 69–70.

La Touche, C. J. (1952). The Leeds campaign against microsporosis in children and domestic animals. *Vet. Record* **64**: 398–399.

Lewis, G. M., M. E. Hopper, J. W. Wilson, and O. A. Plunkett. (1958). "An Introduction to Medical Mycology, 4th ed. Year Book Publ., Chicago, Illinois.

Littman, M. L., and L. E. Zimmerman. (1956). "Cryptococcosis." Grune & Stratton, New York. [For a supplement, see Littman, M. L. (1959). *Am. J. Med.* **27**: 976–998.]

Lodder, J., and N. J. W. Kreger-van Rij. (1952). "The Yeasts: A Taxonomic Study." North-Holland Publ., Amsterdam.
Mackenzie, D. W. R. (1963). "Hairbrush diagnosis" in detection and eradication of non-fluorescent scalp ringworm. *Brit. Med. J.* **II**: 363–365.
Mackinnon, J. E. (1949). The dependence on the weather of the incidence of sporotrichosis. *Mycopathologia* **4**: 367–374.
Mackinnon, J. E., and I. A. Conti-Díaz. (1962). The effect of temperature on sporotrichosis. *Sabouraudia* **2**: 56–59.
Mackinnon, J. E., I. A. Conti-Díaz, L. A. Yarzabal, and N. Tavella. (1960). *Anales Fac. Med., Montevideo* **45**: 310–318.
Marples, M. J. (1961). Some extra-human reservoirs of pathogenic fungi in New Zealand. *Trans. Roy. Soc. Trop. Med.* **55**: 216–220.
Negroni, P. (1960). "Micosis Profunda (Cutaneas y Visceriales)," Vol. 2. Comisión de Investigación Científica (Publ. Esp. No. 1), La Plata. (English translation by S. McMillan, "Histoplasmosis. Diagnosis and Treatment." Thomas, Springfield, Illinois. 1965.)
Nordén, A. (1951). Sporotrichosis. *Acta Pathol. Microbiol. Scand.* Suppl. 89: 1–119.
Sabouraud, R. (1910). "Les Teignes." Masson, Paris.
Sanderson, P. H., and J. C. Sloper. (1953). Skin disease in the British Army in S.E. Asia. *Brit. J. Dermatol.* **65**: 7–8, 252–264, 300–309, and 362–372.
Staib, F. (1962a). Vogelkot ein Nährsubstrat für die Gattung Cryptococcus. *Zentr. Bakteriol., Parasitenk. Abt. I. Orig.* **186**: 233–247.
Staib, F. (1962b). Keratinin-Assimilation, ein neues Spezificum für *Cryptococcus neoformans. Zentr. Bakteriol., Parasitenk., Abt. I. Orig.* **186**: 274–275.
Stockdale, P. M. (1961). *Nannizzia curvata* gen. nov., a perfect state of *Microsporum gypseum* (Bodin) Guiart et Grigorakis. *Sabouraudia* **1**: 41–48.
Stockdale, P. M. (1967). *Nannizzia persicolor* sp. nov., the perfect state of *Trichophyton persicolor* Sabouraud. *Sabouraudia* **5**: 355–359.
Sweaney, H. C., ed. (1960). "Histoplasmosis." Thomas, Springfield, Illinois.
Vanbreuseghem, R. (1952). Technique biologique pour l'isolement des dermatophytes du sol. *Ann. Soc. Belge Med. Trop.* **33**: 173–178.
Van Uden, N. (1962). Factors of host-yeast relationships. *Recent Progr. Microbiol.* **8**: 635–643.
Van Uden, N., and R. C. Branco. (1963). Distribution and population densities of yeast species in Pacific water, air, animals and kelp of Southern California. *Limnol. Oceanog.* **8**: 323–329.
Van Uden, N., and L. Do Carmo Sousa. (1957). Yeasts from the bovine caecum. *J. Gen. Microbiol.* **16**: 385–395.
Van Uden, N., M. de Matos Faia, and L. Assis-Lopes. (1956). Isolation of *Candida albicans* from vegetable sources. *J. Gen. Microbiol.* **15**: 151–153.
Van Uden, N., L. Do Carmo Sousa, and M. Farinha. (1958). On the intestinal yeast flora of horses, sheep, goats, and swine. *J. Gen. Microbiol.* **19**: 435–445.
Willis, M. J. (1952). *Public Health Monograph* **39**: 322 pp.
Winner, H. I., and R. Hurley. (1964). "Candida albicans." Churchill, London.
Winner, H. I., and R. Hurley, eds. (1966). "Symposium on Candida Infections." Livingstone, Edinburgh and London.

CHAPTER 9

Fungal Parasites of Invertebrates

1. Entomogeneous Fungi

M. F. MADELIN

Department of Botany
The University
Bristol, England

I. INTRODUCTION

Fungus diseases of insects are both common and widespread, and sometimes are severe enough almost to eliminate a population of insects in a given habitat. Such epizootic outbreaks are generally attributable to a conjunction of circumstances that favor the disease. Important among these are a humid environment and a dense host population. Although from time to time, and sometimes at more or less regular intervals, a mycosis is for many sorts of insect the major mortality factor in a given population, fungi are usually only one of a number of factors limiting their numbers.

II. THE INSECT HOST

The insect body is invested in an integument. This comprises a continuous layer of epidermal cells covered by a relatively thick chitinous procuticle, at the surface of which there is a thin nonchitinous epicuticle that generally contains waxes. The procuticle may be hardened by a tanning reaction involving polyphenols. The integument is continuous with structurally similar but thinner membranes which line the various invaginations of the body surface, namely tracheae, various glands, reproductive openings, and foregut and hindgut. A chitinous cuticle is absent from the midgut, but in some insects a loose chitin-containing peritrophic membrane lies between the gut wall and its contents.

The musculature and organs lie within the integument. In the absence of confining blood vessels, the blood, which is the only extracellular body fluid, is free to flow among the organs and tissues within the body cavity. Its circulation plays no significant part in respiration, for the tracheae appear to conduct gases directly to the tissues.

III. INSECT-PARASITISM IN THE FUNGI

Insect parasites are distributed widely throughout the groups of true fungi. The parasitic habit appears to have arisen independently in these different groups, though in some there has been considerable speciation subsequent to its assumption, e.g., in the Laboulbeniales, the Entomophthoraceae, *Cordyceps,* and *Septobasidium.* Table I lists the major taxa containing parasitic fungi. A more complete list can be compiled from the publications of Charles (1941), Kobayasi (1941), and Petch (1948).

TABLE I

LIST OF THE MAJOR TAXA WHICH CONTAIN INSECT-PARASITIZING SPECIES

CHYTRIDIOMYCETES	*Hypocrella*	*Beauveria*
Coelomomyces	*Myriangium*	*Cephalosporium*
Myiophagus	*Nectria*	*Gibellula*
ZYGOMYCETES	*Ophiocordyceps*	*Hirsutella*
Culicicola	*Podonectria*	*Hymenostilbe*
Entomophaga	*Sphaerostilbe*	*Isaria*
Entomophthora	*Torrubiella*	*Metarrhizium*
Massospora	Laboulbeniales[a]	*Microcera*
Strongwellsea	BASIDIOMYCETES	*Paecilomyces*
Tarichium	*Septobasidium*	*Penicillium*
Triplosporium	*Uredinella*	*Spicaria*
Zoophthora	DEUTEROMYCETES[b]	*Synsgliocladium* (*Sorosporella*)
Zygaenobia	*Acrostalagmus*	*Synnematium*
ASCOMYCETES	*Aegerita*	*Tetracrium*
Ascosphaera (*Pericystis*)	*Aschersonia*	*Verticillium*
Calonectria	*Aspergillus*	
Cordyceps		

[a] Approximately 125 genera.
[b] Many species in the genera listed are asexual states of ascomycetous insect-parasites.

The nomenclature of parasites formerly classified as species of *Entomophthora* and *Empusa* merits special comment. Taxonomic problems have arisen in classifying insect-parasitizing members of the Entomophthoraceae because *Empusa* is invalid as a name for a fungus genus, and because the genus *Entomophthora* appears inadequate to accommodate properly the species formerly contained in *Empusa* (see MacLeod, 1963). Weiser and Batko have suggested the use of a particular series of features for differentiating a number of genera in this family (see Batko and Weiser, 1965), and the genera listed under Zygomycetes in Table I reflect the views of these authors.

References to original papers dealing with points only briefly touched upon here may be traced through two recent and comprehensive surveys (Steinhaus, 1963; Madelin, 1966a).

IV. MODES OF PARASITISM

A. Ectoparasitism

The thallus in a large group of insect-parasitizing fungi is mainly superficial. Such penetration into the host's body as has been seen is haustorial. Of the described ectoparasites, about 1500 are species of the Laboulbeniales, and the remaining few dozen are deuteromycetes. Except for one or two structurally quite unspecialized ectoparasitic deuteromycetes, such as *Trichothecium acridiorum* (Madelin, 1966b), no ectoparasite has been artificially cultured.

The Laboulbeniales produce nonfatal, contagious cutaneous diseases. They usually appear as minute dark-colored or yellowish bristles or bushy hairs projecting from the integument. The thallus consists of a septate filament which elongates and branches in a definite fashion within a general enveloping membrane, and which gives rise to antheridia or perithecia or both. The enveloping membrane is highly impervious and protects the fungus against desiccation (Faull, 1912). It is thinner and more permeable in aquatic species (Faull, 1911). Thaxter (1896) believed the membrane to be derived from the gelatinous envelope which surrounds the ripe ascospore, but calculations by Richards and Smith (1956), based on its dimensions in *Herpomyces stylopygae,* show that it must be secreted during growth.

The majority of laboulbeniales are attached basally to the host's integument by a blackened foot (Fig. 1,E). Thaxter (1896) concluded that most forms which possessed such a foot did not penetrate the host's body. In certain species, however, which are almost exclusively parasites of soft-bodied hosts, a foot is lacking, and in its place occur various haustorial penetrations which may provide physical as well as nutritional support (see Dodge, in Gäumann and Dodge, 1928, p. 392). These haustoria range from the stout tapering filaments of *Dimeromyces rhizophorus,* through the branching haustoria of *Moschomyces, Rhizomyces, Ceraiomyces dahlii,* and *Arthrorhynchus* species, to the extensive system of bulbs and filaments of *Trenomyces histophtorus.* The latter permeate the fat-bodies of bird lice, but apparently do little harm (Chatton and Picard,

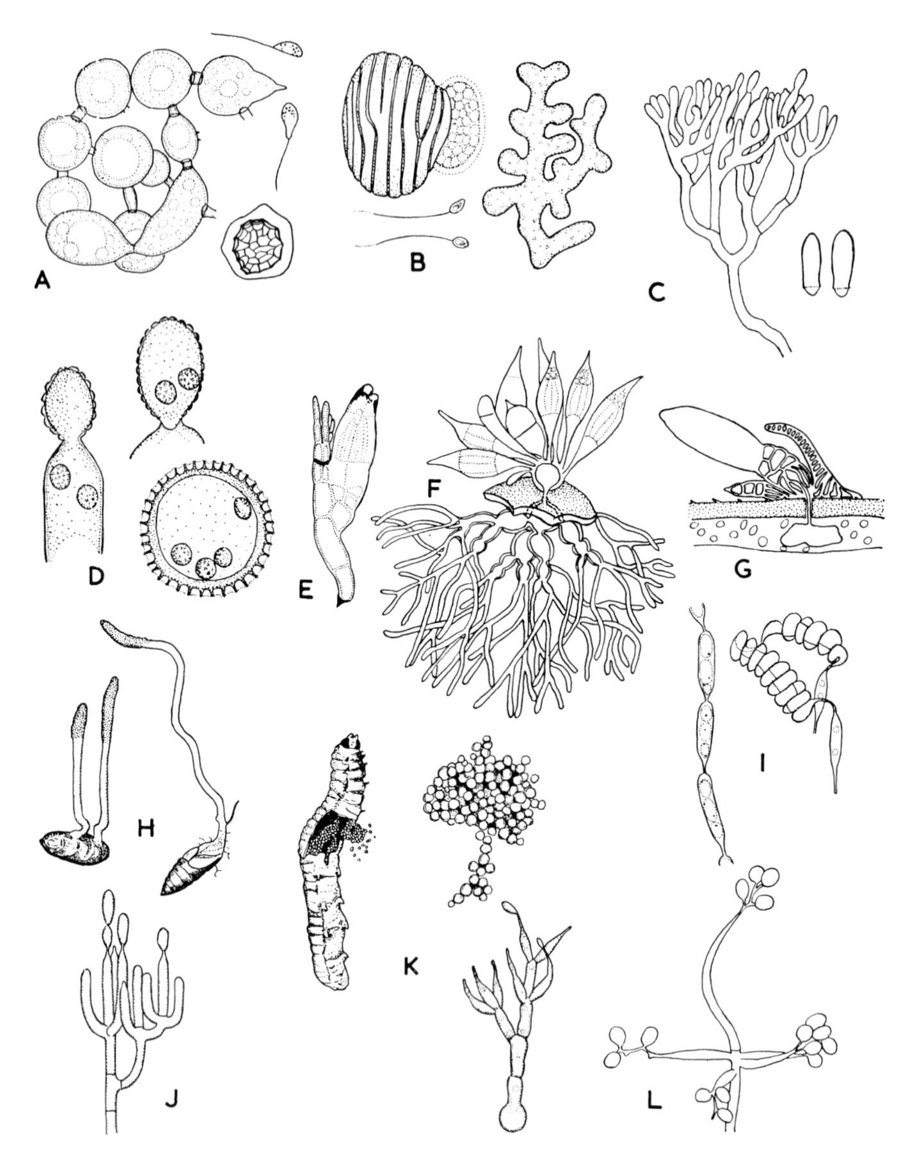

FIG. 1. Insect-parasitizing fungi. A. *Myiophagus* sp.: Thallus, showing isthmuses and sporangia; zoospores and resting sporangium. After Karling (1948). B. *Coelomomyces:* dehiscing resistant sporangium and zoospores of *C. lativittatus*: piece of mycelium of *C. pentangulatus*. After Couch and Dodge (1947). C. *Entomophthora sphaerosperma:* conidiophore and conidia. After Thaxter (1888). D. *Massospora cicadina:* developing and mature conidia, and tetranucleate resting spore. After Goldstein (1929). E. *Laboulbenia tapirina:* plant (monoecious) showing blackened foot. After Benjamin and Shanor (1952). F. *Trenomyces histophtorus:*

1909) (Fig. 1,F). *Herpomyces* is considered by Thaxter (1908) to be unique in possessing both the usual foot *and* slender rhizoidal penetrations. More recently, Richards and Smith (1956) have recognized in species of *Herpomyces* the additional presence of coarser rhizoidal filaments which expand into haustorial bulbs in the host's epidermis (Fig. 1,G).

The mode of nutrition of the majority of laboulbeniales is still problematical. Thaxter (1914) assumed that the few forms which possessed penetrant haustoria used them to draw nourishment from the host's body fluid, and he believed that those species in which no haustoria had been seen were nourished by direct passage of nutrients through the insect's integument into the foot of the parasite. Richards and Smith (1956), consider this to be impossible in view of what is now known of the permeability of insect cuticle. Like Thaxter, they discount the possibility that the cuticle itself is the source of food, but in addition consider that growth on the external surfaces of insects is hardly feasible unless penetrant haustoria are present. Special techniques and careful observation may reveal more species with small haustoria similar to those seen in some species by Thaxter (1908) and others.

Many, but not all, laboulbeniales appear to be highly host specific. Some species are even specific for position—e.g., the 16 species of *Chitonomyces* which occur on the water beetle *Orectogyrus specularis* (Thaxter, 1926)—and may even be restricted to left or right sides of hosts from a particular population (see Benjamin and Shanor, 1952). Benjamin and Shanor demonstrated specificity for the *sex* of the host, and also found that *Laboulbenia odobena* occupies different positions on male and female insects. Thaxter (1896) suggested that position specificity might be partly explained by spores being transmitted by definitely recurring movements of the host, especially during mating. The distribution of *L. odobena* is in accord with this hypothesis. However, this explanation cannot hold for *Herpomyces stylopygae* on cockroaches, where Richards and Smith (1955) saw ascospores all over the hosts' body surfaces, yet found mature plants on only the antennae and palps.

---

female plant, showing haustorium. After Chatton and Picard (1909). G. *Herpomyces stylopygae:* showing haustorium penetrating to epidermis of host. After Richards and Smith (1956). H. *Cordyceps militaris:* perithecial stromata on lepidopterous pupae. After Kobayasi (1941). I. *Septobasidium burtii:* spindle-shaped cells and coiled haustoria from within host. After Couch (1938). J. *Metarrhizium anisopliae:* conidiophore and conidia. After Madelin (1963). K. *Sorosporella uvella:* infected cutworm torn open to expose aggregates of resting spores; a portion of such an aggregate; and a mature resting spore germinating in water to produce the *Syngliocladium* stage. After Speare (1920). L. *Beauveria bassiana:* conidiophore from slide culture. After Madelin (1963).

Adult insects do not molt, and, on these, laboulbeniales seem to survive until the insect dies. However, in cockroach nymphs infected with *Herpomyces,* all is completely lost at molting except the large haustorial bulbs. The bulbs which are left behind appear to be anucleate and do not regenerate new plants (Richards and Smith, 1956).

Almost all our knowledge of nonperithecial ectoparasites is due to Thaxter (1914, 1920). Most of the described species possess a blackened foot like that so common in the laboulbeniales. *Muiogone* and *Muiaria* form tufts bearing multicellular spores. *Chantransiopsis* bears an intriguing, but according to Thaxter, wholly superficial, resemblance to the monospore-producing *Chantransia* forms among the Rhodophyceae (Algae). *Termitaria* produces endoconidia from compact hymenia of conidiophores formed on termites. *Amphoromorpha* species comprise single cells attached to the host's integument by a foot and a peglike haustorium and, like the Laboulbeniales are invested by a continuous general envelope (Thaxter, 1914, 1920). Thaxter noted certain points of similarity between *Amphoromorpha* and chytrids, but saw no flagellate spores.

The thallus in the imperfect genera *Thaxteriola, Entomocosma,* and *Laboulbeniopsis* consists of a few-celled axis anchored by a foot and bearing a distal sporogonium. Gäumann regarded *Thaxteriola* and *Endosporella* as male plants of dioecious Laboulbeniales, but Thaxter considered that there was no evidence for this view (see Gäumann and Dodge, 1928). If these fungi and *Coreomycetopsis,* another imperfect form, are unrelated to the Laboulbeniales, then their resemblances to this order must be considered remarkable instances of parallel evolution.

Although members of the class Trichomycetes live attached by some sort of specialized device to the gut lining or the external cuticle of insects or other arthropods, they are generally considered to be commensals rather than parasites insofar as no penetration into the living tissues of the host has been observed. Recently a number of species have been cultured artificially so an understanding of the relationship between these curious fungi and their hosts may soon be acquired. Biphasic cultures in which a layer of nutrient solution overlies a nutrient agar have proved particularly suitable for culturing them.

B. Endoparasitism

The mycelium of many insect-parasitizing fungi lives within the host's body. Such endoparasitic fungi commonly kill the host within a week or two of infection. Attempts to culture them artificially have generally succeeded, but there have been failures such as with *Coelomomyces* and many entomophthoraceous species. Gustafsson (1965) however has recently succeeded in culturing no fewer than 16 out of 24 species of

Entomophthora (*sensu lato*) occurring in Sweden. He employed a modification of the method described by Müller-Kögler (1959). Spores discharged from freshly collected mycotic insects were allowed to fall on autoclaved egg yolk. If after a few days a culture had been established, it was then subcultured into Sabouraud's maltose or dextrose agar.

Endoparasitic infection is usually initiated by spores, though in *Aegerita webberi,* hyphae may spread from diseased to healthy insects (Morrill and Back, 1912). Penetration of the host's integument by germ tubes has been observed in *Entomophthora muscae* (Schweizer, 1947), *E. coronata* (Yendol and Paschke, 1965), *Septobasidium burtii* (Couch, 1938), *Beauveria bassiana* (Fig. 1L), *Metarrhizium anisopliae* (Fig. 1J), *Spicaria* (*Isaria*) *farinosa* and *Aspergillus flavus* (references in Madelin, 1963), and has been inferred in many other species. In aphids and mosquitoes, which are attacked by species of *Entomophthora* (*E. aphidis, E. culicis*), it seems unlikely that infection could be via the mouth, the main alternative infection route, because of the insects' feeding habits (Skaife, 1925).

The view that penetration of the integument is assisted by secretion of a chitinase is widely held. Huber (1958) has shown that in artificial culture *Metarrhizium anisopliae, Beauveria bassiana, Cordyceps militaris* (Fig. 1H), and *Aspergillus flavus* can all hydrolyze chitin, and Cordon and Schwartz (1962) have shown that *B. tenella* does likewise. The chitinase of *B. bassiana* is firmly bound to the cell during the early phase of the fungus' growth (Claus, 1961). Germ tubes in penetrating appear also to exert mechanical pressure. The way in which the waxy epicuticle is pierced is however unknown. This thin layer is the site of factors giving resistance to infection, and its removal may render insects susceptible (Sussman, 1951; Koidsumi, 1957).

Infection through the integument can be accomplished also by zoospores, e.g., those of *Myiophagus* (Karling, 1948). Whether zoospores are the agents of infection in species of *Coelomomyces,* most of which attack mosquito larvae, has not been discovered.

Integumental wounds may lead to infection by ordinarily pathogenic fungi, and sometimes to infection by casual invaders, such as *Trichothecium roseum, Mucor hiemalis,* and species of *Penicillium, Fusarium,* and *Aspergillus.* Fungi may also infect through the tracheae (Lepesme, 1938; Schaerffenberg, 1957).

Infection via the gut by ingested spores is difficult to demonstrate with certainty, but it has been seen with *Beauveria bassiana* and *Aspergillus flavus,* and with *Entomophthora coronata* in termites (Yendol and Paschke, 1965), and is suspected in a number of other species. Attempts to infect insects by feeding them spores have produced various results, even when a single species is used (in Madelin, 1963). The fact that humid conditions are usually necessary for the initiation of insect mycoses suggests that the integument is the commoner natural infection path, but much uncertainty remains.

Infection brings the fungus into the hypodermal regions or hemocoel of the host, where it begins to proliferate in one way or another. The chytrid *Myiophagus* forms a branched thallus with swellings which, after delimitation by isthmuses, eventually become zoosporangia (Fig. 1A) (Karling, 1948). *Coelomomyces* species form nonseptate, irregularly branched hyphae which appear to lack a cell wall (Couch, 1945; Couch and Umphlett, 1963) (Fig. 1B). Fragmentation of the thallus spreads the fungus within the host. Fungi with true hyphae may colonize either by typical filamentous growth, as in *Aspergillus* species (references in Madelin, 1963) and *Entomophthora sphaerosperma* (Boczkowska, 1932; Ullyett and Schonken, 1940) or by proliferation of free cells or hyphal fragments in the blood in a more or less yeastlike manner as in most parasitic species of Entomophthoraceae, in *Cordyceps,* and in many deuteromycetes other than *Aspergillus. Septobasidium* species are somewhat intermediate, forming some free cells, but mostly chains of spindle-shaped cells connected by fine threads (Couch, 1938) (Fig. 1I). Fungi which form free cells commonly revert to hyphal growth after the host dies. It appears likely, but has yet to be demonstrated, that properties of the hemolymph largely govern the form adopted by the fungus during its parasitic phase. Loughheed (1963) has found that yeast-like growth can be induced in *Hirsutella gigantea* in artificial culture by incorporation of appropriate levels of EDTA into the medium. Experimental studies on yeast-mycelium dimorphism (e.g., Bartnicki-Garcia, 1963; Nickerson, 1963) point the way for further investigations with endoparasites of insects.

Sooner or later the insect succumbs to the infection, but death is preceded by a number of symptoms, including restlessness, cessation of feeding, and loss of coordination. Diseased insects commonly climb to high places, e.g., on vegetation, or, if subterranean, rise to the soil surface. Their death in such situations facilitates dispersal of the parasites' spores.

Those spores which by aerial or subaerial transport serve to spread the pathogen rapidly under favorable conditions, are almost always formed outside the host, e.g., the conidia of *Entomophthora* species (Fig. 1C) and deuteromycetes. The conidia of *Massospora* species (Goldstein, 1929; Soper, 1963) (Fig. 1D) and *Strongwellsea castrans* (Batko and Weiser, 1965) are exceptions, being formed within the abdomen of the host. However, they are released by special mechanisms, namely disintegration or perforation, respectively, of the abdominal walls of the host. In contrast to conidia, resting spores usually form *within* the host's body, e.g., those of *Myiophagus* (in Karling, 1948), *Coelomomyces* (Couch, 1945), *Sorosporella* (the resting spore stage of *Syngliocladium*) (Speare, 1920) (Fig. 1K), *Massospora,* and *Entomophthora.* Nevertheless in *E. echinospora* and *E. megasperma* they sometimes also arise externally (Thaxter, 1888; MacLeod, 1956).

Entomophthora infections can culminate in the formation of either conidia or resting spores, but very little is known about the factors that govern the form of sporulation. Speare (1912) found that, in artificial culture, hyphal bodies of the homothallic species *E. pseudococci* formed either gametangia (and thereafter, zygospores) or conidiophores according to whether they were in darkness or light, respectively.

Propagative spores can usually be germinated readily, but, with certain notable exceptions including *Sorosporella* (Fig. 1K), attempts to germinate resting spores have generally failed. Nevertheless dehiscence of resting spores has been observed in certain *Coelomomyces* species (in Couch and Umphlett, 1963), and Schweizer (1947) found that resting spores of *Entomophthora muscae* could be rendered germinable by exposure to the action of chitinovorous bacteria.

Although sporulation of endoparasitic fungi usually occurs only after the host's death, it sometimes precedes it. The principal records of premortem sporulation in deuteromycetes relate to *Aspergillus* species, whose conidiophores sometimes emerge through the integuments of live insects. Sometimes resting spores of *Sorosporella* form within live hosts (Speare, 1920). Endoparasitic ascomycetes do not sporulate before their hosts are dead, but a number of lower fungi do, e.g., *Coelomomyces* species, *Massospora cicadina* (Goldstein, 1929) and *M. levispora* (Soper, 1963), *Entomophthora erupta* (Hall, 1959), and *Strongwellsea castrans* (Batko and Weiser, 1965).

Species of *Septobasidium* show special features in their mode of parasitism. *S. burtii* is the best understood example (Couch, 1938). Only part of a population of scale insects on a branch of a tree is parasitized, the remainder being not merely unharmed, but even protected beneath a mat of hyphae from natural enemies such as parasitic wasps. The insects furnish the fungus with food and a means of distribution. Both insect and fungus benefit from their association at the expense of the tree. Young insects sheltering beneath the fungal mat become infected via the integument by spores, or buds therefrom, but never by mycelium. Within the hemocoel, the fungus first forms strings of spindle-shaped cells and then, after several weeks, coiled haustoria (Fig. 1I). Simultaneously other hyphae emerge through the integument, where they anastomose with mycelium from the general fungal mat. Individually endoparasitized scale insects thereby become connected to a common crust of mycelium beneath which are also sheltered unparasitized insects. The infected insects are stunted and sterilized, but not killed. The curious pillars, spines, chambers, and tunnels produced by species of *Septobasidium* under natural conditions, never appear in cultures on agar media. Couch considers it probable that such structures are formed as a result of an influence of the scale insects.

V. THE LIFE CYCLE OF THE PARASITE

In general our knowledge of the *natural* life cycles of insect-parasitizing fungi is meager (Madelin, 1963). Some parasites which are inexacting in their nutritional and environmental requirements are probably able to interchange between parasitism and saprophytism. For instance, *Aspergillus flavus* is a readily cultured parasite which is also a common saprophyte, and even *Mucor hiemalis* can become parasitic when insects are stressed or injured (Heitor, 1962). By contrast, parasitic Chytridiomycetes and Laboulbeniales have so far resisted all attempts to culture them axenically; and even though many members of the Entomophthoraceae have now been artificially cultured, the difficulty in initiating such growth suggests unresolved special requirements likely to limit severely any saprophytic development under natural conditions. Such fungi probably pass directly from insect to insect with perhaps an occasional intervening phase of dormancy. Our views on the natural life cycles of the majority of insect parasites must remain largely speculative until more detailed studies have been made.

REFERENCES

Bartnicki-Garcia, S. (1963). Mold-yeast dimorphism of *Mucor*. *Bacteriol. Rev.* **27**: 293–304.

Batko, A., and J. Weiser. (1965). On the taxonomic position of the fungus discovered by Strong, Wells, and Apple: *Strongwellsea castrans* gen. et sp. nov. (Phycomycetes; Entomophthoraceae). *J. Invert. Pathol.* **7**: 455–463.

Benjamin, R. K., and L. Shanor. (1952). Sex of host specificity and position specificity of certain species of *Laboulbenia* on *Bembidion picipes*. *Am. J. Botany* **39**: 125–131.

Boczkowska, M. (1932). Zmiany w organizmie gasienicy bielinka kapustnika (*Pieris brassicae* L.) wskutek porazenia owadomorkiem korzonkowym (*Entomophthora sphaerosperma* Fres.). *Roczniki Nauk Rolniczych* **27**: 1–20.

Charles, V. K. (1941). A preliminary check list of the entomogenous fungi of North America. *U.S. Dept. Agr., Bur. Entomol. Plant Quarantine, Insect Pest Survey Bull.* **21**, 707–785.

Chatton, E., and F. Picard. (1909). Contribution à l'étude systématique et biologique des Laboulbéniacées: *Trenomyces histophtorus* Chatton et Picard, endoparasite des poux de la poule domestique. *Bull. Soc. Mycol. France* **25**: 147–170.

Claus, L. (1961). Untersuchungen über die Chitinasewirkung des insektentötenden Pilzes *Beauveria bassiana* (Bals.) Vuill. *Arch. Mikrobiol.* **40:** 17–46.

Cordon, T. C., and J. H. Schwartz. (1962). The fungus *Beauveria tenella. Science* **138:** 1265–1266.

Couch, J. N. (1938). "The Genus *Septobasidium*," 480 pp. Univ. of North Carolina Press, Chapel Hill, North Carolina.

Couch, J. N. (1945). Revision of the genus *Coelomomyces,* parasitic in insect larvae. *J. Elisha Mitchell Sci. Soc.* **61:** 124–136.

Couch, J. N., and H. R. Dodge. (1947). Further observations on *Coelomomyces* parasitic on mosquito larvae. *J. Elisha Mitchell Sci. Soc.* **63:** 69–79.

Couch, J. N., and C. J. Umphlett. (1963). *Coelomomyces* infections. *In* "Insect Pathology" (E. A. Steinhaus, ed.), Vol. II, pp. 149–188. Academic Press, New York.

Faull, J. H. (1911). The cytology of the Laboulbeniales. *Ann. Botany* (*London*) **25**: 649–654.

Faull, J. H. (1912). The cytology of *Laboulbenia chaetophora* and *L. Gyrinidarum. Ann. Botany* (*London*) **26:** 325–355.

Gäumann, E. A., and C. W. Dodge. (1928). "Comparative Morphology of Fungi," 701 pp. McGraw-Hill, New York.

Goldstein, B. (1929). A cytological study of the fungus *Massospora cicadina,* parasitic on the 17-year cicada, *Magicicada septendecim. Am. J. Botany* **16:** 394–400.

Gustafsson, M. (1965). On species of the genus *Entomophthora* Fres. in Sweden. II. Cultivation and physiology. *Kgl. Lantbruks-Högskol. Ann.* **31:** 405–457.

Hall, I. M. (1959). The fungus *Entomophthora erupta* (Dustan) attacking the Black Grass Bug, *Irbisia solani* (Heidemann) (Hemiptera, Miridae), in California. *J. Insect Pathol.* **1:** 48–51.

Heitor, F. (1962). Parasitisme de blessure par le champignon *Mucor hiemalis* Wehmer chez les insectes. *Ann. Epiphyties* **13**: 179–205.

Huber, J. (1958). Untersuchungen zur Physiologie insektentötender Pilze. *Arch. Mikrobiol.* **29:** 257–276.

Karling, J. S. (1948). Chytridiosis of scale insects. *Am. J. Botany* **35**: 246–254.

Kobayasi, Y. (1941). The genus *Cordyceps* and its allies. *Sci. Rept. Tokyo Kyoiku Daigaku* **B5**: 53–260.

Koidsumi, K. (1957). Antifungal action of cuticular lipids in insects. *J. Insect Physiol.* **1**: 40–51.

Lepesme, P. (1938). Recherches sur une aspergillose des Acridiens. *Bull. Soc. Hist. Nat. Afrique Nord* **29**: 372–381.

Loughheed, T. C. (1963). Morphological changes induced in *Hirsutella gigantea* Petch by ethylenediaminetetraacetate. *Can. J. Botany* **41**: 1155–1157.

MacLeod, D. M. (1956). Notes on the genus *Empusa* Cohn. *Can. J. Botany* **34:** 16–26.

MacLeod, D. M. (1963). Entomophthorales infections. *In* "Insect Pathology" (E. A. Steinhaus, ed.), Vol. II, pp. 189–231. Academic Press, New York.

Madelin, M. F. (1963). Diseases caused by hyphomycetous fungi. *In* "Insect Pathology" (E. A. Steinhaus, ed.), Vol. II, pp. 233–271. Academic Press, New York.

Madelin, M. F. (1966a). Fungal parasites of insects. *Ann. Rev. Entomol.* **11**: 423–448.

Madelin, M. F. (1966b). *Trichothecium acridiorum* (Trabut) comb. nov. on red locusts. *Brit. Mycol. Soc. Trans.* **49:** 275–288.

Morrill, A. W., and E. A. Back. (1912). Natural control of white flies in Florida. *U.S. Dept. Agr., Bur. Entomol. Bull.* **102**: 1–78.

Müller-Kögler, E. (1959). Zur Isolierung und Kultur insektenpathogener Entomophthoraceen. *Entomophaga* **4**: 261–274.

Nickerson, W. J. (1963). Molecular bases of form in yeasts. *Bacteriol. Rev.* **27**: 305–324.

Petch, T. (1948). A revised list of British entomogenous fungi. *Brit. Mycol. Soc. Trans.* **31**: 286–304.

Richards, A. G., and M. N. Smith. (1955). Infection of cockroaches with *Herpomyces* (Laboulbeniales). I. Life history studies. *Biol. Bull.* **108**: 206–218.

Richards, A. G., and M. N. Smith. (1956). Infection of cockroaches with *Herpomyces* (Laboulbeniales). II. Histology and histopathology. *Ann. Entomol. Soc. Am.* **49**: 85–93.

Schaerffenberg, B. (1957). *Beauveria bassiana* (Vuill.) Link als Parasit des Kartoffelkäfers (*Leptinotarsa decemlineata* Say). *Anz. Schaedlingskunde* **30**: 69–74.

Schweizer, G. (1947). Über die Kultur von *Empusa muscae* Cohn und anderen Entomophthoraceen auf Kalt sterilisierten Nährboden. *Planta* **35**: 132–176.

Skaife, S. H. (1925). The locust fungus, *Empusa grylli,* and its effects on its host. *S. African J. Sci.* **22**: 298–308.

Soper, R. S. (1963). *Massospora levispora,* a new species of fungus pathogenic to the cicada, *Okanagana rimosa. Can. J. Botany* **41**: 875–878.

Speare, A. T. (1912). Fungi parasitic upon insects injurious to sugar cane. *Hawaiian Sugar Planters' Assoc. Expt. Sta. Pathol. Physiol. Ser. Bull.* **12**: 1–62.

Speare, A. T. (1920). Further studies of *Sorosporella uvella,* a fungous parasite of noctuid larvae. *J. Agr. Res.* **18**: 399–440.

Steinhaus, E. A., ed. (1963). "Insect Pathology," Vol. II, 689 pp. Academic Press, New York.

Sussman, A. S. (1951). Studies on an insect mycosis. I. Etiology of the disease. *Mycologia* **43**: 338–350.

Thaxter, R. (1888). Entomophthoreae of the United States. *Mem. Boston Soc. Nat. Hist.* **4**: 133–201.

Thaxter, R. (1896). Contribution towards a monograph of the Laboulbeniaceae. I. *Mem. Am. Acad. Arts Sci.* **12**: 189–429.

Thaxter, R. (1908). Contribution towards a monograph of the Laboulbeniaceae. II. *Mem. Am. Acad. Arts Sci.* **13**: 219–469.

Thaxter, R. (1914). On certain peculiar fungus-parasites of living insects. *Botan. Gaz.* **58**: 235–253.

Thaxter, R. (1920). Second note on certain peculiar fungus-parasites of living insects. *Botan. Gaz.* **69**: 1–27.

Thaxter, R. (1926). Contribution towards a monograph of the Laboulbeniaceae. IV. *Mem. Am. Acad. Arts Sci.* **15**: 431–580.

Ullyett, G. C., and D. B. Schonken. (1940). A fungus disease of *Plutella maculipennis* Curt. in South Africa, with notes on the use of entomogenous fungi in insect control. *Union S. Africa, Dept. Agr., Sci. Bull.* **218**: 1–24.

Yendol, W. G., and J. D. Paschke. (1965). Pathology of an *Entomophthora* infection in the eastern subterranean termite *Reticulitermes flavipes* (Kollar). *J. Invert. Pathol.* **7**: 414–422.

CHAPTER 10

Fungal Parasites of Invertebrates

2. Predacious Fungi

C. L. DUDDINGTON

Biological Laboratories
The Polytechnic
London, England

I. INTRODUCTION

The predacious fungi form a taxonomically mixed, yet ecologically natural, group. Most of them belong either to the Zoopagales or the Moniliales, and their principal victims are protozoans, especially soil amoebae, and nematodes. A few species have been described that prey on rotifers. They all capture their prey alive and feed on their bodies while moribund, or after they are dead.

The Moniliales that capture nematodes are particularly interesting on account of the morphological adaptations that they have developed for the capture of their prey. These vary from sticky networks, knobs, or hyphal branches to short branches ending in rings which, by the sudden swelling of their cells, capture nematodes by constriction.

Besides the true predacious fungi, there are many species that are internally parasitic. Their hosts again are nearly always protozoans or nematodes, and the fungi belong mainly to the Zoopagales and the Moniliales, although several of the Lagenidiales have also adopted this habit, which is also found in the Chytridiales and several other groups, including at least one member of the Entomophthorales (Drechsler, 1940).

The term "predacious fungi" is commonly used to include both endozoic and strictly predacious species, and in some instances it is impossible to distinguish clearly between them. *Nematoctonus haptocladus* (Drechsler, 1946), for instance, behaves as an internal parasite of nematodes, gaining entry into their bodies by the germination of spores that stick to their integuments; but when a nematode has finally succumbed, hyphae grow out of its carcass and form sticky appendages by which more nematodes are captured.

II. FUNGI ATTACKING PROTOZOANS

Of the fungi that attack protozoans, the greatest interest has centered round the Zoopagales (Drechsler, 1935a; Duddington, 1956a). On agar plates these fungi form a sparse mycelium of branched, nonseptate hyphae, no more than 1–2 μ in diameter. Small amoebae become attached to the hyphae, apparently by adhesion, and the fungus puts out haustoria into their endoplasm and gradually absorbs their contents. As the absorption proceeds the amoebae gradually assume a rounded shape, their contractile vacuoles cease to operate, and death ensues. Finally the whole contents of the animals are absorbed by the fungus, leaving only the shriveled pellicles attached to the mycelium.

The fungi reproduce by means of conidia. In *Zoopage* these are fusiform and catenulate, long chains of them being attached to short sterigmata projecting from the hyphae. In *Acaulopage* they are formed singly on short sterigmata, and the spores usually bear empty appendages. In *Stylopage* the conidia are carried aloft on long conidiophores that bear from one to several spores. Sexual reproduction is unknown in many species; when it does occur it is by the conjugation of two gametangia, much as in the Mucorales. There is a strong tendency to anisogamy in the group, one gametangium being longer than the other, and conjugation between a gametangium from a conidium with one produced by the mycelium is common.

Although first described by Drechsler (1933), the Zoopagales are extremely common in leaf mold, dung, and decaying vegetable matter generally and in the soil. Probably they were not discovered earlier because of their small size, and still more because their observation requires the examination of dirty plate cultures such as are not normally kept in a mycological laboratory.

None of the Zoopagales has yet been isolated into pure culture, and our knowledge of their physiology is small. They appear to be obligate predators, for their spores, when placed aseptically onto sterile agar, fail to germinate. Probably some substance given off, either by their hosts, or by other organisms in their environment, is a prerequisite for germination, for the spores of many species can readily be seen to germinate on the surface of the agar in the original cultures. Research on this point is greatly needed.

Most of the Zoopagales appear to be host specific, or nearly so, having been described as attacking one, or at the most two, species of prey on plates where there exists an abundant and mixed protozoan fauna (Drechsler, 1947). This, however, has never been tested by direct experiment—for example, by transferring spores or mycelium to pure cultures of different protozoans to find out how many species are attacked. This is another promising line of research.

Besides attacking amoebae, species of Zoopagales have been recorded as capturing other protozoans, mostly testaceous rhizopods. Some of the larger species capture nematodes.

The Zoopagales also include species that have adopted the endozoic habit, amoebae and other protozoans again being the principal hosts. In *Cochlonema* and *Endocochlus* (Drechsler, 1935a) the host becomes infected either through one or more of the fusiform spores of the fungus sticking to its pellicle, or by a spore being ingested. Germination of the spore gives rise to a minute blob of protoplasm which, growing at the expense of the endoplasm of the host, becomes first sausage shaped, then bent in the middle, and finally coiled in a helical thallus. Multiple infection is common in most species. At first the host appears to be little perturbed, even by infection with a number of developing thalli; as time goes on, however, its movements are slowed down and finally cease, the contractile vacuole disappears as the endoplasm is progressively absorbed by the fungus, and the amoeba becomes increasingly transparent until in the end only the pellicle, if one is present, is left.

After the death of the host, reproductive hyphae grow out from the spirally coiled thallus of the fungus. In *Cochlonema* these bear long chains of fusiform conidia which, when mature, become disrupted and litter the surface of the medium, where they are easily picked up by wandering protozoans. In *Endocochlus* the fertile hyphae lie prostrate on the surface of the substratum, giving off at intervals lateral conidia on short sterigmata. In those species where sexual reproduction is known there is isogamous conjugation between two gametangia formed on suspensors that grow out of the carcass of the host, into the air. In *Cochlonema verrucosum,* and possibly other species, where the same host is invaded by more than one thallus, the two gametangia often come from different thalli, suggesting the possibility of heterothallism (Duddington, 1940).

An interesting intermediate stage between the endozoic and the predacious habit *sensu stricto* is shown by *Bdellospora* (Drechsler, 1935a). In this genus the fusiform spore becomes attached to the pellicle of an amoeba and protrudes a branched haustorium into its endoplasm. The spore then swells to form an ellipsoidal thallus which remains outside the host, drawing nourishment from the endoplasm through its haustorium.

The endozoic Zoopagales appear, from their mode of life, to be obligate parasites. They seem to show the same kind of host specificity as the predacious members of the group, but this again has never been proved. They occur in the same types of habitat as the predacious species. Species of *Cochlonema* are common in Britain, but *Endocochlus* has been observed only twice in this country, and *Bdellospora* has been reported only from America.

Among the predacious Moniliales, several species prey upon protozoans. *Dactylella tylopaga* (Drechsler, 1935b) captures amoebae, and *D. passalopaga* (Drechsler, 1936), *Pedilospora dactylopaga* (Drechsler, 1934), and *Tridentaria carnivora* (Drechsler, 1937a), all prey upon *Difflugia* and other testaceous rhizopods. A few other fungi have been reported in the literature as endozoic in protozoans, but most of them are dubious. It is worthy of note that the elaborate adhesive networks, constricting rings, or other organs of capture by which the predacious Moniliales capture nematodes are not found in the species that prey on protozoans, presumably because they are not needed in dealing with such sluggish animals.

III. FUNGI ATTACKING ROTIFERS

Only a few species of predacious fungi have been reported as attacking rotifers—a fact that at first sight seems strange when we consider the number that capture protozoans and nematodes. This, however, may be because nobody has seriously looked for them. Those species that have been described have been found by workers who were looking for something else. There may well be a rich field of research awaiting the person who cares to make an *ad hoc* study of rotifers. The fact that most rotifers are aquatic need deter nobody; the work of Peach (1950, 1952, 1954) has shown that both the Zoopagales and the predacious Moniliales are common in water.

The best-known fungus attacking rotifers is *Zoophagus insidians* (Sommerstorff, 1911; Sparrow, 1929). This fungus captures its prey by means of peglike outgrowths from its hyphae, which are probably sticky. *Zoophagus insidians* has been observed to form laterally biflagellate zoospores in a vesicle, and probably belongs to the Pythiaceae. A second species, *Z. tentaculum* (Karling, 1936) also captures rotifers by short outgrowths from the mycelium which bear at their apices from one to five tentacles that may well be adhesive organs. There is some doubt whether this species is in fact correctly placed in the genus *Zoophagus,* for the account of its reproductive organs given by Karling suggests that it may in fact be a member of the Zoopagales.

Sommerstorffia spinosa (Arnaudow, 1923) has a less well-developed mycelium than *Zoophagus,* and it captures rotifers by adhesion to the ends of its rather ill-defined hyphae. It lives, like *Zoophagus insidians,* among aquatic algae, and preys on the rotifers that tend to congregate there.

A few other phycomycetes have been described as attacking rotifers or rotifer eggs. Among these may be mentioned *Endochytrium oophilum, Myzocytium zoophthorum, Olpidium macrosporum, Woronina elegans,* and *Catenaria anguillulae.* Some of the early records of fungi attacking rotifers are dubious, especially with regard to the systematic position of the fungi.

IV. FUNGI ATTACKING NEMATODES

The nematophagus predacious fungi belonging to the Moniliales have attracted considerable attention during the past fifteen years. This is partly because of their remarkable morphological adaptations for catching nematodes and partly because a number of workers have attempted to use them for the control of plant parasitic nematodes (Duddington, 1950b, 1962).

The most common type of eelworm trap is the adhesive network (Drechsler, 1937b), found in *Arthrobotrys oligospora* and others. The mycelium of the fungus bears short branches which, by curling round and anastomosing with other similar branches, or with the parent hypha, form networks in three dimensions. The networks are sticky, and if a wandering nematode should happen to come into contact with one it is held fast by adhesion. For a time it struggles violently, but after an hour or so its struggles gradually cease, and it becomes moribund, if not actually dead. Then a fine process from the network pierces the integument of the nematode, and swells within it to form an infection bulb from which trophic hyphae spread to all parts of the victim (Shepherd, 1955). In a few hours the entire contents of the body of the nematode are absorbed, the final event being the evacuation of the trophic hyphae themselves. Only the integument of the nematode is left attached to the networks (Fig. 1).

A simpler form of eelworm trap consists of short lateral branches which are sticky, as in *Dactylella lobata* (Duddington, 1951a). Here the adhesive branches normally consist of only one, two, or three cells, although occasional proliferation of the branches may give rise to simple hyphal loops, indicating the relationship of the sticky branches with the more common adhesive networks. The capture of nematodes by the adhesive branches follows the same course as with the networks, and the branches seem to be just as effective as the networks in capturing prey.

The third type of adhesive trap is the sticky knob. This consists of a small, subspherical knob carried on a short stalk consisting of two, or

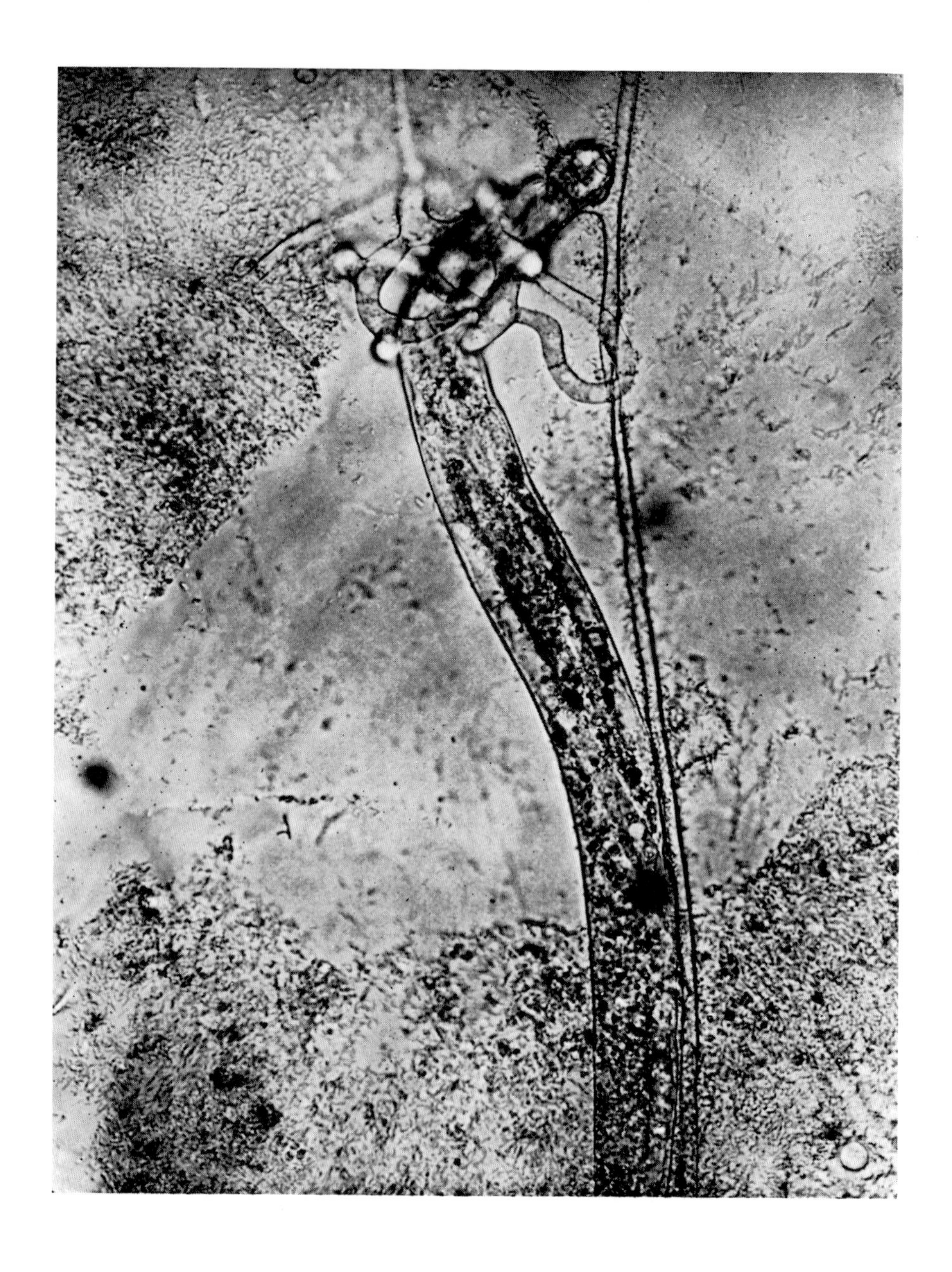

sometimes three, cells. The knob is sticky, and eelworms adhere to them and are consumed in the usual way. *Monacrosporium ellipsosporum* (Drechsler, 1937b) is a common predacious fungus with this type of trap.

Some of the predacious Moniliales depend upon mechanical rather than sticky traps for the capture of their prey. These are of two types: the nonconstricting ring and the constricting ring.

Nonconstricting rings can be seen in *Dactylaria candida* (Drechsler, 1937b). They consist of three-celled rings, attached to the hyphae of the fungus by short, usually three-celled stalks. Should a nematode, in the course of its travels, push its anterior end into a ring it lacks the sense to withdraw and instead tries to force its way through the ring. The result is that it becomes firmly wedged. There follows the usual period of violent struggling by the prey, followed by quiescence and the invasion of the nematode's body by trophic hyphae from the ring cells, which consume its contents.

Sometimes a nematode, in the course of its initial struggling, manages to tear the ring from its moorings, and proceeds on its way, wearing the ring like a life belt. This may happen more than once to the same nematode. Its escape, however, is short-lived, for trophic hyphae still invade its body from the ring cells, so that its death is certain. The death of the nematode is followed by the growth of hyphae out of its carcass, forming a new mycelium—an interesting case of a nematode trap serving as a means of vegetative reproduction.

In *Dactylaria candida,* stalked adhesive knobs are formed in addition to the rings. This is by no means uncommon in predacious fungi with the nonconstricting type of rings.

The nonconstricting ring is entirely passive in its action, depending on the action of the nematode itself to secure capture. There is no evidence whatever that the rings are sticky. The constricting rings, on the other hand, capture nematodes by the garroting action of the ring cells which, by swelling, grasp the nematode in a stranglehold from which there is no possibility of escape. The constricting rings are much like the rings of the nonconstricting type, consisting of three curved cells attached to the mycelium by a short stalk. The ring cells are thicker, however, and the stalk shorter and stouter. The ring cells are sensitive along their inner edges. When a nematode enters a ring the friction of its body stimulates the ring cells to swell suddenly inward to about three times their previous volume. This almost obliterates the opening of the ring, so that the body of the nematode is deeply constricted. Events then follow their usual

FIG. 1. A nematode captured in the adhesive networks of *Arthrobotrys robusta.*

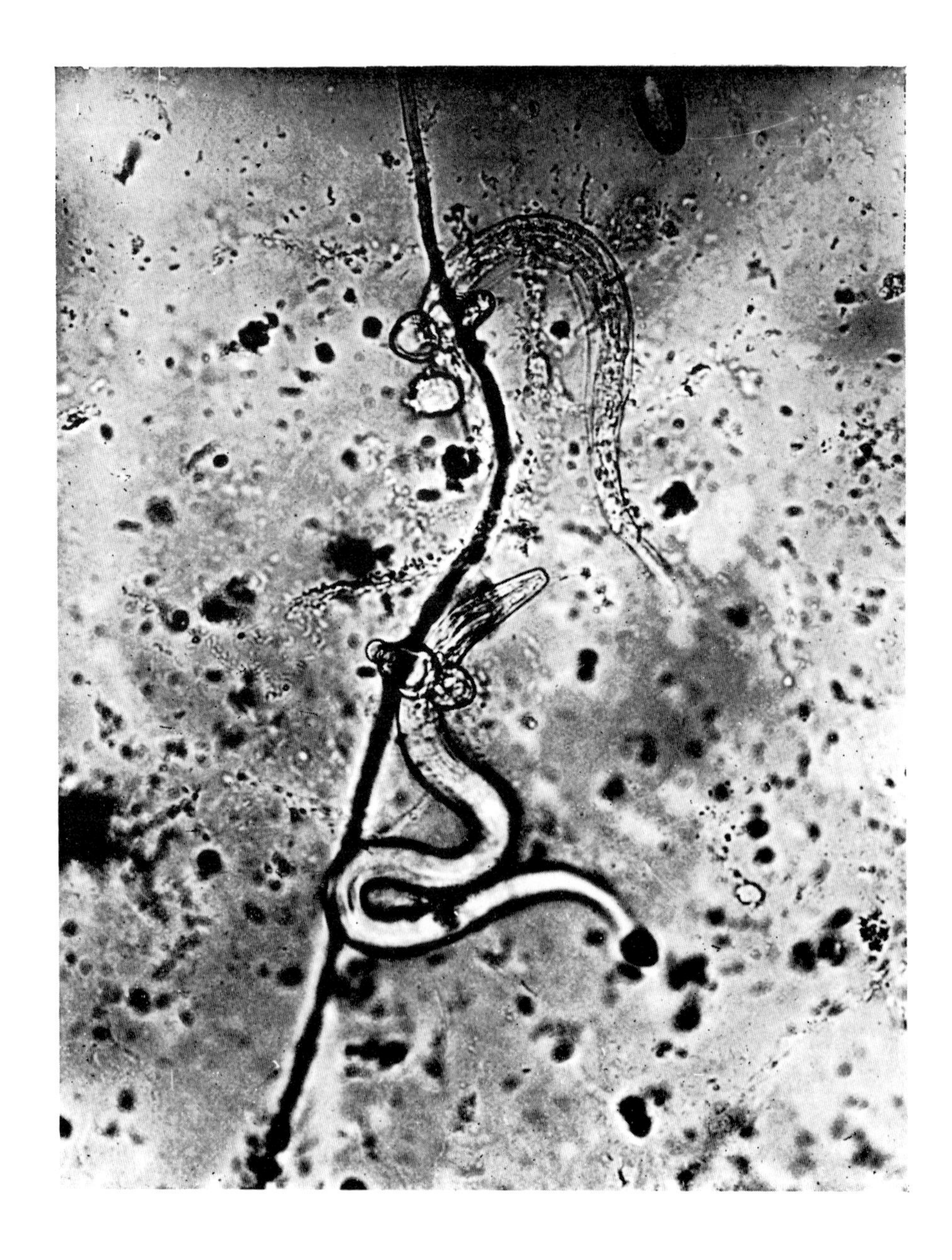

course: after a period of struggling the nematode becomes still, and trophic hyphae from the ring cells invade it and consume its body contents (Fig. 2).

The swelling of the ring cells is extremely rapid. When they are stimulated by rubbing, there is a lag period of some seconds, after which the actual swelling takes no more than a tenth of a second. Just after the ring has closed, a number of small vacuoles in the cytoplasm coalesce to form a single large vacuole, filled with some highly refractive substance. The swelling of the ring cells is irreversible under normal conditions.

Several workers have investigated the mechanism of the constricting rings. Couch (1937) found that the mechanism could be triggered by heat. Comandon and de Fonbrune (1938, 1939) caused the rings to close by rubbing them with a micromanipulator needle. Rees (1955) found that their reactions to acetylcholine showed a certain resemblance to animal muscle. Muller (1958) showed that the closure of the rings could be slowed down by immersion in a sugar solution, but his conclusions from his experiments are open to question. Nobody yet, however, has found a convincing explanation of this remarkable reaction.

The predacious Moniliales, unlike the Zoopagales, show no difficulty in living without their nematode hosts; they should be described as facultatively predacious. They can easily be isolated in pure culture by picking off their conidia, which rise to a height of half a millimeter or more on the ends of erect conidiophores. Conidia transferred to sterile agar usually germinate readily, and the pure cultures can be kept alive indefinitely without nematodes. The fungi grow well and sporulate abundantly in pure culture, but the spores, although produced in large numbers, are usually somewhat smaller than spores produced in the presence of nematodes. In describing a new species of the predacious Moniliales, therefore, it is important to state whether the spores were measured in a pure or a nematode infested culture.

When the predacious Moniliales are growing in pure culture they do not normally form their characteristic nematode traps, although there are certain exceptions, especially among the fungi with constricting rings. On adding nematodes, the traps are usually formed, and nematodes are captured. It is better, however, to add a small amount of mycelium to a

---

FIG. 2. Two nematodes captured by the constricting rings of *Dactylaria gracilis*. The nematode shown below has recently been captured and so shows little disorganization of its internal organs, whereas that shown above, which has been caught for at least 24 hours, consists virtually of an empty integument containing trophic hyphae.

culture containing abundant nematodes rather than the converse (Duddington, 1955a). It appears that something given off by the nematodes stimulates trap formation, and Pramer and Stoll (1959) have isolated a substance, which they call nemin, capable of stimulating trap formation. Trap formation does not appear to depend solely on response to morphogenetic substances, especially when the fungus is living in the soil (Cooke, 1964). *Monacrosporium ellipsoporum* responds poorly to such stimuli (Feder *et al.,* 1963) and yet is sensitive in the soil, while the converse is true of *Arthrobotrys conoides* (Winkler *et al.,* 1961).

Certain fungi with constricting rings are particularly liable to form traps in pure culture, and there is evidence that the phenomenon is connected with heterokaryosis (Feder *et al.,* 1960). Certain substances of animal origin, including aqueous extracts of animal tissues, can stimulate ring formation (Roubaud and Deschiens, 1939).

The predacious Moniliales show less sign of host specificity than the Zoopagales. Most of them appear to be able to capture several different species of nematodes, and their ability to catch a given species probably depends more on the size of the nematode and the structure of its integument than upon anything else.

The ecology of the predacious Moniliales has been studied by Duddington (1951b, 1954) and more recently by Cooke (1962a,b, 1963a,b, 1964) and Wyborn (1966). While little is known yet about their habitat relations, we are gradually building up a picture of their life in the soil through the work of Cooke and his co-workers.

Besides the predacious series of Moniliales, there are several of the Zoopagales that capture nematodes. *Stylopage grandis* (Duddington, 1955b), for example, produces a sticky fluid on its mycelium to which nematodes adhere. Those members of the Zoopagales that prey upon nematodes do not produce specialized nematode traps, and they appear to differ little from the species that capture protozoans except in the greater diameter of their hyphae.

Many of the Moniliales have adopted the endozoic habit, the commonest being *Harposporium anguillulae* and *Acrostalagamus obovatus.* All attack nematodes. They usually gain entry into their hosts by means of sticky spores that adhere to the integuments of the nematodes, penetrating by a germ tube that gives rise to an endozoic mycelium of branched, septate hyphae. A few species have spores that are swallowed by the host. After the death of the nematode, the endozoic mycelium gives off fertile branches that grow out through the integument of the host and form conidia outside it.

Endozoic fungi attacking nematodes are also found among the Lagenidiales. *Protascus subuliformis, Myzocytium vermicolum,* and *Haptoglossa heterospora* are not uncommon in England. A significant feature of the endozoic Lagenidiales is that most of them have nonmotile, sticky spores instead of the zoospores that are characteristic of the group. Even *Myzocytium vermicolum,* which normally forms laterally biflagellate zoospores, often gives rise instead to nonmotile, moniliform spores that adhere to their hosts (Karling, 1942). There can be little doubt that the nonmotile spores are an adaptation to life in a host that is both numerous and gregarious.

Euryancale (Drechsler, 1939, 1951) is an endozoic member of the Zoopagales that infects nematodes. It has an endozoic mycelium of rather wide, nonseptate hyphae. Narrower fertile hyphae emerge from the dead host, bearing curiously curved conidia, slightly reminiscent of a species of *Harposporium.* Other endozoic fungi that attack nematodes include several chytrids, and *Pythium anguillulae,* which was observed by Sadeheck parasitizing the vinegar eelworm in a vat of vinegar. The systematic position of *P. anguillulae* is dubious in the extreme; it may have been identical with a species of *Phytophthora* that was observed in a nematode from England (Duddington, 1942).

V. FUNGI ATTACKING OTHER INVERTEBRATES

Protozoans, rotifers and nematodes appear to be the animals that usually are the hosts of predacious fungi, but there are occasional records of other invertebrates suffering attack, and no doubt the number of records would be multiplied if a mycological study were made of the smaller invertebrates. Nobody who knows the predacious fungi could believe that their activities are concentrated against three phyla of the animal kingdom. In particular, the possibility of marine predacious fungi should not be overlooked. They are common enough among nematodes in old, dried-up saltmarshes (Duddington and Wyborn, 1966), and there seems to be no reason why they should not be found in the sea.

Mention should be made of that curious group of fungi, the Eccrinales, and their associated groups, the Amoebidiales, Harpellales, Genistallales, and Asellariales (Lichtwardt, 1960). These are organisms that are mainly parasitic in or on various arthropods, especially Crustacea and Myriapoda. Little is known about them, and they would well repay further study.

REFERENCES

Arnaudow, N. (1923). Ein neue Rädertiere (Rotatoria) fangender Pilze (*Sommerstorffia spinosa* nov. gen., nov. sp.). *Flora* (*Jena*) **116**: 109–113.

Comandon, J., and P. de Fonbrune. (1938). Recherches expérimentales sur les Champignons prédateurs de Nématodes du sol. Les pièges garotteurs. *Compt. Rend. Soc. Biol.* **129**: 620–622.

Comandon, J., and P. de Fonbrune. (1939). De la formation et du fonctionnement des pièges de Champignons prédateurs de Nématodes. Recherches effectues à l'aide de la Micromanipulation et de la Cinématographie. *Compt. Rend.* **208:** 304–305.

Cooke, R. C. (1962a). The ecology of nematode-trapping fungi in the soil. *Ann. Appl. Biol.* **50:** 507–604.

Cooke, R. C. (1962b). The behaviour of nematode-trapping fungi during the decomposition of organic matter in the soil. *Brit. Mycol. Soc. Trans.* **45:** 314–319.

Cooke, R. C. (1963a). The predacious activity of nematode-trapping fungi added to soil. *Ann. Appl. Biol.* **51:** 295–299.

Cooke, R. C. (1963b). Ecological characteristics of nematode-trapping Hyphomycetes. I. Preliminary studies. *Ann. Appl. Biol.* **52:** 431–437.

Cooke, R. C. (1964). Ecological characteristics of nematode-trapping Hyphomycetes. II. Germination of conidia in soil. *Ann. Appl. Biol.* **54:** 375–379.

Couch, J. N. (1937). The formation and operation of the traps in the nematode-catching fungus, *Dactylella bembicodes* Drechsler. *J. Elisha Mitchell Sci. Soc.* **53:** 301–309.

Drechsler, C. (1933). Morphological diversity among fungi capturing and destroying nematodes. *J. Wash. Acad. Sci.* **23:** 138–141.

Drechsler, C. (1934). *Pedilospora dactylopaga* n. sp., a fungus capturing and consuming testaceous rhizopods. *J. Wash. Acad. Sci.* **24:** 395–402.

Drechsler, C. (1935a). Some conidial phycomycetes destructive to terricolous amoebae. *Mycologia* **27:** 6–40.

Drechsler, C. (1935b). A new mucedinaceous fungus capturing and consuming *Amoeba verrucosa*. *Mycologia* **27:** 216–223.

Drechsler, C. (1936). A *Fusarium*-like species of *Dactylella* capturing and consuming testaceous rhizopods. *J. Wash. Acad. Sci.* **26:** 397–404.

Drechsler, C. (1937a). A species of *Tridentaria* preying on *Difflugia constricta*. *J. Wash. Acad. Sci.* **27:** 391–398.

Drechsler, C. (1937b). Some hyphomycetes that prey on free-living terricolous nematodes. *Mycologia* **29:** 447–552.

Drechsler, C. (1939). Five new Zoopagaceae destructive to rhizopods and nematodes. *Mycologia* **31:** 388–415.

Drechsler, C. (1940). Three fungi destructive to free-living terricolous nematodes. *J. Wash. Acad. Sci.* **30:** 240–254.

Drechsler, C. (1946). A clamp-bearing fungus parasitic and predaceous on nematodes. *Mycologia* **38:** 1–23.

Drechsler, C. (1947). Three zoopagaceous fungi that capture and consume soil-inhabiting rhizopods. *Mycologia* **39:** 253–281.

Drechsler, C. (1951). Various zoopagaceous fungi subsisting on protozoans and eelworms. *Mycologia* **43:** 161–185.

Duddington, C. L. (1940). Predacious fungi from Cotswold leaf mould. *Nature* **145:** 150–151.

Duddington, C. L. (1942). Unpublished observations.

Duddington, C. L. (1951a). *Dactylella lobata,* predacious on nematodes. *Brit. Mycol. Soc. Trans.* **34:** 489–491.

Duddington, C. L. (1951b). The ecology of predacious fungi. I. Preliminary survey. *Brit. Mycol. Soc. Trans.* **34:** 322–331.

Duddington, C. L. (1954). Nematode-destroying fungi in agricultural soils. *Nature* **173:** 500.

Duddington, C. L. (1955a). Notes on the technique of handling predacious fungi. *Brit. Mycol. Soc. Trans.* **38**: 97–103.
Duddington, C. L. (1955b). A new species of *Stylopage* capturing nematodes. *Mycologia* **47**: 245–248.
Duddington, C. L. (1956a). The predacious fungi: Zoopagales and Moniliales. *Biol. Rev.* **31**: 152–193.
Duddington, C. L. (1956b). "The Friendly Fungi." Faber & Faber, London.
Duddington, C. L. (1962). Predacious fungi and the control of eelworms. *Viewpoints Biol.* **1**: 151–200.
Duddington, C. L., and C. H. E. Wyborn. (1966). Unpublished studies.
Feder, W. A., C. O. R. Everard, and C. L. Duddington. (1960). Heterocaryotic nature of ring formation in the predacious fungus *Dactylella doedycoides*. *Science* **131**: 922–924.
Feder, W. A., C. O. R. Everard, and L. M. O. Wooton. (1963). Sensitivity of several species of the nematophagus fungus *Dactylella* to a morphogenic substance derived from free-living nematodes. *Nematologica* **9**: 49–51.
Karling, J. S. (1936). A new predacious fungus. *Mycologia* **28**: 307–320.
Karling, J. S. (1942). "Simple holocarpic biflagellate Phycomycetes." Karling, New York.
Lichtwardt, R. W. (1960). The taxonomic position of the Eccrinales and related fungi. *Mycologia* **52**: 410–428.
Muller, H. G. (1958). The constricting ring mechanism of two predacious Hyphomycetes. *Brit. Mycol. Soc. Trans.* **41**: 341–364.
Peach, M. (1950). Aquatic predacious fungi. *Brit. Mycol. Soc. Trans.* **33**: 148–153.
Peach, M. (1952). Aquatic predacious fungi. II. *Brit. Mycol. Soc. Trans.* **35**: 19–23.
Peach, M. (1954). Aquatic predacious fungi. III. *Brit. Mycol. Soc. Trans.* **37**: 240–247.
Pramer, D., and N. R. Stoll. (1959). Nemin: A morphogenic substance causing trap formation by predacious fungi. *Science* **129**: 966–967.
Rees, J. R. (1955). Unpublished observations.
Roubaud, E., and R. Deschiens. (1939). Sur les agents de formation des dispositifs de capture chez les Hyphomycètes prédateurs des nématodes. *Compt. Rend.* **209**: 77–79.
Shepherd, A. M. (1955). Formation of the infection bulb in *Arthrobotrys Oligospora* Fresenius. *Nature* **175**: 475.
Sommerstorff, H. (1911). Ein tierefangender Pilz (*Zoophagus insidians,* nov. gen., nov. sp.). *Oesterr. Botan. Z.* **61**: 361–373.
Sparrow, F. K., Jr. (1929). A note on the occurrence of two rotifer capturing phycomycetes. *Mycologia* **21**: 90–96.
Winkler, E. J., S. Kuyama, and D. Pramer. (1961). A nemin assay procedure. *Nature* **191**: 155.
Wyborn, C. H. E. (1966). Unpublished studies.

CHAPTER 11

Fungi Parasitic on Other Fungi and Lichens

M. F. MADELIN

Department of Botany
The University
Bristol, England

I. INTRODUCTION

Fungi enter into a number of mutualistic relationships with other fungi (DeVay, 1956); among them is that in which one fungus absorbs nutriment from another. For some fungi this appears to be an incidental supplement to a generally saprobic mode of nutrition. In others it is a usual, but not exclusive, habit. For yet others, such mycoparasitism is obligatory.

Different degrees of morphological adaptation toward mycoparasitism may be recognized. Some fungi merely produce seemingly unspecialized hyphae; these contact or penetrate the host cells, which commonly they damage or kill. Others introduce haustoria, rhizoids, or specialized filaments into the host, and sometimes establish balanced parasitic relationships in which there is little or no damage to the host. Yet others, usually with holocarpic thalli, are entirely contained within their hosts. These and other modes of parasitism will be illustrated in the following consideration of the occurrence and nature of the mycoparasitic habit in the major groups of fungi. Fungi which parasitize lichens are treated separately in Section IV.

II. MYCOPARASITIC FUNGI

A. Plasmodiophoromycetes

Several plasmodiophoraceous organisms are intracellular parasites of other fungi. *Woronina polycystis* was the first to be discovered (Fig. 1A). It produces unequally biflagellate zoospores which infect saprolegniaceous hosts. Naked protoplasts are introduced into the tips of the host's hyphae or even into its antheridia or oogonia. The invaded hypha reacts to the parasite's presence by swelling, the swollen part becoming delimited by a septum. Cook and Nicholson (1933) report that the parasitic plasmodium becomes fragmented by the repeated formation of septa by the host so that a row of infected segments results, but the possibility exists that the observed series of parasitized segments are the result of multiple infections (Sparrow, 1960). Mature plasmodia develop into sori of either zoosporangia or resting spores. A second species, *W. pythii,* is an obligate parasite of *Pythium.* The latter reacts to infection by forming galls which are often arranged in series. *Sorodiscus cokeri* is another parasite of *Pythium* species, but causes little or no hypertrophy, while *Octomyxa achlyae* and *O. brevilegniae* (Fig. 1B) complete their life cycles in their respective saprolegniaceous hosts in ways similar to *W. polycystis* (Karling, 1942b; Pendergrass, 1950). [Other references are in Sparrow (1960).]

B. *Chytridiomycetes*

1. Chytridiales

In the Chytridiales there are parasites of both aquatic and nonaquatic fungi, and even of other chytrids. Three sorts of mycoparasitic chytrid may be recognized, namely ectoparasites, parasites with epibiotic reproductive parts but endobiotic rhizoidal systems, and endoparasites.

Solutoparies pythii is an ectoparasite with rhizoids that encircle but apparently do not penetrate the hyphae of its pythiaceous host, which becomes stimulated to branch abnormally.

There are a number of mycoparasitic chytrids which have epibiotic sporangia nourished through rhizoidal systems inserted into the host. *Phlyctochytrium synchytrii* is such a parasite on the resting sporangia of *Synchytrium endobioticum,* as are *Chytridium rhizophydii, Septosperma anomalum,* and *S. rhizophidii* on other chytrids. Of those chytrids which parasitize filamentous fungi in this way, *Chytriomyces parasiticus* causes localized swelling and branching of the mycelium of *Aphanomyces laevis,* while *Rhizophydium carpophilum,* which can also grow saprophytically, is a virulent parasite of the oogonia and oospores of a number of water molds. Another species of *Rhizophydium, R. fungicola,* attacks the mycelium of the imperfect fungus *Gloeosporium theobromae.*

Internal mycoparasitic chytrids include species of *Rozella* and *Olpidium. R. cladochytrii,* which may be taken as an example of the former, parasitizes saprophytic species of the Cladochytriaceae (Fig. 1C). Zoospores of the parasite introduce their contents into the sporangia or rhizomycelium of the host, where they grow as naked protoplasts which sometimes induce considerable enlargement of the host's rhizomycelium.

Later, each parasite develops its own wall, but this may be difficult to see if the parasite has filled a sporangium of the host. The mature parasite becomes a zoosporangium or a resting spore (Karling, 1942a). Other species of *Rozella* attack various aquatic fungi. Three species of *Olpidium* are known to be mycoparasitic, namely *O. uredinis* which infects the uredospores of several *Puccinia* species, *O. rhizophlyctidis* which inhabits species of *Rhizophlyctis,* and *O. allomycetos* which infects *Allomyces* species and the chytrid *Karlingia rosea. O. allomycetos* has a predilection for the resting sporangia of *A. anomalus* (Fig. 1D). Thin-walled sporangia and hyphae of the latter react to the introduction of the parasite's germ tubes by enclosing them within ingrowing pegs of wall material, whereas thick-walled sporangia only occasionally react in this way. Other internally parasitic chytrids include *Pleotrachelus fulgens* and *P. zopfianus* which form their sporangia within species of *Pilobolus,* and *Pringsheimiella dioica* which parasitizes *Achlya* species. *P. dioica* forms its resting spores only when two sexually opposite or compatible strains of parasite are present. [References to the chytrids mentioned above can be located in Sparrow (1960).]

2. *Blastocladiales*

Catenaria allomycis was discovered growing within *Allomyces anomalus* in the soil; it can also infect both generations of certain other *Allomyces* species, and also *Blastocladiella simplex* (Fig. 1E). The mature parasite consists of a series of rounded sporangia or resting spores linked by short one- or two-celled isthmuses (Sparrow, 1960).

C. *Hyphochytridiomycetes*

Rhizidiomyces apophysatus, which parasitizes organisms besides fungi, can attack species of *Saprolegnia* and *Achlya.* The apophysis and the branched rhizoidal system which sustain the epibiotic sporangial rudiment are located within the hosts' oogonia. *Rhizidiomycopsis japonicus* is a somewhat similar parasite of the oogonia of a species of *Aplanes.* Yet a third mycoparasite in this small class, namely *Hyphochytrium infestans,* was discovered inhabiting the ascocarp of a discomycete (Sparrow, 1960).

D. *Oomycetes*

1. *Saprolegniales*

Parasitism of other fungi is known among the Saprolegniaceae, particularly in the genus *Aphanomyces.* Hyphae of *A. parasiticus* invade the mycelium, young sporangia and young oogonia of certain other sapro-

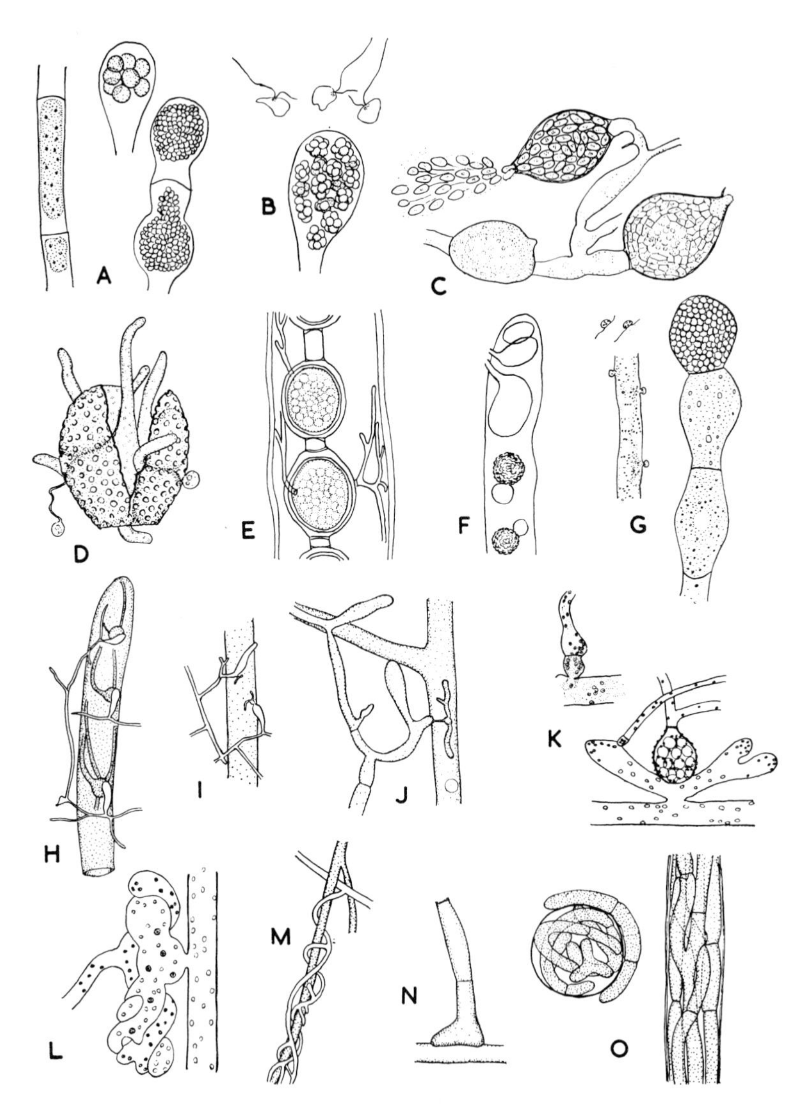

FIG. 1. Mycoparasitic fungi. A. *Woronina polycystis:* plasmodia, and sori of zoosporangia and resting spores in host filaments. After Cook and Nicholson (1933). B. *Octomyxa brevilegniae:* active zoospores, and groups of resting spores. After Pendergrass (1950). C. *Rozella cladochytrii:* thallus and sporangia in rhizomycelium of *Nowakowskiella profusum*. After Karling (1942a). D. *Olpidium allomycetos:* seven parasites in resting sporangium of *Allomyces anomalus*. After Karling (1948), in Sparrow (1960). E. *Catenaria allomycis:* resting spores and rhizoids in hypha of *Allomyces*. After Couch (1945), in Sparrow (1960). F. *Olpidiopsis vexans:* empty sporangia, and two mature oospores in slightly swollen hypha of *Saprolegnia*. After Barrett (1912). G. *Rozellopsis septigena:* zoospores, early stage of

legniaceous fungi and emerge only after they have exhausted the host hyphae. Efforts to grow this species apart from its host have been unsuccessful (Coker, 1923). *A. exoparasiticus* (Couch, 1926), *A. cladogamus,* and *Plectospira myriandra* (Drechsler, 1943) parasitize pythiaceous hosts by elaborate enwrapment with branches of the mycelium. Drechsler comments that unless the externally applied filaments are more efficient absorptive structures than appearances suggest, the attack of these saprolegniaceous fungi appears to serve more in thwarting the development of competing fungi than in utilizing their substance as nourishment.

Among the Ectrogellaceae, *Pythiella besseyi* is an endobiotic, holocarpic hyperparasite of *Olpidiopsis schenkiana,* in its turn parasitic in *Spirogyra.* The thallus of the hyperparasite is a bilobed or ellipsoidal cell which becomes a sporangium and liberates diplanetic zoospores (Sparrow and Ellison, 1949). The allied *P. vernalis* parasitizes and causes galls on the filaments of certain species of *Pythium.*

2. *Lagenidiales*

A number of endobiotic mycoparasites are classified as Lagenidiales. Indeed, two species of the type genus *Lagenidium* itself are mycoparasites, one, *L. destruens,* being a particularly virulent parasite on a species of *Achlya* (see Sparrow, 1960). Further, the genus *Olpidiopsis* is chiefly composed of parasites of freshwater fungi. Evidence from collected material and experimental studies suggests that the host range of any one species is restricted, even to a particular genus (Srivastava, 1966). Protoplasts of *Olpidiopsis* species on entering saprolegniaceous hosts by way of germ tubes produced by the biflagellate zoospores of the parasite quickly induce deformation of their hosts. The parasitic protoplast becomes walled and develops into a zoosporangium or fuses sexually with another parasite of opposite sex (Fig. 1F) (Barrett, 1912). Parasitism of other hosts is

---

infection of *Saprolegnia* hypha, and formation of a series of sporangia in host. After Prowse (1951). H. *Syncephalis* sp.: appressoria forming haustorial bladders and hyphae within sporangiophore of *Pilobolus crystallinus.* After Zopf (1890), in Buller (1934). I. *Piptocephalis xenophila:* appressoria with haustoria on hypha of *Mucor hiemalis.* After Dobbs and English (1954). J. *Dispira cornuta:* haustorium within hypha of *Sporodinia grandis.* After Ayers (1935). K. *Parasitella simplex:* parasitism of mucorine host; fusion of cupping cell with host hypha, and late stage (diagrammatic) showing sicyospore and secondary invasion of lobe of cupping cell. After Burgeff (1924). L. *Chaetocladium brefeldii* var. *macrosporum:* late stage of parasitism of mucorine host. After Burgeff (1924). M. *Sclerotinia* sp.: hyphae entwining a hypha of a *Mucor.* After Reinhardt (1892). N. *Gonatobotryum fuscum:* holdfast-shaped absorptive hypha contacting hypha of *Graphium* sp. After Shigo (1960). O. *Rhizoctonia solani:* mycelium attacking conidium of *Pythium splendens,* and sporangiophore of *Mucor recurvus.* After E. E. Butler (1957).

similar. Slifkin (1961) reports that once a saprolegniaceous thallus begins to reproduce, it becomes immune to infection by *O. incrassata.* If made to resume vegetative growth, the thallus again becomes susceptible. *Olpidiopsis* species appear to be obligate parasites, although Diehl (1935) reported the cultivation to maturity of some immature thalli of *Olpidiopsis* transferred from their saprolegniaceous host to artificial media.

The genus *Rozellopsis* contains *Rozella*-like parasites with biflagellate zoospores (Karling, 1942a). When the long trailing posterior flagellum of a *Rozellopsis* zoospore contacts a potential host, it becomes attached and then contracts, drawing the zoospore down to rest. The contents of the zoospore then enter the host to form a protoplast indistinguishable from the host's. Only in the transformation of the thallus of the parasite into a sporangium does a perceptible membrane develop around it. *R. inflata* (=*Pleolpidium inflatum*), which parasitizes various pythiaceous hosts, forms its sporangia singly in much-swollen terminal or intercalary regions of the host hypha which are delimited by septa (Prowse, 1954). *R. waterhousei* likewise forms its sporangia singly. However *R. septigena,* which appears to be confined to *Saprolegnia* species, forms chains of sporangia separated by cross walls which are apparently produced by the hypertrophied host hyphae themselves (Prowse, 1951) (Fig. 1G). It is not known whether the basipetal series of sporangia of *R. septigena,* and of the rather similar *R. simulans,* are derived by segmentation of single thalli or from multiple infections.

3. *Peronosporales*

Although no member of the Peronosporales is known to be *characteristically* a parasite of other fungi, mycoparasitism has been observed to occur in dual cultures of certain *Pythium* species (Drechsler, 1943). Parasitism by *P. oligandrum* may be taken as an example. Delicate branches of the fungus enwrap filaments of the host species, soon penetrating them and forming hyphae that grow lengthwise and assimilate the degenerating contents. Young oogonia, zoosporangia, and conidia may also be invaded, but oospores, once surrounded by their thick walls, seem to be immune. Haskins (1963) described a species of *Pythium* which in laboratory trials parasitized 79 of 98 species of fungi. On 69 hosts it produced oogonia, an event which depends on the presence of particular exogenous sterols (Haskins *et al.,* 1964).

E. *Zygomycetes*

Within the Mucorales are displayed biotic interactions with other fungi which range from almost fortuitous parasitism to highly specialized obligate parasitism. Such a range exists, for example, among those mucors which grow on the fruit bodies of higher fungi. While a number of species of *Absidia, Mucor,* and *Rhizopus* which invade the fruit bodies of higher fungi are certainly not always parasitic, other mucors such as *Sporodinia grandis* (=*Syzygites megalocarpus*), *Dicranophora fulva,* and *Spinellus* spp., although capable of saprophytic growth, are regularly found on basidiomycete sporophores. Spores of *Spinellus* spp. usually germinate only under special circumstances, but thereafter cultures are easily maintained by mycelial transfers. P. Watson (1964) has found that spores of *S. macrocarpus* will germinate on the surface of basidiomycete fruit bodies, or if ascorbic, arabo-ascorbic, or gluconic acids are present.

Parasitism by mucors of other mucors is common. It is accomplished in three major ways: by the proliferation of endoparasitic mycelium as in *Syncephalis;* by the insertion into the host of haustoria arising from an extramatrical mycelium as in species of *Piptocephalis, Dispira, Dimargaris,* and *Tieghemiomyces;* and by hyphal fusions between parasite and host as in *Parasitella* and *Chaetocladium.*

Except for *Syncephalis wynneae* which parasitizes the discomycete *Wynnea macrotis* (Thaxter, 1897), all species of *Syncephalis* are facultative parasites of mucors. Hyphae of the parasite form swollen appressoria in contact with the host's sporangiophore (Fig. 1H). From each appressorium arise one or more fine hyphae which penetrate the host and enlarge therein to form haustorial bladders from which springs the internal mycelium of the parasite. Later, hyphae of the parasite emerge from the host to form a superficial mycelial mat which bears sporangiophores (Buller, 1934).

Species of *Piptocephalis* have a fine extramatrical mycelium nourished by way of haustoria inserted generally into vegetative filaments of the host (Fig. 1I). Species of *Piptocephalis* parasitize only mucorales, except for *P. xenophila,* which develops better on ascomycetes (Dobbs and English, 1954). Though able to germinate on certain media, the spores of *Piptocephalis* need to establish a parasitic relationship with a susceptible host to continue their growth. Berry (1959) found that most hosts of *P. virginiana* seem to suffer little harm from this parasite, susceptibility to which is much affected by the culture medium. *Dispira cornuta* (=*D. americana* = *D. circinata,* fide Ayers, 1935), which, unlike *Piptocephalis,* may be cultured axenically, parasitizes only mucorales, into whose vegetative hyphae it inserts digitate haustoria (Fig. 1J). Reports that it has a mode of parasitism like that of *Parasitella* (e.g., Zycha, 1935) are evidently based on an account by Thaxter, who confused the parasitic organs of a species of *Parasitella* with those of *Dispira* (Ayers, 1935). *D. parvispora* likewise parasitizes only mucorales, but *D. simplex* is known to parasitize only the ascomycete *Chaetomium bostrychodes* (Benjamin, 1961, 1963).

Species of *Parasitella* and *Chaetocladium* are morphologically specialized but culturable parasites. *P. simplex* and *C. brefeldii* var. *macrosporum* were closely studied by Burgeff (1924). When a hypha of one of these contacts a suitable host, it delimits a terminal "cupping cell" ("cupping" in the sense of "bleeding") which fuses with the host hypha, the intervening cell walls disappearing. Nuclei of host and parasite mingle within the cupping cell. In *Parasitella,* the portion of the parasitic hypha adjacent to the cupping cell swells to become a thick-walled, food-laden storage cell, the sicyospore, around which extend processes arising from the cupping cell (Fig. 1K). The sicyospore eventually germinates like a zygospore to form mycelium or a sporangiophore. In *Chaetocladium,* the cupping cell enlarges and produces lateral processes which become entwined by branches arising from the region of the parasite adjacent to the cupping cell. Sporangiophores of *Chaetocladium* arise from this tangled gall. There is no sicyospore (Fig. 1L). Burgeff concluded that parasitism of *Absidia glauca* and *A. caerulea* by *Parasitella* and *Chaetocladium* was strictly sex-limited in that single strains of the heterothallic parasites attacked only complementary strains of these two heterothallic hosts. Furthermore, Burgeff conjectured that the parasitism of these fungi probably originated by their making use of their sexual reactions to attack their hosts. However Satina and Blakeslee (1926), working with a larger number of strains of these organisms, concluded that the parasitic reaction was not truly sex-limited since they found numerous exceptions.

A few members of the Kickxellaceae occur in association with other fungi and may prove to be mycoparasitic (Benjamin, 1959).

F. Ascomycetes

Many ascomycetes are mycoparasitic (in Hansford, 1946; Nicot, 1962). Among those which attack basidiomycetous fructifications are species of *Hypomyces. H. chrysospermum* is common on boletes on which it most frequently appears in its chlamydospore state (*Sepedonium*). Early stages of infection may show a true conidial state, but perithecia are rare.

Besides parasites of insects, the genus *Cordyceps* contains five species (including the familiar *C. ophioglossoides* and *C. capitata*) which live upon the subterranean ascocarps of *Elaphoglossum,* and two which live upon the sclerotia of *Claviceps* (Kobayasi, 1941). *C. ophioglossoides* grows readily in artificial culture. *Battarina inclusa* is another parasite of hypogeous ascocarps which forms its astomate perithecia within the hymenium of *Tuber puberulum*.

Eudarluca caricis (=*E. australis*) in both perithecial and pycnidial (=*Darluca filum*) stages is a cosmopolitan parasite of many macrocyclic and microcyclic rusts, although Eriksson (1966), who summarizes the extensive literature on this fungus, notes that one cannot eliminate the possibility that it may also to some extent feed directly upon the vascular plant as a parasite or saprophyte. It fructifies most commonly in uredosori, but also in aecidia and teleutosori. Its perfect state is generally found on *Puccinia* spp. on members of the Gramineae and Cyperaceae (Eriksson, 1966). Keener (1934) showed that isolates of this easily cultured parasite differed in their virulence toward different species of rusts.

A few discomycetes are mycoparasitic, for example, *Micropyxis geoglossi* which grows and fruits on the living apothecia of another discomycete, *Trichoglossum*. Attempts to culture it artificially have failed (Seeler, 1943). The parasitism displayed by certain *Sclerotinia* species is quite different. Reinhardt (1892) found that in dual culture their hyphae envelop and kill the hyphae of a number of other fungi, although no special parasitic organs are developed (Fig. 1M).

G. *Basidiomycetes*

The few basidiomycetes which are known to be mycoparasitic are all hymenomycetes. *Claudopus subdepluens* fruits on the pores and stipe of *Polyporus perennis*. The parasite's mycelium partially fills some of the hymenial pores of the host and extends to a considerable depth into its tissues, even perhaps into the soil. Neither enzymatic digestion of the host nor parasitic haustoria have been seen. *Boletus parasiticus* attacks the fruit bodies of *Scleroderma* species, while *Asterophora lycoperdoides* and *A. parasitica* (sometimes classified as species of *Nyctalis*) live and fructify on a number of agarics (especially *Russula* and *Lactarius* spp.). *Asterophora* species rarely form basidiospores, reproducing instead by chlamydospores.

The above parasites of fruit bodies, and others like *Claudopus parasiticus* and *Volvariella surrecta,* cause little or no deformation of their hosts, but *Stropharia epimyces* dwarfs and renders more or less sterile the sporophores of *Coprinus comatus* and *C. atramentarius* on which it grows (Buller, 1924).

There are also examples of hymenomycetes attacking nonbasidiomycetous fungi. *Corticium solani* is described in Section H, 3 below under the name of its imperfect state, *Rhizoctonia solani*. Barnett (1963) has recently recorded that in laboratory tests some wood-rotting polypores and agarics penetrate and damage the endoconidia of *Ceratocystis* spp. He suggests that mycoparasitism would have some survival value for these fungi.

H. Deuteromycetes

1. Sphaeropsidales

Ampelomyces quisqualis (=*Cicinnobolus cesatii*) is a parasite which forms pycnidia within the conidiophores, ascocarps, and even vegetative cells of powdery mildews. Slender hyphae of the parasite grow rapidly through those of the mildew, at first having little effect, but later killing them. It is possible that the hyperparasite overwinters as a saprophyte on the leaves bearing the mildew. *A. quisqualis* grows and sporulates on various nutrient agar media (Emmons, 1930). A number of other hyperparasitic species of *Ampelomyces* have been described, but it seems doubtful that they are distinct from *A. quisqualis* (Hansford, 1946).

Coniothyrium minitans is a parasite of the sclerotia, and sometimes the apothecia, of certain species of *Sclerotinia*. The parasite at first produces little effect in its attack on sclerotia in the soil, but it opens the way to secondary parasites so that the sclerotia eventually disintegrate (Tribe, 1957).

A number of other pycnidial fungi parasitize leaf-inhabiting ascomycetes (Hansford, 1946) and other higher fungi (Seeler, 1943).

2. Moniliales

Various hyphomycetes are capable of mycoparasitism, but for many of these it is probably not their predominant habit. This is probably true for certain species of *Trichoderma, Penicillium,* and *Cephalosporium. T. lignorum* parasitizes a number of different soil fungi in artificial culture by encircling their hyphae with its own. This is sometimes followed by penetration and growth within the host (Weindling, 1932; K. D. Butler, 1935). *T. viride* in artificial culture on acid media parasitizes the hyphae of *Armillaria mellea* and *Polyporus schweinitzii* in a similar way (Aytoun, 1953). This sort of parasitism evidently occurs under more natural conditions too, for Boosalis (1956) found that a *Trichoderma* species was able to parasitize the mycelium of *Rhizoctonia* (*Corticium*) *solani* in unsterilized field soil, as also could *Penicillium vermiculatum*. The latter species developed penetration pegs from which internally parasitic mycelium originated. Species of *Penicillium* and *Aspergillus* have also been observed to invade the sporangiophores of mucoraceous fungi, just as species of *Cephalosporium* invade the hyphae, conidiophores, and conidia of certain species of *Helminthosporium* (Kenneth and Isaac, 1964).

A greater degree of physiological specialization for mycoparasitism is shown by *Gonatobotryum fuscum* (Shigo, 1960), *G. simplex* (Whaley and Barnett, 1963), and *Calcarisporium parasiticum* (Barnett and Lilly, 1958), all of which are unable to grow in the absence of appropriate hosts. These species contact the hyphae of their hosts by means of special hyphal branches which appear not to penetrate at all (Fig. 1N).

A rather differently specialized form of mycoparasitism is shown by *Dactylella spermatophaga* and *Trinacrium subtile,* which invade the oospores of root-rotting and other soil-inhabiting oomycetes (Drechsler, 1938). Hyphae penetrate the walls of oogonia and oospores without regard for thickness, and form haustoria within. Over extended periods of time, such fungi presumably contribute effectively to the eradication from the soil of oospores of root-rotting oomycetes. A comparable degree of mycoparasitic specialization is shown by certain hyphomycetous hyperparasites of rust fungi. *Tuberculina maxima* is the "purple mold" which invades the spermogonia and aecidia of, principally, certain *Cronartium* species including *C. ribicola.* Though culturable, it is slow growing (Hubert, 1935). In tropical Africa, certain species of *Titaea* are likewise parasitic in the sori of rusts, *T. hemileae* invading *Hemileia* on coffee (Hansford, 1946).

Several hyphomycetes which parasitize the cultivated mushroom are economically important. *Mycogone perniciosa* is an important pest which causes enlargement of the stipe, reduction or suppression of the cap, and eventually, rapid decomposition of the flesh of the mushroom. The hyphae of the parasite are intercellular and are reported to cause at first an intense multiplication of the nuclei in the cells of the host. The later breakdown of the mushroom hyphae adjoining those of the parasite has been attributed to physical pressure resulting from the enlargement of the parasitic hyphae, and also to enzyme secretion (Smith, 1924; Chaze and Sarazin, 1936). Other hyphomycetous parasites of mushrooms include *Verticillium malthousei* and *Cephalosporium costantinii,* both of which can deform the host, though not like *Mycogone* causing rapid decomposition; and *C. lamellaecola* which causes fasciation and mildewing of the gills (Smith, 1924; Ware, 1933).

Under natural conditions, too, many hyphomycetes are associated with the fruit bodies of higher basidiomycetes (Nicot, 1962). Although harmless saprophytes sometimes grow on perennial or coriaceous fruit-bodies, the relationship of many hyphomycetes is undoubtedly a parasitic one. Parasitism of larger ascomycetous fruit-bodies is also known. For example *Fusidium parasiticum* attacks the stromata of *Xylaria* species; it sporulates abundantly over the surface but does little harm to the underlying tissues (Backus and Stowell, 1953).

Many hyphomycetes which parasitize leaf-inhabiting ascomycetes are listed by Hansford (1946).

Like so many true fungi, myxomycetes too may be attacked by fungal parasites. These are principally hyphomycetes. *Stilbum tomentosum* is common and forms abundant white coremia on the fructifications of *Trichia* and other slime molds (Petch, 1945).

3. *Mycelia Sterilia*

As well as parasitizing higher plants, *Rhizoctonia solani* can parasitize other fungi, in spite of its own susceptibility to certain mycoparasites (E. E. Butler, 1957). Mycoparasitism has been observed in sclerotial strains as well as strains which have produced the perfect state referable to *Corticium solani*. *R. solani* exhibits one or other of two modes of parasitism, depending on the host. On some, including *Pythium* species, the parasite coils tightly about the host hyphae causing their protoplasm to disappear or coagulate. On mucorales and the imperfect fungus, *Amblyosporium botrytis*—the only higher fungus *R. solani* is known to attack—the hyphae of the parasite penetrate the host hyphae apparently by mechanical pressure, and establish an extensive internal mycellium (Fig. 1O). There may also be some coiling of hyphae around the host. A study of 20 isolates revealed the existence of races specialized with respect to host range. Establishment of the parasitic relationship was greatly influenced by the nutrition of the parasite and potential host prior to their encounter. While conditions inducing poor growth of either the host or the parasite served to reduce the amount of infection, good vegetative growth did not of itself ensure that parasitism would occur.

Chlamydospores of species of the hypogeous zygomycete *Endogone,* frequently contain septate hyphae of parasites which in their hosts and in cultures form no spores themselves. They apparently have no effect on the form of the surrounding fruit body (Godfrey, 1957).

III. THE HOST-PARASITE RELATIONSHIP

So widespread is the distribution of mycoparasitism in the fungi and so varied are its physical manifestations that a diversity of physiological interrelationships between host and parasite is to be expected. Reference to such works as Oudemans' "Enumeratio Systemica Fungorum" (1919) indicates how large is the number of species of fungi found growing on fungi. However, it may be better, as Barnett (1963) suggests, to refer to most of these fungi as merely fungicolous. Intimate physical juxtaposition of two fungi does not necessarily signify a host-parasite relationship, i.e., one which is favorable to one fungus and usually detrimental to the other.

Any one of a number of biological relationships might exist, such as have been discussed by DeVay (1956). Parasitism is just one form of symbiosis which involves heterotrophic organisms. Among the true mycoparasites there are those which obtain nutrients from living hosts (biotrophic parasites) and those able to kill host cells and then use their nutrients (necrotrophic parasites). Unfortunately very little is known of the qualitative and quantitative aspects of the transfer of materials from host to parasite. To many parasites, and especially to those which are destructively parasitic, the host probably represents a local concentration of general or particular nutrients that are available to the parasite but not to its competitors. Where a more balanced host-parasite relationship exists, we can with few exceptions at present do little more than use our usually limited knowledge of the cultural characteristics of the parasite to speculate as to the nature of the relationship. It is a matter of conjecture whether the transfer between a particular pair of fungi contributes general nutrients for the parasite, or particular essential substances required by a deficient metabolism in the parasite. *Calcarisporium parasiticum* and *Gonatobotryum simplex* both appear to require the same vitamin-like growth factor for axenic growth (Barnett and Lilly, 1958; Whaley and Barnett, 1963). This factor is present in many ascomycetes and deuteromycetes and some basidiomycetes, but has not been found in phycomycetes. The basic factor underlying the successful parasitism by *C. parasiticum* and *G. simplex* appears to be their ability to absorb the required nutrient from the living host cells, probably by altering the permeability of the cell membrane (Barnett, 1964). For certain obligate parasites it appears that the continued metabolic activity of the host is more important than the actual content of nutrients at the time the parasitic relationship is established. The importance to the parasite of continued functioning of the host is well illustrated by *Rozellopsis inflata* when its zoospores infect, as occasionally they do, the encysted zoospores of *Zoophagus insidians* (Prowse, 1954). The infected zoospore enlarges and becomes converted in entirety into a zoosporangium of the parasite. It appears that the continued activity of the small amount of enveloping host material is essential to the growth of the obligately parasitic *Rozellopsis*.

Principally physiological aspects of host-parasite relationships are reviewed and discussed by Barnett (1963, 1964) and Boosalis (1964).

IV. FUNGI PARASITIC ON LICHENS

A substantial body of information has accrued relating to fungi which have been found growing in lichen thalli of which they are not a usual fungal component. The biological relationships of many such fungi to the thalli in which they have been found are far from clear and have been interpreted in divers ways. This is perhaps hardly surprising in view of the different interpretations of the relationship between fungus and alga in a normal lichen. Thus a number of fungi now recognized as parasites were themselves formerly regarded as lichens. Further the pycnidia formed by some lichens as secondary fruit forms have sometimes been misinterpreted as parasitic fungi (W. Watson, 1948). Interpretations notwithstanding, curious multiple associations exist.

Some fungi are clearly parasitic in view of the way their attack causes decomposition of the lichen thallus, e.g., *Coniothecium graphideorum* on *Opegrapha* species (in W. Watson, 1948). Others, however, inhabit a lichen thallus without killing its normal components. A curious form of this relationship has been observed in which the algal cells of a lichen become entangled not only with hyphae of the lichen-fungus proper, but also with those of a second fungus, but without harmful effect. This relationship has been termed parasymbiosis. Some fungi which do not damage the normal components of the lichen induce various sorts of hypertrophy, such as the tubercle-like galls induced in *Cladonia destricta* and *C. cornuta* by *Phoma uncialicola* and *Diplodina sandstedei,* respectively; the wart-like galls on *Parmelia* species induced by the parasymbiotic discomycete *Abrothallus parmeliarum;* and the galls variously shaped like spoons, fists, spheres, bladders, horseshoes, and hooks observed in other parasitized lichens.

Von Keissler (1930), in his monumental work on lichen parasites, discusses the relationships of lichens to their parasites, and provides an extensive systematic treatment of the latter. Of the parasites, most are ascomycetes or deuteromycetes, a few are basidiomycetes, and—with one possible exception which may be a saprobe—none are lower fungi.

REFERENCES

Ayers, T. T. (1935). Parasitism of *Dispira cornuta*. *Mycologia* **27**: 235–261.

Aytoun, R. S. C. (1953). The genus *Trichoderma:* Its relationship with *Armillaria mellea* (Vahl ex Fries) Quél. and *Polyporus schweinitzii* Fr., together with preliminary observations on its ecology in woodland soils. *Trans. Proc. Botan. Soc. Edinburgh* **36**: 99–114.

Backus, M. P., and E. A. Stowell. (1953). A *Fusidium* disease of *Xylaria* in Wisconsin. *Mycologia* **45**: 836–847.

Barnett, H. L. (1963). The nature of mycoparasitism by fungi. *Ann. Rev. Microbiol.* **17**: 1–14.

Barnett, H. L. (1964). Mycoparasitism. *Mycologia* **56**: 1–19.

Barnett, H. L., and V. G. Lilly. (1958). Parasitism of *Calcarisporium parasiticum* on species of *Physalospora* and related fungi. *West Va., Univ. Agr. Expt. Sta., Bull.* **420**: 1–37.

Barrett, J. T. (1912). Development and sexuality of some species of *Olpidiopsis* (Cornu) Fischer. *Ann. Botany (London)* **26**: 209–238.

Benjamin, R. K. (1959). The merosporangiferous Mucorales. *Aliso* **4**: 321–433.

Benjamin, R. K. (1961). Addenda to "The merosporangiferous Mucorales." *Aliso* **5**: 11–19.

Benjamin, R. K. (1963). Addenda to "The merosporangiferous Mucorales" II. *Aliso* **5**: 273–288.

Berry, C. R. (1959). Factors affecting parasitism of *Piptocephalis virginiana* on other Mucorales. *Mycologia* **51**: 824–832.

Boosalis, M. G. (1956). Effect of soil temperature and green-manure amendment of unsterilized soil on parasitism of *Rhizoctonia solani* by *Penicillium vermiculatum* and *Trichoderma* sp. *Phytopathology* **46**: 473–478.

Boosalis, M. G. (1964). Hyperparasitism. *Ann. Rev. Phytopathol.* **2**: 363–376.

Buller, A. H. R. (1924). "Researches on Fungi," Vol. III, 611 pp. Longmans, Green, New York.

Buller, A. H. R. (1934). "Researches on Fungi," Vol. VI, 513 pp. Longmans, Green, New York.

Burgeff, H. (1924). Untersuchungen über Sexualität und Parasitismus bei Mucorineen I. *Botan. Abhandl. Herausgegeben von Dr. K. Goebel* **4**: 1–135.

Butler, E. E. (1957). *Rhizoctonia solani* as a parasite of fungi. *Mycologia* **49**: 354–373.

Butler, K. D. (1935). The cotton root rot fungus, *Phymatotrichum omnivorum*, parasitic on the water melon, *Citrullus vulgaris*. *Phytopathology* **25**: 559–577.

Chaze, J., and A. Sarazin. (1936). Nouvelles données biologiques et expérimentales sur la môle maladie du champignon de couche. *Ann. Sci. Nat.: Botan. Biol. vegetale* **18**: 1–85.

Coker, W. C. (1923). "The Saprolegniaceae, with Notes on Other Water Molds," 201 pp. Univ. of North Carolina Press, Chapel Hill, North Carolina.

Cook, W. R. I., and W. H. Nicholson. (1933). A contribution to our knowledge of *Woronina polycystis* Cornu. *Ann. Botany (London)* **47**: 851–859.

Couch, J. N. (1926). Notes on the genus *Aphanomyces*, with a description of a new semiparasitic species. *J. Elisha Mitchell Sci. Soc.* **41**: 213–227.

DeVay, J. E. (1956). Mutual relationships in fungi. *Ann. Rev. Microbiol.* **10**: 115–140.

Diehl, H. (1935). Beiträge zur Biologie von *Olpidiopsis saprolegniae* Barrett. *Zentr. Bakteriol., Parasitenk. Abt.* **II 92**: 229–249.

Dobbs, C. G., and M. P. English. (1954). *Piptocephalis xenophila* sp. nov. parasitic on non-mucorine hosts. *Brit. Mycol. Soc. Trans.* **37**: 375–389.

Drechsler, C. (1938). Two Hyphomycetes parasitic on oospores of root-rotting Oomycetes. *Phytopathology* **28**: 81–103.

Drechsler, C. (1943). Two species of *Pythium* occurring in southern states. *Phytopathology* **33**: 261–299.

Emmons, C. W. (1930). *Cicinnobolus cesatii*, a study in host-parasite relationships. *Bull. Torrey Botan. Club* **57**: 421–442.

Eriksson, O. (1966). On *Eudarluca caricis* (Fr.) O. Eriks,, comb. nov., a cosmopolitan uredinicolous pyrenomycete. *Botan. Notiser* **119**: 33–69.

Godfrey, R. M. (1957). Studies on British species of *Endogone*. II. Fungal parasites. *Brit. Mycol. Soc. Trans.* **40**: 136–144.

Hansford, C. G. (1946). The foliicolous Ascomycetes, their parasites and associated fungi. *Mycol. Papers, Imp. Mycol. Inst.* **15**: 1–240.

Haskins, R. H. (1963). Morphology, nutrition, and host range of a species of *Pythium*. *Can. J. Microbiol.* **9**: 451–457.

Haskins, R. H., A. P. Tulloch, and R. G. Micetich. (1964). Steroids and the stimulation of sexual reproduction of a species of *Pythium*. *Can. J. Microbiol.* **10**: 187–195.

Hubert, E. A. (1935). Observations on *Tuberculina maxima,* a parasite of *Cronartium ribicola*. *Phytopathology* **25**: 253-261.

Karling, J. S. (1942a). Parasitism among the chytrids. *Am. J. Botany* **29**: 24–35.

Karling, J. S. (1942b). "The Plasmodiophorales," 144 pp. Published by the author, New York.

Keener, P. D. (1934). Biological specialization in *Darluca filum*. *Bull. Torrey Botan. Club* **61**: 475–490.

Kenneth, R., and P. K. Isaac. (1964). *Cephalosporium* species parasitic on *Helminthosporium* (sensu lato). *Can. J. Plant Sci.* **44**: 182–187.

Kobayasi, Y. (1941). The genus *Cordyceps* and its allies. *Sci. Rept. Tokyo Kyoiku Daigaku* **B5**: 53–260.

Nicot, J. (1962). Les moisissures des champignons supérieurs. Liste préliminaire des espèces récoltées en 1959, 1960, 1961. *Bull. Soc. Mycol. France* **78**: 221–238.

Oudemans, C. A. J. A. (1919). "Enumeratio Systematica Fungorum," Vol. 1, 1230 pp. Martinus Nijhoff, The Hague.

Pendergrass, W. R. (1950). Studies on a plasmodiophoraceous parasite, *Octomyxa brevilegniae*. *Mycologia* **42**: 279–289.

Petch, T. (1945). *Stilbum tomentosum* Schrad. *Brit. Mycol. Soc. Trans.* **28**: 101–109.

Prowse, G. A. (1951). On *Rozellopsis septigena*. *Brit. Mycol. Soc. Trans.* **34**: 400–405.

Prowse, G. A. (1954). *Sommerstorffia spinosa* and *Zoophagus insidians* predacious on rotifers, and *Rozellopsis inflata* the endoparasite of *Zoophagus*. *Brit. Mycol. Soc. Trans.* **37**: 134–150.

Reinhardt, M. O. (1892). Das Wachsthum der Pilzhyphen. Ein Beitrag zur Kenntnis des Flächenwachsthums vegetabilischer Zellmembranen. *Jahrb. Wiss. Botan.* **23**: 478–563.

Satina, S., and A. F. Blakeslee. (1926). The Mucor parasite *Parasitella* in relation to sex. *Proc. Natl. Acad. Sci. U.S.* **12**: 202–207.

Seeler, E. V., Jr. (1943). Several fungicolous fungi. *Farlowia* **1**: 119–133.

Shigo, A. L. (1960). Parasitism of *Gonatobotryum fuscum* on species of *Ceratocystis*. *Mycologia* **52**: 584–598.

Slifkin, M. K. (1961). Parasitism of *Olpidiopsis incrassata* on members of the Saprolegniaceae. I. Host range and effects of light, temperature, and stage of host on infectivity. *Mycologia* **53**: 183–193.

Smith, F. E. V. (1924). Three diseases of cultivated mushrooms. *Brit. Mycol. Soc. Trans.* **10**: 81–97.

Sparrow, F. K., Jr. (1960). "Aquatic Phycomycetes," 2nd ed., 1187 pp. Univ. of Michigan Press, Ann Arbor, Michigan.

Sparrow, F. K., Jr., and B. Ellison. (1949). *Olpidiopsis schenkiana* and its hyperparasite *Ectrogella besseyi* n. sp. *Mycologia* **41**: 28–35.

Srivastava, G. C. (1966). The host range of four species of *Olpidiopsis*. *Brit. Mycol. Soc. Trans.* **49**: 69–72.

Thaxter, R. (1897). New or peculiar zygomycetes. 2. *Syncephalastrum* and *Syncephalis*. *Botan. Gaz.* **24**: 1–15.

Tribe, H. T. (1957). On the parasitism of *Sclerotinia trifoliorum* by *Coniothyrium minitans*. *Brit. Mycol. Soc. Trans.* **40**: 489–499.

von Keissler, K. (1930). Die Flechtenparasiten. *In* "Kryptogamen-Flora" (L. Rabenhorst, ed.), Vol. VIII, 712 pp. Akad. Verlagsges., Leipzig.

Ware, W. M. (1933). A disease of cultivated mushrooms caused by *Verticillium malthousei* sp. nov. *Ann. Botany* (*London*) **47**: 763–786.

Watson, P. (1964). Spore germination in *Spinellus macrocarpus*. *Brit. Mycol. Soc. Trans.* **47**: 239–245.

Watson, W. (1948). List of British fungi parasitic on lichens or which have been included as lichens (or vice versa), with some notes on their characters and distribution. *Brit. Mycol. Soc. Trans.* **31**: 305–399.

Weindling, R. (1932). *Trichoderma lignorum* as a parasite of other soil fungi. *Phytopathology* **22**: 837–845.

Whaley, J. W., and H. L. Barnett. (1963). Parasitism and nutrition of *Gonatobotrys simplex*. *Mycologia* **55**: 199–210.

Zycha, H. (1935). Pilze II. Mucorineae. *In* "Kryptogamenflora der Mark Brandenburg," Vol. VIa, 264 pp. Bornträger, Berlin.

Ecology

FUNGI UNDER DOMESTICATION

CHAPTER 12

Fungi under Domestication

GEORGE SMITH[1]

Department of Biochemistry
London School of Hygiene and Tropical Medicine
London, England

I. INTRODUCTION

From very early times man has domesticated wild animals and improved their usefulness by selection. In the same way wild plants, which were found to be of value as food or as sources of clothing materials, have been cultivated and gradually improved to give higher yields and superior products. Certain fungi, also, have been used by man from time immemorial, albeit without any knowledge of the organisms themselves, to effect fermentations to give potable liquors, or to improve the flavor of foodstuffs. In more recent times, as knowledge of the fungi themselves has developed, species which are mainly destructive in the wild have been domesticated and have been trained to serve man's purpose.

II. THE TRADITIONAL PROCESSES USING FUNGI

A. *Alcoholic Fermentation*

In the West, fermentation of carbohydrates to give alcoholic beverages has been carried out with the aid of yeasts; the traditional processes of making both beer and wine utilize strains of *Saccharomyces cerevisiae.* Until after the middle of the nineteenth century the processes were entirely empirical. Between 1876 and 1906 E. C. Hansen published a very long series of papers, from the Carlsberg Laboratories in Copenhagen, which did much to put brewing on a scientific basis. Hansen investigated contaminants, mostly of atmospheric origin, which infect beer and introduce undesirable flavors, or spoil the liquor completely. Eventually, he introduced pure culture methods into the brewery. One of the worst contaminants is *S. pastorianus,* since this destroys alcohol and taints the liquor.

[1] Died March 29, 1967.

In the wine industry the introduction of pure culture methods was somewhat slower than in the breweries, but at present both industries are on a completely scientific basis.

For particular beverages yeasts other than *S. cerevisiae* are used, either to increase the percentage of alcohol or to introduce particular flavors. In some Belgian and English beers an after fermentation is effected by means of species of *Brettanomyces,* which is more tolerant of alcohol than *S. cerevisiae* and hence carries the fermentation further. In the manufacture of sherry the so-called "flor," which gives the characteristic bouquet, consists of species of *Kloeckera* and *Hansenula.* A good account of this process of ripening sherry is given by Hohl and Cruess (1940).

The strains of yeasts used for brewing are usually classed as top and bottom yeasts. The top yeasts, which carry out a vigorous fermentation, in which the yeast cells are carried to the top of the liquor and form a surface pellicle, are used in the manufacture of typical English beers. The bottom yeasts ferment more slowly, and the cells stay at the bottom of the liquor. These are used in the manufacture of the so-called "lager beer," and are commonly known as *S. carlsbergensis.*

Another important method of producing alcohol is the "amylo" process. *S. cerevisiae* ferments sugars but does not secrete diastase, the starch-splitting enzyme. In the preparation of alcohol from starch various Mucoraceae are used, chiefly *Rhizopus japonicus* and *R. tonkinensis,* to hydrolyze the starch to glucose. The same species will also ferment the sugar to give alcohol, but the process is too slow, and usually yeast is added when a large proportion of the starch has been broken down, since this ferments much faster than *Rhizopus.*

In the Far East, alcoholic beverages are made from rice, and the active agents are not yeasts but strains of *Aspergillus oryzae* and the related *A. tamarii.* Japanese koji is a starter made by growing *A. oryzae* on cooked rice, usually mixed with other cereals, and the alcoholic beverage saké is manufactured by the bulk fermentation of rice, using the koji as starter.

B. *Soybean Fermentations*

Soy sauce, the basis of many European bottled sauces, is made in the Far East by fermenting soybeans by means of *Aspergillus tamarii.* The fungus is first grown on cooked soybeans, often mixed with other starchy material in order to aid rapid growth, and this product is used as a starter for the main fermentation.

Miso, an important commodity in Japan, is made by the fermentation of soybeans. It is sold as a pale brownish paste, from which is made a kind of thick soup popular as a nursing dish. The amount of miso produced in Japan exceeds 500,000 tons per annum. Cooked soybeans, koji made from rice, and 10–12% of salt are ground together with a little miso from a previous batch and allowed to ferment at 35–40°C, without admission of air, for 3–5 months. It is then aged for several weeks at the ambient temperature, before being packed for sale.

A large number of other fermentations are carried out in Far Eastern countries, some utilizing members of the *A. flavus* group, others using various Mucoraceae, still others species of *Monascus*. A full account of these is given in the long paper by Hesseltine (1965).

C. *Baking*

Like the production of alcoholic beverages, baking is a process of great antiquity using yeast, but, instead of alcohol, the main product of fermentation is carbon dioxide. The production of pressed yeast for the baking industry is carried out on a very large scale; in modern times, strains of *Saccharomyces cerevisiae* have been selected for their ability to produce little alcohol, but to decompose most of the soluble carbohydrate to CO_2. At one time yeasts from brewers and distillers were used for baking, the latter being the more suitable since it does not contain the bitter principles of hops. Now pressed yeast is manufactured specially for baking. In the production of beverages the aim is to produce as much alcohol as possible, with a fair amount of CO_2, and to limit the growth of the yeast cells. In pressed yeast manufacture, the aim is to obtain maximum growth of the yeast itself, with minimum production of alcohol, this being achieved by vigorous aeration and the addition of nutrients in stages, to keep pace with their removal from solution by the multiplying yeast cells. In the traditional process, still carried out in many homes, the yeast is first allowed to ferment a warm sugar solution, the number of cells being thus increased. This is used as a starter for the main fermentation of the dough.

D. *Mold-Ripened Cheese*

The manufacture of a variety of mold-ripened cheeses is another industry of unknown origin. Until the present century their production was on a purely empirical basis, the different flavors of cheese made in particular districts being due to variations in the milk used for the primary bacterial fermentation, and the presence of a local infection of a strain of the mold with distinct biochemical properties. There are two types of these cheeses, the blue-veined, more or less firm-textured type, such as Roquefort, Gorgonzola, and Stilton, and the soft, uncolored type, of which Camembert and Brie are the best known.

With a view to introducing the manufacture of the cheeses into America, Thom in 1905 (see Raper and Thom, 1949) began a study of the cheese molds. He showed that the molds of the blue-veined cheeses are all to be regarded as strains of *Penicillium roquefortii,* differences between the various cheeses being due to local differences in the curd. During the very long period during which these cheeses have been made in particular localities, there has continually been unconscious selection of strains. Where the manufacture has been deliberately introduced, as in the United States, selection of strains has been deliberate, and pure culture methods have been adopted.

During recent years the industry has been troubled by the appearance of a tan-colored mutant of *P. roquefortii.* When this supplants the blue mold the cheese is practically unsalable. The remedy is obvious—pasteurization of the milk, and inoculation with pure cultures.

The small soft cheeses are ripened either with *P. camemberti* or *P. caseicola,* the two species giving somewhat different flavors. The curd is made into small cakes, 3–4 cm thick, salted on the surface, and either inoculated with the desired species or placed in an infected room. The secret of success is strict attention to physical conditions, a temperature of 55–60°F, and a relative humidity of 88%. Any serious variation from these conditions usually results in infection, most commonly with *Scopulariopsis brevicaulis,* the infection being first indicated by the production of an ammoniacal odor.

III. MUSHROOM GROWING

As noted in Volume I (page 4), some of the larger fungi have for long been greatly esteemed as food. The supply of these esculents was originally dependent on naturally occurring fruit bodies, and although the practice of collecting wild fungi still continues the increasing urbanization and higher population has led, at least in Europe and temperate North America, to most of the larger fungi offered for sale being grown commercially and to a decline in diversity of the species eaten. In the United Kingdom and the United States the mushroom (*Agaricus bisporus*), fresh or canned, is the usual article of trade. Similarly, the paddy straw mushroom (*Volvariella volvacea*) predominates in India and the Far East, and the shiitake (*Lentinus edodes*) in Japan and China. Recently Singer (1961) has discursively reviewed the cultivation of mushrooms throughout the world and his monograph is a useful source book. Here space permits only some of the salient features of the cultivation of mushrooms to be summarized.

A. *Mushroom Cultivation*

The origins of mushroom culture are obscure. Mushrooms were being cultivated at the beginning of the eighteenth century in France, where by the mid-nineteenth century there was a flourishing mushroom-growing industry, particularly in caves resulting from quarrying in the Paris region. These caves afforded the cool even temperature required for cultivating mushrooms on composted stable manure. The inoculum was either mycelium ("spawn") collected in the wild ("virgin spawn") or inoculum derived from the crop before it begins to bear, and the procedures then adopted are essentially those in use today. The main difference in modern practice is that the spawn is derived from pure laboratory cultures maintained under strictly controlled conditions so as to preserve the characteristics of a particular strain.

Briefly, mushroom culture involves the composting of horse manure (to which gypsum is frequently added at 15 kg per ton and if necessary additional straw) by turning a heap of manure at intervals and allowing it to heat. When it has cooled sufficiently the compost is either spread in layers in suitable flat trays in windowless mushroom sheds or made into ridges out of doors. The compost is then inoculated by the insertion of small portions of spawn and when the spawn is seen to be established ("running"), the bed or the ridge is then covered ("cased") with a 2–3 inch layer of soil. A few weeks later sporophores push up through the casing soil and are harvested. Several successive series ("flushes") of sporophores are developed to give a total average yield of 1.5–2.0 pounds of mushrooms per square foot of bed (7.5–9.4 kg/m^2). The optimum temperature for mushroom culture is an even 16–18°C (60–65°F). There is of necessity, because of the replacement of the horse by the internal combustion engine, current interest in finding a suitable replacement for stable manure as a substrate. Much has been written about mushroom culture, and there are many practical handbooks. Typical examples are those by Atkins (1966), Lambert (1956), Anonymous (1960), and Hunte (1966).

Finally, mention must be made of the identity of the fungi used. The cultivated mushroom is distinct from the classical field mushroom, *Agaricus campestris,* which as every student knows has four terminal spores on each basidium so that when presented with fruit bodies of cultivated mushrooms as class material he usually also records four-spored basidia although the cultivated form has typically only two spores on each basidium. The confusion between the field and cultivated mushroom is one of long standing, and it was not until 1951 that the name *Agaricus bisporus* was proposed for the latter. The two-spored form does occur in the wild, but it is under cultivation that, by intensive selection for color, shape, size, and other desirable commercial qualities, much variation has occurred and many variants and cultivars are available from spawn-producing firms. Two varieties—*A. bisporus* var. *albidus* and *A. bisporus* var. *avellaneus,* white and brown forms, respectively—have been given scientific names. Although *A. campestris* has probably never been cultivated, the four-spored *A. bitorquis* and *A. subperonatus* are occasionally grown (Singer, 1961).

B. Paddy Straw Mushroom Culture

Both the taxonomy and the nomenclature of the paddy [padi (the Malayan spelling), or rice] straw mushroom, like that of the common mushroom, have been confused. The paddy straw mushrooms have often been given the generic name *Volvaria* which, as it is a homonym of the generic name for a lichen, must be replaced by *Volvariella* for a genus which includes a complex of species. Following Singer (1961) and tradition, the two species commonly cultivated are *V. volvacea* and *V. diplasia,* especially the former of which several varieties can be distinguished [see Singer (1961) for details].

The cultivation of the paddy straw mushroom, as practiced from tropical Africa, to India and the Far East, is simple. Bundles of rice ("paddy") straw are soaked, then made into beds approximately 3½ by 3½ feet square and 2 feet high; either infection is left to chance, or the beds are inoculated with the mycelium of the agaric, either as "natural spawn" derived from another bed or pure culture spawn. Fruit bodies appear 2–3 weeks later, and one bed may yield up to 8 pounds or so. A minimum temperature of 21°C (70°F) is a prerequisite for success. The fruit bodies are marketed either fresh or after drying over a charcoal fire.

C. Shiitake Cultivation

The shiitake is another agaric but differs from those so far considered in being lignicolous and its cultivation in Japan is undertaken not on compost but on suitable logs of hardwood, which are inoculated with the fungus and stored out-of-doors in clearings of the forest or in other suitable situations. The logs, approximately 1 meter in length and 5–15 cm in diameter, are typically of shiis [species of *Pasania* (or *Shiia*)] but oak (*Quercus*) and chestnut (*Castanea*) are also widely employed. Holes are made in the logs with special tools, inoculum of spores or infected wood is inserted, and the logs are then stored in the open. Two years or so later fruit bodies begin to appear and flushes continue twice yearly, in spring and fall, for several years. The fruit bodies are of a firm texture and are usually marketed dry. According to Singer (1961), who can be consulted for further details, 2775 long tons of dried shiitake were produced in Japan in 1953.

Once again, the nomenclature is confused. *Lentinus edodes* is the preferred name for the shiitake, but synonyms of *L. edodes* include *Armillaria edodes, Cortinellus edodes, C. berkleyanus,* and *C. shiitake.*

D. Truffle Cultivation

Attention is drawn to truffle (species of *Tuber*) "cultivation" merely to complete the series. Mushrooms and straw mushrooms are intensively grown on compost—that for the former being more elaborate than for the latter—and mushroom mycelium suitable for soups can be grown in synthetic media by the deep culture technique (Humfeld and Sugihara, 1949, 1952). The shiitake is grown under controlled conditions on its natural substrate, and the same applies to the growing of truffles, but under conditions that leave much more to chance. The species involved, of which the best known is *Tuber melanosporum,* the Périgord truffle, are associated with a series of broad-leaved trees, particularly species of *Quercus*. Truffle production is a by-product of the afforestation of suitable soils in France, Italy, and Spain when some ten years after planting truffles may be expected to develop in the soil surrounding the trees in sufficient numbers to yield an annual spring crop (see Malençon, 1938; Singer, 1961).

IV. INDUSTRIAL FERMENTATIONS

Most of these are based on purely academic research on the biochemistry of the lower fungi. It is, however, no simple matter to transfer a laboratory discovery to the factory. Frequently the yields are not sufficiently high for large-scale production. Methods of enhancing the yield are either by selection of strains of the particular species, by finding other species which give greater yields or which work faster, or by obtaining mutants by means of mutagenic chemicals or by irradiation. Also it is important that the product should be obtained in good yield when the fungus is grown in submerged culture, since this is the only satisfactory method of fermentation with very large volumes of fluid culture medium.

A. Citric Acid

Wehmer (1893) showed that some molds produced citric acid from sugar. He made one of these, now considered to be a monoverticillate species of *Penicillium,* the type of a new genus *Citromyces*. It has since been shown that citric acid is produced by many species of *Penicillium,* but always in yields too low for commercial exploitation. Currie (1917) showed that species of the *Aspergillus niger* group produced both oxalic and citric acids. Methods were soon worked out for suppressing the production of oxalic acid, and increasing the yield of citric acid, the chief conditions being a high concentration of sugar (15%), a low concentration of nitrogen, and a highly acid reaction (pH 3.5 or lower). Exact details of commercial methods have never been published. However, one very interesting process has certainly been used, and may still be in operation. Initially the culture medium is inoculated and the fungal mycelium established in the fluid. The conversion of the remaining sugar is then allowed to take place, then the fluid is separated from the mycelium for isolation of the citric acid, and a fresh batch of culture medium is run onto the old mycelium. In this way the loss of sugar incurred in establishing mycelium is minimized (Perlman and Sih, 1960).

B. *Gluconic Acid*

This acid is produced by many species of molds. The first species to be used in attempting the large-scale production of the acid was *Penicillium purpurogenum* var. *rubri-sclerotium* (May *et al.*, 1927, 1929; Herrick and May, 1928). Later *P. chrysogenum* was found to give better yields, and finally, selected strains of *Aspergillus niger* were used. By submerged culture very good yields are obtained. Citric acid is used chiefly in medicinal and food preparations.

C. *d-Lactic Acid*

The fungus used is *Rhizopus oryzae* (Lockwood *et al.*, 1936), and a careful laboratory study of the fermentation led to a process taking only 30–35 hours, with a yield of up to 75% of the sugar consumed (Ward *et al.*, 1936, 1938).

D. *Gallic Acid*

This has been obtained since 1902, when Calmette showed that a clear tannin extract is readily fermented by a strain of *Aspergillus niger* [described by Calmette (1902) as *A. gallomyces*]. The medium must be well aerated and vigorously agitated, but exact details are not available. Gallic acid is used for making blue-black ink.

E. *Itaconic Acid*

Itaconic acid was originally obtained as a metabolic product by Kinoshita (1920), using a member of the *Aspergillus glaucus* series. The fungus currently used is *A. terreus,* the medium contains approximately 6% glucose, the fermentation is carried out in submerged culture, and yields of about 50% are obtained (Perlman and Sih, 1960). The acid is used in the plastics industries. As in other fermentation industries, yields have been improved first by selection of strains, and secondly by ultraviolet irradiation to give mutants.

F. Fumaric Acid

In this fermentation, which is described by Perlman and Sih (1960), the fungus is *Rhizopus arrhizus,* the medium contains 10–16% sugar, the temperature of operation is 33°C, and the acid is continuously neutralized by calcium carbonate as it is produced. Yields are upward of 65%.

G. Fat

Many species of microfungi produce fat, but the yield from different species varies enormously. The first successful large-scale production, using *Endomyces vernalis* (=*Trichosporon pullulans*), was developed in Germany toward the end of the first world war. Since then many investigations have been carried out (Lockwood *et al.,* 1934; Lundin, 1948; Woodbine, 1959). The conclusions of most workers have been that microbial fat cannot compete in normal times, on the basis of yields and costs, with animal and vegetable fats, but may become of importance on account of its content of the essential unsaturated acids.

H. Glycerol

Glycerol is produced in small amounts during the normal alcoholic fermentation. The yield is much improved by carrying out the fermentation in an alkaline medium, or, better, by adding sodium sulfite to the culture medium. The latter method has also the advantage of inhibiting the growth of contaminating bacteria, without affecting the activity of the yeast. The sulfite is added to the medium gradually during the fermentation. The method was worked out in Germany during the first world war. Later, a process developed in the United States used a specially selected strain of yeast and a medium kept alkaline by the gradual addition of sodium carbonate to a final concentration of about 5% (see Smith, 1960).

I. Proteins

Proteins are synthesized by a number of fungi, usually as cell constituents. The yeasts *Saccharomyces cerevisiae* and *Candida utilis* (formerly *Torulopsis utilis*) contain in the cells considerable amounts of high quality proteins. Thaysen (1953) has described the production of the so-called "food yeast," using specially selected strains of *C. utilis,* capable of growing well at 39°C, so that the manufacture could be carried on in hot countries. The first experimental plant was erected in Jamaica, with a view to supplementing the native diet, which was deficient in proteins and vitamins. The yeast contains about 45% protein and considerable amounts of B group vitamins. At the present time very little of the yeast is manufactured for human consumption, because the addition of more than a trace gives a flavor which soon palls. The yeast is, however, manufactured in Jamaica, South Africa, and the United States for adding to the feed of domestic animals, particularly to cattle fodder.

J. Vitamins

Compressed brewers' or distillers' yeast is widely used as a source of the B complex.

One of the B group, riboflavine, is now manufactured in the pure form by fermentation. The fungi used are *Ashbya gossypii* and *Eremothecium ashbyi* (Pridham and Raper, 1950). Yaw (1952) describes the production of riboflavine by *E. ashbyi* when grown on a synthetic medium, from which the product is readily isolated.

Although vitamin C and ergosterol, the precursor of vitamin D, are produced by molds, neither is manufactured by fermentation. Vitamin B_{12}, first isolated from liver, was soon found to be present in the broth on which *Streptomyces griseus* had been grown for production of streptomycin. At present most of the vitamin is obtained as a by-product in the manufacture of streptomycin, and of Aureomycin by *S. aureofaciens*. Yields have been improved by mutagenic agents acting on the organisms, and also by adding to the broth small amounts of cobalt.

K. Antibiotics

The first really successful antibiotic to be produced was, of course, penicillin, produced by species of the *Penicillium chrysogenum* group. The story of its discovery, and large-scale manufacture, and the elucidation of its chemical structure has often been told and need not be elaborated here (see Raper, 1952). It should, however, be noted that there are a number of penicillins, related but differing in structure, and produced mainly by adding suitable precursors to the fermenting liquor.

The most successful antibiotics are all produced by actinomycetes, particularly species of *Streptomyces*. Such are streptomycin, Aureomycin, Chloromycetin (chloramphenicol), and Terramycin. However, the agents producing them are not fungi and hence there is no point in other than a bare mention here.

Two metabolic products which are of considerable promise are obtained from a species of *Cephalosporium,* which was isolated from the sea near a sewage outfall in Sardinia. One substance, cephalothin (trade name Keflin) has been developed in the United States; the other, cephaloridine (trade name Ceporin), in England. Both are marked by low toxicity. The original metabolic product, cephalosporin C, had several disadvantages, but a large number of chemically modified derivatives have been made, and the substances undergoing clinical trials are the best of these. A good account of the cephalosporins is given by Abraham (1957). The antibiotics mentioned above are all antibacterial agents. In addition to these there are a number of antifungal substances which have met with some success. Weindling and Emerson (1936) isolated from *Gliocladium virens* (which they misidentified as both *Trichoderma viride* and *Gliocladium fimbriatum;* see Webster and Lomas, 1964), an inhabitant of wet soils—a substance, gliotoxin, which inhibits the growth of the damping-off fungi, species of *Pythium.* They had moderate success in controlling attacks by *Pythium,* by means of heavy inoculations of *G. virens* into wet soils. Van Luijk (1938) investigated a number of species of molds, all isolated from soil, as to their inhibitory effect on various species of *Pythium.* He found that the medium upon which *Penicillium expansum* had been grown was very successful in protecting seedlings from attack by *Pythium,* but that inoculation of the *Penicillium* into soil had no effect. The active substance was isolated and characterized as patulin by Anslow *et al.* (1943), who obtained it from *P. expansum* and, in better yield, from *P. patulum.*

Another antifungal agent is griseofulvin, produced by *Penicillium griseofulvum* and *P. nigricans* (for reviews, see Brian, 1960; Rhodes, 1963). This has been used in recent years for the cure of ringworm in man by oral administration (see Chapter 8). Another substance for the same purpose was isolated by Takeuchi *et al.* (1959, 1960) from a strain of *Paecilomyces variotii,* and called "variotin," but it has not so far come into general use.

L. Modifications of Sterols

The sterols occurring in greatest abundance in natural products have no useful physiological action. The active sterols are found in comparatively small amounts and are not easy to extract. The molecules of most of the latter have a hydroxy group at carbon-11, whereas the abundant natural steroids lack this group. The introduction of an —OH at C-11, if performed chemically, requires a large number of reactions, with losses at each stage. Peterson and Murray (1952) showed that progesterone is hydroxylated at C-11, in one step, by *Rhizopus arrhizus.* Since then thousands of microfungi have been screened for their possible useful transformation of steroids. At the present time it is possible to effect hydroxylation at many different points in the molecule, ketone formation, epoxidation, hydrogenation, cleavage of the side chain, and various combinations of these reactions. A comprehensive review of these reactions is given by Peterson (1963).

REFERENCES*

Abraham, E. P. (1957). The cephalosporins. *In* "Biochemistry of Some Peptides and Steroid Antibiotics," CIBA Lectures Microbial Biochem., pp. 30–63. Wiley, New York.

Anonymous. (1960). Mushroom growing. *Min. Agr. Fish. Food Bull.* **34:** 1–66.

Anslow, W. K., H. Raistrick, and G. Smith. (1943). Anti-fungal substances from moulds. Part I. Patulin (anhydro-3-hydroxymethylene-tetrahydro-1:4-pyrone-2-carboxylic acid), a metabolic product of *Penicillium patulum* Bainier and *Penicillium expansum* (Link) Thom. *J. Soc. Chem. Ind.* (*London*) **62:** 236–238.

Atkins, F. C. (1966). "Mushroom Growing Today," 5th ed. Faber & Faber, London.

Brian, P. W. (1960). Presidential address. Griseofulvin. *Brit. Mycol. Soc. Trans.* **43:** 1–13.

Calmette, A. (1902). German Patent 129,164.

Currie, J. N. (1917). The citric acid fermentation of *Aspergillus niger. J. Biol. Chem.* **31:** 15–37.

Herrick, H. T., and O. E. May. (1928). The production of gluconic acid by the *Penicillium luteum-purpurogenum* group. II. Some optimal conditions for acid formation. *J. Biol. Chem.* **77:** 185–195.

Hesseltine, C. W. (1965). A millennium of fungi, food, and fermentation. *Mycologia* **57:** 149–197.

Hohl, L. H., and W. V. Cruess. (1940). Observations on certain film-forming yeasts. *Zentr. Bakteriol., Parasitenk., Abt. II* **101:** 65–78.

Humfeld, H., and T. F. Sugihara. (1949). Mushroom mycelium production by submerged propagation. *Food Technol.* **3:** 355–356.

Humfeld, H., and T. F. Sugihara. (1952). The nutrient requirements of *Agaricus campestris* grown in submerged culture. *Mycologia* **44:** 605–620.

Hunte, W. (1966). "Champignon-Anbau im Haupt- und Nebenerwerb," 126 pp. Parey, Berlin and Hamburg.

Kinoshita, K. (1920). Formation of itaconic acid and mannitol by a new filamentous fungus. *J. Chem. Soc. Japan* **50:** 583–593.

Lambert, E. B. (1956). Mushroom growing in the United States. *U.S. Dept. Agr. Farmers' Bull.* **1875:** 1–12.

Lockwood, L. B., G. E. Ward, O. E. May, H. T. Herrick, and H. T. O'Neill. (1934). Production of fat by *Penicillium javanicum* van Beyma. *Zentr. Bakteriol., Parasitenk., Abt. II* **90:** 411–425.

Lockwood, L. B., G. E. Ward, and O. E. May. (1936). The physiology of *Rhizopus oryzae. J. Agr. Res.* **53:** 849.

Lundin, H. (1948). Über Fettsynthesen durch Mikroorganismen und Moglichkeiten für ihre industrielle Anwendung. *Jahrb. Hochschule Bodenk. Wien* **2:** 410–420.

Malençon, G. (1938). Les truffes europèenes, historique, morphogénie, organographie, classification, culture. *Rev. Mycol.* (*Mem. Hors. Ser.*) pp. 1–92.

May, O. E., H. T. Herrick, C. Thom, and M. B. Church. (1927). The production of gluconic acid by the *Penicillium luteum-purpurogenum* group. I. *J. Biol. Chem.* **75:** 417–422.

May, O. E., H. T. Herrick, A. J. Moyer, and R. Hellbach. (1929). Semi-plant scale production of gluconic acid by mold fermentation. *Ind. Eng. Chem.* **21:** 1198–1203.

Perlman, D., and C. J. Sih. (1960). Fungal synthesis of citric, fumaric, and itaconic acids. *Progr. Ind. Microbiol.* **2:** 167–194.

* For additional references see Smith (1960).

Peterson, D. H. (1963). Microbiological transformations of steriods and their application to preparation of hormones and derivatives. *In* "Biochemistry of Industrial Microorganisms" (C. Rainbow and A. H. Rose, eds.), pp. 538–606. Academic Press, New York.

Peterson, D. H., and H. C. Murray. (1952). Microbiological oxidation of steroids at carbon-11. *J. Am. Chem. Soc.* **74:** 1871.

Pridham, T. G., and K. B. Raper. (1950). *Ashbya gossypii*—its significance in nature and in the laboratory. *Mycologia* **42:** 603–623.

Raper, K. B. (1952). A decade of antibiotics in America. *Mycologia* **44:** 1–59.

Raper, K. B., and C. Thom. (1949). "Manual of the penicillia," 875 pp. Baillière, London.

Rhodes, A. (1963). Griseofulvin production and biosynthesis. *Progr. Ind. Microbiol.* **4:** 167–187.

Singer, R. (1961). "Mushrooms and Truffles," 272 pp. Leonard Hill (Books), London.

Smith, G. (1960). "An Introduction to Industrial Mycology," 5th ed., 399 pp. Arnold, London.

Takeuchi, S., *et al.* (1959). Variotin. *J. Antibiot.* (*Tokyo*) **A12:** 195–251.

Takeuchi, S., H. Yonehara, H. Umezawa, and Y. Sumiki. (1960). Chemistry of variotin. *J. Antibiot.* (*Tokyo*) **A13:** 289–290.

Thaysen, A. C. (1953). Food and the future. Part 3 (B). Food and fodder yeast. *Chem. & Ind.* (*London*) May 9, pp. 446–447 (rev.).

Van Luijk, A. (1938). Antagonism between various micro-organisms and different species of the genus *Pythium* parasitizing upon grasses and lucerne. *Mededeel. Phytopathol. Lab. Scholten* **14:** 45–83.

Ward, G. E., L. B. Lockwood, O. E. May, and H. T. Herrick. (1936). Studies in the genus *Rhizopus.* I. The production of dextro-lactic acid. *J. Am. Chem. Soc.* **58:** 1286.

Ward, G. E., L. B. Lockwood, B. Tabenkin, and P. A. Wells. (1938). Rapid fermentation process for dextro-lactic acid. *Ind. Engn. Chem.* **30:** 1233.

Webster, J., and N. Lomas. (1964). Does *Trichoderma viride* produce gliotoxin and viridin? *Brit. Mycol. Soc. Trans.* **47:** 535–540.

Wehmer, C. (1893). "Beiträge zur Kenntnis einheimischer Pilze." Hansche Buchhandlung, Hannover and Jena.

Weindling, R., and O. H. Emerson. (1936). The isolation of a toxic substance from the culture filtrate of a Trichoderma. *Phytopathology* **26:** 1068–1070.

Woodbine, M. (1959). Microbial fat; micro-organisms as potential fat producers. *Progr. Ind. Microbiol.* **1:** 179–245.

Yaw, K. E. (1952). Production of riboflavin by *Eremothecium ashbyi* grown on *synthetic medium. Mycologia* **44:** 307–317.

Ecology

METHODS OF ADJUSTMENT TO THE ENVIRONMENT

CHAPTER 13

Physiological and Biochemical Adjustment of Fungi to Their Environment

JOHN SAVILLE WAID[1]

Department of Botany
University of New England
Armidale, New South Wales, Australia
and
Department of Agronomy
Cornell University
Ithaca, New York

I. INTRODUCTION

The fungi include some very heterogeneous groups of organisms. It is, therefore, impossible to generalize about their ecology or the ways in which they have adapted to life in different habitats. In this chapter it will be possible only to describe what appear to constitute adaptive responses of fungi to the influence of environmental factors. For, as Neidhardt (1963) emphasized recently, "The nature of the selective advantage conferred on the cell is, in most instances, only an educated guess. Information at the requisite physiological and ecological levels is wanting." My aim is to survey selected aspects of our knowledge of this complicated subject, and it will be necessary to simplify various types of phenomena. One should keep in mind the limitations mentioned above and not draw conclusions of a general nature from the examples given here.

When sufficient biochemical and physiological information on the fungi has been accumulated we should be able to explain why some fungi occur in certain environments, how they are maintained, and how they have become adapted to prevailing conditions. Such adaptation probably comes about when these organisms perform physiological processes more effec-

[1] Department of Soil Science, Reading University, Reading, England.

tively or acquire the ability to carry out additional ones. Yet, before we can explain these events more fully, we must first overcome the obstacles which beset those interested in organisms within natural ecosystems (Smith, 1964).

The fungal ecologist, like other ecologists, requires accurate quantitative techniques to describe not only natural populations of fungi, but also the environments in which they exist. Fungi, other than the more advanced parasites, such as rusts and dermatophytes, generally occur in complex mixed populations of animals and plants. It is frequently impossible to observe them in their natural habitats, even in those where they are abundant, such as soil and water. This is because the vegetative structure of most fungi is simple and is immersed in its substrate, which makes study of them in their microhabitats very difficult (Garrett, 1956; Menzies, 1963; Park, 1963; Warcup, 1960). In consequence we know very little about changes in fungal populations with time relative to environmental factors in nature. Less is known about the rates at which fungal material is synthesized in natural communities, and this is in marked contrast to the wealth of information that has been obtained about communities of photosynthetic organisms. Though something is known about the auto-ecology of various fungi, in particular those forming parasitic or symbiotic associations, there is little quantitative information on the physiology and biochemistry of fungi in other than laboratory systems. And such knowledge has been applied to events in nature by inference and analogy. By studying the relationship between a fungus and its environment, we may be fortunate enough to determine how it has become adapted to live in a particular range of habitats. A fungus could be investigated at the several levels specified by Marjory Stephenson (Woods, 1955; Gibson, 1957; Knight, 1962).

These are:

A. Mixed cultures growing in natural environments.
B. Pure growing cultures in undefined laboratory media.
C. Nonproliferating cells in pure culture on chemically defined substrates.
D. Pure growing cultures in highly purified media.
E. Cell-free enzymes and coenzymes on pure substrates.

One level involves a detailed study of the fungus in its natural environment. The nature of the environment, its living inhabitants and physical and chemical nature should be described. The effects of changing or manipulating the environment in several ways should be investigated; this has been done, for example, by Hora (1959), who studied the influence of adding nutrients to forest soils on the production of basidiocarps. The next level is physiological and is concerned with growing pure cultures of the fungus in the laboratory and determining the influence of various physical factors on its growth and survival as well as a detailed study of its growth requirements. Pure culture studies may indicate what appear to be optimum conditions for the growth of an organism. But these conditions may be unlike those of the ecological situations in which the organism grows naturally, and for this reason extrapolation from one level to another level of investigation may become difficult. Laboratory experiments generally involve the use of controlled environments, but these fail to mimic the seasonal, daily, and momentary fluctuations that occur in the physical and chemical regimes of natural environments. Worse, interactions with other individuals are usually ignored completely or imitated poorly. As with other organisms, in particular crop plants (Evans, 1963), laboratory experiments fail generally to predict fungal performance under natural conditions. It must be remembered too that most laboratory experiments are made with fungal strains that have been grown for some time in culture and, because they have been subjected to artificial selection, they may have been altered, both physiologically and morphologically, from the field specimens.

Hawker (1957) has pointed out, quite rightly, that laboratory studies with pure cultures are valuable when combined with field observations carried out over an extended period. For a proper understanding of the effects of environmental changes on growth and survival of fungi it is essential that they should be analyzed experimentally in the field. There is a very real need for facts to be verified at several levels, and to do this requires the development of new approaches and methods applicable to these studies. A very productive approach has been the use of enrichment techniques, such as in Tribe's (1957, 1960) studies on the ecology of microorganisms colonizing cellulose film buried in soil.

Other levels of investigation are of a biochemical nature and involve studies of metabolic pathways, metabolic end products, the isolation and study of cell-free enzymes and organelles such as mitochondria. Those components, or metabolic end products of the fungal cell, that have some effect on the external environment interest the ecologist. Within this category can be included materials released from the cell, such as surface-localized and extracellular enzymes, antibiotics, and other organic molecules, as well as nutrients selectively absorbed by the cell.

Such investigations have been carried out, but only to a limited extent, and we do not yet know enough about any fungus to understand its adaptation to particular environments. Unfortunately laboratory studies often fail to provide hypotheses that survive investigation in the field. A simple explanation for such disappointments is that field and laboratory investigations have been inadequate or are not closely related to one another. This difficulty has been discussed by di Menna (1962), who could find no marked or consistent difference between the physiological characters of yeast floras from New Zealand soils and from leaf surfaces although the leaf yeasts were taxonomically distinct from the soil yeasts. She has suggested that interactions between the yeasts and other inhabitants of these habitats may explain why the yeast populations of leaf surfaces and soils are distinct, but lack of precise information about such interrelationships and the physical and nutritional environment of the yeasts hampers interpretation of her observations.

Too often, perhaps, fundamental problems of fungal ecology and physiology have been neglected for the sake of questions of practical importance. Yet, an investigation into a practical problem often involves objective research, and thus may provide information that serves a practical end as well as being of scientific interest (Russell, 1963), such as theoretical aspects of fungicidal chemistry (Rich, 1960; McNew, 1960) and the physiology of fungitoxicity (Sisler and Cox, 1960).

Ecology and physiology are closely related, yet the amount of reliable information about the mechanisms by which fungi adjust to environmental conditions in their natural habitat is rather limited. We need to know how to determine which adaptations confer on a particular organism the ability to become dominant in certain ecological situations, and why the organism disappears or becomes insignificant in other situations. This has not prohibited speculation, often based on groundless assumptions, about the mechanisms of adjustment involved. Accordingly, conclusions about the methods of adjustment of fungi in nature are rarely based upon adequate experimental evidence. Before generalizations can be made we need experimental evidence for numerous fungi from a wide variety of ecosystems.

II. MECHANISMS OF PHYSIOLOGICAL AND BIOCHEMICAL ADJUSTMENT OF FUNGI

A. Nature of Viable Material and Establishment of the Vegetative Phase

The establishment of a fungus in a new habitat is a critical phase in its life cycle. While becoming established on fresh substrata, young fungal thalli, like seedlings of green plants, are very susceptible to adverse conditions. A germinating propagule must rely upon endogenous food reserves until the organism has developed to the stage where it can assimilate nutrients from the environment, unless it can absorb materials while in the dormant state.

Fungi can colonize suitable environments in numerous ways. The propagules of many fungi bring about the widespread dispersal of the species, and local spread can be effected by hyphae, mycelial strands, and rhizomorphs (cf. Chapters 21 and 22, by C. T. Ingold and P. H. Gregory, respectively, in Volume II), whereas survival over a period of time in environments unfavorable for germination can be brought about by spores, resting hyphae, and sclerotia (cf. Chapter 18 by Sussman, in this volume). The different methods of dispersal and survival enable fungi to endure adverse conditions and, when the opportunity arises, to exploit a wide range of ecological situations. It is appropriate here to consider some of the means by which fungi are established in certain environments and some of the hindrances to their establishment.

Few fungi form spores that can germinate as soon as they are formed. Most spores, although appearing normal and fully developed, cannot germinate until after a period of rest (cf. Sussman, Chapter 23, Volume II).

1. *Self-inhibition of Spore Germination*

There are a few reports that inhibition of spore germination is brought about by the activity of the parent mycelium, perhaps through the formation of a diffusible germination inhibitor (Cochrane, 1958; Carlile and Sellin, 1963). Self-inhibition of spore germination has more frequently been observed in dense populations of spores when it reduces not only the germination rate but also the proportion of spores that ultimately germinate (see pp. 740–741, Volume II). In the case of *Puccinia graminis* f. sp. *tritici* there is evidence that the inhibitor of uredospore germination is a volatile spore metabolite. Both types of inhibition of spore germination can occur when the spores are crowded together within a fungal fructification where spore germination is a rarity. Removal of the inhibition allows spores to germinate normally, so it would seem the inhibitor does not affect the spores permanently. Cochrane has pointed out that a possible ecological function of the inhibition of spore germination is that it minimizes germination of spores within the fructification before dispersal. A germinated spore, besides being an inefficient dispersal agent, may be more susceptible to adverse environments than an ungerminated one. Carlile and Sellin found that many fungi can form inhibitory factors to which the spores of other fungal species respond. This may confer an advantage on vegetatively active fungi as it would reduce competition for nutrients with other fungi. Of considerable interest was their finding that the spores of *Chaetocladium jonesii,* which normally parasitizes other members of the Mucoraceae, were insensitive to inhibitory factors formed by the mycelia of *Mucor plumbeus, Rhizopus stolonifer,* and *Phycomyces blakesleeanus*. This insensitivity may well be biologically advantageous to

C. jonesii as it may be correlated with its parasitic habit; its spores must be insensitive in order to germinate on a host mycelium producing a spore-inhibiting factor.

2. *Influence of the Amount of Viable Material*

The propagules of fungi may consist of either fungal spores, which may be single-celled or aggregates of cells, or of fungal hyphae, which may be solitary or organized into aggregates, such as sclerotia, mycelial strands, or rhizomorphs. The chance of becoming established in a habitat becomes greater as the amount of propagating material is increased. This subject has received considerable attention by plant pathologists studying the influence of inoculum density on disease establishment. Once a disease of the type where the pathogen multiplies at a rapid rate, such as potato blight (*Phytophthora infestans*), has become established, the amount of initial inoculum has a negligible influence on the ultimate size of an epidemic. But when a pathogen multiplies slowly, the amount of inoculum at the onset of the disease may be used to predict crop losses (van der Plank, 1960). Many of the diseases caused by root-infecting fungi, in particular those of trees and shrubs, seem to be successfully established only by means of hyphal aggregates, such as rhizomorphs, and these structures appear to provide a mechanism whereby the volume and nutritional status of the inoculum is increased and perhaps maintained by translocation of nutrients from a food base (Garrett, 1960).

3. *Substances Influencing Germination*

There is evidence that substances excreted by higher plants can reduce or increase the rate of germination of the propagules of saprophytic and parasitic fungi present on their seeds, stems, or leaves or in soil adjacent to their roots (Spencer, 1962; see also pp. 743–744, Volume II). If such substances are excreted continuously, under natural conditions, they may accumulate and reach significant concentrations at liquid-solid interfaces and influence the germination of propagules of parasites. The germination of the propagules of certain root infecting parasites is activated by the root excretions of susceptible hosts (Buxton, 1957), although activation can also be caused by nonsusceptible species (Schroth and Snyder, 1961). In general, the sclerotia of root parasites are not inhibited by root exudates (Garrett, 1956) but Coley-Smith and Hickman (1957) found that the sclerotia of *Sclerotium cepivorum* germinated in soil or sand only in the presence of, but not in contact with, onion roots. Water extracts of onions, shallots, and leeks had the same effect, but extracts of plants other than *Allium* spp. did not. It would be an obvious biological advantage to a parasite, whose infective units lie dormant in a soil in which disease-resistant plants grow, for dormancy to be broken by a specific substance, such as an essential metabolite produced by a susceptible host plant. Since such propagules would fail to germinate in the absence of a supply of the activating substance, this mechanism would be partial insurance against germination in the absence of a host plant. There is, however, little evidence of the existence of such a mechanism in nature.

It has been shown that germination of certain fungal spores can be accelerated by external supplies of sugars, amino acids, growth factors and other substances (Cochrane, 1958, 1960; Hawker, 1950; see also pp. 745–757, Volume II), and the fact that such substances are commonly excreted by plants (Rovira, 1962; Spencer, 1962) may be a reason why activation can be caused by a number of plants (Flentje, 1959). It has been suggested by Garrett (1956) that it could be an advantage for parasites to be activated in environments where nutrients are available because external supplies of food may maintain young mycelia while they penetrate into the host tissues and establish themselves therein; success would be less likely in an impoverished environment. There is also the possibility that dependence on an essential nutrient exuded from a host would ensure that the young mycelia follow the concentration gradients of the activating materials right up to the host surfaces.

4. *Fungistasis in Soil*

It has been known for some time that viable fungal spores nearly always fail to germinate when added to soils that lack easily decomposable organic matter (pp. 743–744, Volume II). This has been shown to be due to the widespread occurrence in soil of fungistatic factors of biological origin. These substances include metabolic products excreted by microorganisms and plants as well as substances originating from decomposing organic residues (Brian, 1960; Dobbs and Hinson, 1953; Jackson, 1960; Park, 1960; Winter, 1948; Winter *et al.*, 1960). It has been suggested by Lingappa and Lockwood (1961) that the fungus spores release nutrients which could activate the growth of antagonistic microorganisms. A localized accumulation of the growth inhibitors produced by these satellite organisms could prevent germination. They also confirmed earlier observations (Stover, 1959, 1962) that inhibited fungal spores rapidly decompose in soil as a result of the activities of lytic bacteria.

5. *Rate of Germination*

Rapid germination is one step toward ensuring the production of a fungal colony when fungal spores reach a suitable new habitat. The spores of many freshwater hyphomycetes when released from the parent thallus seem to be capable of immediate germination, for appressoria develop, which anchor spores when they come to rest on a surface; shortly afterward, germ tubes grow out from the appressoria. Successful anchorage followed by rapid germination would seem to be important in the turbulent environments of the rapidly flowing streams inhabited by such fungi. Webster (1959) believes that tetraradiate spores become anchored more efficiently than spores of more conventional shape because of the three-point contact of the former with the substratum. A different mechanism serves the same function for ascomycetes living in fresh water and in sea water. Their ascospores generally bear a sticky mucilage which permits firm attachment of the spores to surfaces and may also assist in suspending the spores and aiding their dispersal (Ingold, 1953).

B. Vegetative Growth and Utilization of the Environment

1. Hyphal Structure and Organization in Relation to Utilization of the Environment

Hyphae are the basic vegetative structures of filamentous fungi. What then are the significant physiological properties of hyphae? How do they fulfill the functions they are supposed to serve? How are they modified to meet the requirements of different environmental situations? And what are the limits to which their physiology can be modified to meet extreme environmental conditions?

Hyphae present large surfaces through which substances can be interchanged with the environment. If growth is favored, hyphal apices are generally packed with protoplasm, lack prominent vacuoles, and are thin-walled. As portions of hyphae age, they become vacuolate and their protoplasm streams toward the younger growing region. The evacuated, older region consists, in the main, of dead hyphal segments although resistant survival structures, such as chlamydospores may have been formed therein.

Extension growth takes place in a short zone at the tip of a hypha. If a hyphal tip is severed and transferred to a medium favoring growth, a new thallus will develop indicating that individual tips are units, like spores, capable of independent growth. Robertson (1961) has observed that severing a hypha of *Fusarium oxysporum* just behind the last-formed septum has no effect on its rate of extension growth. In such experiments severed hyphal tips continue to utilize their immediate environment and their manner of growth remains unaffected although they are no longer united with the parent thallus. Hyphae, once formed, generally remain separate from others in the same mycelium in a constant and orderly way. Robertson suggests that their spatial relationships may be determined by influences such as the accumulation of toxic substances, but there is a lack of experimental evidence to support his hypothesis.

The observation that in certain environments the apical regions of a hyphal system can grow independently of the rest of the parent thallus is of physiological significance. One must attempt to determine, therefore, those factors which confer efficiency, in terms of successful growth, and those which limit the efficiency of such small units of living material.

All fungi appear to be chemo-organotrophs, for their growth depends upon oxidation of exogenously supplied organic substances. They scavenge for preformed materials, and one measure of their efficiency is their ability to remove potentially useful materials from the environment. The utilization of materials in the immediate environment of the fungal cell depends primarily upon such surface-related activities as the ability to take up water, nutrient ions, and other molecules (cf. Rothstein, Volume I, Chapter 15). The fine, threadlike structures of hyphae and the ovoid shapes of yeastlike cells give a relatively large surface-to-volume ratio which permits essential interchanges of materials between the environment and the cell. But to maintain itself in an active state over an extended period, the living material, if it consists entirely of a mycelial system lacking storage structures, must be supplied with nutrients to support continued growth. The uptake and accumulation of materials from the environment is achieved by the growth of hyphae from regions where nutrients are becoming depleted, or where staling substances are accumulating, to other regions. Unfortunately, as Robertson (1961) points out, we lack information about the relationship between the rate of movement of nutrient particles in substrates supporting growth and the rate of extension of the hyphal apex and, in consequence, we do not know to what extent the growth of hyphae is influenced by localized nutrient stress rather than by other factors, such as water potential and concentration of toxic substances. As they withdraw nutrients from the environment, a deficit is set up in the vicinity of the hyphae. This deficit tends to become rectified by the diffusion of nutrients. The possible ecological implications of changes caused by absorption have been discussed by Harley (1960), who suggested that in situations where the concentrations of essential nutrients are low, as may occur in soil, the rate of spread of a fungus may be a factor affecting its ability to dominate or otherwise influence the local microbial population.

Living hyphae with their large, thin-walled surfaces have limited means of conserving water, and most fungi are obliged to exist either in water, or in moist or extremely humid conditions; it is, of course, in such environments that fungi reach their greatest abundance (Brown and

Wood, 1953). Because of their delicate construction, hyphae cannot resist undue mechanical stress, but in general this is no disadvantage. Hyphae are thin and the substrates in which they grow, such as soil or decaying wood, often have pores through which hyphae can pass with ease. When a mechanical barrier composed of organic materials is encountered many fungi possess the necessary extracellular enzymes to digest or weaken the barrier and utilize it as a source of food.

2. *Extracellular and Surface-Localized Enzymes*

Fungi can decompose organic compounds of high molecular weight by synthesizing enzymes, located at the hyphal surfaces or secreted into the growth medium. The ability to form extracellular or surface-localized enzymes, catalyzing the decomposition of exogenous substances, is of undoubted adaptive and ecological significance. In situations where certain organic compounds are abundant, members of the associated microflora will produce specific enzymes catalyzing transformations of the various components of the substrate which are then utilized by the microflora. For example, dead woody tissues will support a microflora containing characteristically many fungi-forming cellulases,[2] lignin-decomposing enzymes, and phenolases; these enzymes break down into smaller water-soluble molecules, the large polymers, that form the substrate.

The rate of reactions catalyzed by extracellular enzymes depends upon two important factors: the amount of enzymes in the immediate vicinity of the hyphal surfaces, and the rate at which each enzyme can act. Although the total amount of enzymes is determined by the rates at which they are synthesized and destroyed, the effectiveness of the enzymes depends on whether they are present in an active or an inactive state. Various mechanisms of enzyme activation and inactivation have been described by Pardee (1959) and are discussed by Zalokar (Chapter 14, Volume I).

Cells of certain genotypes synthesize certain enzymes only in the right chemical environment, a phenomenon known as induced enzyme biosynthesis (Pollock, 1959). This phenotypic modification is induced while the cells are exposed to specific chemicals, especially the substrate of the enzyme, and is affected by other environmental conditions (Spiegelman and Halvorson, 1953). Inducible enzymes contrast with the constitutive enzymes that are present as the normal endowment of cells. Exposure of the cells to compounds related to substrates can also induce enzyme biosynthesis. Because this modification of the cell physiology has no apparent adaptive advantage, the term "enzyme induction" is regarded as

[2] Enzyme nomenclature follows that of Long (1961).

preferable to "enzyme adaptation" (Sussman, 1957; Phaff, 1959; Vogel, 1959). Therefore, induced enzyme biosynthesis is a phenotypic response to the chemical composition of the environment.

Many of the extracellular or surface-localized enzymes of fungi are synthesized in significant amounts only in the presence of inducing substances (Sussman, 1957). For example, the cellulases of most fungi are induced by cellulose or related substances (Siu, 1951), and a similar situation occurs with pectinesterase, formed in the presence of pectin, and phenolase, induced by monophenols, such as tyrosine and *p*-cresol. The experimental evidence suggests that such enzymes are not formed in the absence of their inducers, but there are alternative explanations. There is the possibility that a genetic mechanism is in operation, such as selection of a haploid nuclear component of a heterokaryon, or a mutation arising at random, and subsequent selection of the genes determining formation of the given enzyme (Buxton, 1959, 1960).

The relationship between extracellular and surface-localized enzymes and their substrates provides a convincing explanation of the abundance of certain types or physiological groups of fungi in various situations, such as, for example, the dominance of cellulose and lignin-decomposing basidiomycetes on decaying wood, but it is impossible to explain on enzymological grounds alone why only a restricted number of species can become locally dominant.

Hirsch (1954) suggested that a more detailed enzymological approach to some problems of ecology may provide reasons for the distribution of certain organisms. In an experimental investigation an organism may grow well under a wide range of conditions on a variety of defined media, but in nature the organism may, because of the constraining influence of a variety of unknown ecological factors, be restricted to a more limited range of metabolites. In the case of most fungi, the source of organic carbon seems to be of considerable, if not of paramount, ecological importance. The utilization of the substrate would, at all events, be limited by the characteristics of the enzyme systems involved. Hirsch investigated the influence of temperature on the production of cellulase and conidia by *Neurospora crassa* when grown on cellulose and found that some strains formed the enzyme and developed conidia at 35°C, but not at 25°C. Apart from artificially warm habitats, such as bakeries, strains of *N. crassa* have always been collected from tropical and subtropical areas, most frequently from burnt trees. Perhaps this is due to the ability of certain strains to synthesize cellulase and to form conidia at higher temperature ranges, but not in cooler.

Not only is there a tendency for cells to form certain enzymes when they are needed, but there is also a tendency for them not to form such enzymes when they are not needed (Pardee, 1959). Exposure of cells to certain chemicals can repress the synthesis of enzymes, one example being the suppression of cellulase formation by fungi growing on cellulose in the presence of glucose above a certain critical concentration. Such repression has obvious advantages where the metabolism of the fungus can be directed toward acquisition of the more readily utilizable form of a metabolite. Regulation of enzyme formation, however it occurs (Pardee, 1959), has the added usefulness that the environmental resources can be used ultimately for the synthesis of the more complex enzyme systems. For example, cellulase formation by fungi can be induced in the presence of glucose and cellulose when the concentration of glucose begins to fall below that which represses cellulase induction (Siu, 1951).

3. *Hyphae and Mechanical Forces*

The germinating spores of many taxonomically unrelated parasites can exert mechanical force to penetrate the physical barrier of the leaf cuticle. They use a characteristic mechanism consisting of an adhesive surface formed by an appressorium. From the central region of this surface a very slender penetration tube develops. The reaction of the germ tube to physical contact, thigmotropism, is probably a major factor inducing adhesion to the host and the formation of the appressorium. Not only leaf cuticle, but films of collodion, gold, and other substances have been shown to stimulate appressorium formation and subsequent penetration by the germ tubes of pathogens. But even though the experimental materials were pierced by physical means, it is doubtful whether subsequent penetration of leaf cuticle is entirely a physical process; with many fungi it may be abetted by chemical degradation and consequent weathering of the cuticle by exogenous fungal enzymes (Dickinson, 1960).

The general lack of differentiation, other than of cell walls and septa, in the construction of the vegetative portions of the thalli of most fungi is in marked contrast to the development of specialized cells and even highly organized structural tissues within the fruit-bodies, especially in the Agaricales and the Gasteromycetes (Ingold, 1953; see also, Hickman, Volume I, Chapter 2; and Smith, this volume, Chapter 12).

Fungal cells adhere closely to their substrata. Anchorage in nonturbulent, microenvironments is effected efficiently because a large proportion of the cell surface is formed in contact with a preexisting surface. Hyphae are in some way bound to the substratum by attractive forces between the contiguous surfaces. Such forces may be chemical adhesion (intermolecular attraction), which may be brought about by mucilage production (Dickinson, 1960), or cohesion (intramolecular attraction), for example, where water molecules exist as bridges between a moist substratum and moist hyphal surfaces. Anchorage of fungal thalli in turbulent environments is augmented by mechanical adhesion such as by the development of rhizoids or rooting hyphae. The primary function of appressoria and haustoria of surface-dwelling parasites would seem to be nutrient absorption but anchorage of the thallus may be an additional role.

The essential vegetative structure of the fungi is the hyphal filament or its equivalent, such as the chytrid thallus or the yeast cell. Such structures show little differentiation at the cellular level, although anchoring or absorbing units may be formed by simple morphological modification of the basic cell construction. Despite the apparent simplicity of construction, the living fungal cell meets the requirements both adequately and economically for a self-replicating, nutrient-absorbing structure.

C. Fungi in Ecological Successions

One aim of ecological research is to determine in what manner the selective nature of the habitat influences the structure of natural communities of organisms. One important aspect of the habitat is the interaction between the inhabitants of its communities, but, as yet, our understanding of such relationships is extremely limited. It is true that, through the interpretation of laboratory experiments, we know a great deal about the mechanisms of interaction between microorganisms, but apart from some cases of hyperparasitism, such as *Eudarluca* on rust fungi, such mechanisms have rarely been observed in operation in natural habitats; accordingly, we lack sufficient basic information to decide which mechanisms are of importance, or even operative, in natural situations.

1. Influence of Hyphae on Their Environment

A natural environment will change during the life cycle of a fungus although, in certain circumstances, such as in ocean or freshwater habitats, these changes may be gradual or slight. Environmental changes may be cyclic, such as those that occur from day to day, or random, and the rhythm and pattern of fungal growth may be altered to meet these environmental fluctuations. The growth of a fungus brings about alterations of the environment. Such environmental changes can be detrimental to the growth and survival of the fungus. For example, *Phytophthora infestans* may kill off sprouting blighted potato tubers so that the shoots never emerge above soil level; thus, the parasite, because it is unable to form conidiophores on the leaves, fails to spread to other potato plants. There are, then, changes occurring with the passage of time to which the fungus may have to adjust in order to survive.

Fungal mycelia can alter the chemical composition of the environment through the absorption and release of substances by the hyphae. Such chemical alterations may be accompanied by changes in the physical nature of the environment. Therefore, the presence of a fungus may have an indirect but appreciable effect on the life of other organisms growing in the zone affected by the activities of the hyphae. The effects may be harmful or beneficial depending upon the nature of the affected organism. One example is the beneficial influence of cellulolytic fungi on the development of noncellulolytic microorganisms within habitats enriched with cellulose. The influence of a fungus on other organisms may vary from an alteration of the concentration of nutrients, oxygen or carbon dioxide, to more complex changes resulting from the production of substances acting in very low concentrations, such as enzymes, reproductive hormones, growth factors, and antibiotics.

It is recognized that, in general, the alteration of a single component of the environment may affect other factors of ecological importance, and this is illustrated by the possible effects of an increase in carbon dioxide concentration in the vicinity of an active fungal hypha (Harley, 1960) on the well-being of microorganisms in the immediate environment. An increase in the supply of carbon dioxide would influence those organisms which require it as an essential metabolite. A possible result of increased carbon dioxide fixation would be that the concentrations of metabolites in the affected organisms are altered, in particular the nature and yield of amino acids formed *via* the citric acid cycle, as well as other organic acids such as citric and lactic in fungi, and pyruvic and propionic in bacteria. If these metabolites are excreted and decomposed biologically, they in their turn will modify the environment. An increase in carbon dioxide concentration could also affect the rate of growth and reproduction of microorganisms, some being favored, but others inhibited, by high concentrations of carbon dioxide.

Accumulation of carbon dioxide is accompanied generally by a local depletion of oxygen. A poorly aerated environment, such as would occur in very moist soil, may thus be transformed to one favoring anaerobic or microaerophilic organisms. Accumulation of organic acids may increase the acidity of the medium if it is insufficiently buffered, and through changes in the pH of the medium may affect indirectly a myriad of processes and factors, including the solubility and availability of essential nutrients, the activities of surface and extracellular enzymes, the entry of essential and toxic substances into the cell (Jennings, 1963), and, in the case of many fungi, the production and the germination of spores.

Without further elaboration of the possible direct effects and subsidiary influences of other metabolic end products of fungi, it is certain that the growth of hyphae can bring about alterations of their environments which profoundly affect the development of contemporary and successive members of the community to which they belong, but we are not certain exactly how these changes are brought about.

2. *Interactions among Microorganisms in Ecological Successions*

There are many known instances of ecological successions of microorganisms. It is believed that such successions develop through the action of primary colonizers modifying the substrate so that it becomes more favorable for secondary colonizers which, in turn, may modify the substrate still further and thus favor subsequent colonizers, and so on. In a parasitic successional series, a pathogen attacks living plant tissues and the lesions so formed permit the entrance of other, perhaps more severe, parasites, and saprophytes are often implicated in the later stages of the succession. Studies of successions of saprophytic fungi and associated organisms have been receiving increasing attention in recent years; there is considerable evidence that the course of the succession is modified by such factors as the composition of the microenvironment, in particular the nature of the substrate (Caldwell, 1963; Chesters, 1960; Hudson, 1962; Kendrick and Burges, 1962; Tribe, 1957, 1960; Winston, 1956).

There are strong indications that among the pioneer organisms of a succession are some which, through decomposition, transform the original chemical constituents of the substrate so that it supports the growth of secondary colonizers lacking the necessary enzymes to decompose the original substrate. Alternatively, early colonizers may synthesize substances, such as growth factors, essential for the development of secondary colonizers which, because of some metabolic deficiency, were unable to synthesize them from the original substrate.

Many fungi are equipped to make use of habitats containing nutrients present in relatively unavailable forms. They often colonize organic residues at a later stage in the microbial succession so that their maximum development follows the peak in the activity of the "sugar fungi." The ability to decompose cellulose is a characteristic attribute of many of these fungi, and here I would like to use this ability to delimit two broad groups of fungi: cellulolytic and noncellulolytic.

In a natural environment, such as soil, where a fungus competes with other individuals for limited supplies of nutrients, it is inevitable that the more readily available nutrients, in particular water-soluble substances containing carbon and nitrogen, would be depleted rapidly. As their further development at the expense of the more-available nutrients becomes restricted, fungi appear to possess several mechanisms to overcome these difficulties. For example, certain fungi germinate and develop rapidly in environments rich in fresh organic matter which they invest with hyphae having a very rapid rate of linear growth. As the nutrients disappear, hyphal growth ceases, metabolism is reduced to a low level, and large numbers of resting or dispersal structures are formed. These propagules become distributed in various ways and thus provide the fungus with many opportunities for further colonization when fresh substrates become available (Garrett, 1956).

This is typical of the growth of many saprobic members of the Mucorales, such as *Mucor* and *Rhizopus*. As the supply of nutrients diminishes they can form three, possibly four, different types of survival structures: sporangiospores, which are small and light and can be dispersed in a variety of ways (Ingold and Zoberi, 1963); chlamydospores, which are thick-walled; resting spores formed within the aging hyphae; and, fast growing hyphae which grow outward from the nutrient source and rarely branch, so that their resources are conserved to afford maximum spread. Although rarely observed on natural materials, zygospores may be formed under certain circumstances.

Some penicillia and aspergilli have a similar way of life but grow less rapidly and survive by forming very large numbers of small, light conidia that are readily dispersed in air currents. Cleistothecia and sclerotia may also be formed.

Both ways of life are characteristic of the ecological group of fungi first called "sugar fungi" in 1937 by Thom and Morrow (Burges, 1939, 1958; Garrett, 1956). Such fungi are commonly among the early colonizers of habitats such as dung and green manures which, when fresh, contain copious supplies of readily available nutrients, but such fungi may be prevalent in habitats where supplies of such nutrients are not very abundant initially. In this case, they occur in the later stages of the ecological succession. It is likely that these fungi use the products of the hydrolytic breakdown of complex substances carried out by bacteria, fungi, and other microorganisms concurrently occupying the same habitat (Hawker, 1957). It has been claimed that "sugar fungi" are able to utilize only simple carbohydrates, amino acids, and other relatively simple organic compounds and lack the ability to decompose complex organic materials such as cellulose, lignin, chitin, and possibly keratin. For example, none of the Mucorales have been shown capable of decomposing either cellulose or lignin (Cochrane, 1958). But E. E. Taylor and Marsh (1963) find that *Pythium*, which has been described as a "sugar fungus," can decompose certain types of cellulose and they cite reports of cellulose decomposition by chytrids.

The dependence of certain fungi on other saprophytes is well illustrated by microorganisms associated with cellulose decomposition described in Siu's summary (1951, Table 24) of the order of abundance of the most common fungal species isolated from exposed cotton textiles. Cotton fibers consist typically of about 94% crystalline cellulose together with very small amounts of protein (1.3%), pectin (0.9%), wax (0.6%), organic acids (0.8%), and sugars (0.3%). Out of a total of 1604 fungal isolates, 56.6% were assigned to ten species or taxonomic series with definite cellulolytic activity, and the remainder belonged to nine species which do not show any cellulolytic activity on crystalline cellulose. Of additional interest is Siu's list (1951, Table 29) of noncellulolytic species of fungi isolated from cotton fabrics. A high proportion of these species (76%) belong to the three typical groups of "sugar fungi," namely, aspergilli (21%), penicillia (35%) and mucorales (21%).

The fact that certain fungi occur among the dominant microorganisms in situations where cellulose is abundant is obviously not acceptable as evidence that they are capable of decomposing cellulose. The appropriate evidence must be obtained by reliable controlled experiments (Cochrane, 1958).

This example emphasizes one of the difficulties involved in investigations of the organisms concerned in the transformation of a particular nutrient where enrichment culture techniques are used, in this case the crystalline cellulose of cotton textiles. Frequently, secondary organisms develop in such cultures and live at the expense of those organisms that carry out the primary transformation of the nutrient. The noncellulolytic, or "sugar fungi," in the situation described above may be living on the products formed by cellulolytic bacteria and fungi.

Cellulose is an important constituent of most photosynthetic plants and is a major structural component of terrestrial ones. On land, cellulose forms the largest reserve of organic carbon in a form that can be used by organisms. Its decomposition is of great ecological importance and the widespread occurrence of fungi on decomposing cellulosic materials (Siu, 1951; Tribe, 1957, 1960) suggests that they are important members of aerobic mesophilic microfloras taking part in cellulose decomposition.

Only a very small proportion of fungi have been suitably tested for cellulolytic activity and there does not seem to be any convincing correlation between their taxonomy and ability to decompose cellulose. However there is some relationship, albeit a slight one, between ecological behavior and the possession of cellulolytic enzymes (Cochrane, 1958). Thus, it can be said that more species of fungi which produce cellulolytic enzymes develop in habitats where cellulose occurs than species possessing no cellulolytic enzymes, but it is not possible to be more definite. To quote data from Siu (1951, Tables 27 and 28), 33.2% of the 295 fungal species isolated from decomposing cotton textiles, and tested for their ability to decompose cellulose, are noncellulolytic and thus form a large proportion of the population dwelling in a restricted habitat.

D. Mechanisms of Antagonism and Tolerance

Antagonism, in its widest sense, has been defined by Wood and Tveit (1955) "to include any activity of one organism which in some way adversely affects another growing in association with it." Antagonistic activities can include parasitism, predation, mycophagy, the production of toxins (including antibiotics) and competition. Accounts of early work on antagonism among fungi have been given by D'Aeth (1939), Waksman (1947), and DeVay (1956), who have reviewed knowledge gained from experimental studies of the interactions between two or more fungi parasitizing living or decomposing plant tissue. They each recognized that the type of interaction occurring between two organisms in culture may be quite different from that occurring between the same organisms in nature. This difficulty is illustrated rather well by an experimental study carried out by Elarosi (1957a,b) of the associations between *Rhizoctonia* [*Corticium*] *solani* and *Fusarium solani,* which parasitize potato tubers. Elarosi demonstrated that the relationship between these fungi altered under various conditions of artificial culture and included active parasitism of *C. solani* by *F. solani,* inhibition of the former resulting from antibiotic production by the latter; commensalism where the growth of *Corticium* was improved by the presence of *Fusarium,* which remained unaffected by the association; as well as competition, possibly for food, where either fungus could be antagonized, depending on the environmental conditions. Potato tubers, a natural substrate for both fungi, were rotted far more extensively when *Fusarium* infection followed *Corticium* infection than when the double inoculation was carried out in the reverse order, or when tubers were inoculated singly.

1. Parasites and Predators of Fungi

Parasitic and predatory activities of fungi are described in great detail in other chapters of this volume, but some mention should be made here of parasites and predators of fungi.

There are a number of disorders of cultivated mushrooms and other fungi whose causes are unknown. Hollings (1962) described a series of investigations of an infectious disease, called dieback, of the cultivated mushroom *Agaricus bisporus.* He has shown that affected mushroom tissues contain virus particles. Furthermore, affected tissue may contain three morphologically different types of virus particles. His finding is of extreme importance as this is the first authenticated demonstration of virus infecting a fungus. It remains to be seen whether virus infections of fungi occur with significant frequency in natural populations. If so, the biology of these viruses should become a fascinating new field for research.

Fungal mycelia quite often disappear quickly from their natural habitats even though their hyphae are quite young. This disappearance may be due to autolysis of the young filaments or, alternatively, lysis could be due to the production of toxins and enzymes formed by pathogenic (Barnett, 1963) or competing fungi, actinomycetes, bacteria, or invertebrates. There is, indeed, one report of an odoriferous insect, *Scaptocoris talpa,* emitting a volatile fungicidal material antagonistic to *Fusarium* and other fungi in soil and in culture (Timonin, 1961). It is not clear why some fungi succumb more readily than others to specific growth inhibitors.

Fungal hyphae and yeast cells are a major component of the diet of many small animals, especially species of nematodes, mites, termites, fruit flies, and even some rodents. Mycophagous animals, in habitats such as decaying plant residues, will consume or disperse fungal hyphae and spores (Winston, 1956). There is, unfortunately, no quantitative information about the rate at which fungal material is destroyed by animals in natural communities.

2. *Antibiotics*

The use of complex inhibitory substances of microbial origin, known as antibiotics, to control selectively the growth of microorganisms pathogenic to man and animals has been so successful that there has been considerable interest in their use to control plant pathogens. The utilization of antibiotic-producing organisms to man's advantage has resulted in many attempts to demonstrate the existence of selective antibiotics in natural environments. There has also been considerable speculation about the ecological significance of antibiotic production to those microorganisms forming antibiotics in laboratory tests (Brian, 1957, 1960; Waksman, 1961).

It must be emphasized that in the following context the term "antibiotic" is being used in a narrow sense to refer to potent, selective, highly complex substances produced by microorganisms and does not include nonspecific substances, often having a simple chemical structure, that may be toxic to fungi, such as nitrite, sulfide, cyanide, bicarbonate, and lactic acid (Park, 1960).

Particular attention has been paid to antagonistic fungi inhabiting soil, root, and seed habitats. This is because a wide selection of antibiotics have been obtained from cultures of fungi isolated from such habitats and it is a common observation that numerous species of these fungi inhibit the growth of bacteria and other fungi in tests for antibiotic activity. In contrast only a few of the fungi which are confined to, or which reach their greatest abundance in, aquatic habitats, particularly aquatic phycomycetes and hyphomycetes, exhibit antagonism in culture.

Therefore, interest has developed in determining whether forming antibiotics is of importance for the growth and survival of fungi in their natural habitats.

Numerous observations indicate that a significant proportion of the organisms which appear to bring about an effective reduction in the inoculum potential of root-infecting fungi in the soil environment will form antibiotics *in vitro*. There are indications too that the antagonistic activities of such antibiotic-producing organisms are reduced when soil conditions are unfavorable either for growth or for the production and accumulation of antibiotics. However, there is insufficient evidence to show whether the adverse effect of the antagonist on the root parasite is the direct result of antibiotic action. When a fungus is the first colonizer of a substrate, the ability to form antibiotics may be advantageous to it because the accumulation of a growth inhibitor might restrict the entry and subsequent colonization by secondary organisms (Brian, 1957). Such a situation may occur in diseased or rotting bulky plant materials where a fungus, known to form antibiotics *in vitro,* such as *Penicillium expansum* on fruit (Brian, 1957), or *Armillaria mellea* in wood (Oppermann, 1951), may become the sole or principal inhabitant. Yet even here the antagonistic activities of the organisms may be due to alteration of host metabolism or to the release of substances from the substrate, such as acids, resins, tannins, or phenolic compounds, and not directly due to the formation of antibiotics.

Antibiotics have never been detected throughout the soil mass but there have been a few convincing demonstrations that they can be found in localized habitats enriched with organic materials, such as plant fragments, or in the rhizosphere. Yet antibiotics have been found only when conditions are favorable for the growth of the antagonists. Antibiotics have never been shown to accumulate except within the organic substrate, possibly because of their chemical instability, their tendency to be inactivated by adsorption on colloids, and their susceptibility to biological decomposition (Brian, 1957, 1960; Wright, 1956; Waksman, 1961; Krywolap *et al.*, 1964).

To form significant amounts of an antibiotic an antagonist would need sufficient concentrations of specific nutrients. The chances of an environment, such as soil, meeting these exacting requirements are rather remote but are most probably met when organic materials become available for decomposition by the microflora. But, because of the dynamic nature of the soil environment, conditions favoring antibiotic production by a specific antagonist are not likely to persist. Even if conditions remain favorable for antibiotic production, it is very probable that resistant members of the local microflora will be able to decompose the antibiotic and thus nullify its effects. Where a mixed population of microorganisms occurs the production of antibiotics by fungal mycelia may have no more than an extremely local effect limited to the zone immediately surrounding the hyphae themselves. However, this may be of real advantage to a fungus because in the hyphal region, especially on the hyphal surfaces, the concentration of antibiotic substances may reach sufficiently high concentrations to neutralize the activities of microorganisms, such as lytic bacteria, that could adversely affect the growth of the fungus. The antibiotic might provide an external, but extremely narrow, defensive screen in which active hyphae can develop whereas potential invaders of the living hyphae are discouraged (Novogrudsky, 1948). If so, then it is possible that in natural habitats these metabolites are of little use as weapons against surrounding competitors for nutrient supplies but the survival of antibiotic-forming hyphae may be prolonged and, as a result, may influence the composition of natural microbial populations.

3. Competition

Here attention will be focused on some of the mechanisms by which a fungus can grow in the face of competition from either different organisms (interspecific competition) or other individuals of the same species (intraspecific competition). In this context, competition will be taken to be the endeavor of two or more organisms to gain the same object. Competition among organisms can be more precisely defined by Donald's (1963) admirable definition, which he derived from those of Clements *et al.* (1929) and Milne (1961). Donald's definition is: "Competition occurs when each of two or more organisms seeks the measure it wants of any particular factor or thing and when the immediate supply of the factor or thing is below the combined demand of the organisms." Competition used in this sense describes an activity where the objects of competition are particular factors, such as water or nutrients.

The existence of competition between organisms is difficult to demonstrate unless some adverse effect is manifest; this, in the case of a fungus, could be a reduction in the rate of mycelial growth or the alteration of other activities, for example, an alteration of metabolism due to oxygen deficiency. Even so, precautions have to be taken to ensure that any adverse effect on the growth or activity of an organism, apparently induced by the presence of another organism, is the result of competition, not of chemical inhibition, such as antibiotic production. Chemical inhibition can operate in a favorable environment where the supplies of factors are adequate and, therefore, competition is nonexistent. For example, antagonism can occur between pairs of fungal species cultured under ideal conditions for growth.

There are several means by which a fungus could compete successfully with other organisms for supplies of water, energy, nutrients, and oxygen. One is to grow rapidly from regions where the supply of a factor is low into regions uninhabited by other organisms and there exploit the available supply of the factor before competitors arrive. In habitats such as soil and water, where local environments can become enriched by the deposition of fresh organic debris, it is an advantage for resting or dispersal structures to germinate rapidly and utilize the substrate before other competitors do so. Also advantageous is the ability to withdraw the limiting factor from the environment more rapidly than do competing organisms. In situations where supplies of a factor approach depletion, or are present in forms of low availability, a fungus would be at an advantage if it possessed the means to obtain supplies from these sources of lesser availability.

a. Competition for Space. Microorganisms and plants, as Clements *et al.* (1929), Park (1960), and Donald (1963) have pointed out, compete rarely, if at all, for space. It is conceivable that a situation might arise, for example in soil, in which hyphae of different fungal individuals may appear to compete for growth channels, such as soil pores. A similar situation might occur on plant surfaces with the hyphae of invading parasites apparently competing for stomata or other portals of entry into the host. In both instances the outcome of this rivalry could be that the hyphae of one individual occupy the passage and block it so that other individuals are excluded. However these are likely to be cases of competition not for space per se, but for other factors, because tropisms toward water, nutrients, or other factors could be operating (Flentje, 1959). Therefore, the physical exclusion of some of the interacting hyphae could be an incidental result of hyphae competing for factors other than space.

b. Competition for Water. Competition among fungi for water can become apparent when moisture stress is severe. Griffin (1963) has shown that in soils drier than the permanent wilting point for mesophytic plants (pF 4.2) the ability of soil fungi to absorb water and grow will be likely to differ from one species to another and may lead to ecological diversification. Such diversification has been shown in a variety of studies of microbiological spoilage of materials, such as cotton textiles (Siu, 1951) or grain. There are a few fungi, notably some in the *Aspergillus glaucus* group, whose spores germinate when stored in containers with relative humidities of 75% (Griffin, 1963) and in wheat grain having moisture contents of 14.5% (Christensen, 1957). Such organisms have a competitive advantage over fungi whose spores will not germinate until the moisture stress is less severe. The spores of most fungi will germinate and form active mycelia only in saturated or near-saturated atmospheres.

Christensen, therefore, provides a reason for the abundance of aspergilli in corn that is stored when relatively dry but later deteriorates. It is not known what physiological features of such aspergilli permit them to grow at water potentials so different from those needed for the growth of most other fungi.

c. *Competition for Nutrients.* Most investigations of microbial competition have been concerned with competition between photosynthetic plants and microorganisms for supplies of inorganic nutrients, such as occurs when large quantities of decomposable organic matter are added to soil or water. It is well known that as a result of assimilation of the inorganic nutrients by the microflora a large proportion of the nutrients can become immobilized and rendered temporarily unavailable to other organisms that may suffer to a lesser or greater degree (Alexander, 1961).

There have been few investigations of the significance of competition between microorganisms although the possible role of antibiotics as factors involved in antagonism has received much more attention. Most investigations of this subject have been concerned with competition for inorganic nutrients. In particular, competition between root-infecting fungi and soil microorganisms for supplies of inorganic nitrogen has been examined in experiments where there was an abundance of decomposable organic matter which would intensify competition for inorganic nutrients (Garrett, 1956). The factor which most often limits growth of an organism is the supply of energy source. In the case of fungi and other heterotrophs, the supply of decomposable organic carbon may be the focal point for competition and, therefore, would be expected to be of great ecological significance. Finstein and Alexander (1962) examined the interaction between *Fusarium oxysporum* f. sp. *cubense* and soil bacteria for supplies of carbon and inorganic nitrogen and showed that the bacteria could suppress the growth of the fungus at limiting concentrations of carbon and nitrogen. There was no growth inhibition in the presence of high levels of these nutrients, and competition was more severe for carbon than for nitrogen. Additional experiments showed that, with one exception, none of the antagonists inhibited the growth of *Fusarium* by antibiotic action.

The mechanisms which enable a fungus to compete successfully with other organisms for nutrients presumably change as the status of the substrate changes. When fresh organic materials become available for decomposition, as when plant residues are added to soil, there is a very rapid development of an active microbial population in the region of the added substrate. This population may be very different in composition from those that are active in neighboring regions not supplemented by fresh organic material. Exploitation of a fresh substrate is favored if a colonist has resting hyphae that can recommence growth quickly or spores which germinate rapidly to form a mycelium having a rapid rate of growth. Through the rapid production of suitable enzymes and efficient uptake of nutrients, mycelium can convert organic substances into living matter before competing organisms can do so.

During this early stage of decomposition, competition between the colonists is mainly for utilizable substrate. The most favored organisms would be those able to form appropriate extracellular and surface enzymes as well as those able to overcome any mechanical barrier and to resist toxic materials present in the substrate. If the substrate is deficient in one or more nutrients, then organisms that can maintain themselves on a reduced nutrient supply would be favored. So would fungi able to obtain nutrients from sources of low availability. For example, where supplies of liquid phase soil phosphate are limited, fungi may increase the solubility of solid phase phosphates by various mechanisms. These include the production of either inorganic or organic acids, such as carbonic and lactic acids, which can act upon certain forms of inorganic phosphate, as well as the excretion of a wide variety of phosphatases, such as polyphosphate depolymerase and phytase.

There is evidence that severe competition for nitrogen can be detrimental to the mycelia of several fungal plant parasites which characteristically ramify throughout tissues of moribund or dead plants. Apparently these fungi are dependent on large supplies of nitrogen for their saprophytic existence (Garrett, 1956; Marshall and Alexander, 1960; Roncadori, 1962; Snyder, 1960). Their survival in the absence of living host tissues depends not upon the formation of specific survival structures, but upon slow mycelial development within organic substrates where presumably the effects of toxic substances in the environment and competition for nutrients are reduced considerably.

In time, conditions in the substrate tend to become less favorable for fungal growth. There is a decline in the volume of substrate available for colonization and in the amount of energy sources. The concentration of individual inorganic nutrients and of oxygen can fall to low levels as a result of microbial utilization. Concurrently, carbon dioxide, bicarbonate, ammonia, hydrogen sulfide, antibiotics, and other toxic materials can increase. In limited regions these substances could reach levels inhibiting nutrient uptake or the growth of many of the colonizing fungi so that their hyphae could become predisposed to lysis and, in consequence, die.

d. Competition for Oxygen. One way of adjustment to a decrease in oxygen supply would be a decline in respiratory activity and the acquisition of a fermentative enzyme system, a response typical of many yeasts which can involve induced enzyme biosynthesis (Spiegelman and Halvorson, 1953). But if the organism is auxotrophic, enzyme synthesis may be dependent on an external supply of an essential metabolite necessary for the synthesis of the new protein, and, if this is limited, growth may cease.

Another method of adjustment to a decrease in oxygen supply may involve a reduction in physical resistance to the movement of oxygen into mycelium. Experience gained in laboratory and industrial investigations has shown that if fungal pellets form in aerated liquid culture, the rate of diffusion of oxygen into the interior of the pellets may limit growth when the pellets exceed a certain diameter (Arnold and Steel, 1958; Darby and Goddard, 1950). In nature such barriers may be formed by hyphal aggregates, such as strands and rhizomorphs. These structures generally grow in well-aerated situations, such as among soil and litter, where they spread over the surfaces of the substrates. From these structures small hyphal strands or single branch hyphae, which may be more permeable to oxygen than the bulky parent tissues, invade substrates in which oxygen deficits can occur. Most fungi in static water or in waterlogged environments where aeration is poor do not form rhizomorphs or complex hyphal aggregates, such as fruiting structures. *Armillaria mellea* is an exception because it can form rhizomorphs deep within waterlogged timber. But these rhizomorphs are unusual as they have a central cavity in which gases can diffuse freely, and this ventilation system must give this fungus a competitive advantage over others less able to cope with an oxygen deficiency (Reitsma, 1932).

e. Competition for Carbon Dioxide. Carbon dioxide appears to be essential for the growth of some fungi (Cochrane, 1958; Burges and Fenton, 1953). Carbon dioxide assimilation, through dark fixation reactions, can supply part of the carbon in many of the organic acids formed in fungal cells and has been shown to contribute a significant proportion of the carbon requirement of growing yeast cells (Morris, 1958). In most ecological situations supplies of carbon dioxide should not limit dark fixation reactions but low concentrations of dissolved carbon dioxide may occur in static water well populated with green plants when environmental factors, such as sunlight, favor photosynthesis. Under such circumstances, competition for carbon dioxide between photosynthetic organisms and aquatic fungi may occur and might limit fungal activity and development.

4. *Tolerance of Suboptimal Conditions*

Tolerance of suboptimal conditions would be advantageous to a fungus during a declining phase of substrate colonization. There is the possibility that the phenotype alters in response to changes in the nutritional condition of the substrate and to toxic materials as they accumulate. This might be achieved, directly, through enzyme induction or, indirectly, as a result of a shift in the genotype through mutation or through an alteration in the balance between nuclei forming a heterokaryon. Demonstrations of adjustment which appear to involve heterokaryotic mechanisms have been made *in vitro* (Buxton, 1959, 1960; Jinks, 1952). If the mycelium is intolerant of suboptimal conditions, then the ability to form resting or dispersal structures would be a means of ensuring survival.

Mention should be made of the intensive investigations by Cantino (1956, 1961) and his colleagues of the relationships between biochemical patterns and morphological development in fungal thalli. Cantino has shown that the metabolism and type of reproductive structures formed by the freshwater phycomycete *Blastocladiella emersonii* are altered when the concentration of bicarbonate ions in the growth medium exceeds a critical concentration. Then bicarbonate initiates the production of carotene, melanin, and phenolase, an accelerated production of isocitric dehydrogenase, and an increased deposition of fat and chitin. This increase in metabolic activity is accompanied by the loss of some enzyme systems, including chitinase, α-ketoglutarate dehydrogenase, succinic dehydrogenase, and cytochrome oxidase, with a concurrent reduction in the rate of oxygen consumption. Cantino (1961) has suggested that metabolic events are correlated with the formation of resistant, brown, thick-walled sporangial thalli in place of thin-walled, colorless thalli that are formed in media containing subcritical levels of bicarbonate.

Ultimately, when the substrate has been fully exploited and the energy source has become exhausted there is a very marked decline in microbial activity. Only hyphae that can endure starvation levels of nutrients, or which have the appropriate enzymes to decompose the more resistant types of organic material, will remain in an active state.

5. *Tolerance of Toxic Materials*

Fungi vary considerably in their sensitivity to toxic materials and, in the case of a few chemical agents, it is possible to provide reasons for their selective action. For example, application of griseofulvin, an antibiotic produced by several species of *Penicillium,* to growing hyphae can bring about abnormal cell wall extension and, hence, profound disturbances in hyphal development. But, with few exceptions, this effect of griseofulvin occurs only in those fungi with chitin in their cell walls, but not in yeasts and oomycetes having cellulosic or nonchitinous walls (Brian, 1949).

There are two main ways by which the cell resists the action of toxic materials and antimetabolites. The first is where the toxic substance, as a result of the impermeability of the cell membrane, and perhaps by the development of other barriers, is excluded from the cell or enters at a reduced rate and is detoxified. Sisler and Cox (1960) suggest that the barrier formed by the fungal cell wall and membrane may play a significant role in limiting the penetration of compounds of high molecular weight, for example, enzymes that could hydrolyze essential cell components. Copper tolerance is associated with tolerance toward hydrogen ions and other cations. One possible mechanism of copper tolerance is a general exclusion of cations from the cell acting through selective impermeability of the cell membrane. Species sensitive to fungicides may possess sites on the cell surface on which a toxicant may act without penetrating into the cytoplasm, but resistant strains may possibly arise through the loss or alteration of such sensitive sites.

The second type of resistance is through detoxication of the fungicide by various mechanisms which have been described by Sisler and Cox (1960). Many toxicants can be inactivated through the action of specific enzymes that hydrolyze, oxidize, or polymerize toxic substances. In some fungi certain toxicants are metabolized. Another general type of mechanism is the reaction of a metabolite and a toxicant to form a nontoxic complex. An example is the chelation of copper ions by cysteine and certain other organic nitrogen compounds. The sulfhydryl groups of cysteine and glutathione can protect proteins by binding toxicants that interfere with the sulfhydryl groups of proteins. Other mechanisms include the loss of metabolic sites sensitive to toxicants and the development of new biosynthetic pathways not inhibited by toxicants (Brian, 1960).

It is often possible to "train" cultures of sensitive fungi to tolerate concentrations of inorganic and organic toxic substances that would normally inhibit growth. This is done by repeated subculturing into media containing low concentrations of the toxic chemical agent. The acquisition of tolerance toward toxic materials has been attributed either to the induced production of enzymes controlling a detoxication system or to mutation. The adapted strains are generally unstable and can soon lose their tolerance toward the inhibitor when subcultured in media in which the inducing substance is absent.

There is little doubt of the existence of natural populations of fungi which can resist toxic materials, but it is not known how they acquire their resistance. In a classical investigation of the reasons why flax varieties differ in their susceptibility to wilt, Timonin (1941) produced evidence that the rhizosphere of a nonsusceptible variety of flax contained hydrocyanic acid which depressed the growth of the pathogen, *Fusarium lini*, but supported the growth of harmless saprophytes. Plant pathogens can become tolerant to toxic materials under field conditions. J. Taylor (1953) found that spores of *Physalospora obtusa* collected from apple orchards sprayed with Bordeaux mixture for periods exceeding eight years were more tolerant of this fungicide than spores collected from unsprayed orchards. It is of interest, therefore, that Kendrick (1962) in a study of the fungal flora of a Canadian swamp found that thirteen species of fungi were confined to areas containing large amounts of copper (more than 7500 ppm). In marked contrast, he found that nine species were absent from swamp areas containing more than 5 ppm but another nine were unaffected by copper concentrations in the swamp. Those organisms confined to the areas rich in copper appeared to possess an advantageous tolerance to copper which enabled them to become established in this unfavorable habitat; they are most probably at some disadvantage in habitats where copper is present in low concentrations. The most common fungus in this group, *Penicillium ochro-chloron* Biourge, has been isolated repeatedly from habitats rich in copper, such as solutions of copper sulfate.

E. Propagation, Dissemination, and Survival

Propagation, dissemination, and survival are topics that receive thorough treatment in other chapters of this volume and have been mentioned in various sections of this chapter. However, I would like to give some examples of propagation by means of spores which demonstrate the effectiveness of two different spore dispersal systems in ensuring the continued existence of fungal parasites.

It is by chance that the spores of most fungi are dispersed to habitats that favor their germination, and the establishment of new mycelium depends on events that occur as the spores germinate. Under suitable environmental conditions spores are produced in great numbers and various agents, such as water, wind, and insects, disperse the species efficiently and rapidly. For example, *Puccinia triticina* [*P. recondita*], the causal agent of brown rust of wheat leaves, once established on a crop in the susceptible phase of growth, will develop uredia from which airborne uredospores (conidia) are set free in very large numbers. The rate of multiplication of this organism within the wheat population can be measured by counting the numbers of uredial pustules on the leaves as the crop develops. Chester (1946) estimated that the pustules must multiply 3×10^7-fold after winter in order to reach epidemic proportions. Van der Plank (1960) estimated that the rate of increase during this early stage of the disease, when the number of leaves increased tenfold and the number of pustules per leaf rose from an average of 0.001 to 10, was 12.5% per day. The multiplication of local lesions of the blight of potatoes caused by *Phytophthora infestans* can be as high as 10^9-fold in a season. In susceptible potato crops it has been shown that the disease can originate and spread from infected plants developing from infected seed tubers. One infected plant per square kilometer of potatoes was sufficient to cause an epidemic that destroyed all the foliage of the crop (van der Zaag, 1956).

In both the above examples the rapid rate of multiplication of the living material of these fungal parasites is achieved by the formation of many spores which germinate rapidly under suitable conditions and form a mycelium that sporulates a few days after establishment on its host. In this way the organisms manage to rapidly colonize all suitable substrates, in this case photosynthetic tissues. The production of such spores ceases when adverse conditions set in, as when the food supply of the parasite becomes inadequate because of debility of the host, or in temperate regions with the onset of winter.

Some fungi have managed to reduce spore wastage. For example, the ascospores of members of the Laboulbeniales (minute parasites of insects) are covered with sticky gum and will adhere to objects with which they come in contact such as the body of an insect. This may be a reason why some of these fungi occupy restricted positions on the exoskeleton of the host. Shanor (1955) mentions several bizarre species of *Laboulbenia* parasitizing a ground beetle *Bembidion picipes* and suggests a reason why the thalli of one species occupy almost unbelievably rigid positions on the male and female hosts, as follows: This species "had a much more restricted position, being found normally, and almost without exception, only on the humeral angle of the right elytron of females and only on the inner distal surface of the femur of the right front leg of males. The spores of the species are expelled from the perithecium only when pressure is applied. It seems to be clearly indicated for this species that the regularly recurring movement in mating behavior determines the localization to restricted areas of the exoskeleton." Events at the time of ascospore discharge determine the position that the thalli occupy on the host beetle, for it is possible for them to develop on other parts of the host. The distribution of the thalli does not seem to be limited physiologically as, for example, by availability of food materials in only one region of the host.

III. CONCLUSIONS

One aim of this treatise is to try to illuminate those features that characterize fungi and distinguish them from other groups of organisms. Therefore, it is appropriate to finish this essay by asking and attempting to answer two questions. First, do fungi possess means of adjustment to their environment that are different from those of other organisms? Failing this, do some or all fungi make greater use of certain mechanisms of adjustment than do other organisms?

The answer to the first question is that fungi do not appear to possess unique biochemical or physiological mechanisms of adjustment to their environments. Therefore, we must decide which mechanisms, out of a wide selection of possible ones, are widespread or have become highly developed among fungi. These would include adjustments involved in activities such as nutrient absorption and assimilation, aerobic metabolism, propagation, survival, and tolerance to toxic materials.

The fungi are adapted to life in a very wide variety of situations. They may generally be found wherever supplies of decomposable organic materials, moisture, and oxygen are plentiful and temperatures are moderate. Apart from the oceans, where a major proportion of the earth's decomposable organic material abounds, fungi form a significant fraction of the saprophytic population of most ecosystems suggesting that many mechanisms of adjustment must have been involved.

In the case of a fungal symbiont or a parasite, survival must depend on adjustment throughout the vegetative phase of the life cycle so that its functioning harmonizes with that of its host or partner and the association is prolonged. The ability of many fungi to form such associations is, perhaps, one of the most striking features of their biology and one which must involve intricate, delicate, and little understood mechanisms of adjustment. Yet similar mechanisms of adjustment must be used by other saprophytic, parasitic, and symbiotic organisms, in particular bacteria, so it is not likely that they are more widespread among fungi than among other taxonomic groups of organisms.

REFERENCES

Alexander, M. (1961). "Introduction to Soil Microbiology," 472 pp. Wiley, New York.

Arnold, B. H., and R. Steel. (1958). Oxygen supply and demand in aerobic fermentations. *In* "Biochemical Engineering" (R. Steel, ed.), pp. 149–182. Heywood, London.

Barnett, H. L. (1963). The nature of mycoparasitism by fungi. *Ann. Rev. Microbiol.* **17**: 1–14.

Brian, P. W. (1949). Studies on the biological activity of griseofulvin. *Ann. Botany (London)* [N.S.] **13**: 59–77.

Brian, P. W. (1957). The ecological significance of antibiotic production. *Symp. Soc. Gen. Microbiol.* **7**: 168–188.

Brian, P. W. (1960). Antagonistic and competitive mechanisms limiting survival and activity of fungi in soil. *In* "Ecology of Soil Fungi" (D. Parkinson and J. S. Waid, eds.), pp. 115–129. Liverpool Univ. Press, Liverpool.

Brown, W., and R. K. S. Wood. (1953). Ecological adaptations in fungi. *Symp. Soc. Gen. Microbiol.* **3**: 326–337.

Burges, N. A. (1939). Soil fungi and root infection. *Broteria* **8**: 64–81.
Burges, N. A. (1958). "Micro-organisms in the Soil," 188 pp. Hutchinson, London.
Burges, N. A., and E. Fenton. (1953). The effect of carbon dioxide on the growth of certain soil fungi. *Brit. Mycol. Soc. Trans.* **36**: 104–108.
Buxton, E. W. (1957). Some effects of pea root exudates on physiologic races of *Fusarium oxysporum* Fr. f. *pisi* (Linf.) Snyder and Hansen. *Brit. Mycol. Soc. Trans.* **40**: 145–154.
Buxton, E. W. (1959). *Plant Pathol., Probl. Progr., 1908–1958* pp. 183–191.
Buxton, E. W. (1960). *Plant Pathol.* **2**: 359–405.
Caldwell, R. (1963). Observations on the fungal flora of decomposing beech litter in soil. *Brit. Mycol. Soc. Trans.* **46**: 249–261.
Cantino, E. C. (1956). The relation between cellular metabolism and morphogenesis in *Blastocladiella. Mycologia* **48**: 225–240.
Cantino, E. C. (1961). The relationship between biochemical and morphological differentiation in non-filamentous aquatic fungi. *Symp. Soc. Gen. Microbiol.* **11**: 243–271.
Carlile, M. J., and M. A. Sellin. (1963). An endogenous inhibition of spore germination in fungi. *Brit. Mycol. Soc. Trans.* **46**: 15–18.
Chester, K. S. (1946). "The Cereal Rusts," 269 pp. Chronica Botanica, Waltham, Massachusetts.
Chesters, C. G. C. (1960). Certain problems associated with the decomposition of soil organic matter by fungi. *In* "Ecology of Soil Fungi" (D. Parkinson and J. S. Waid, eds.), pp. 223–238. Liverpool Univ. Press, Liverpool.
Christensen, C. M. (1957). Deterioration of stored grains by fungi. *Botan. Rev.* **23**: 108–134.
Clements, F. E., J. E. Weaver, and H. Hanson. (1929). Plant competition. *Carnegie Inst. Wash. Publ.* **398**: 1–340.
Cochrane, V. W. (1958). "Physiology of Fungi," 524 pp. Wiley, New York.
Cochrane, V. W. (1960). *Plant Pathol.* **2**: 167–202.
Coley-Smith, J. R., and C. J. Hickman. (1957). Stimulation of sclerotium germination in *Sclerotium cepivorum* Berk. *Nature* **180**: 445.
D'Aeth, H. R. X. (1939). A survey of interaction between fungi. *Biol. Rev.* **14**: 105–131.
Darby, R. T., and D. R. Goddard. (1950). Studies on the respiration of the mycelium of the fungus *Myrothecium verrucaria. Am. J. Botany* **37**: 379–387.
DeVay, J. E. (1956). Mutual relationships in fungi. *Ann. Rev. Microbiol.* **10**: 115–140.
Dickinson, S. (1960). *Plant Pathol.* **2**: 203–232.
di Menna, M. E. (1962). The antibiotic relationships of some yeasts from soil and leaves. *J. Gen. Microbiol.* **27**: 249–257.
Dobbs, C. G., and W. H. Hinson. (1953). A widespread fungistasis in soils. *Nature* **172**: 197–199.
Donald, C. M. (1963). Competition among crop and pasture plants. *Advan. Agron.* **15**: 1–114.
Elarosi, H. (1957a). Fungal associations. I. Synergistic relations between *Rhizoctonia solani* Kühn and *Fusarium solani* Snyder and Hansen in causing a potato tuber rot. *Ann. Botany (London)* [N.S.] **21**: 555–568.
Elarosi, H. (1957b). Fungal associations. II. Cultural studies on *Rhizoctonia solani* Kühn, *Fusarium solani* Snyder and Hansen, and other fungi and their interactions. *Ann. Botany (London)* [N.S.] **21**: 569–585.

Evans, L. T. (1963). Extrapolation from controlled environments to the field. *In* "Environmental Control of Plant Growth" (L. T. Evans, ed.), pp. 421–437. Academic Press, New York.

Finstein, M. S., and M. Alexander. (1962). Competition for carbon and nitrogen between *Fusarium* and bacteria. *Soil Sci.* **94**: 334–339.

Flentje, N. T. (1959). *Plant Pathol., Probl. Progr., 1908–1958* pp. 76–87.

Garrett, S. D. (1956). "Biology of Root-Infecting Fungi," 293 pp. Cambridge Univ. Press, London and New York.

Garrett, S. D. (1960). *Plant Pathol.* **3**: 23–56.

Gibson, J. (1957). Nutritional aspects of microbial ecology. *Symp. Soc. Gen. Microbiol.* **7**: 22–41.

Griffin, D. M. (1963). Soil moisture and the ecology of soil fungi. *Biol. Rev.* **38**: 141–166.

Harley, J. L. (1960). The physiology of soil fungi. *In* "Ecology of Soil Fungi" (D. Parkinson and J. S. Waid, eds.), pp. 265–276. Liverpool Univ. Press, Liverpool.

Hawker, L. E. (1950). "Physiology of Fungi," 360 pp. Univ. of London Press, London.

Hawker, L. E. (1957). Ecological factors and the survival of fungi. *Symp. Soc. Gen. Microbiol.* **7**: 238–258.

Hirsch, H. M. (1954). Temperature-dependent cellulase production by *Neurospora crassa* and its ecological implication. *Experientia* **10**: 180–181.

Hollings, M. (1962). Viruses associated with a die-back disease of cultivated mushroom. *Nature* **196**: 962–965.

Hora, F. B. (1959). Quantitative experiments on toadstool production in woods. *Brit. Mycol. Soc. Trans.* **42**: 1–14.

Hudson, H. J. (1962). Succession of micro-fungi on ageing leaves of *Saccharum officinalis. Brit. Mycol. Soc. Trans.* **45**: 395–423.

Ingold, C. T. (1953). "Dispersal in Fungi," 197 pp. Oxford Univ. Press, London and New York.

Ingold, C. T., and M. H. Zoberi. (1963). The asexual apparatus of Mucorales in relation to spore liberation. *Brit. Mycol. Soc. Trans.* **46**: 115–134.

Jackson, R. M. (1960). Soil fungislasis and the rhizospore. *In* "Ecology of Soil Fungi" (D. Parkinson and J. S. Waid, eds.), pp. 168–176. Liverpool Univ. Press, Liverpool.

Jennings, D. H. (1963). "The Absorption of Solutes by Plant Cells," 204 pp. Oliver & Boyd, Edinburgh and London.

Jinks, J. L. (1952). Heterokaryosis—a system of adaptation in wild fungi. *Proc. Roy. Soc.* **B140**: 83–99.

Kendrick, W. B. (1962). Soil fungi of a copper swamp. *Can. J. Microbiol.* **8**: 639–647.

Kendrick, W. B., and N. A. Burges. (1962). Biological aspects of the decay of *Pinus sylvestris* leaf litter. *Nova Hedwigia* **4**: 313–344.

Knight, B. C. J. G. (1962). The growth of microbiology. *J. Gen. Microbiol.* **27**: 357–372.

Krywolap, G. N., L. F. Grand, and L. E. Casida. (1964). The natural occurrence of an antibiotic in the mycorrhizal fungus *Cenococcum graniforme. Can. J. Microbiol.* **10**: 323–328.

Lingappa, B. T., and J. L. Lockwood. (1961). The nature of the widespread soil fungistasis. *J. Gen. Microbiol.* **26**: 473–485.

Long, C. (1961). "Biochemists' Handbook," 1192 pp. Spon, London.

McNew, G. L. (1960). Fungicides and bactericides for controlling plant diseases. *In* "Biological and Chemical Control of Plant and Animal Pests," Publ. No. 61, pp. 49–72. Am. Assoc. Advanc. Sci., Washington, D.C.

Marshall, K. C., and M. Alexander. (1960). Competition between soil bacteria and *Fusarium*. *Plant Soil* **12**: 143–153.

Menzies, J. D. (1963). The direct assay of plant pathogen populations in soil. *Ann. Rev. Phytopathol.* **1**: 127–142.

Milne, A. (1961). Definition of competition among animals. *Symp. Soc. Gen. Microbiol.* **15**: 40–61.

Morris, E. O. (1958). Yeast growth. *In* "The Chemistry and Biology of Yeasts" (A. H. Cook, ed..), pp. 257–322. Academic Press, New York.

Neidhardt, F. C. (1963). Effects of environment on the composition of bacterial cells. *Ann. Rev. Microbiol.* **17**: 61–86.

Novogrudsky, D. M. (1948). The colonization of fungal hyphae by soil bacteria. *Mikrobiologiya* **17**: 28–35.

Oppermann, A. (1951). Das antibiotische Verhalten einiger holzzersetzender Basidiomyceten zueinander und zu Bakterien. *Arch. Mikrobiol.* **16**: 364–409.

Pardee, A. B. (1959). The control of enzyme activity. *In* "The Enzymes" (P. D. Boyer, H. Lardy, and K. Myrbäck, eds.), 2nd ed., Vol. 1, pp. 681–716. Academic Press, New York.

Park, D. (1960). Antagonism—The background to soil fungi. *In* "Ecology of Soil Fungi" (D. Parkinson and J. S. Waid, eds.), pp. 148–159. Liverpool Univ. Press, Liverpool.

Park, D. (1963). The ecology of soil-borne fungal disease. *Ann. Rev. Phytopathol.* **1**: 241–258.

Phaff, H. J. (1959). The production of certain extracellular enzymes by microorganisms. *In* "Handbuch der Pflanzenphysiulogie" (W. Ruhland *et al.*, eds.), Vol. 11, pp. 76–116. Springer, Berlin.

Pollock, M. R. (1959). Induced formation of enzymes. *In* "The Enzymes" (P. D. Boyer, H. Lardy, and K. Myrbäck, eds.), 2nd ed., Vol. 1, pp. 620–680. Academic Press, New York.

Reitsma, J. (1932). Studien uber *Armillaria mellea* (Vahl) *Quèl. Phytopathol. Z.* **4**: 461–522.

Rich, S. (1960). *Plant Pathol.* **2**: 553–603.

Robertson, N. F. (1961). Mycology. *In* "Contemporary Botanical Thought" (A. M. MacLeod and L. S. Cobley, eds.), p. 133–148. Oliver & Boyd, Edinburgh and London.

Roncadori, R. W. (1962). The nutritional competition between *Hypoxylon punctulatum* and *Ceratocystis fagacerum*. *Phytopathology* **52**: 498–502.

Rovira, A. D. (1962). Plant-root exudates in relation to the rhizosphere microflora. *Soils Fertilizers* **25**: 167–172.

Russell, R. S. (1963). The extent and consequences of the uptake by plants of radioactive nuclides. *Ann. Rev. Plant Physiol.* **14**: 271–294.

Schroth, M. N., and W. C. Snyder. (1961). Effect of host exudates on chlamydospore germination of the bean root rot fungus *Fusarium solani* f. *phaseoli*. *Phytopathology* **51**: 389–393.

Shanor, L. (1955). Some observations and comments on the Laboulbeniales. *Mycologia* **47**: 1–12.

Sisler, H. D., and C. E. Cox. (1960). *Plant Pathol.* **2**: 507–552.

Siu, R. G. H. (1951). "Microbial Decomposition of Cellulose," 531 pp. Reinhold, New York.

Smith, H. (1964). Microbial behavior in natural and artificial environments. *Symp. Soc. Gen. Microbiol.* **14**: 1–29.

Snyder, W. C. (1960). Antagonism as a plant disease control principle. *In* "Biological and Chemical Control of Plant and Animal Pests," Publ. No. 61, pp. 127–136. Am. Assoc. Advanc. Sci., Washington, D.C.

Spencer, D. M. (1962). Antibiotics in seeds and seedling plants. *In* "Antibiotics in Agriculture" (M. Woodbine, ed.), pp. 125–145. Butterworth, London and Washington, D.C.

Spiegelman, S., and H. O. Halvorson. (1953). The nature of the precursor in the induced synthesis of enzymes. *Symp. Soc. Gen. Microbiol.* **3**: 98–125.

Stover, R. H. (1959). *Plant Pathol. Probl. Progr., 1908–1958* pp. 339–355.

Stover, R. H. (1962). "Fusarial Wilt (Panama Disease) of Bananas and other *Musa* Species," 117 pp. Commonwealth Mycolo. Insti., Kew.

Sussman, A. S. (1957). Physiological and genetic adaptability in the fungi. *Mycologia* **49**: 29–43.

Taylor, E. E., and P. B. Marsh. (1963). Cellulose decomposition by *Pythium*. *Can. J. Microbiol.* **9**: 353–358.

Taylor, J. (1953). The effect of continual use of certain fungicides on *Physalospora obtusa*. *Phytopathology* **43**: 268–270.

Timonin, M. I. (1941). The interaction of higher plants and soil microorganisms. III. Effect of by-products of plant growth on activity of fungi and actinomycetes. *Soil Sci.* **52**: 395–413.

Timonin, M. I. (1961). Effect of volatile constituents of *Scaptocoris talpa* Champ. on the growth of soil fungi. *Plant Soil* **14**: 323–334.

Tribe, H. T. (1957). Ecology of micro-organisms in soil as observed during their development upon buried cellulose film. *Symp. Soc. Gen. Microbiol.* **7**: 287–298.

Tribe, H. T. (1960). Decomposition of buried cellulose film. *In* "Ecology of Soil Fungi" (D. Parkinson and J. S. Waid, eds.), pp. 246–256. Liverpool Univ. Press, Liverpool.

van der Plank, J. E. (1960). *Plant Pathol.* **3**: 229–289.

van der Zaag, D. E. (1956). Overwintering an epidemiologie van *Phytophthora infestans,* tevens enige nieuwe bestrijdingsmogelijkheden. *Tijdschr. Plantenziekten* **62**: 89–156.

Vogel, H. J. (1959). Induction and repression of enzyme formation. *In* "Handbuch der Pflanzenphysiologie" (W. Ruhland *et al.,* eds.), Vol. 11, pp. 117–131. Springer, Berlin.

Waksman, S. A. (1947). "Microbial Antagonisms and Antibiotic Substances," 2nd ed., 415 pp. The Commonwealth Fund, New York.

Waksman, S. A. (1961). The role of antibiotics in nature. *Perspectives Biol. Med.* **4**: 271–287.

Warcup, J. H. (1960). Methods for isolation and estimation of activity of fungi in soil. *In* "Ecology of Soil Fungi" (D. Parkinson and J. S. Waid, eds.), pp. 3–21. Liverpool Univ. Press, Liverpool.

Webster, J. (1959). Experiments with spores of aquatic Hyphomycetes. I. Sedimentation and impaction on smooth surfaces. *Ann. Botany* (*London*) [N.S.] **23**: 595–611.

Winston, P. W. (1956). The acorn microsere, with special reference to arthropods. *Ecology* **37**: 120–132.

Winter, A. G. (1948). Untersuchungen uber die Beziehungen Zwischen *Ophiobolus graminis* und anderen Organismen mit Hilfe der Aufwuchsplattenmethode. *Arch. Mikrobiol.* **12**: 240–270.

Winter, A. G., H. Peuss, and F. Schonbeck. (1960). The influences of biotic factors on the development of soil fungi. *In* "Ecology of Soil Fungi" (D. Parkinson and J. S. Waid, eds.), pp. 76–83. Liverpool Univ. Press, Liverpool.

Wood, R. K. S., and M. Tveit. (1955). Control of plant diseases by use of antagonistic organisms. *Botan. Rev.* **21**: 441–492.

Woods, D. D. (1955). The integration of research on the nutrition and metabolism of micro-organisms. *J. Gen. Microbiol.* **9**: 151–160.

Wright, J. M. (1956). Biological control of a soil-borne *Pythium* infection by seed inoculation. *Plant Soil.* **8**: 132–140.

CHAPTER 14

Survival of Fungi after Freezing and Desiccation

PETER MAZUR

Biology Division
Oak Ridge National Laboratory
Oak Ridge, Tennessee

I. INTRODUCTION

Organisms require liquid water in order to function. Because of this, all growth and reproduction is restricted to narrow temperature limits between about −20°C and 100°C, and in most cases to an even narrower range between 0°C and 35°C (Michener and Elliott, 1964).

Biological function is further restricted by the requirement that cells be in contact with water having an activity (a_W) above some minimum, the definition of activity being the ratio of the vapor pressure of the water in the environment to that of pure water at the same temperature. Most organisms require an a_W above about 0.96, but a few can function at activities as low as 0.62 (Scott, 1957). Since these lower limits of temperature and a_W are exceeded in many terrestrial environments, it is fortunate that *survival* is not as stringently restricted as function. Some organisms can withstand the terrestrial minimum of −75°C, and many can withstand water activities that approach zero.

The ability of cells to survive adverse temperatures and water activities is not only ecologically important, but also makes feasible the long-term preservation of viability. If a cell or organism can be cooled to, say, −196°C and rewarmed without damage, or if it can be dehydrated and rehydrated without damage, it should be possible to maintain it for long periods of time either at low temperatures or while desiccated. The purposes of this chapter are in part to discuss the basic factors involved in freezing and dehydration injury and the conditions under which injury can be avoided. The fungi are particularly interesting in this regard because many species survive wider ranges of environments than do the species of almost any other group. Furthermore, because of their economic importance and their usefulness as genetic and biochemical material, there has been considerable interest in devising procedures for preserving viable cultures with minimal attention for long periods of time. Procedures for preservation by freezing and freeze-drying have been developed empirically, and for the most part they have been successful in the sense that enough cells survive to serve as seed inocula for new cultures.

If the empirical approach had always been successful or if occasional failures were of no importance, it might be superfluous to urge a mechanistic understanding of the factors responsible for success. But there have been failures, and even more important, there are uncertainties. There is no assurance that a technique that preserves one species will preserve another. There is no certainty that treated suspensions that yield viable cells after one week will do so after one year. And there is no certainty that cultures derived from frozen or freeze-dried cells will be identical to the original, especially if only small fractions of the cells survive treatment.

Finally, the empirical approach sheds little or no light on the means by which fungi in nature withstand subzero temperatures and desiccation. In nature, fungi are exposed either to air or to very dilute suspending media; in most preservation techniques, they are suspended in substances like 10% horse serum, 10% sucrose, or 10% glycerol. In nature, fungi are subjected to cooling and warming rates best measured in degrees per hour; in preservation techniques, the rates are measured in degrees per minute or degrees per second. In nature, a desiccated organism may be slowly rehydrated by exposure to moist air; in preservation techniques, it is likely to be rehydrated in a fraction of a second by direct immersion in water.

Some of the factors that affect survival always operate during low-temperature exposure and dehydration no matter how they are carried out; others are critically dependent on the way in which temperature is changed or on the way in which water is removed. The first section will discuss the basic factors that operate on all cells during freezing and drying. The discussion will then consider the factors involved in freezing and dehydration injury in fungi. The techniques used to preserve viable cells will be then analyzed in terms of the mechanisms that underlie injury, and suggestions will be given as to ways in which injury can be minimized. Finally, some comments will be made on how an understanding of mechanisms of injury is pertinent to an understanding of ecological hardiness.

II. BIOPHYSICAL ASPECTS OF FREEZING AND DEHYDRATION

A fungus subjected to desiccation or subzero temperatures is subjected to one or more of three events; namely, water loss with a concomitant rise in the concentration of low and high molecular weight solutes, low temperatures, and ice formation.

A. Low Temperatures without Ice Formation

The fact that growth and reproduction slow and eventually stop as temperature is lowered is ample evidence for the importance of temperature in biological function. In most cases the resulting changes are reversible; restoring the temperature to normal restores normal function.

However, reversibility is by no means universal, and two general classes of chilling injury and death have been reported. One is a rather slow sequence of changes that occurs in some cells when they are actively metabolizing at reduced temperatures. The other is a rapidly developing injury that occurs in certain cells under certain conditions when they are cooled rapidly to temperatures near 0°C. This latter usually is referred to as "thermal shock." The slowly developing type of injury is unlikely to appear rapidly enough to be a factor in the injury resulting from freezing or freeze drying, but thermal shock could be a factor and hence deserves some comment. As mentioned, it is injury produced by rapid chilling to near or below 0°C. It does not occur with slow chilling even in susceptible cells, and not all cells are susceptible. Susceptibility depends, in part, on species; thus, bull sperm are highly sensitive but human sperm are not (Sherman, 1962). It depends also on the growth phase; log phase cells of *Escherichia coli,* for example, are highly sensitive whereas stationary phase cells are completely resistant (Meynell, 1958). Finally, susceptibility depends on the suspending medium and culture conditions (Meynell, 1958; Gorrill and McNeil, 1960; Strange and Dark, 1962).

Under conditions that maximize sensitivity, the effects of thermal shock can be profound. For example, rapid chilling can kill high proportions of cells of *E. coli* (Meynell, 1958) and *Aerobacter aerogenes* (Strange and Ness, 1963).

Information on the sensitivity of fungi to thermal shock is scanty, but the little available indicates that they are resistant. Thus, 100% of the spores of *Aspergillus flavus* and stationary-phase vegetative cells of *Saccharomyces cerevisiae* survive rapid cooling to —9 to —15°C as long as the water in which they are suspended remains supercooled (Berry, 1933;

Mazur, 1960a, 1961a; Araki and Nei, 1962). They might remain unharmed at even lower temperatures if it were possible to keep the suspending medium unfrozen. Concentrated eutectic solutions of $MgCl_2$ and $CaCl_2$ do remain unfrozen below —26 and —45°C, respectively, and as many *Aspergillus* spores suspended in the two solutions survive rapid cooling to these temperatures (about 80%) as survive at room temperature (Mazur, 1953, 1960b).

B. *Low Temperatures with Ice Formation*

Since the supercooled state is metastable, ice will form in cell suspensions cooled sufficiently below 0°C. Freezing immediately subjects the cells to three new factors: (1) the physical consequences of the ice crystals themselves, (2) the progressive desiccation produced by the conversion of water into ice, and (3) the rise in the concentration of low and high molecular weight solutes that accompanies the desiccation. Any one of these events could be lethal.

Since cells are partially isolated from their environment by a semipermeable membrane, these factors can occur outside or inside the cell, a distinction that will be seen to be of particular importance in evaluating the role of ice formation on survival.

1. The Sequence of Events during Freezing

Investigators who have observed the freezing of cells under the microscope report without exception that the external medium always freezes before the cells. Although no direct observations have been made on fungi, they have been made on a variety of other cells, including guinea pig and rabbit tissues (Smith and Smiles, 1953), *Amoeba* (Chambers and Hale, 1932; Smith *et al.,* 1951), sea urchin eggs (Asahina, 1961), various higher plant cells (Asahina, 1956; Sakai, 1961, 1962), and frog muscle fibers (Chambers and Hale, 1932).

Even after they have been surrounded by ice, cells often remain unfrozen for minutes or hours, provided the temperature remains above about —10°C (Mazur, 1965b, 1966). With the exception of the halophiles and osmophiles, the concentration of solutes in the protoplasm in most cells is below 1 osmolar, and the freezing point, therefore is above —1.8°C. Accordingly, since cells remain unfrozen at temperatures below —1.8°C, they must be supercooled—at least initially.

Supercooled water ordinarily freezes immediately when it comes in contact with ice; hence, the fact that supercooled cells can remain supercooled when surrounded by ice shows that cells possess a barrier that prevents extracellular ice from seeding them at temperatures above about —10°C. In all likelihood that barrier is the plasma membrane (Mazur,

1960b, 1965b). The barrier is a peculiar one in that it disappears below about −10°C, as evidenced by the fact that most cells freeze intracellularly below that temperature. The basis of the temperature dependence of the barrier properties is not known, although I have speculated that it may be related to the depression of the freezing point of water in the very small (4–8 Å radius) water-filled channels that are believed to exist in membranes (Mazur, 1960b, 1965b).

Regardless of what allows a cell to become supercooled, a supercooled cell surrounded by ice is unstable. Even if equilibrium cannot be restored initially by intracellular freezing, it can be restored by water leaving the cell and freezing externally. The vapor pressure of supercooled water exceeds that of ice; accordingly, in response to this vapor pressure differential, supercooled water will flow out of a cell at the rate

$$-\frac{dV}{dt} = \frac{kART}{v_1} \ln (p_i/p_e), \tag{1}$$

where V is the volume of cell water, t is time, k is the permeability of the cell to water, A is its surface area, R is the gas constant, T is temperature, v_1, the molar volume of water, and p_i and p_e are the vapor pressures of internal supercooled water and external ice (and any solution in equilibrium with ice). As the cell loses water, the concentration of intracellular solutes rises, and this in turn lowers p_i. Water will continue to leave the cell at a progressively lower rate until equilibrium is attained when p_i falls to p_e.

Clearly, if cooling is infinitely slow, the contents of a supercooled cell will dehydrate continuously so as to remain in vapor pressure equilibrium with the external ice. However, this will not be true at finite cooling rates, the reason being that a drop in temperature tends to *increase* the vapor pressure ratio, p_i/p_e. If no water left the cell in response to the vapor pressure differential, the increase in the ratio p_i/p_e with decreasing temperature would be

$$\ln (p_i/p_e) = \frac{L_f}{R}\left(\frac{T_f - T}{TT_f}\right) \tag{2}$$

where L_f is the latent heat of fusion and T_f the original freezing point of the protoplasm.

Hence, the amount of water remaining in the cell and the extent to which it is supercooled (degree to which p_i exceeds p_e) will depend on the extent to which the increase in p_i/p_e given by Eq. (2) is counterbalanced by the decrease in p_i/p_e given by Eq. (1). If cooling is sufficiently slow, the cell will lose water sufficiently rapidly to keep p_i nearly equal to p_e. Such a cell will not freeze internally; instead it will dehydrate.

On the other hand, if the cell is cooled too rapidly, the water will not be able to leave the cell rapidly enough to maintain vapor pressure equilibrium. The ratio of p_i/p_e will remain greater than unity, which is the same thing as saying that the protoplasm will remain supercooled. Equilibrium will eventually be restored below a certain temperature by intracellular freezing.

To quantify the terms "sufficiently" rapidly and "sufficiently" slowly and to calculate the extent of supercooling in a given cell at a given cooling rate and temperature, it is necessary to have numerical values for the parameters in Eqs. (1) and (2) and to solve the equations simultaneously. The resulting combined differential equation is

$$Te^{b(T_g-T)}\frac{d^2V}{dT^2} - \left[(bT+1)e^{b(T_g-T)} - \frac{ARK_g n_2}{B(V+n_2v_1)}\cdot\frac{T^2}{V}\right] \times \frac{dV}{dT} = \frac{L_f A k_g}{Bv_1} \quad (3)$$

Besides the parameters already defined, the equation also contains the temperature coefficient of the permeability constant (b), the permeability to water (k_g) at a known temperature (T_g), the cooling velocity (B), and the osmoles of solute in the cell (n_2). The derivation of Eq. (3) and the several assumptions underlying it have been published previously (Mazur, 1963b).

Numerical solutions to Eq. (3) give the volume of water in a cell as functions of temperature and the several parameters. The solutions for a cell with the properties of yeast are presented in Fig. 1. The curves show the calculated percentage of the initial intracellular water remaining in the cell at various temperatures and cooling rates. The curve labeled *Eq.* shows the water content in a cell that is maintaining continuous equilibrium with the external ice by dehydration, i.e., a cell cooled at an infinitesimal rate. The water content of a cell cooled at 1°C per minute remains close to equilibrium, whereas that of a cell cooled at 100°C per minute or faster does not. We would, therefore, expect that the former cell would not freeze internally but that the latter would. The expectation is supported by experiments with *Saccharomyces cerevisiae*. The dotted curve in Fig. 2 shows the calculated extent to which the water in yeast is supercooled as a function of cooling velocity. This curve was obtained from the curves in Fig. 1. The left and right photomicrographs show the appearance of yeast cooled at 1° and 300°C per minute, respectively, to −79°C and fixed at those temperatures by freeze-substitution with ethanol (the solid curve represents cell survival, and will be discussed in Section III). The supercooling curve indicates that cells cooled at 10°C per minute or slower will contain no supercooled water by the time the temperature has reached −15°C. In other words it predicts that slowly cooled cells will equilibrate by losing all their free water. Measurements of the volumes of yeast after cooling at 1°C per minute and freeze-substitution (left micrograph) indicate they have, in fact, lost about 90% of their intracellular water (Mazur, 1961b, 1967a). Since only 90% of the water in yeast is capable of freezing (Wood and Rosenberg, 1957; Souzu *et al.*, 1961; Mazur, 1963a), these slowly cooled cells contain little, if any, intracellular ice. On the other hand, the volume of the cells cooled at

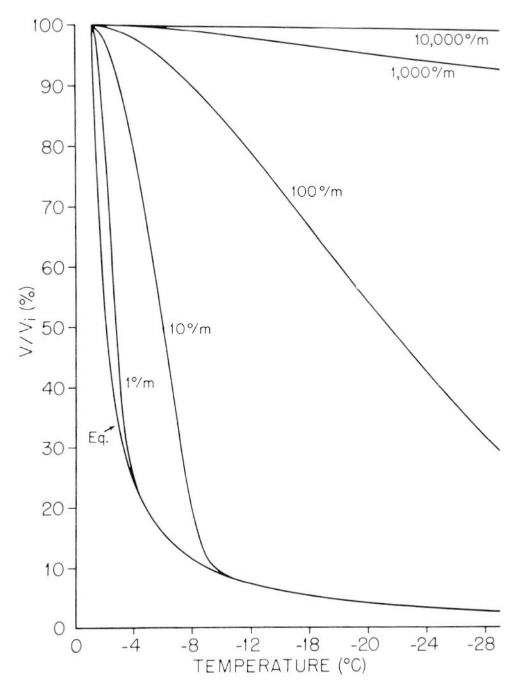

FIG. 1. Calculated percentages of intracellular water (V/V_i) remaining in yeast cells as a function of temperature and cooling velocity. The curve *Eq.* represents the equilibrium water content. From Mazur (1965a).

300°C per minute is nearly twice as great (right micrograph), which indicates that they contain about 33% of their original water after cooling. Two-thirds of that water must have been frozen (Mazur, 1967a).

Table I compares the calculated minimum cooling rates required for intracellular freezing in several cells with those observed experimentally. The agreement is within an order of magnitude. In view of the simplifying assumptions underlying Eq. (3), the uncertainty in the correct values of several of the parameters, (particularly b and k_g), and the errors involved

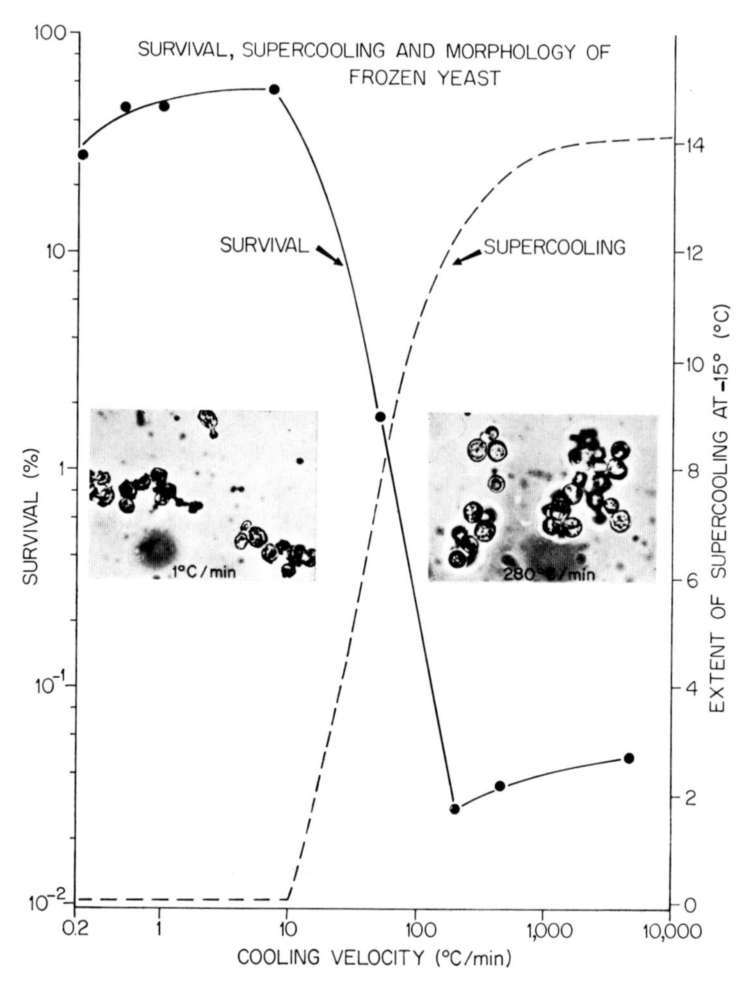

FIG. 2. Survival, morphology, and extent of supercooling of cells of *Saccharomyces cerevisiae* as a function of cooling velocity. The survival curve is experimental; the supercooling curve is calculated from Fig. 1. Survivals are those for cells suspended in distilled water, cooled at the indicated rates to −70°C, cooled rapidly to −196°C, and warmed rapidly at 1400°C per minute. The photomicrographs are taken from Mazur (1961b) and depict freeze-substituted cells. From Mazur (1967b).

in quantifying cooling rates experimentally, this rough agreement is considered to support the basic validity of Eq. (3).

In summary, then, an initially supercooled cell will eventually equilibrate with the external freezing solution. It can equilibrate either by freezing internally or by having its water leave the cell and freeze externally. Which

TABLE I

MINIMAL COOLING VELOCITIES FOR THE FORMATION OF INTRACELLULAR ICE

Organism	Cooling velocity: Calculated[a] (°C/minute)	Cooling velocity: Observed (°C/minute)	Observer
Amoeba	<1	<1	Smith *et al.* (1951)
Sea urchin egg (*Strongylocentrotus nudus*, unfertilized)	1	1–9	Asahina (1961)
Yeast (*Saccharomyces cerevisiae*)	20	20–50	Mazur (1961a; Fig. 2 this chapter); Araki and Nei (1962)
Escherichia coli	~500	>100	Rapatz and Luyet (1963)
Red cells (mammalian)	5000	4000	Luyet *et al.* (1963)

[a] The calculated cooling rate was considered to be that for which the cell still contained 20% of its intracellular water at −12°C according to solutions to Eq. (3). Known values for the parameters are given by Mazur (1963b). Assumed values were used in other cases, viz. (a) sea urchin eggs: $b = 0.1034$ (the measured value for *Arbacia*); (b) yeast: $b = 0.065$; (c) *E. coli*: $k_g = 0.3$, $b = 0.0325$ (from Mazur, 1965b).

occurs will depend on the cooling velocity and on biological parameters such as the permeability of the cell to water.

2. *The Concentration of Solutes*

Whether equilibration is by dehydration or intracellular freezing, it results in the progressive conversion of intracellular water into ice. The decreasing quantity of liquid water, in turn, produces a progressive increase in the concentration of solutes, both within the cell and outside of it; and it produces a progressive decrease in the separation between macromolecules.

Since the stability of both proteins and DNA is known to be influenced by the concentrations of ions (von Hippel and Wong, 1964; Leibo and Mazur, 1966), large increases in the concentration of electrolytes during the freezing of cells could well lead to irreversible damage. Evidence on this point is discussed in a recent book (Meryman, 1966). Furthermore, many proteins can undergo irreversible denaturation when they are merely cooled to below 0°C (Brandts, 1967a). Freezing would aggravate the situation because the concentration of proteins produced by ice formation is likely to accelerate the rate at which a reversible denaturation becomes irreversible aggregation (Brandts, 1967b).

It is important to note that at atmospheric pressure the concentration of solutes in an ideal aqueous solution undergoing freezing is determined solely by temperature; namely

$$m \approx \frac{273 - T}{1.86} \tag{4}$$

where m is the total osmolal concentration of solutes (molecules and ions). Similarly for any given ideal solution, the fraction (q) of unfrozen water present at any temperature depends only on temperature and the initial osmolal concentration of the solution before freezing (m_i); i.e.,

$$q \approx \frac{1.86 m_i}{273 - T} \tag{5}$$

These equations hold only approximately for real solutions; nevertheless, they illustrate two points that are applicable to any freezing solution, including protoplasm: (a) a change in T must alter both m and q; (b) the value of q will be primarily determined by the low molecular weight solutes and not the macromolecules, since it is the former that contribute preponderantly to m_i.

One consequence of these interrelations is that it is not possible to predict *a priori* what the effect of temperature will be on reaction rates in partly frozen biological systems. Although a drop in temperature slows reaction rates in most unfrozen systems, it can actually accelerate reactions in partly frozen systems because of the mass action effect of the increase in the concentration of the reactants (Bruice and Butler, 1965; Tappel, 1966; Kiovsky and Pincock, 1966).

During freezing, the temperature will eventually drop to the point where the concentration of solutes exceeds their solubility. At that point, the eutectic point, all residual liquid free water freezes. For a simple aqueous solution, the eutectic point is a specific temperature, characteristic of the solute; e.g., −21.1°C for NaCl solution. But for complex solutions such as protoplasm there is no unique eutectic point, but rather a eutectic zone smeared over a range of temperatures. When eutectic points are determined experimentally, as for example by measurements of the electrical conductivity of a solution, the temperature at which the last liquid water disappears during cooling is about 5–10°C lower than the temperature at which the first liquid water appears in a frozen solution during warming. The latter temperature is the true eutectic point; the former temperature is lower because the solution becomes supersaturated with respect to solute during cooling (Rey, 1960; Mazur, 1961a, 1963a; Greaves and Davies, 1965).

3. *Events in the Solid State*

Even though a solution is completely solid below its eutectic point or eutectic zone, it can still undergo change. For example, rapid cooling produces small imperfect ice crystals, which are thermodynamically unstable relative to large perfect ones (Mazur, 1966). If the temperature is appropriate and the time sufficiently long, the small imperfect crystals will become converted into large perfect ones by a variety of processes referred to by such terms as recrystallization, grain growth, sintering, and regelation. These recrystallization processes have been shown to occur in pure water, aqueous solutions, and cells at temperatures above —100°C, and to occur in a matter of seconds at temperatures above about —50°C (Meryman, 1957; Luyet, 1966; Mazur, 1966, 1967a).

C. *Freeze-Drying and Dehydration*

The technique of freeze-drying or lyophilization involves three steps: (1) a cell suspension is frozen (either by immersion in a low-temperature bath or by evaporative cooling *in vacuo*); (2) the system is evacuated to a pressure of less than 100 μ Hg; and (3) the frozen sample is maintained at a temperature such that the vapor pressure of ice in the sample exceeds that of water that is trapped either by a chemical desiccant such as P_2O_5, or by a refrigerated condenser held at a lower temperature than the sample. Then, because of the vapor pressure difference, water sublimes out of the sample and condenses or freezes in the trap.

Freezing itself removes water from a cell suspension and deposits it as ice, and the drying portion of freeze-drying simply serves to transfer that ice from the sample to the trap. Because the initial freezing dehydrates the cells, one might expect most of the injury to occur during freezing and little or none during sublimation. Although this is true in some instances, freeze-drying is often decidedly more injurious than freeze-thawing. The increased damage probably has several causes:

1. In most freeze-drying procedures the sample is kept frozen solely by evaporative cooling. As a result, the temperature of the sample depends on the mass of ice and the rate of sublimation. Since both of these are continuously changing during the course of dehydration, the sample temperature may also vary considerably.

2. Although freezing dehydrates a cell, it does not dehydrate it completely. Calorimetric measurements show that only about 90% of the water in *Saccharomyces cerevisiae* and *Escherichia coli* freezes regardless of the temperature to which the cells are cooled (Wood and Rosenberg, 1957; Souzu *et al.,* 1961; Mazur, 1963a). Freeze-drying, in contrast,

usually removes some 98–99% of the water in the sample. The 10% of the water that does not freeze is referred to as "bound," and there is evidence that the removal of this "bound" fraction is decidedly injurious (Nei *et al.,* 1965; Webb, 1965).

3. Water is reintroduced into a frozen suspension by thawing it. Water is reintroduced into a freeze-dried preparation by exposing it to water vapor or by adding liquid water. Although thawing and rehydration are alike in that they both add liquid water, they differ in the temperature and rate at which they convert the dry system to a fully hydrated one.

D. *Summary*

During freezing, a cell will be subjected to lowered temperature, dehydration, and ice formation. All these can affect its survival. The rate at which the cell is cooled will determine the likelihood of intracellular freezing. It will also determine the length of time it is exposed to concentrating solutes, and the length of time that its proteins are being increasingly compacted. During cooling, the concentration of solutes will increase continuously and the fraction of unfrozen water will decrease continuously. If cells are held at any constant temperature above the eutectic zone, the concentration of solutes and fraction of water will be fixed at a value determined by that temperature. Below the eutectic zone, there will be no liquid free water, but there may be a certain amount of "bound" water. Even if the cell suspension becomes completely solid, solid-state chemical reactions, free radical reactions, and changes in the size and shape of ice crystals can still occur.

III. CAUSES OF FREEZING INJURY IN FUNGI

A. *Yeast*

Although yeast (*Saccharomyces cerevisiae*) is not a "typical" fungus, there is more information on its response to freezing and thawing than on other microorganisms, and from this information has developed some concept of the physical and chemical basis of injury. Hopefully many of the mechanisms that underlie injury in these cells also underlie the injury of cells in general.

1. Factors Determining Injury and Survival

The current picture of injury in yeast can perhaps be best understood by reference to Fig. 3. The curves depict survival after initial cooling at various rates to —70°C, further rapid cooling to —196°C and subsequent slow, rapid, or ultra-rapid warming and thawing. The dotted curve depicts

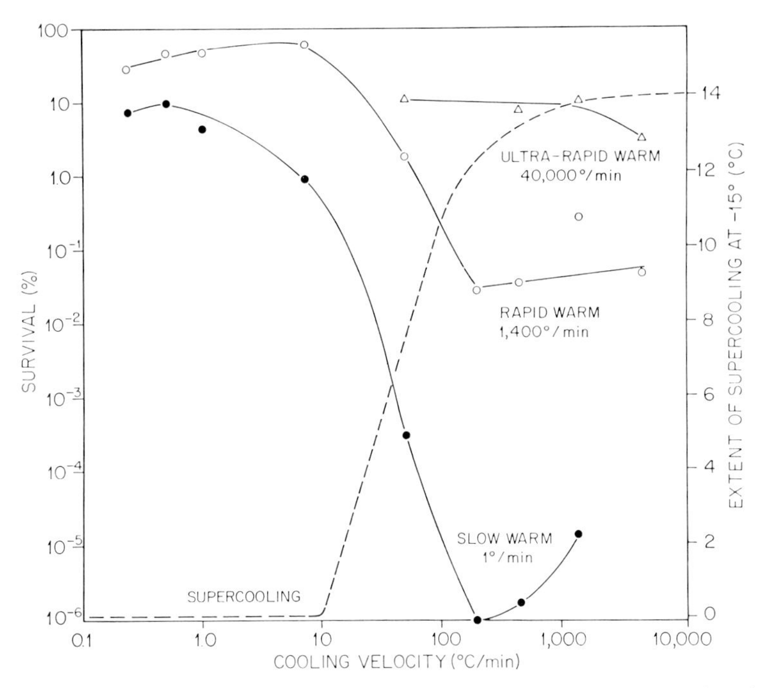

FIG. 3. Survival and supercooling of *Saccharomyces cerevisiae* as a function of cooling velocity. Cells were suspended in triple-distilled water, cooled at various rates to −70°C, transferred to liquid nitrogen, and warmed at the rates indicated. The supercooling curve was derived from the calculated curves in Fig. 1. From Mazur (1967a).

the calculated extent of supercooling (Section II, B). The first point of interest is that survivals vary over a 100 million-fold range. The second point is that the survival curves for slow and rapid warming show a maximum at a cooling velocity of 1°C or 10°C per minute and a minimum at a cooling velocity of 200°C per minute. Similar results were reported by Araki and Nei (1962). A third point is that the rate of warming affects rapidly cooled cells more than slowly cooled cells.

I believe the explanation for these data to be the following: The low survivals at the very low cooling velocities of 0.2°C per minute are probably due to the fact that this treatment subjects the yeast for long periods of time to the increasing concentrations of solutes produced during freezing (Section II, B). Faster cooling reduces this contributiton to injury by shortening the exposure time, but concomitantly, it increases the probability of intracellular freezing, with the result that survivals drop at cooling rates above 10°C per minute. The full evidence for this interpretation has been presented in several publications (Mazur, 1961a,b, 1963a,b,

1966, 1967a). One piece of evidence is that the cooling rate at which survival begins to drop coincides with the calculated cooling rate at which the cells begin to contain supercooled water; and it is known that as the extent of supercooling increases, so too does the likelihood of freezing. Another piece of evidence, the volumes of slowly and rapidly frozen cells, was discussed in Section II, B.

The higher the cooling rate, the greater the certainty that all the cells freeze internally; but higher cooling velocities also tend to produce smaller, more imperfect crystals. It is believed that changes in the size and form of these small crystals are responsible for the increased effect of warming rate observed in rapidly cooled yeast. Since 10–40% of ultra-rapidly warmed cells survive after rapid cooling (Fig. 3) (Doebbler and Rinfret, 1963; Anderson *et al.,* 1966), intracellular ice does not appear to be invariably lethal as long as the ice crystals remain small or imperfect. However, small crystals are thermodynamically unstable, and during slow warming, they will tend to stabilize by decreasing their surface to volume ratio, i.e., by increasing in size and in smoothness of contour. A discussion of how these changes in size and form could lead to injury has been presented elsewhere (Mazur, 1967a). In contrast, when rapidly cooled cells are warmed ultrarapidly, the crystals presumably melt before this grain growth can occur, and survival remains rather high. There is no direct proof that grain growth occurs in yeast cells that are warmed at 1°C per minute and does not occur in cells warmed ultrarapidly, but, as mentioned in Section II, B, grain growth has been observed in other slowly warmed cells and in solutions.

Although the observation that 10% or more of yeast cells survive ultrarapid cooling and warming is of considerable mechanistic interest, it is of less interest in considering the factors responsible for the survival or death of fungi in nature or in most procedures for preservation by low-temperature storage. On the other hand, since cooling rates of 0.1° to 200°C per minute are met in ecological situations and in the preservation of fungi by low-temperature storage, the factors involved in the survival of yeast subjected to these cooling rates are of more general interest. The pertinent findings are given below.

a. Effects Occurring in the First Few Hours of Low-Temperature Exposure. (1) *Temperature.* As shown in Fig. 4, nearly 100% of yeast survive cooling to —10°C regardless of the cooling and warming rate. Between —10°C and —70°C, survival drops to an extent determined by the cooling and warming rate, but most of the cells that survive cooling to —70°C and thawing, also survive cooling to at least —196°C.

Survivals are high above —10°C because intracellular freezing is prevented by the cell membrane's ability to prevent nucleation of the super-

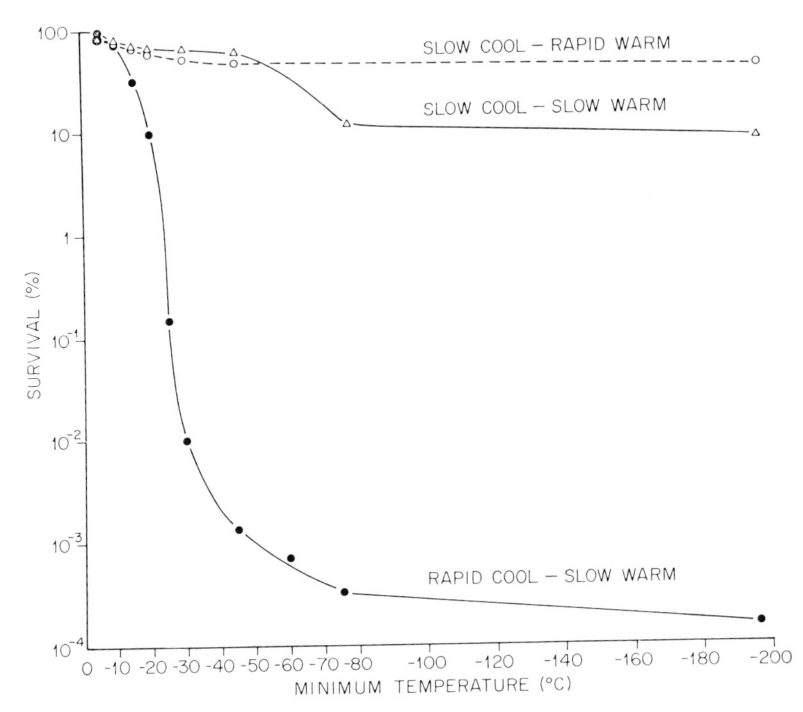

FIG. 4. Survival of *Saccharomyces cerevisiae* as a function of temperature. Cells were suspended in distilled water, cooled to various temperatures at 1°C per minute (slow cooling) or 50°C per minute (rapid cooling), and warmed at 1°C per minute (slow warming) or 500°–1400°C per minute (rapid warming). From Mazur and Schmidt (1966).

cooled cell contents (Mazur, 1960b, 1965b), and because extracellular freezing produces no injury for an hour or so. (It must be emphasized, however, that prolonged storage at −10°C could become deleterious because it would subject the cells to prolonged exposure to concentrated solutes.) By the time the cells have been cooled to about −70°C, either they have frozen intracellularly or they have dehydrated without internal freezing. In either case, cooling to −196°C produces little or no further alteration. Again, this statement applies only to the first few minutes of exposure. Prolonged storage at −70°C for hours or days could be considerably more harmful than storage at −196°C (see below).

(2) *Cooling and warming rates.* If cells are cooled slowly to below −40°C at 1°C per minute, survivals are between 10 and 50% when warming is slow and about 50% when warming is rapid (Fig. 4). On the other hand, if cells are cooled rapidly at 50° to 300°C per minute, survivals are 10^{-3} to 10^{-6}% when warming is slow and 0.1 to 1% when

warming is rapid (Figs. 3 and 4). As already indicated, the damaging effects of rapid cooling are associated with intracellular freezing.

The basis of the damage accompanying slow cooling is uncertain. The drop in survival from 100% at —5°C to about 50% at —30°C may be due to the long duration of exposure to concentrating solutes; however, when slow cooling is carried to lower temperatures, slowly warmed cells undergo a second drop in survival whereas rapidly warmed cells do not. The cause of this second drop is unknown.

The above findings are in general supported by most investigators who have determined quantitative survivals of yeast after freezing and thawing. Survivals are higher at temperatures above —10°C than below (Baum, 1943; Campbell, 1943; Devik and Ulrich, 1948–1949; Nei *et al.,* 1954; Wood and Rosenberg, 1957); slow cooling is less damaging than rapid cooling (Ulrich and Halvorson, 1946–1947; Devick and Ulrich, 1948–1949; Nei *et al.,* 1954; Wood and Taylor, 1957; Benedict *et al.,* 1961; Smith, 1961; Bradley, 1963; Greaves and Davies, 1965), but not necessarily less damaging than ultrarapid cooling and ultrarapid warming (Doebbler and Rinfret, 1963; Moor and Mühlethaler, 1963); and slow thawing is more harmful to rapidly cooled cells than is rapid thawing (Lund and Lundberg, 1949–1950).

Some investigators, however, have reported contrary findings, especially as to the effects of warming rate. These findings and possible reasons for the discrepancies have been discussed elsewhere (Mazur, 1966, p. 262).

b. Damage during Storage. Yeast can survive the initial effects of exposure to low temperatures and still succumb to long-term storage. For example, in the previous section it was mentioned that nearly 100% survive freezing to —10°C; yet storage at temperatures above —10°C results in a progressive decline in viability according to Stille (1950). He found that the number of viable yeast dropped more than 5 log units after 77 days at —4°C. Survivals also decreased at —15 and —24°C, although less rapidly than at —4°C (0.4%, 1.7%, and 3×10^{-4}%, respectively, after 77 days). The finding that decay rates decrease with decreasing storage temperatures is a common observation with microorganisms (Haines, 1938; Straka and Stokes, 1959; Woodburn and Strong, 1960), but it is by no means universal (Arpai, 1963; A. P. Harrison and Pelczar, 1963). There is no theoretical reason why it should be universal, for although a drop in temperature tends to decrease reaction rates, it also increases the concentration of solutes in the unfrozen liquid. It is quite possible for the deleterious consequences of increased solute concentration to more than compensate for any beneficial effects of lowered temperature.

Cells cooled to below their eutectic zone (approximately —30°C to —50°C) should contain little or no free liquid water and should, therefore, be much less subject to injury from concentrated solutes. In agreement with this prediction the viability of most cells remains unaltered after prolonged storage at —78°C, and to date there has been no clear demonstration of a drop in survival of any cells stored at —196°C in liquid nitrogen. On the other hand, there is one reported case in yeast and a number of cases in animal cells in which survival fell with time even at temperatures as low as —78°C (Wallace and Tanner, 1935). The simplest explanation is that enough liquid water (free or bound) existed even at —78°C to permit deleterious reactions to occur. This supposition has been supported recently by M. V. Sussman and Chin's (1966) finding that nuclear magnetic resonance signals characteristic of liquid water are observable in cod muscle down to —70°C. Injury could also conceivably occur as low as —78°C as a result of recrystallization of ice crystals, especially if cells are cooled rapidly enough to contain intracellular ice.

2. *Manifestations of Injury*

Yeast cells that are killed by freezing and thawing are not physically disintegrated (Haines, 1938; Nei, 1960; Mazur, 1961b), but the thawed cells exhibit marked morphological and permeability changes. Their volume is halved, the conspicuous central vacuole disappears, intracellular solutes of molecular weight below 500–1000 leak into the surrounding medium, and the cells become permeable to solutes that are normally nonpenetrating (Lund, 1951–1952; Foulkes, 1954; Hansen and Nossal, 1955; Sakagami, 1959; Armstrong, 1961; Conway and Armstrong, 1961; Mazur, 1961b,c, 1963a, 1965b; Araki, 1965; Souzu, 1965).

These observations are consistent with the view that lethal freezing or thawing damages or destroys the plasma membrane and various internal membranes. As a result of this damage, the cells lose most of the solutes that contribute to their internal osmotic pressure. They shrink because turgor pressure is no longer present to maintain the cell wall in a stretched state (Mazur, 1961c). The question whether or not membrane damage is a direct consequence of ice formation, and is, therefore, the immediate cause of death, is unanswered. However, permeability damage is observable during the course of warming even before the frozen suspensions are completely thawed (Mazur, 1965b).

Yeast cells that are dead in the sense of being unable to form colonies on agar plates are, nevertheless, capable of a certain amount of enzymatic activity. Their catalase activity is not impaired (Ogawa, 1953). They can degrade phosphates and ferment glucose to a certain extent (Tonino and Steyn-Parvé, 1963; Souzu, 1964, 1965; Araki, 1965), and they can dehydrogenate succinate, lactate, citrate, isocitrate, malate, fumarate, and glutamate (Hansen and Nossal, 1955). On the other hand, they can not carry out oxidative phosphorylation (Hansen and Nossal, 1955) and apparently can not synthesize DNA (Souzu and Araki, 1962). The former process is associated with mitochondrial membranes.

B. *Freezing Injury in Other Fungi*

Although there have been many studies on the effects of freezing on cells of animals and higher plants, and on bacteria, there have been few on fungi other than yeast, and even fewer that provide the type of data from which one can draw conclusions about mechanisms of injury. Nevertheless, some information is available. Most of it pertains to spores.

1. *The Effects of Freezing on Fungus Spores*

It has been known for many years that a fraction of spores in a population will survive cooling to temperatures as low as —185°C, but only more recently have investigators determined percentage survivals.

a. Freezing of Aqueous Suspensions of Spores. Alexopoulos and Drummond (1934) rapidly froze water suspensions of spores of *Melanconium, Coniothyrium, Eurotium,* and *Cytospora* to —185°C and reported that germination took place in all cases after thawing; but they made no estimate of the percentage survival. Akai (1954) did measure percentage survivals of uredospores of *Puccinia triticina* [*P. recondita*] after suspensions of spores in water had been frozen at —10°C. Survivals (percent germination treated/percent germination unfrozen controls) were about 25% immediately after freezing, but dropped rapidly with storage time.

As discussed in the preceding section on yeast, survival after freezing and thawing can be affected by cooling rate, temperature, storage time, and warming rate. These factors were found to influence the survival of spores of *Aspergillus flavus* profoundly (Mazur, 1953), with results quite parallel to those for yeast.

1. No injury occurred when suspensions of spores in water were cooled to —8.5°C regardless of whether the suspension was supercooled or frozen (Mazur, 1960a). Moreover, 100% survived exposure to temperatures as low as —45°C as long as the suspending medium had a sufficiently high concentration of salts to remain unfrozen (Mazur, 1960b). On the other hand, if the suspending medium was frozen, and if the spores were cooled rapidly and warmed slowly, survival dropped abruptly from 85% to 10% as the minimum temperature was lowered from —9.5°C to —40°C. Cooling to temperatures below —40°C engendered little additional damage (Mazur, 1960a).

These findings lead to three conclusions: (a) injury requires the presence of external ice; (b) the presence of external ice is not sufficient in itself to produce injury (temperatures below −10°C, rapid cooling, and slow warming are also required); and (c) the spores are more injured by being frozen than by being exposed to concentrated salt solutions.

2. When suspensions were frozen to −65°C, lowering the rate of cooling from 350° to 0.4°C per minute increased the percentage survival from 7 to 37% (Table II). To be protected, the spores had to be cooled

TABLE II

EFFECT OF COOLING AND WARMING VELOCITY ON SURVIVAL OF FROZEN AND THAWED SPORES OF *Aspergillus flavus*[a]

	Survival[c] after	
Cooling velocity[b] (°C/minute)	Rapid warming (1400°C/minute) (%)	Slow warming (1°C/minute) (%)
0.3–0.4	73.5[d]	37.5
6–7	72.9	11.4
350	77.6	6.7

[a] From Mazur (1953).

[b] Spores were suspended in distilled water and cooled to −65°C to −75°C. Cooling rates were based on the rate of temperature drop from 23°C to −35°C.

[c] Percent germination/percent germination of controls. The percentage of germination of controls was 86–95%.

[d] Cooled only to −32°C.

slowly to at least −30°C; they could then be cooled rapidly to lower temperatures without incurring further damage (Fig. 5).

3. The above findings applied to cases where the spores were warmed slowly at 1°C per minute. Increasing the warming rate increased the survival of rapidly cooled cells and eliminated the difference between the effects of rapid and slow cooling (Table II).

Haskins (1957) studied the effects of rate of warming on the spores of *Alternaria, Aspergillus, Fusarium, Gliocladium, Penicillium,* and *Pestalotia* (Table III). All responded similarly to *Aspergillus flavus* in that survivals were higher after rapid thawing than after slow, but the differences were less striking with *Gliocladium* and *Penicillium* than with the other genera.

These results have recently been confirmed and extended by Goos *et al.* (1967). The survival of frozen and slowly thawed spores of several species was higher when cooling was slow than when it was rapid, but was high and usually independent of cooling rate when thawing was rapid. The species were *Aspergillus niger, Botrytis bifurcata, Cephaliophora irregularis, Fusarium solani, Gloeosporium musarum, Helminthosporium sativum, Penicillium megasporum, Syzygites megalocarpus,* and *Tricho-*

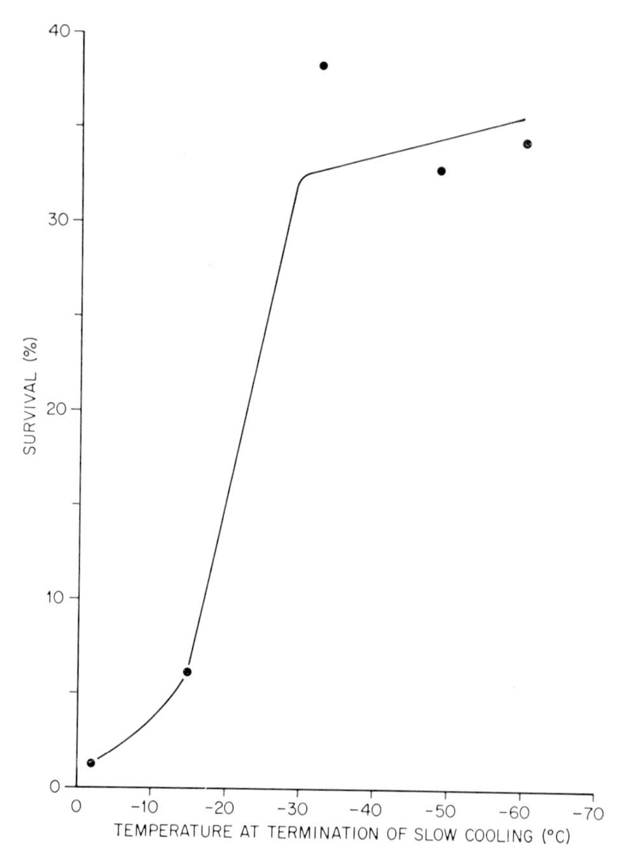

FIG. 5. Effect of temperature at termination of slow cooling on the survival of spores of *Aspergillus flavus*. Spores were suspended in distilled water, cooled at 1°C per minute to the indicated temperatures, and then cooled rapidly to —75°C at more than 50°C per minute and warmed slowly. Survival is calculated as percent germination/percent germination of controls. The percent germination of controls was 87. Drawn from data of Mazur (1953).

phaea abundans. In *Rhizopus stolonifer,* however, survival approached 100% regardless of the cooling and warming rate.

As with yeasts, these findings for *A. flavus* and the other species are consistent with the hypothesis that the chief cause of injury in fungus spores suspended in aqueous solutions is intracellular freezing (Mazur, 1953, 1956, 1960a,b). However, unlike the case with yeast, the evidence supporting this view is circumstantial.

b. Freezing of "Air-Dry" Spores. One might expect "air-dry" conidia to survive freezing better than spores suspended in water or aqueous solutions, and in general this is so. Faull (1929) observed that air-dry

TABLE III

PERCENTAGE GERMINATION OF SPORES AFTER BEING SUSPENDED IN SERUM OR WATER, RAPIDLY FROZEN TO −65°C, AND WARMED AT SEVERAL RATES[a,b]

	In water			In serum		
Organism	Rapid warm	Medium warm	Slow warm	Rapid warm	Medium warm	Slow warm
Alternaria	22.9	6.5	6.1	38.4	48.8	3.9
Aspergillus	54.0	31.6	18.3	70.6	19.3	10.4
Fusarium	67.7	43.9	30.7	50.8	44.4	35.6
Gliocladium	84.3	85.9	72.2	90.1	87.8	72.8
Penicillium	74.6	53.8	43.7	78.8	83.0	56.9
Pestalotia	60.5	53.2	31.7	83.9	73.7	26.9

[a] From Haskins (1957).
[b] Rapid: 5 minutes; immersion in 35°C bath. Medium: 1 hour; left in air at 21°C. Slow: 6 hours; left in freezing bath until it reached 21°C.

conidia of *Neurospora crassa* were more resistant than "wet" spores, but the results were qualitative. Mazur (1953) found that air-dry spores of *A. flavus* were highly resistant to low temperatures. It can be seen from Table IV that about 80% survived freezing to −73°C or −196°C regardless of the warming rate. Graham (1956) obtained similar results with spores of *Ustilago tritici* [*U. nuda*] frozen to −38°C. Only 6% survived when the spores were suspended in water, whereas 90% survived when the spores were air-dry. Faull's suggestion that air-dry conidia of *N. crassa* are relatively resistant to freezing was confirmed by Wellman and Walden (1964). They froze sporulating cultures of *N. crassa*

TABLE IV

COMPARATIVE EFFECTS OF FREEZING ON THE SURVIVAL OF AIR-DRY AND WET SPORES OF *Aspergillus flavus*[a,b]

Condition of spores	Percentage germination after			
	Rapid cool[c]		Ultrarapid cool[d]	
	Rapid warm[e]	Slow warm[e]	Rapid warm	Slow warm
Air-dry	78.9	75.2	86.0	75.2
Wet[f]	66.7	3.2	91.1	13.0

[a] From Mazur (1953).
[b] The percentage germination of untreated controls was 94.7%.
[c] Cooled to −73°C at about 270°C per minute.
[d] Cooled to −196°C at about 500°C per minute.
[e] Rapid and slow warming were about 1400 and 1°C per minute.
[f] Spores suspended in distilled water.

and *Sordaria fimicola* to −196°C at rates between 60 and 900°C per minute, held them for 0 to 9 months, and thawed them rather slowly in air. The spores were then collected and the percentage germination was determined. Germination was 95–98% for *Neurospora* and 78% for *Sordaria,* the same as for untreated controls.

The reduced sensitivity of air-dry spores may be due to the fact that ice formation does not occur because of their low water content. This assumption is reasonable since many air-dry fungus spores only contain about 0.06 gm to 0.3 gm of H_2O per gram dry weight (Table V), and calorimetric measurements have shown that about 0.25 gm of H_2O per gram dry weight of yeast or *E. coli* is incapable of freezing (Wood and Rosenberg, 1957; Souzu *et al.,* 1961; Mazur, 1963a). Furthermore, Somers and Horsfall (1966) have shown by nuclear magnetic resonance that *Erysiphe* conidia contain no free water even though their water content is quite high.

If air-dry spores survive because they do not freeze and if most of the injury in "wet" spores results from intracellular freezing, one would have to conclude that the water content of air-dry spores rises rapidly when they are suspended in water. The data in Table V and the observation of Somers and Horsfall (1966) that the water content of *Erysiphe* conidia rises rapidly with rise in relative humidity (RH) suggest that this may be so. The question whether ice can form in air-dry spores can be settled only by direct calorimetric measurements. Calorimetry can also determine how much of the intracellular water in wet spores can freeze, but unfortunately it cannot determine whether the water freezes within the spore or leaves the spore and freezes externally. It would be informative to know, however, whether the time-course for the increase in freezing susceptibility of air-dry spores upon their transfer to water is paralleled by the time course of water uptake.

The response of air-dry uredospores of *Puccinia* and *Uromyces* to low temperatures is more complex than that of the spores discussed so far. Survival has been found to depend on the procedures followed after warming. Melander (1935) and Flor (1954) observed that low-temperature exposure markedly reduced the percentage germination of air-dry *Puccinia* and *Melampsora lini* (flax rust) uredospores. Akai (1954) found that exposure to −10°C for 1 day was more harmful to air-dry uredospores of *P. triticina* [*P. recondita*] (2.7% germination) than to suspensions of spores in water (18% germination). It would have been reasonable to assume that the low survivals represented irreversible low-temperature injury, but two observations in 1962 showed that this is not the case. Loegering and Harmon (1962) found that the survival of air-dry spores of *P. graminis* after rapid cooling to −196°C depended critically on the

TABLE V

WATER CONTENTS OF FUNGUS SPORES

Organism	State of spore	Water content (Grams H_2O per gram wet weight)	Water content (Grams H_2O per gram dry weight)	Reference
Erysiphe sp.	Air-dry	0.52–0.75	1.1–2.6	Yarwood (1950)
Uromyces appendiculata	Air-dry	0.12	0.14	Yarwood (1950)
Peronospora destructor	Air-dry	0.17	0.20	Yarwood (1950)
Botrytis cinerea	Air-dry	0.17	0.20	Yarwood (1950)
Monilinia fructicola	Air-dry	0.25	0.33	Yarwood (1950)
Penicillium digitatum	Air-dry	0.06	0.06	Yarwood (1950)
Aspergillus niger	Air-dry	0.13	0.15	Yarwood (1950)
Aspergillus terreus	Air-dry	0.43	0.75	Stapleton and Hollaender (1952)
Penicillium cyclopaeum	Suspended in protein sol'n	0.50–0.78	0.96–3.5	Barer (1956, p. 63)
P. notatum	Suspended in protein sol'n	0.45	0.82	Barer (1956, p. 63)
P. notatum (pregermination)	Suspended in protein sol'n	0.79	3.6	Barer (1956, p. 63)
Puccinia sp. (uredospores)	Air-dry	0.08–0.16	0.09–0.019	Sharp and Smith (1957)
Puccinia sp.	Equilibrated at RH 32–79%	0.35–0.60	0.54–1.5	Schwinghamer (1958)
Erysiphe sp.	Equilibrated at 100% RH	0.66–0.69	1.9–2.2	Somers and Horsfall (1966)
	Equilibrated at ~50% RH	0.31–0.35	0.45–0.54	

temperature of the thawing bath. Survival increased from below 2% to 100% when the temperature of the thawing bath was raised from 20°C to between 34°C and 60°C. The increase was not due to the increased warming rate in the higher temperature baths, for high survivals were also obtained when the spores were first transferred from liquid nitrogen to baths at 0°C or 20°C, and then 5 minutes later to a bath at 40°C. In fact, survival was 100% even when as much as 1 hour lapsed between the initial warming in a 20°C bath and the transfer to a 40°C bath. Besides this reversible injury induced by cooling the spores to −196°C, Loegering and Harmon also observed irreversible freezing injury associated with storage at subzero temperatures. Storage for 108 days at −5°C or −20°C reduced survival to about 40%. No such loss occurred at −196°C.

The second observation was that of Schein (1962), who found that the survival of "frozen and thawed" air-dry uredospores of the bean rust *Uromyces phaseoli* [*U. appendiculatus*] could be raised significantly by a different procedure, namely, by exposing the "thawed" spores to 100% relative humidity for 1–4 days before placing them on agar plates. For example, hydration for 24 hours increased the percentage germination of spores stored at −60°C for 21 months from 40% to 65%. As far as freezing damage per se is concerned, Schein found that *Uromyces* uredospores, like those of *Puccinia,* died more rapidly when stored at higher subzero temperatures. For example, none survived storage after 7–15 months at −16°C regardless of whether or not they were hydrated before plating, whereas some 40–65% survived at −60°C.

The thermal reactivation observed by Loegering and Harmon has been studied in more detail by Bromfield (1964) who found first that although the *Puccinia* spores had to be cooled to below 0°C to induce reversible dormancy, they did not have to be cooled to −196°C; cooling to −1 to −3°C was sufficient. He confirmed Loegering and Harmon's observations that (a) the spores could be subjected to multiple cycles of inactivation and reactivation, (b) a considerable period of time (up to 34 days) could elapse between warming the chilled spores to 20°C and reactivation at 40°C, and (c) the rate of warming or chilling had little or no effect on the results. A hydration procedure similar to that used by Schein was usually even more effective in reversing cold-induced dormancy than was a 5-minute heat shock at 40°C. The combination of heat shock and hydration raised the percentage of germination slightly over that obtained with either alone, but the effect was not additive. The dormant spores respire at a normal rate, suggesting that cold-induced dormancy involves a blockage of germination rather than a general inhibition of metabolism. The block was not eliminated by exposing the spores to 10^{-4} *M* solutions of nonanol, heptanol, octanol, or decanol, all of which have been found effective in inducing the germination of spores rendered dormant by other means.

The question remains whether the dormancy is induced by lowered temperatures per se or by ice formation (i.e., freezing). The fact that dormancy is induced only below 0°C and that it occurs even after very rapid cooling to —196°C favors the latter hypothesis. (When small sample tubes are immersed in liquid nitrogen, only a few seconds elapse before the temperature drops so low as to preclude chemical reactions.) On the other hand, although it seems very unlikely that the water in spores can freeze at —1°C, cooling to —1°C induced dormancy.

The induction of reversible dormancy appears peculiar to "air-dry" uredospores. When suspensions of uredospores of *Puccinia graminis* in water are frozen to —196°C and thawed, survivals are low regardless of the cooling velocity, the warming velocity, or the temperature of the thawing bath (Davis *et al.,* 1966). Nor is dormancy induced in the conidia of a variety of other fungi when suspensions of the spores in 10% glycerol are frozen to —196°C and thawed (Goos *et al.,* 1967).

2. *Effects of Freezing on Vegetative Fungal Cells*

Apart from the studies of yeast already discussed, there have been few quantitative studies of the effects of freezing on vegetative fungal cells, undoubtedly because of the difficulty in quantifying hyphal survival. However, some fraction of the hyphae of at least some genera can survive exposure to subzero temperatures, for several authors have reported that nonsporulating cultures or fragments of mycelium can produce viable cultures after freezing to —10°C (Melander, 1935), —20°C (Carmichael, 1962), or —196°C (Hwang, 1960). Bartetzko (1910) was one of the first, and one of the very few, to thoroughly study the effects of freezing on individual hyphae. He did so by microscopic observation of the staining and osmotic properties of young (70–200 μ) hyphae of *Aspergillus, Penicillium, Botrytis,* and *Phycomyces* that had been suspended in various solutions and cooled to temperatures between —0.3 and —26°C. He found, first, that no injury occurred for the first 2 hours at temperatures as low as —11°C as long as the suspending medium remained unfrozen. Longer exposures in the supercooled state, however, were deleterious. On the other hand, rapid injury did occur when the suspending medium froze, and the lower the temperature the greater the injury. There was also a correlation between the temperature that produced a 50% kill and the freezing point (or concentration) of the suspending medium. For example, when hyphae of *A. niger* were frozen in 1, 10, 20, 30, 40, or 50% glucose with measured freezing points —0.3, —1.3, —2.9,

−4, −6.7, and −8.9°C, the temperatures below which 50% of the hyphae were killed were −2, −3, −7, −13, −19, and below −26°C, respectively. He reported similar results with the other organisms tested and with other suspending media (glycerol, and mixtures of KNO_3 and $NaNO_3$). Most of the experiments were carried out using slow thawing, but rapid thawing produced similar results.

It is difficult to draw any clear conclusions from the data as to mechanisms, other than the obvious one that the presence of ice in the medium produced injury or was required for injury. Actually, the results are rather at odds with the tendency of most other cells to become injured only below fixed temperatures. The concentration of solutes often affects the degree of injury or death, but it does not usually affect the temperatures at which injury occurs (Mazur, 1966).

Cochrane (1958) has summarized the results of several other older studies on the freezing of mycelia. In general, mycelium appears to be considerably more sensitive than spores. However, Doebbler and Rinfret (1963) obtained survivals of 22% when mycelial fragments of *A. niger* in growth medium were sprayed on a moving surface of liquid nitrogen and thawed in 37°C saline. They estimated that this procedure yielded cooling and warming rates of several hundred degrees per second. Wellman and Walden (1964) examined mycelial fragments and isolated hyphae from agar slant cultures of *Neurospora* and *Sordaria* that had been frozen at 60–900°C per minute to −196°C and thawed slowly rather than rapidly. They reported that the fraction of fragments or tips that grew was the same as in unfrozen controls. This result is rather surprising in view of the abundant evidence with other microorganisms that the sequence of rapid cooling and slow warming is maximally harmful (Mazur, 1966). In fact, Wellman and Walden, themselves, found this to be the case in frozen and thawed sporulating cultures of *Pythium* and *Rhizopus*. The cultures often failed to survive the combination of rapid freezing and slow thawing, but survivals were improved by slow cooling at 1°C per minute and by rapid thawing. One possible explanation for the apparent lack of injury in rapidly frozen and slowly thawed mycelia might be that freezing and thawing physically destroyed a large fraction of the mycelial cells. This would have resulted in an overestimate of the fraction of surviving cells since this estimate was based on the assumption that freezing did not reduce the number of morphologically intact units.

IV. DEHYDRATION AND FREEZE-DRYING

The concept of preserving cell viability by dehydration was predicated on the fact that liquid water is essential for active biological processes.

Freeze-drying was thought to be advantageous because it would permit water to be removed at temperatures low enough to stop or slow deleterious chemical reactions. Furthermore, it was believed that cells should be frozen as rapidly as possible to keep their structure normal during cooling. On the basis of this reasoning and the earlier successful freeze-drying of bacteria, Wickerham and Andreasen (1942) freeze-dried yeast, and Raper and Alexander (1945) dried spores of filamentous fungi. Their techniques proved to be eminently successful for the preservation of cultures of most species (see Section V); however, when the percentage survivals in freeze-dried samples of yeast (Atkin *et al.*, 1949) and fungal conidia (Weston, 1949) were determined, they were found to be low, usually below 5%. Since then, low survivals of freeze-dried fungus spores have been reported by Haskins and Anastasiou (1953), Mazur (1953), Mazur and Weston (1956), Graham (1956), and Haskins (1957); and low survivals of freeze-dried yeast have been reported by Kirsop (1955), Guibert and Bréchot (1955), and Nei *et al.* (1961). The remainder of this section will be concerned with the possible causes of injury.

A. *Comparison of Freeze-Drying and Freezing*

It was pointed out in Section II that freezing itself dehydrates cells by depositing cellular water in a biologically nonutilizable form, i.e., as ice. The sublimation then merely serves to remove the ice from the sample. One might expect, therefore, that most of the damage from freeze-drying would be due to damage incurred during freezing. Experimental data have shown that this supposition is partly, but not completely, true.

1. *Freezing Damage in Freeze-Drying*

In the standard freeze-drying procedure, cell suspensions are rapidly frozen to about −60°C and then held at about −10°C during sublimation. We have seen in Section II that this sequence of steps is maximally deleterious to yeast, and to spores of *A. flavus* and several other molds. Obviously, no cell will survive freeze-drying if it cannot survive the initial freezing; hence, if freezing is a major factor in injury, survivals after freeze-drying ought to be markedly improved by freezing under optimum conditions. This supposition has been borne out.

a. Spores. When *A. flavus* spores are frozen and thawed, survivals are maximal if the cells are cooled no lower than −10°C, and they are minimal when the cells are cooled below −40°C. The findings for freeze-drying are comparable. Survivals are usually higher when spores are cooled to no lower than −18°C than when they are initially cooled to −60°C (Table VI).

TABLE VI

Effect of Initial Freezing Temperature and Suspending Medium on Survival of Freeze-Dried Fungal Spores

Organism	Percentage germination of spores suspended in								
	Distilled water			Horse serum			Horse serum + sucrose		
	Control	−15°C[a]	−65°C[a]	Control	−15° to −18°C	−59° to −65°C	Control	−16° to −18°C	−59° to −63°C
Aspergillus flavus[b]	96.6	25.7	2.4	96.9	45.2	7.1	—	—	—
Aspergillus niger[c]	—	—	—	55.9	28.5	9.3	50.7	30.7	8.1
Fusarium	—	—	—	87.3	3.2	0.0	89.6	57.4	2.3
Gliocladium	—	—	—	99.1	0.0	0.0	99.4	32.3	27.4
Penicillium	—	—	—	99.4	1.9	1.8	94.4	60.7	40.6
Pestalotia	—	—	—	95.5	2.2	5.5	94.9	64.0	2.2

[a] Initial freezing temperature.

[b] From Mazur (1953); samples were held at about −10°C during sublimation.

[c] All other data are from Haskins (1957); samples were frozen at indicated temperatures and then dried in a vacuum jar at room temperature.

Haskins and Anastasiou (1953), Haskins (1957), and Graham (1956) also found that survivals after freeze-drying were significantly higher when spore suspensions were allowed to freeze by evaporative cooling instead of by immersion in baths at temperatures below —35°C. Haskins and Anastasiou obtained survivals of 57 and 34% for the two procedures in one experiment with suspensions of *A. niger* spores in serum, and Graham obtained survivals of 42 and 4.5% with suspensions of *Ustilago* spores in water. Haskins (1957) found that the lowest temperature reached with evaporative cooling in his apparatus was about —12°C. This is in accord with the supposition that the procedure yielded higher survivals because the temperature was above the region where maximum freezing injury occurs. But there are other possible explanations. One is that evaporative cooling protected by producing lower cooling rates than those produced by direct immersion of sample tubes in a cold liquid bath. Another is that it protected because it concentrated the suspending medium before freezing occurred. Weston (1949) reported that when spore suspensions were subjected to preliminary evaporation from the liquid state (presumably without freezing), they were better able to survive subsequent rapid cooling to —60°C and sublimation at —10°C.

A further parallel between the effects of freezing and thawing and freeze-drying is found in the relative response of air-dry and wet spores to the two treatments. Percentage germinations of air-dry and wet conidia of *Aspergillus flavus* were 75 and 3.2, respectively, after freezing and slow thawing (Table IV) and 91 and 2.4 after freeze-drying (Mazur, 1953). Similarly, percentage germinations of air-dry and wet spores of *Ustilago tritici* [*U. nuda*] were 90 and 5.6 after freezing and thawing and 93 and 4.5 after freeze-drying (Graham, 1956). Water was the suspending medium for the wet spores, and the first step both in the freeze-thawing and the freeze-drying was to cool the spores rapidly to —38°C (Graham) or to —70°C (Mazur).

Finally, if freezing is a major factor in the injury produced by freeze-drying, then dehydration at temperatures above 0°C might yield higher survivals than does freeze-drying. In some cases it has been found to do so. For example, 65–100% of spores of *Aspergillus flavus* and *Pestalotia palmarum* survived spray-drying at 80–100°C, whereas only 2–10% survived freeze-drying by the Wickerham-Raper technique (Mazur and Weston, 1956; Weston *et al.,* 1949). Although moisture contents of the spray-dried samples were not determined, survivals were not reduced by increasing the length of exposure to a flow of heated air, a fact that suggests that the higher survivals obtained with spray-drying are not ascribable to incomplete dehydration.

Mazur and Weston (1953) also determined the viability of *A. flavus*

TABLE VII

PERCENTAGE GERMINATION OF SPORES OF *Aspergillus flavus* AFTER SLOW DEHYDRATION FROM THE LIQUID STATE

Suspending medium	Control[a] (%)	Dehydrated[b] (%)
None (air dry)	—	89.6
Distilled H_2O	96.6	74.6
Horse serum	90.0	79.9
0.3 *M* sucrose	91.8	50.7
0.16 *M* NaCl	98.5	18.2

[a] Exposed to ambient humidity for 21 hours at 25°C.

[b] Held over Drierite for 8 days at 25°C. Rehydrated in a solution of 0.1% Naccanol in water.

spores after thin layers of suspensions had been dehydrated at room temperature (Table VII). Survivals were considerably higher than after freeze-drying. The residual water contents of the samples were not determined, but the desiccator-dried samples appeared dry after the first day of the 8-day desiccation. Woodward and Swarup (1956) and Klingmüller (1963) obtained similar results with conidia of *Neurospora*. About 50–100% of spores suspended in water survived dehydration for 1–6 days over P_2O_5 at room temperature. Similarly, Sharp and Smith (1957) found that higher percentages of air-dry uredospores of *Puccinia* survived vacuum drying at room temperatures than at —50 to —10°C. Although it is possible that the former actually froze by evaporative cooling, the authors were unable to observe a drop in temperature with thermocouples immersed in the spore mass.

b. Vegetative Cells. I mentioned on p. 351 that only small percentages of yeast cells survive the standard freeze-drying procedure developed by Wickerham and Andreasen. Greaves and Davies (1965) investigated the contribution of freezing to freeze-drying injury in yeast and found that two factors are involved, one associated with freezing, the other not. Figure 6 compares the survivals of yeast dried by direct pumping at temperatures between +2 and —40°C with that of cells frozen rapidly to the same temperatures and thawed slowly. Unlike survivals after freezing and thawing, survivals after freezing and drying increased as the drying temperature was reduced from +2 to —15°C (between —5°C and —10°C, some samples froze and others did not; survivals were the same in both cases). But below —15°C, the slope of the survival curve suddenly changed sign and became parallel to that for freezing and thawing. This parallelism suggests that below —15°C the improvement in survival produced by reducing the temperature was counteracted by the appearance of freezing

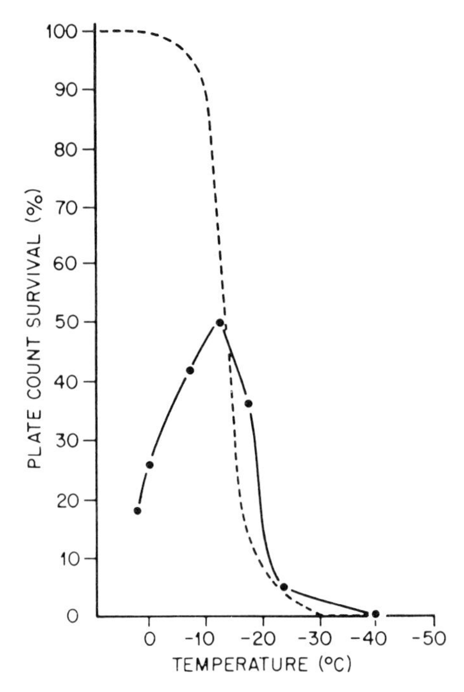

FIG. 6. Percentage survival of *Saccharomyces cerevisiae* after drying at indicated temperatures (solid line) and after rapid freezing to various temperatures and slow thawing (dotted curve). The freezing data are from Mazur (1960b). Frozen-thawed cells were suspended in water; dried cells were suspended in 1% bovine albumin. From Greaves and Davies (1965).

injury. Since freezing injury is reduced by cooling slowly at 1°C per minute, slow cooling ought to reduce freeze-drying injury. In fact, Greaves and Davies found this to be so, for samples of cells cooled at 1°C per minute to —25 and —35°C and dried at those temperatures survived as well or better than those cooled to and dried at —12.5°C (Table VIII).

The reduced survival produced by drying yeast at temperatures above —15°C contrasts with results just reviewed for spores. The difference is probably due to the higher susceptibility of yeast cells to the concentrated solutions bathing the cells at those temperatures. As noted earlier, *A. flavus* spores can withstand concentrated salt solutions for at least an hour.

Paradoxically, although Greaves and Davies found that few cells of *Saccharomyces cerevisiae* survive dehydration from the liquid state at say +2°C, others have found that nearly 100% survive the rapid dehydration at elevated temperatures used in preparing "active-dry" yeast (Sant and Peterson, 1958; Koga *et al.,* 1966). The discrepancy may be due to differences in the temperature and rate of dehydration. On the other hand,

TABLE VIII

PERCENTAGE SURVIVAL IMMEDIATELY AFTER DRYING *Saccharomyces cerevisiae* IN DIFFERENT DRYING MEDIA[a,b]

Suspending medium	Percentage survival immediately after drying at −12.5°C	−25°C	−35°C
Distilled water	1	19	18
Glucose 7.5%	71	70	85
Sucrose 12.5%	63	72	75
Peptone 10%	59	63	83
Na glutamate 5%	31	16	52
PVP 10%	4	50	49
Glucose 7.5%, Peptone 5%, PVP 10%	70	100	85
Sucrose 10%, Na glutamate 2%, PVP 10%	71	85	74
Sucrose 12.5%, PVP 10%	80	94	84
Na glutamate 5%, PVP 10%	26	10	18

[a] From Greaves and Davies (1965).
[b] Suspensions were cooled slowly at 1°C per minute to indicated temperatures.

as discussed in Section 2 below, the survival of active dry yeast is critically dependent on the final water content of the product and on the method of rehydration, and it is possible that Greaves and Davies dried the yeast beyond the critical point (8 gm of water per 100 gm dry weight), or rehydrated it under suboptimal conditions. However, the point germane to the present discussion is that it is *possible* to dry yeast to low water contents without killing the cells if freezing injury is avoided.

This may also be the case with fungal hyphae. Perkins (1962) reports that nonconidiating strains of *Neurospora* survive room temperature dehydration by silica gel better than freeze-drying.

2. *Differences between Freeze-Drying and Freezing and Thawing*

Although freezing injury contributes importantly to freeze-drying injury, it is not the only factor, for the sequence of freezing and drying often yields lower survivals than the sequence of freezing and thawing, even when the freezing procedures are the same (Table IX).

Three factors could be responsible for the increased injury observed with freezing and drying: (a) the sample temperature during sublimation,

TABLE IX

COMPARATIVE EFFECTS OF FREEZE-THAWING AND FREEZE-DRYING ON THE SURVIVAL OF FUNGI

Organism	Cell type	Suspending medium	Freezing temp. (°C)	% Survival[a] after: Slow thawing	% Survival[a] after: Drying	Reference
Aspergillus flavus	Conidia	H_2O	−15	65	26	Mazur (1963c)
			−65	7	2.4	
A. niger	Conidia	Serum	−65	10.4	9.3	Haskins (1957)
Fusarium	Conidia	Serum	−65	35.6	0	Haskins (1957)
Gliocladium	Conidia	Serum	−65	72.8	0	Haskins (1957)
Penicillium	Conidia	Serum	−65	56.9	1.8	Haskins (1957)
Pestalotia	Conidia	Serum	−65	26.9	5.5	Haskins (1957)
Saccharomyces cerevisiae	Vegetative cells	H_2O	−12	60	1	Mazur (1961a); Greaves and Davies (1965)

[a] Survivals of the spores refer to percentage germination.

(b) the fraction of cellular water removed by sublimation, and (c) the rehydration of the dried material.

a. Sample Temperature during Sublimation. Most fungi have been freeze-dried by one of two procedures: the sample tubes have either been held in a bath at about —10°C during sublimation, or they have been held in air at room temperature. In the former case, the sample temperature probably remains close to the bath temperature because the rate of heat flow from bath to sample is probably enough to supply the necessary heat of sublimation. But this is not the case for sample tubes held in air. The heat of sublimation is initially drawn from the sample itself, and as a result, the temperature of the sample drops until the rate of sublimation is reduced to the point where the necessary heat can be supplied from the surrounding air. The equilibrium temperature attained depends on a number of factors including the area of subliming surface relative to the area for heat transfer, the efficiency of removal of water vapor through the vacuum system, and the nature of the dried material overlying the subliming surface. Probably, the only generalization that can be made is that the temperature of the frozen portion of the sample usually remains below 0°C. Only thermocouple measurements can tell how far below 0°C, and even they are difficult to interpret because of the complex thermal fluxes within the sample. Haskins' (1957) published temperature-time curves are probably representative.

It is impossible to predict how cells will respond to being maintained for variable intervals of time at variable temperatures in the range of 0° to —30°C, but some cells may be badly injured. For example, Fig. 7 shows the rapid drop in viability that occurs when cells of the bacterium *Pasteurella tularensis* are held at —15°C after being exposed for 3–5 minutes at —45 or —75°C.

As mentioned in connection with Greaves and Davies' (1965) work on yeast, the most probable cause of freeze-drying injury in the temperature range 0 to —15°C is contact with concentrated intra- and extracellular solutes. It was pointed out in Section II that the concentration of solutes in the unfrozen portion of any given frozen solution above its eutectic point is uniquely determined by temperature; the concentration remains constant as long as the temperature is constant, and it varies inversely with temperature. But the situation is different in freeze-drying at a constant temperature. Since the concentration of solutes in the unfrozen portion of the solution must remain constant, the ice has to sublime before any water is removed from the liquid portion. But once all the ice has sublimed, the liquid will begin to evaporate, and the solute concentration will be raised higher and higher. This may explain why Greaves and Davies found that drying at, say, —5°C was so much more harmful than freezing to the same temperature.

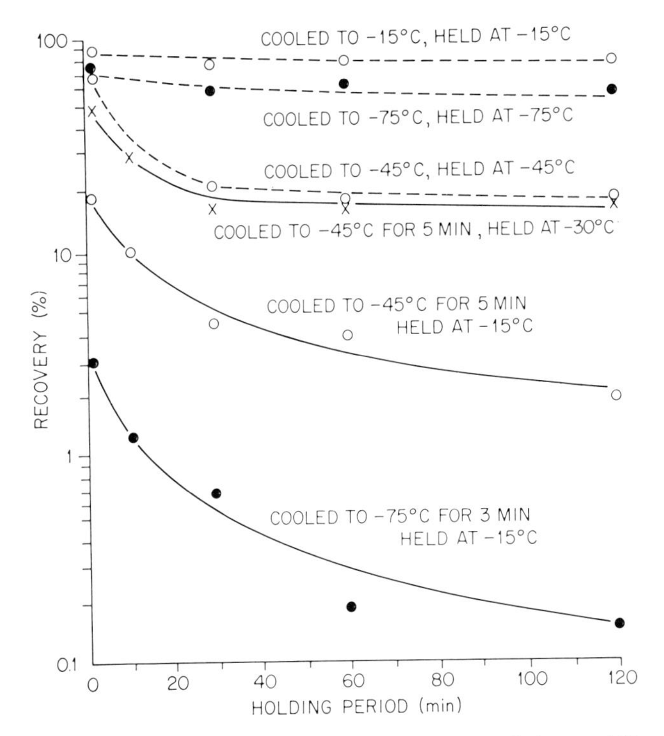

FIG. 7. Survival of *Pasteurella tularensis* cells initially cooled to −15°, −45°, or −75°C and then held at these or higher temperatures for various times. Dotted lines: cells held at initial cooling temperatures. Solid lines: cells held at initial cooling temperatures for 3–5 minutes and then held at −15° or −30°C. All cooling and warming was rapid. From Mazur *et al.* (1957a).

One way to eliminate injury from concentrated solutes is to dehydrate samples below the eutectic point or eutectic range of the solutes present inside and outside the cells; and as was seen in Section II, this means below −35 to −50°C. To my knowledge Greaves and Davies (1965) are the only ones to have freeze-dried fungi at temperatures this low, and they found that survivals were in fact improved (Table VIII).

b. Extent of Dehydration. Freezing and freeze-drying differ in another respect; namely, in the amount of water removed from solution. The calorimetric evidence reviewed in Section II shows that some 10% of the water in yeast and *Escherichia coli* remains unfrozen at temperatures as low as −70°C. This residual unfrozen water is presumably bound to proteins and nucleic acids, perhaps as water of hydration. Freeze-drying, on the other hand, removes not only the 90% of the water sequestered as ice, but most of the bound water as well. Residual moisture contents are usually 1–3% of the original wet weight of the cells. In many microorganisms, the 90% or so of the water that is free (i.e., capable of freezing) can be removed without must loss in viability, but the removal of part of the residual 10% is highly deleterious. Webb (1965, p. 13) has reported such findings for cells of *Serratia marcescens*, and Nei *et al.* (1965) for *E. coli*. Sakurada (1958) found that 50% of a population of yeast withstood having their water content lowered from the normal value of 2.3 gm per gram dry weight to 0.4 gm per gram dry weight by drying from the liquid state, but that fewer than 5% survived the removal of the remaining 20% of the cell water.

It should be emphasized that cells are not invariably killed when their water content is reduced below 10% of normal. As already mentioned, some 96% of the water in yeast can be removed (residual water content 0.08 gm H_2O per gram dry weight) by a stream of warm air without loss in viability; but when the water content is reduced to this value, the viability and enzymatic capabilities of the yeast become critically dependent on rehydration procedures.

c. *Method of Rehydration.* When a frozen cell suspension is warmed and thawed, the water converted to ice during freezing begins to return to the cell as the temperature rises above the eutectic zone. Since rate of thawing (and therefore the rate of introduction of water) can have profound effects on the survival of frozen and thawed cells, the method of rehydration could also have profound effects on the survival of dried cells. It does, but the effects are different.

A number of investigators have found that the activity and viability of active dry yeast are greatly affected by both the temperature of the rehydrating fluid and the rate of rehydration (Ebbutt, 1961; J. S. Harrison and Trevelyan, 1963; Herrera *et al.,* 1956; Mitchell and Enright, 1957; Sant and Peterson, 1958). Table X clearly shows the interacting effects of the temperature of the rehydrating fluid and the moisture content of the product on the viable count. When dried yeast with a water content of 0.08 gm/gm was rehydrated by the direct addition of water, the viable count went up 20-fold (from 0.5 to 10×10^9 cells/gm) as the temperature of the water was raised from 4.5° to 37°C. On the other hand, when the water content of the dried product was first raised to 0.20–0.25 gm/gm by equilibration with water vapor before liquid water was added, viability was high regardless of the temperature of the added water. The production of CO_2 by dried yeast exhibited a similar response. (It is important to note in relation to subsequent discussions that viability becomes sensitive to the temperature of the rehydrating fluid only when the dried cells contain less than 10% of the water content of normal undried yeast; we have noted earlier that 10% of the water in normal yeast is incapable of freezing.)

Mitchell and Enright (1957) showed that it is even possible to dry yeast to a final water content of 0.022 gm of H_2O per gram wet weight (at which point 99% of the original water has been removed) without impairing the ability of the yeast to produce CO_2. However, the CO_2 production remains unimpaired only if the moisture content of the yeast is raised to 0.08 gm of H_2O per gram wet weight by equilibration with water vapor prior to adding liquid water.

The survival of the dehydrated spores of a number of filamentous fungi is also raised appreciably by allowing the spores to equilibrate with water vapor at high relative humidity before adding liquid water (Table XI).

The causes of the injury produced by the direct addition of low-temperature liquid water to dried cells are uncertain. Record *et al.* (1962) have suggested that the damage in gram-negative bacteria may be due to

TABLE X
SURVIVAL OF ACTIVE-DRY YEAST AS A FUNCTION OF MOISTURE CONTENT AND TEMPERATURE OF THE REHYDRATING MEDIUM[a]

Moisture content		Viable count ($\times 10^9$/gm) after rehydration at		
Grams per gram wet weight	Percent of normal[b]	4.5°C	26°C	37°C
0.08	4	0.5	9.9	10.0
0.17	9	4.0	10.4	10.4
0.20	11	9.2	8.8	11.0
0.25	14	11.0	9.8	10.0

[a] Modified from Sant and Peterson (1958).
[b] Based on a normal water content of 0.7 gm of H_2O per gram of wet cells or 2.33 gm of H_2O per gram of solids.

a type of osmotic shock. They observed with the microscope that cells of *Escherichia coli* were plasmolyzed in concentrated glucose or sucrose solutions and became converted into spheroplasts upon sudden transfer to dilute media. The plasmolysis indicates that when the cells were suspended in the concentrated solutions, the sugars permeated the space between the cell wall and the plasma membrane. They believe that when the cells were subsequently transferred to dilute media, water permeated into this space faster than the sugars could diffuse out. The resulting osmotic pressure caused the cell wall to rupture and resulted in the conversion of the cells to nondividing spheroplasts. Since *E. coli* cells freeze-dried in glucose are subjected to a similar sequence of changes in the concentration of extracellular solutes during drying and rehydration, they reason that a similar mechanism could be responsible for injury.

An analogous type of osmotic shock occurs in T4 bacteriophage and appears to be a contributing factor in freezing injury (Leibo and Mazur, 1966). On the other hand it is difficult to see how it could occur in gram-

TABLE XI

EFFECT OF METHOD OF REHYDRATION ON THE SURVIVAL OF DEHYDRATED SPORES

Organism	Spore type	Drying conditions		Percent survival after rehydration with		Reference
		Suspending medium	Freezing	No vapor equilibration	Vapor equilibration	
Neurospora crassa	Conidia	H_2O	No	14	80–100	Klingmüller (1963)
Ustilago nuda	Teliospore	H_2O	Yes	43	59	Graham (1956)
Puccinia coronata	Uredospores	None	Yes	<1	64	Sharp and Smith (1952, 1957)
Puccinia graminis	Uredospores	None	Yes	5	97–99	Haskins (1957)
Puccinia graminis	Uredospores	?	Yes	~10	~40	Rowell (1956)

positive microorganisms, since gram-positive bacteria and yeast are difficult or impossible to plasmolyze (Record *et al.*, 1962; Mazur, 1961c). According to Thimann (1963), most fungi are gram positive.

Another possible basis for sensitivity to rehydration procedures is that dehydration induces a type of dormancy in fungi analogous to that induced in rust spores by low temperatures (Section III, B). Spores which have been made dormant by low temperatures are like dried cells in that germination can be initiated either by exposing the spores to high relative humidities or to temperatures around 40°C. However, Bromfield (1964) has found that spores rendered dormant by low-temperature exposure continue to respire, whereas yeast rendered nonviable by drying and rapid rehydration produce little or no CO_2. The degree to which other apparently nonviable fungi can respire after freezing, drying, and rapid rehydration has not been studied.

Koga *et al.* (1966) have made measurements of the physical properties of water in partially dried yeast wtih results that may be pertinent to the question of why their viability is sensitive to conditions of rehydration. They find that the sorption isotherms, heats of vaporization, dielectric increments, and proton magnetic resonance spectra of dried samples show abrupt changes when the sample water content is reduced below 0.11 gm of H_2O per gram of wet sample (or to less than 5% of the water in fully hydrated yeast). The changes all indicate that the residual water molecules have considerably less rotational and translational freedom than those in bulk water. If these molecules are removed during drying, cell viability could well be critically dependent on how they are reintroduced during rehydration. Koga *et al.* also studied the physical properties of samples with higher water contents (0.11–0.20 gm of H_2O per gram of wet sample, or 5–10% of the normal water content of yeast) but the properties of the water molecules were like those of bulk water.

B. *Summary and Conclusions on the Cause of Damage from Dehydration*

There seems to be little question that the survival of fungi after freeze-drying partly depends on the injury engendered by freezing. In other words, higher percentages of cells survive freeze-drying when the cooling velocities and minimum temperatures are chosen to minimize lethality from freezing and thawing. There is, however, one striking difference between freeze-thawing and freeze-drying. In most microorganisms, survival after freezing is higher when thawing is rapid than when it is slow; but in the case of freeze-drying, survival is either higher after slow rehydration than after rapid, or is unaffected by the rate of rehydration. I have already mentioned one reason for the difference. In freeze-dried and dehydrated cells the important factor in rehydration appears to be the rate at which the water content of the cell is raised from around 1% to 5–10% of its original value before desiccation. In freezing, on the other hand, the cell water content never drops below 10% of normal, since only 90% of the original water in the cell is capable of freezing. Slow warming seems to be damaging to frozen cells either because it permits the growth of intracellular ice crystals in the case of rapidly cooled cells, or because it exposes the cells to concentrated solutes as the cell water content is raised from 10% to 100% of its normal value. This long exposure normally never occurs during the rehydration of desiccated cells. According to the adsorption isotherm published by Koga *et al.* (1966), the water content of dried *Saccharomyces cerevisiae* after equilibration at 98% RH is 0.24 gm of H_2O per gram of cell solids. This corresponds to 10% of the cell's normal water content. Hence, even if dried cells are rehydrated in two steps, first slow equilibration with water vapor at close to 100% RH, and then the addition of liquid water, the process is still equivalent to rapid thawing. The first step would raise the cell water content slowly, but only from 1% to 10% of the normal value. The second would raise it rapidly from 10 to 100% of normal.

The effects on dried cells of slowly raising their water contents to 20 to 80% of normal can be studied by special procedures. Studies of this sort have been performed on *Serratia marcescens* by Monk *et al.* (1956), Monk and McCaffrey (1957), and Bateman *et al.* (1961). Maximum sensitivity was found when the water contents of the dried samples were 0.3–0.5 gm of H_2O per gram wet weight of sample (Fig. 8). If the normal water content of *Serratia* is 0.7 gm of H_2O per gram wet weight cells as in yeast, these values correspond to 20–40% of the normal water content.

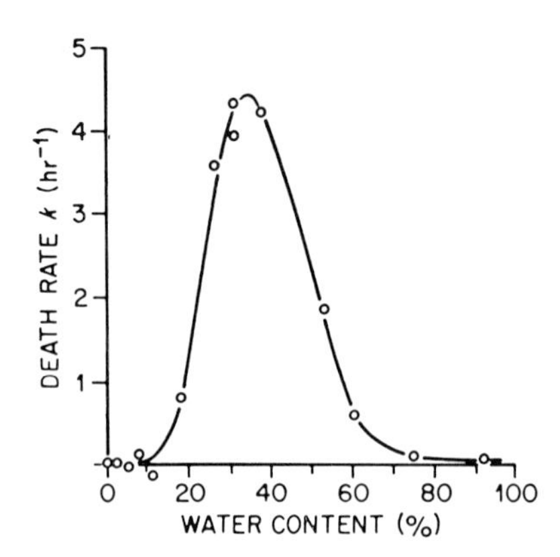

FIG. 8. Effect of water content (grams of H_2O/grams wet weight of sample) on the logarithmic death rate of freeze-dried cells of *Serratia marcescens*. The cells were first freeze-dried to zero water content and then rehydrated to the indicated water contents. From Monk and McCaffrey (1957).

These treatments produced conditions more analogous to those occurring during slow thawing; and, as is the case with slow thawing, they indicate that microorganisms may be quickly injured by having their water contents maintained for more than a short time at 20–40% of normal.

One final conclusion about dehydration is that the removal of water is not necessarily fatal per se. Several instances have been mentioned in which cells can survive the removal of more than 96% of their water. Furthermore, spores of *Bacillus subtilis* and *Aspergillus fumigatus* survive exposure to vacuums of 10^{-8} to 10^{-9} mm Hg for 5–35 days (Portner *et al.*, 1961; Morelli *et al.*, 1962). It is difficult to believe that any biologically significant water would remain after such treatments. What is clear is that survival is often critically dependent on the way water is removed from the cells (e.g., by freezing or by drying from the liquid state), and on the way it is added.

V. PRESERVATION OF FUNGI BY FREEZING AND DEHYDRATION

The labor of maintaining large culture collections by periodic transfer is appreciable. Moreover, if cultures are genetically unstable, there is a risk that desired properties will be lost by mutation and selection. Accordingly, other preservation methods have been developed, chief among which are storage under mineral oil, freeze-drying, freezing, and dehydration over silica gel. Descriptions of these methods and the results achieved with them have been recently reviewed by Fennell (1960), Raper (1963), Simmons (1963), and Perkins (1962). Their reviews indicate that all these techniques can successfully preserve most fungi if one defines success as the maintenance of sufficient viability to initiate a new culture after storage for several years. But if one defines success as the maintenance of a high proportion of viable cells in a culture, then the methods have been deficient.

The present section will be concerned only with freezing, and with freeze-drying or other types of dehydration. An analysis of these techniques in terms of the mechanism of injury will help clarify, I believe, why they have not always yielded high survivals, and how they might be improved.

A. *Preservation by Freezing and Low-Temperature Storage*

1. *Survey of Results*

Table XII lists some of the information on the viability of fungi after storage at subzero temperatures. There is little point in making a detailed

TABLE XII

SURVIVAL OF FUNGI AFTER STORAGE AT SUBZERO TEMPERATURES

Organisms	Cell type	Suspending medium	Freezing rate	Storage temp. (°C)	Storage time	Survival[a]	Comments[b]	References
65 genera		Agar slant	Slow	−20	9 mo	390/400	(1)	Carmichael (1956)
Hyphomycetes						359/371		
Yeasts		Agar slant	Slow	−17 to −21	5 yr	272/279	—	Carmichael (1962)
Phycomycetes						79/80		
Pyrenomycetes						30/35		
Other ascomycetes						21/21		
Flax rust	Uredospores	None	Slow	−10	1 yr	5%	—	Flor (1954)
Gymnosporangium	Teliospores	None	Slow	−10	9 mo	100%	—	Hamilton and Weaver (1943)
	Sporidia	H_2O		−10	3 wk	≪100%	—	
Venturia	Conidia	H_2O	?	−10	15 mo	Good	—	
Uromyces	Uredospores	None	Slow	−20	2 yr	Good		Harter and Zaumeyer (1941)
Rhizoctonia, *Botrytis*, *Pythium*, *Phytophthora*, *Syzygites*, *Choanephora*	Spores and/or mycelium	10% glycerol	1.7°/min	−196	3 days	6/6	(2)	Hwang (1960)

Pathogenic fungi	Yeast and mycelia							
Saprolegniaceae Pythiaceae Mucoraceae Kickxellaceae Choanephoraceae Basidiobolaceae Entomophthoraceae Clavicepitaceae Diaporthaceae 10 other families	Spores and/or mycelium	10% glycerol	1°/min	−165 to −196	6–57 mo	162/162	(3)	Hwang (1966)
Pencillium *Aspergillus*	Spores (?)	H_2O	Slow	−10 −18 −29	6 wk	50–70% 60–90% 65–95%	—	Jones and Fabian (1952)
451 isolates (333 species)	—	Agar slants	Slow	−18°C	5 yr	331/451	(4)	Kramer and Mix (1957)
Puccinia	Uredospores	None	Rapid	−5°C −20°C −196°C	108 days 108 days 108 days	40% 45% 100%	(5)	Loegering and Harmon (1962)
Saccharomyces	Vegetative	Sucrose or H_2O	Slow	−10 to −20°C	28 wk	0–70%	(6)	McFarlane (1941)
Various yeasts *Aspergillus*	Vegetative Spores	Sugars or H_2O	Slow	−18°C	28–60 wk	0–14% 2–80%	—	McFarlane and Goresline (1943)

(Continued)

TABLE XII (*Continued*)

Organisms	Cell type	Suspending medium	Freezing rate	Storage temp. (°C)	Storage time	Survival[a]	Comments[b]	References
Puccinia	Uredospores	None	Moderate	−29 to −40	45 days	0–2%	—	Melander (1935)
Dermatophytes *Microsporum* *Epidermophyton* *Trichophyton*	Mycelium + spores	Plasma + milk	?	−22 to −52	2 yr	58/61	—	E. Meyer (1955)
Puccinia	Uredospores	None	?	−10 to −22	4.5 yr	100%	—	Sackston (1960)
Uromyces	Uredospores	None		−16 −60	15 mo 21 mo	0–10% 45–60%	—	Schein (1962)
Saccharomyces	Vegetative	0.16 *M* NaCl	Moderate	−4 −15 −24	77 days 77 days 77 days	0.0003% 0.4% 2%	—	Stille (1950)
Saccharomyces	Vegetative	15% glycerol in buffer	Slow	−40	1 yr	—	(7)	Tanguay (1959)
Saccharomyces *Zygosaccharomyces* *Torula* *Mycoderma*	Vegetative	Broth or saline	Slow	−13 to −15	160 wk	0–1%	—	Tanner and Williamson (1928)

Aspergillus	Spores	H_2O or cherry juice	Moderate	−40		0.3–1%		
				−80		5–26%		
Saccharomyces	Vegetative	Cherry juice	Moderate	−40	12 wk	0.02%	—	Wallace and Tanner (1935)
				−80		1.4%		
Mycoderma	Vegetative	H_2O or cherry juice	Moderate	−40		4–25%		
				−80		3–30%		
Basidiomycetes	Mycelium	Agar slant cultures	Rapid	−170 to −196	>12 hr	9/15	—	Wellman and Walden (1964)
Ascomycetes	Spores and/or mycelium					30/30		
Fungi Imperfecti	Spores and/or mycelium					51/51		
Phycomycetes	Spores and/or mycelium					43/63		
Neurospora	Conidia				9 mo	100%		

[a] Percentage values refer to the fraction of viable cells in a culture. The other values refer to the number of cultures that were viable.

[b] Numbers in parentheses refer to comments listed below:

(1) Cultures lost were species of *Candida, Chromocrea, Epidermophyton, Gelasinospora, Geomyces, Myxotrichum, Neurospora, Sordaria, Trichophyton.*

(2) None of these genera survived freeze-drying.

(3) The fungi were selected because of fastidious habit or inability to survive freeze-drying.

(4) The agar slants were thawed, sampled, and refrozen every six months. Fifty-five isolates representing 49 species failed to survive one year at −18°C. Four of the species were successfully preserved by Hwang at −196°C (*Absidia, Claviceps* and two species of *Pythium*).

(5) Survivals with optimal techniques of post-thawing treatment.

(6) Survival depended on sucrose concentrations, pH, and temperature.

(7) The rate of growth of treated samples as a function of the concentration of inositol in the medium was the same as for controls.

comparison of the results because they have been influenced by a host of variables, many of which were not controlled by any one investigator, and few of which were common to different investigations. However, the results do illustrate certain points that deserve emphasis.

a. In most cases, sufficient cells survive freezing, storage, and thawing to initiate new cultures regardless of how these operations are carried out.

b. However, in some cases frozen and thawed samples are totally nonviable. Although most of these cases occur in certain families or orders of the Phycomycetes and Basidiomycetes, some also occur in other classes. It appears impossible to predict with assurance whether a given culture of a given species will remain viable after low-temperature storage.

c. The usual frozen sample probably contains 10^7 to 10^9 cells. It is possible, therefore, that even though a frozen and thawed culture is viable, it may contain only a few viable cells. Although there are no reported instances in which the cells that survive low-temperature storage are abnormal (see below), survivals of 10 to 50% would be more reassuring than survivals of 10^{-4} to 10^{-6}%.

d. Every reported case of nonviable fungus cultures has occurred after storage at —4 to —50°C. There is no confirmed case of cells failing to survive storage at —196°C if they can survive the immediate effects of freezing and thawing. There *are* instances, such as those reported by Wellman and Walden (1964), in which entire cultures have failed to survive these immediate effects, but there is good reason to believe from Hwang's (1966) data and from the results reported in Section III that such lethality can be prevented by an appropriate choice of cooling and warming velocities.

The occasional destruction of every cell in samples stored at —4 to —40°C is predictable on the basis of the many studies such as those of Stille (1950) and Wallace and Tanner (1935), which show that viability decreases appreciably and progressively with storage time, even at temperatures as low as —24° to —40°C. (Wallace and Tanner also report an appreciable death of yeast at —80°C. This is unusual, for most bacteria and animal cells are quite stable at that temperture.) In Section II, we noted that biological systems contain liquid water at temperatures above about —50°C. As a result cells stored at —4 to —40°C will be surrounded for long periods of time by highly concentrated solutions—a situation likely to be deleterious.

2. *Optimizing Procedures for Low-Temperature Storage*

An optimum procedure ought to include slow cooling at a rate of 1 to 10°C per minute to prevent intracelluar freezing and thermal shock, an additive in the suspending medium to reduce injury from exposure to concentrated solutes during cooling, storage at temperatures below —130°C, and rapid thawing to prevent injury from recrystallization and to reduce the length of exposure to concentrated solutes during thawing. The reasons for using slow cooling and rapid thawing were given in Sections II and III.

Many fungi, unlike animal cells, can survive slow freezing in the absence of an additive, probably because they are quite resistant to the levels of dehydration produced by freezing (Section IV). However, some fungi may be exceedingly sensitive to dehydration, and in such cases glycerol or DMSO may have to be present for them to survive slow cooling. If these compounds are used, the cells may be injured during storage unless they are held below —46 or —136°C, which are the eutectic points of glycerol and DMSO, respectively (Miner and Dalton, 1953; Farrant, 1965).

Even if additives are not present, storage temperatures below —130°C are still advantageous, for at such temperatures few chemical reactions occur, and ice cannot recrystallize (Mazur, 1966). The only potential sources of injury are direct damage from ionizing radiation and the accumulation of trapped free radicals (Wood and Taylor, 1957).

3. *Genetic Alterations in Cells Surviving Freezing and Thawing*

Although there have been very few careful genetic comparisons between untreated cells and frozen and thawed survivors, the investigators listed in Table XII are almost unanimous in reporting the absence of any morphological or physiological differences. Moreover, Bradley (1963) found that the cells of *Saccharomyces pastorianus* that survived freezing had the same glucozymase activity and the same capacity for adaptive formation of maltozymase as untreated cells. He found no mutants that lacked the ability to form maltozymase among 10^5 colonies derived from frozen-thawed survivors. Mazur (1966) reported that the cells of *S. cerevisiae* that survived freezing and thawing were no more resistant to subsequent freezing and thawing than the original population.

B. *Preservation by Freeze-Drying*

1. *General Procedure*

Although some investigators preserve fungi by freezing and low-temperature storage, most large culture collections are preserved by freeze-drying by the techniques developed by Wickerham and Andreasen (1942) for yeast and Raper and Alexander (1945) for spores. The results with these procedures have on the whole been excellent when judged on the basis of the capacity of freeze-dried inocula to yield viable unchanged cultures. Over 98% of 1161 strains of freeze-dried yeast have yielded viable cultures after storage for 2 years (Wickerham and Flickinger, 1946), and freeze-dried cultures of *Candida* have survived for 10 years (Rhoades, 1958). Similar percentages of viable cultures from freeze-dried spores of filamentous fungi have been obtained after 17 years of storage (Hesseltine *et al.,* 1960) and after 21 years (Davis, 1963). In addition, Ainsworth (1962) found that sporophores of *Schizophyllum commune* freeze-dried by Buller (1913) were still viable 52 years later.

2. *Problems with Freeze-Drying as a Method of Preservation*

In view of the results just surveyed, one might question the need for a section on "problems with freeze-drying." However, some fungi do not survive the immediate effects of freeze-drying and rehydration, and with others the percentage of cells that survive is often very low. Moreover, there is evidence that cells surviving freeze-drying are sometimes physiologically and genetically different from normal.

a. Fungi Failing to Survive the Immediate Effects of Freeze-Drying. The inability of spores of the Entomophthorales to survive freeze-drying was noted by Raper and Alexander and by subsequent investigators. Other instances of negative results have been reported for aquatic phycomycetes, including *Pythium, Plectospira,* and *Achlya,* and for the hymenomycetes *Stereum* (Fennell *et al.,* 1950). Still others have been listed by Hesseltine *et al.* (1960).

b. Low Survival after Freeze-Drying. Even though the standard techniques yield high proportions of viable cultures, the percentage of viable cells in dried populations is often low and variable (Table XIII). As a result, it is very difficult to use freeze-dried samples as direct sources of viable cells, comparable, for example, to the active dry yeast used in the manufacture of bread. There are also cases where one wishes to know how the effects of factors like radiation or temperature are influenced by cell water content. Such studies are precluded if dehydration itself kills large and variable fractions of the cell population.

Furthermore, although cultures containing small fractions of viable cells can give rise to suitable daughter cultures, the viable fraction will continue to drop with storage, and may eventually reach zero. The death rate may be thousands of times lower under the best storage conditions than under suboptimal conditions, but it is difficult to know in advance that a given set of conditions is good, and even then, the death rate is not zero (see below).

c. Alterations in Freeze-Dried Fungi. Many of the papers just summarized state specifically that cultures derived from freeze-dried cells were physiologically and morphologically indistinguishable from untreated parent cultures. However, Atkin *et al.* (1949) reported that fewer than 1% of yeast cells survived freeze-drying and rehydration, and that more than 50% of the cultures derived from dried samples had B-vitamin requirements that differed from the parent population, and Kirsop (1955) reported comparable alterations. Braendle (1963) observed that the proportion of prototrophs in nicotinamide-requiring auxotrophs of *Penicillium chrysogenum* increased 1- to 2-fold after freeze-drying, but the increase did not seem to be correlated with the percentage killed. Several references on alterations in freeze-dried bacteria are mentioned by Fennell (1960, p. 121) and Heckly (1961).

3. *Methods of Reducing Injury from Freeze-Drying*

The conclusion was reached in Section IV that injury from freeze-drying is the resultant of (a) damage during freezing, (b) damage from excessive dehydration, and (c) damage during rehydration. These factors relate to the freeze-drying process itself. To these must be added whatever damage is produced during storage.

a. Reducing Damage from Freezing. Freezing injury in freeze-drying can probably best be minimized by cooling cells slowly (1–10°C per minute) and by carrying out the sublimation below —30 to —40°C. However, the slow sublimation at such low temperatures greatly increases the time required for dehydration, and the first step alone, namely slow cooling, is often sufficient to minimize damage (Section IV, Table VIII). Above all, specimens should *not* be cooled below the temperature at which the water is to be sublimed; to do so is likely to lower survivals markedly.

The centrifugal freeze-drying technique developed by Greaves (1944) has certain advantages from this point of view. It produces relatively slow cooling by evaporation, and it assures equality of the freezing and sublimation temperatures. Furthermore, it usually produces higher survivals than methods involving direct prefreezing (Haskins, 1957; Graham, 1956). The chief disadvantage of a technique dependent on evaporative cooling is that the cooling velocities and sublimation temperatures vary during drying, and depend on factors such as the geometry of the sample, the sample composition, and the mean free path of water molecules in the vacuum system. Alternatively, it would be relatively easy to modify the older techniques involving direct freezing so as to permit slow freezing.

Another way to reduce freezing injury in freeze-dried spores is to eliminate the suspending medium. Those "air-dry" spores that have been examined survive both freeze-thawing and freeze-drying better than wet spores (Sections III and IV).

TABLE XIII

QUANTITATIVE SURVIVALS OF FUNGI AFTER FREEZE-DRYING

Organism	Cell type	Suspending medium	Drying procedure		Survival[c]		Reference
			Standard[a]	Optimum[b]	Standard (%)	Optimum (%)	
Pestalotia palmarum	Spore	Serum	R.A.	(1)	(0.5–15)	(93)	Buell (1948); Weston (1949)
Aspergillus flavus	Spore	Serum	R.A.	(2)	7.3(7)	47 (45)	Mazur (1953)
		H_2O	R.A.		2(2)	27 (26)	
Ustilago tritici [*U. nuda*]	Teliospore	H_2O	R.A.	(3)	(4.5)	(74)	Graham (1956)
Aspergillus niger	Spore	Serum	R.A.		17(9)	60 (31)	
Fusarium	Spore	Serum	R.A.		0	64 (57)	
Gliocladium	Spore	Serum	R.A.	(4)	0	32 (32)	Haskins (1957)
Penicillium	Spore	Serum	R.A.		2(2)	64 (61)	
Pestalotia	Spore	Serum	R.A.		6(6)	68 (64)	
Saccharomyces cerevisiae	Vegetative cell	Serum	W.A.	—	0.02	—	Atkin *et al.* (1949)
Saccharomyces cerevisiae	Vegetative cell	Serum + glucose	C.F.	—	0.02–30	—	
S. carlsbergensis	Vegetative cell	Serum + glucose	C.F.	—	0.3–22	—	
Other *Saccharomyces* spp.	Vegetative cell	Serum + glucose	C.F.	—	0.02–11	—	Kirsop (1955)
Other yeasts	Vegetative cell	Serum + glucose	C.F.	—	0–77	—	

Torula	Vegetative cell	Milk	W.A.	—	0.1	—	Kupletskaya (1961)
Cryptococcus terricola	Vegetative cell	H_2O	C.F.	(5)	0.1	80	Pedersen (1965)

[a] R.A. refers to the freeze-drying procedure of Raper and Alexander (1945), W.A. refers to the procedure of Wickerham and Andreasen (1942), and C.F. refers to centrifugal freeze-drying.

[b] The modifications which yielded optimum survivals were as follows:

(1) Spores were suspended in a mixture of 20% sucrose and 0.3% algin and subjected to preliminary evaporation from liquid state.

(2) Spores were cooled no lower than −15°C.

(3) Spores were suspended in "mist desiccans" plus egg yolk and frozen by evaporative cooling. Vapor phase equilibration before rehydration raised germination to 83%.

(4) Spores were suspended in serum and sucrose and cooled no lower than −18°C.

(5) Ten percent sucrose used as suspending medium.

[c] Values in parentheses are percentage germination; others are percentage survivals (number of viable treated cells/number of viable control cells).

Finally, freezing injury can be completely eliminated by dehydrating cells above 0°C. As we have seen, this procedure often gives higher survivals than freeze-drying.

b. Residual Water Content. It is not clear whether dehydrated fungus cells are *killed* because of the removal of essential water during dehydration or because of the improper addition of water during rehydration. If the final water content remaining after dehydration is critical, the only practical expedient will probably be to include an additive that either maintains the water content at the desired level or reduces its criticality. Certain additives clearly do protect (Table XIII), but the basis of the protection is uncertain. Alternative procedures for drying specimens to a desired final water content would be difficult with any routine laboratory method.

c. Rehydration. There is clear evidence that the survival of freeze-dried fungi can be affected by the rate of rehydration and by the temperature at which it is carried out. Although slow rehydration and higher temperatures usually give superior results, too few organisms have been examined to generalize. It would not be difficult to test the effects of various rehydration procedures on a broader range of fungi, and the resulting information would be of more than casual interest.

The assumption that freeze-drying can be made less injurious by relatively minor changes in procedure is supported experimentally. Table XIII lists some of the modifications that have been used and the percentage survivals obtained through their use.

d. Protection by Additives. The results in Table XIII also show that survival is influenced by the composition of the suspending medium. Nevertheless, much less is known about the effects of various solutes on the survival of fungi after freeze-drying than is known for bacteria. The information on additives has been reviewed by Fry (1954, 1966), Fennell (1960), Heckly (1961), and Greaves (1960).

It will be noted, however, from Tables VI, VIII, and XIII that the survival of fungi seems to be enhanced by the presence of sugars in the suspending medium. Sugars also tend to enhance the survival of freeze-dried bacteria, and some years ago, Fry and Greaves (1951) suggested that they protect by keeping the water content of cells from dropping below a critical level during freeze-drying. In support of this hypothesis Greaves (1960) and Fry (1966) quoted from the work of Ungar *et al.* (1956) the fact that the residual moisture in freeze-dried BCG tuberculosis vaccine drops from 2.1% to 0.1% as the glucose concentration in the suspending medium is lowered from 10% to 0%, and that this drop is accompanied by a drop in percentage survival. However, sugars also can reduce injury from freezing and thawing (Mazur *et al.,* 1957b; Mazur,

1966), and this might form part of the basis of their ability to protect in freeze-drying. Furthermore, the idea that sugars protect by holding water is opposed by the fact noted in Section IV that some fungi survive dehydration and storage in an atmosphere of zero water activity (a_W), and so do some bacteria (Scott, 1960).

If such organisms are in equilibrium with an atmosphere of $a_W = 0$, they contain no water. Of course true equilibrium may never actually be attained. One problem in interpreting data on low water contents is the difficulty in measuring them. Water contents based on oven drying, vacuum drying, electrolytic techniques, Karl Fischer reagent, and nuclear magnetic reasonance all possess certain ambiguities.

e. Storage Conditions. It is important to distinguish the injury occurring as a direct result of freezing, dehydration, and rehydration from that occurring during the storage of dried cells. Although some of the deleterious factors that operate during freeze-drying itself may also contribute to injury during storage (e.g., exposure to concentrated solutes), others, such as the occurrence of intracellular freezing and osmotic shock, are independent of storage time. In addition, some factors that injure during storage act much too slowly to have any effect on cells during the short times required for freeze-drying and rehydration. Two examples are the browning reaction discussed by Scott (1960) and the accumulation of free radicals. Supporting the distinction are many published examples for bacteria in which survivals have been high immediately after drying but have dropped rapidly with storage, and examples in which survivals have been low after drying but have dropped only slowly with storage (Scott, 1960; Greaves, 1960).

Unfortunately there is little quantitative information on the factors affecting the survival of freeze-dried fungi during storage. Haskins (1957) stated that survivals appeared to drop less rapidly at 4°C than at room temperature, but he presented no data. Sharp and Smith (1957) made a similarly cautious statement for *Puccinia* uredospores, but their results are equivocal. Fennell (1960) stated that samples in lyophile tubes that have lost their vacuum are often completely nonviable. Scott (1960) gave data on the survival of cells of *Saccharomyces cerevisiae* dried in various media and stored for periods up to 60 days at $a_W = 0.00$ and $a_w = 0.43$. As can be seen from the plot of his data in Fig. 9, survivals remained high at the lower water activity but dropped appreciably at the higher.

Burns (1962) compared the effectiveness of several suspending media on the survival of a number of species of yeasts after storage at room temperature. The results appeared to depend more on the species than on the suspending medium.

In contrast to the fungi, there is abundant information on the storage

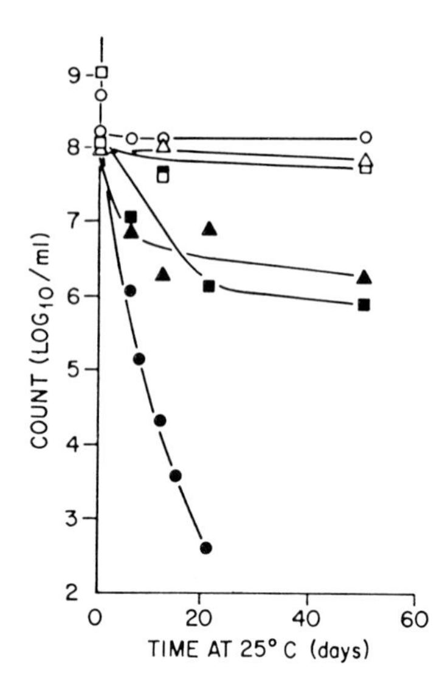

FIG. 9. Effect of storage time on the survival of *Saccharomyces cerevisiae* freeze-dried in various media and stored *in vacuo* at an a_w of 0.00 (open symbols) or 0.43 (closed symbols). The suspending media were papain digest (□, ■), $10^{-1}M$ lysine (△, ▲); or $10^{-1}M$ xylose (○, ●). From Scott (1960).

stability of freeze-dried bacteria. Since much of this is summarized in the reviews cited on page 376 mention will be made only of some of the more general problems and conclusions. Storage stability of bacteria is affected chiefly by temperature, the sample water content, the gaseous environment, and the solutes present in the original suspending medium.

(1) *Effect of temperature.* According to Fry (1966), the consensus is that dried cells stored at 4°C die less rapidly than cells stored at room temperature or higher. However, little attention has been paid to the possibility of storing dried cultures at subzero temperatures. Organisms that survive dehydration can be cooled to close to absolute zero without injury (Luyet and Gehenio, 1940), and the decay rate at −196°C or below is almost certain to be extremely low.

(2) *Effect of the gaseous environment.* Dry bacteria usually die more rapidly when they are exposed to oxygen or air than when they are exposed to nitrogen or kept under high vacuum (see Zentner, 1966, for a recent review). However, Mallett *et al.* (1959), Scott (1960), and Bateman *et al.* (1961) have found that the effect of the atmosphere on bacteria can depend on the residual water content and the additives present. Different combinations of water contents and suspending media yield responses ranging from much greater storage decays in air to greater decay rates *in vacuo*. Lion *et al.* (1961) and Heckly *et al.* (1963) have suggested

that the lethal effect of oxygen may be associated with the production of free radicals in dried cells.

(3) *Effect of moisture content on storage stability.* Although most investigators are agreed that water contents above 5–10% are deleterious (for example, see Fig. 8), there is disagreement as to the optimum water content for storage stability. Some, like Scott (1960), have found that storage survival is best when the a_W of the environment is zero (and, therefore, the water content of the cells must have approached zero). Others maintain that the optimum water content is above zero (Hutton *et al.,* 1951; Ostroukhova, 1961; Fry, 1966).

(4) *Protection by additives.* The storage death rate of freeze-dried bacteria is greatly affected by the additives present. However, additives that protect against the immediate lethality of freeze-drying do not necessarily enhance storage stability.

The selection of a protective additive depends on what one believes to be the injurious factor. Scott (1960) feels that the "browning" reaction is an important cause of storage injury. This is a reaction between compounds containing carbonyl groups and the amino side-chains of cell constituents. He has found that solutes rich in carbonyl groups such as pyruvate, ribose, or glucose tend to increase storage death rates, whereas solutes, like semicarbazide, that combine with aldehydes or ketones tend to decrease death rates.

Since oxygen is quite injurious to dried cells, it has long been considered desirable to have a reducing agent present (Naylor and Smith, 1946) and perhaps a free radical scavenger (Lion *et al.,* 1961; Lion, 1963).

Sugars have often been found to be protective. The protection may result from the maintenance of an optimum concentration of water in dried specimens. However, this explanation is not universally accepted. Webb (1965) suggests that cells are killed by the removal of a certain critical fraction of their bound water. He believes that additives protect by substituting for that water. Finally, high molecular weight solutes often (but not always) improve survival in storage (Heckly, 1961). Although a number of hypothetical explanations have been offered (e.g., Greaves, 1960; Record *et al.,* 1962; Lion, 1963), the mechanistic basis of the protection remains obscure.

4. *Summary*

Enough spores of most fungi survive the standard techniques for freeze-drying to make the method practical for the conservation of cultures. However, in some cases no spores survive the treatment, and in many cases survivals are very low. The causes of injury are well enough understood to make rational guesses as to what steps can be taken to improve survivals. Some of these guesses have been borne out experimentally; others, however, remain to be tested.

C. *Preservation by Dehydration from the Liquid State*

Many fungi survive dehydration from the liquid state (Rhodes, 1950; Annear, 1958, 1963; Perkins, 1962), and as mentioned in Section IV, survival is often higher than after freeze-drying. Hill (1962) found that at least 15% of conidia of *Peronospora tabacina* survived drying in air at 0% RH, and Brockman and de Serres (1962) obtained the survivals shown in Tables XIV and XV for *Neurospora* conidia dried over silica gel at room temperature.

The procedures suggested for improving survival after freeze-drying and after storage should be equally applicable to dehydration from the liquid state, especially when the dehydration is carried out under vacuum. Once the water content of a sample undergoing freeze-drying has dropped below about 10%, the rate of sublimation becomes too low to keep its temperature much below room temperature unless the temperature rise is prevented by a cold bath. Accordingly, once the water content drops below 10%, freeze-drying and drying from the liquid state become identical processes.

D. *Relative Merits of the Various Preservation Techniques*

1. *Advantages of Freezing and Thawing*

The advantages of preserving fungi by freezing techniques are many, provided that freezing and thawing are carried out at proper rates and that storage is below —75°C, or preferably below —130°C.

a. Many of the organisms that do not survive freeze-drying have been shown by Hwang (1966) to survive freezing and thawing.

b. Storage at —196°C almost guarantees that any cell that survives cooling to —196°C and warming can be preserved in the viable state indefinitely. The same guarantee cannot be made for freeze-dried cells stored, for example, at 4°C.

c. Freezing is a simpler procedure than freeze-drying.

d. In most cases, preservation by freezing will not require searching for a protective additive, whereas in freeze-drying the additive is critical.

e. The optimum procedures for thawing are better understood than the optimum procedures for rehydration.

2. *Advantages of Freeze-Drying and Dehydration from the Liquid State*

Special low-temperature equipment is not required for storage near 0°C. Frozen samples, on the other hand, must be kept below —75°C, a

TABLE XIV

SURVIVAL OF CONIDIA OF TWO STRAINS OF *Neurospora* AS A FUNCTION OF STORAGE TIME OVER SILICA GEL[a]

Storage time[b]	Percent survival	
	74A-OR	1-155-0011
0 hours[c]	75.0	74.8
2 hours	82.3	61.2
8 days	18.0	34.8
14 days	12.5	23.2
35 days	16.0	31.9
97 days	13.2	7.1
255 days	9.6	8.0

[a] From Brockman and de Serres (1962).
[b] Storage for the first 7 days was at room temperature; subsequent storage was at 4°C.
[c] Survival immediately before adding conidia to silica gel.

requirement that has ceased to be a great drawback, however, since the advent of liquid nitrogen refrigerators and low-temperature mechanical refrigerators.

The two techniques are probably comparable in cost and in hazards. Freeze-drying has the hazards inherent in any high vacuum system plus those involved in handling dry specimens of pathogenic organisms. Freezing in liquid nitrogen involves the hazards of handling liquefied gases and Dewar flasks, plus the danger of ampules exploding during warming if liquid N_2 has entered through a pinhole leak. The latter danger can be

TABLE XV

SURVIVAL OF CONIDIA FROM SEVERAL STRAINS OF *Neurospora* AFTER STORAGE OVER SILICA GEL AT 4°C AND AT 23°C[a]

Strain	Storage time (days)	Percent survival after storage at	
		4°C	23°C
2-015-0095	223	5.1	0.09
2-015-0128	223	7.7	0.03
1-154-0022	224	6.9	2.9
2-016-0001	212	2.8	2.3
2-016-0006	212	31.7	0.1
1-234-0106	211	48.6	5.4
1-234-0084	211	29.3	0.4
2-017-0002	183	21.7	0.1
2-017-0006	183	10.1	2.1
74-OR21-6a	211	57.6	16.2

[a] From Brockman and de Serres (1962).

eliminated by storing ampules in cold nitrogen vapor rather than in the liquid.

VI. ECOLOGICAL IMPLICATIONS AND CONCLUSIONS

A. *Environmental Extremes for Survival of Fungi*

The terrestrial distribution of fungi is wide. Boyd (1958) obtained 600–7000 fungi per gram of soils from the arctic coast of Alaska. The soil temperatures at the time of collection (August) were —1 to 7°C and the moisture contents 8–67%. (During the winter, soil temperatures in the Point Barrow region drop to about —25°C.) Hagen and Rose (1961) isolated a psychrophilic yeast (*Cryptococcus*) from a decomposing *Laminaria* on a beach at Hebron Fjord in Labrador. Boyd and Boyd (1964) determined the number of microorganisms at various soil depths in permafrost areas near Point Barrow. Molds were found only in the upper 12 inches of the ground, generally above the permafrost.

A number of fungi also have been found in Antarctica, a region that is dry as well as cold (annual rainfall about 2.5 inches according to Boyd and Boyd, 1963). Straka and Stokes (1960) isolated a psychrophilic yeast from glacier ice. It grew optimally at 5–10°C. Sinclair and Stokes (1965) plated material from 37 snow, ice, and soil samples from Antarctica and 4 marine samples from the arctic. Yeast and bacterial colonies formed in 14 of the samples. Four of the yeast species were obligate psychrophiles tentatively identified as new species of *Torulopsis* and *Candida*. G. H. Meyer *et al.* (1962) analyzed the microbial content of a 50-year-old bottle of yeast left by the Scott expedition in 1911. They obtained numerous colonies of *Saccharomyces cerevisiae, Rhodotorula pallida,* several bacteria, and infrequent colonies of *Absidia corymbifera* and *Rhizopus arrhizus*. Analysis of other food stuffs and feces from the same expedition yielded cultures of *Mucor, Penicillium, Rhodotorula,* and *Cryptococcus* (G. H. Meyer *et al.,* 1963). Fungi have also been found in antarctic soils. Boyd and Boyd (1963) isolated molds from soil samples in areas formerly inhabited by man and in one soil sample from an uninhabited area. The latter contained species of *Penicillium* and *Aspergillus*. Di Menna (1966) found that 52 out of 126 soil samples from the Ross Dependency in Antarctica contained yeasts in numbers ranging from 5 to 100,000 per gram. The organisms were species of *Debaryomyces, Cryptococcus, Candida, Trichosporon,* and *Rhodotorula*. Most of the *Candida* were obligate psychrophiles.

Michener and Elliott (1964) give a very extensive list of the lowest temperatures reported for bacteria, yeast, and molds for growth on foods and microbiological media. The lowest values for fungi are —17.8, and —34°C for two yeasts. Of course, numerous fungi remain viable in frozen and freeze-dried foods even though they cannot grow (Gunderson, 1962; Silverman and Goldblith, 1965).

B. *Environmental Factors Favoring Survival*

The most important factor favoring the survival of fungi in nature is probably the rarity of intracellular freezing. As was seen in Sections II and III, intracellular freezing occurs in yeast and *Aspergillus flavus* spores only when the cooling velocity exceeds 1 to 10°C per minute to temperatures below —10°C. Cooling rates in nature are almost never that high.

The ability of fungi to survive subfreezing temperatures in nature, therefore, depends on their ability to withstand extracellular freezing, which, as has been emphasized, is tantamount to resisting dehydration. Fungi, like bacteria, may die most rapidly when their water contents are around 30–40%. This is fortunate if so, because such water contents probably occur only for short periods in nature. Cells are either immersed in liquid water or dilute solutions, in which case their water contents are above this critical zone, or they become exposed to air, in which case their water contents rapidly drop below this zone. The lethal water content is most likely to prevail when cells are surrounded by ice at —2° to about —5°C,[1] but such temperatures are probably relatively infrequent. The high heat of fusion of water tends to hold its temperature at 0°C unless the air is sufficiently cold to freeze all the water. But if the air is that cold, the low heat capacity of ice (0.5 cal gm^{-1} deg^{-1}) is likely to cause the ice to cool rapidly below —5°C.

C. *Frost and Drought Resistant Structures in Fungi*

In her review of ecological factors in the survival of fungi, Hawker (1957) stated that individual hyphae of fungi are rarely able to survive adverse environmental conditions. It is somewhat strange that this is so since vegetative yeastlike organisms are highly resistant to low natural temperatures and to dehydration (Section IV); furthermore, Hawker, herself, has pointed out (p. 240) that many fungal hyphae convert to yeastlike forms in adverse environments. The greater resistance does not seem to be ascribable to decreased water content, for a yeast cell is highly hydrated (0.7 gm of H_2O per gram wet weight). Its basis is unknown.

Most mycelial forms survive by producing a variety of special bodies

[1] If the average value for the osmolarity of a cell is 0.5 *M*, which corresponds to a freezing point of about —0.93°C, then its water content will be halved at —1.8°C and quartered at about —3.6°C (see Eq. 4).

including chlamydospores, sclerotia, cysts, conidia, sexual spores, and teliospores. Many of these have thick cell walls and low water contents (Table V). Because of their low water contents, it is questionable whether "air-dry" spores freeze intracellularly during rapid cooling in laboratory experiments, and it is most unlikely that they freeze during the much lower cooling velocities found in nature.

Since the spores survive the dehydration and solute concentration that occurs during their formation, it is not surprising that they tend to be resistant to low external water activities. To state this, of course, does not explain why they survive the original dehydration during formation, nor does it explain the mechanism by which a highly hydrated region of cytoplasm becomes dehydrated and isolated from the remaining cytoplasm.

It is often thought that the thick cell walls in many spores act as water-impermeable barriers to keep the cytoplasm partially dehydrated. But *Neurospora* ascospores (A. S. Sussman, 1961), *Erysiphe* conidia (Somers and Horsfall, 1966), and bacterial spores (Murrell, 1960; Gerhardt and Black, 1960) have been shown to be permeable to water. Furthermore, Lewis *et al.* (1960) have calculated that even if the walls of bacterial spores were composed of the most water-impermeable organic compounds known, a dehydrated spore would still become hydrated to 90% of saturation after about 3 minutes exposure to water.

However, there is an alternative explanation for the maintenance of low internal water contents that does not require impermeability to water: spore cell walls are mechanically strong and rigid enough to resist the osmotic pressure across them, and because of this, prevent the net flow of water into the spore. The water activity in a spore containing 20% water would be about 0.5. If such a spore were in contact with air at a relative humidity of 95% ($a_W = 0.95$), the osmotic pressure difference across the cell membrane would be

$$\Delta\pi = \frac{RT}{\bar{V}} \ln \frac{a_w \text{ (air)}}{a_w \text{ (spore)}} \tag{6}$$

where R is the gas constant (82 cc atm mole^{-1} deg^{-1}), and $\bar{V}$ the partial molal volume of water in the spore ($\sim$18 cc mole^{-1}). Thus, the osmotic pressure at 300°K would be 876 atm. This osmotic pressure difference would tend to drive water rapidly into the spore; but water can enter only if the spore increases in volume. If the spore wall is sufficiently strong and inflexible, it will prevent the volume increase, and will, thereby prevent the entry of water. Attaining equilibrium of course would necessitate that the spore wall be capable of withstanding the pressure differential of 876 atmospheres.

D. *Conclusions*

The relatively high resistance of fungi to low temperatures in nature and in the laboratory is due to two factors: (1) intracellular ice generally does not form within them, and (2) either they are relatively resistant to dehydration, or else they form resistant bodies. The physical and biological factors that determine the likelihood of intracellular freezing are reasonably well understood. Basically, the likelihood depends on the degree to which the cells become supercooled during cooling, and this in turn depends on the rate of cooling and on the rate at which water can flow out of the cell in response to the vapor pressure differential built up during cooling.

The basis of resistance to dehydration is much more poorly understood, partly because dehydration actually involves three simultaneous processes: the removal of water per se, the concentration of ions and other low molecular weight solutes, and a decrease in the distance separating macromolecules. To this complex situation must be added the possible influence of temperature. Fungi are particularly attractive experimental cells for investigations of the factors underlying resistance since the same organism can change from being susceptible to resistant and back again in a matter of minutes or hours. Any knowledge gained would not only be of interest in understanding mechanisms of freezing and drying injury in fungi, but ought also to be germane to understanding the ecological success of fungi and the nature of dormancy, and to understanding the causes of injury in the cells of higher plants and animals.

REFERENCES

Ainsworth, G. C. (1962). Longevity of *Schizophyllum commune*. II. *Nature* **195**: 1120–1121.

Akai, S. (1954). On the resistance of urediospores of *Puccinia triticina* to low temperatures. *Ann. Phytopathol. Soc. Japan* **19**: 15–17.

Alexopoulos, C. J., and J. Drummond. (1934). Resistance of fungous spores to low temperatures. *Trans. Illinois State Acad. Sci.* **26**: 63.

Anderson, N. G., J. G. Green, and P. Mazur. (1966). Centrifugal freezing. I. A system for rapid freezing of aqueous cell suspensions. *Natl. Cancer Inst. Monograph* **21**: 415–430.

Annear, D. I. (1958). Observations on drying bacteria from the frozen and from the liquid state. *Australian J. Exptl. Biol. Med. Sci.* **36**: 211–222.

Annear, D. I. (1963). Preservation of yeasts by drying. *Australian J. Exptl. Biol. Med. Sci.* **41**: 575–580.

Araki, T. (1965). The effect of freeze-thawing upon the fermentation of yeast cells. *Low Temp. Sci.* (*Sapporo*) **B23**: 97–109.

Araki, T., and T. Nei. (1962). The mechanism of freezing in microorganisms. I. Factors affecting the survival of yeast cells subjected to subzero temperatures. *Low Temp. Sci.* (*Sapporo*) **B20**: 57–68.

Armstrong, W. McD. (1961). Distribution of potassium in Baker's yeast. *Nature* **192**: 65–66.

Arpai, J. (1963). Selective effect of freezing as reflected in growth curves. *Folia Microbiol. (Prague)* **8**: 18–26.

Asahina, E. (1956). The freezing process of plant cell. *Contrib. Inst. Low Temp. Sci., Hokkaido Univ., Sapporo, Japan* **10**: 83–126.

Asahina, E. (1961). Intracellular freezing and frost resistance in egg-cells of the sea urchin. *Nature* **191**: 1263–1265.

Atkin, L., W. Moses, and P. P. Gray. (1949). The preservation of yeast cultures by lyophilization. *J. Bacteriol.* **57**: 575–578.

Barer, R. (1956). Phase contrast and interference microscopy in cytology. *In* "Physical Techniques in Biological Research" (G. Oster and A. W. Pollister, eds.), Vol. 3, pp. 29–90. Academic Press, New York.

Bartetzko, H. (1910). Untersuchungen über das Erfrieren von Schimmelpilzen. *Jahrb. Wiss. Botan.* **47**: 57–98.

Bateman, J. B., P. A. McCaffrey, R. J. O'Conner, and G. W. Monk. (1961). Relative humidity and the killing of bacteria—the survival of damp *Serratia marcescens* in air. *Appl. Microbiol.* **9**: 567–571.

Baum, H. M. (1943). The resistance to low temperatures of a culture of *Saccharomyces cerevisiae* grown from a single cell. *Biodynamica* **4**: 71–74.

Benedict, R. G., E. S. Sharpe, J. Corman, G. B. Meyers, E. F. Baer, H. H. Hall, and R. W. Jackson. (1961). Preservation of microorganisms by freeze-drying. II. The destructive action of oxygen. Additional stabilizers for *Serratia marcescens*. Experiments with other microorganisms. *Appl. Microbiol.* **9**: 256–262.

Berry, J. A. (1933). Destruction and survival of microorganisms in frozen pack foods. *J. Bacteriol.* **26**: 459–470.

Boyd, W. L. (1958). Microbiological studies of arctic soils. *Ecology* **39**: 332–336.

Boyd, W. L., and J. W. Boyd. (1963). Soil microorganisms of the McMurdo Sound Area, Antarctica. *Appl. Microbiol.* **11**: 116–121.

Boyd, W. L., and J. W. Boyd. (1964). The presence of bacteria in permafrost of the Alaskan Arctic. *Can. J. Microbiol.* **10**: 917–919.

Bradley, S. G. (1963). Loss of adaptive enzyme during storage. *In* "Culture Collections: Perspectives and Problems" (S. M. Martin, ed.), pp. 46–52. Univ. of Toronto Press, Toronto.

Braendle, D. H. (1963). Discussion after paper by Bradley (1963, pp. 52–55).

Brandts, J. F. (1967a). Heat effects on proteins and enzymes. *In* "Thermobiology" (A. H. Rose, ed.), pp. 25–72. Academic Press, New York.

Brandts, J. F. (1967b). *Conf. Mech. Freezing Injury, Fairbanks, Alaska, 1966* (unpublished).

Brockman, H. E., and F. J. de Serres. (1962). Viability of Neurospora conidia from stock cultures on silica gel. *Neurospora Newsletter* **1**: 8–9.

Bromfield, K. R. (1964). Cold-induced dormancy and its reversal in uredospores of *Puccinia graminis* var. *tritici*. *Phytopathology* **54**: 68–74.

Bruice, T. C., and A. R. Butler. (1965). Ionic reactions in frozen aqueous systems. *Federation Proc.* **24**: Suppl. 15, S45–S49.

Buell, C. B. (1948). Studies on the effect of the lyophil process on fungous spores. M.A. Thesis, Wellesley College, Wellesley, Massachusetts.

Buller, A. H. R. (1913). Upon the retention of vitality by dried fruit bodies of certain hymenomycetes including an account of an experiment with liquid air. *Brit. Mycol. Soc. Trans.* **4**: 106–112.

Burns, M. E. (1962). Survival of lyophilized yeasts. *Sabouraudia* **1**: 203–213.

Campbell, J. D. (1943). Resistance of yeast to low temperatures. *Biodynamica* **4**: 65–70.

Carmichael, J. W. (1956). Frozen storage for stock cultures of fungi. *Mycologia* **48**: 378–381.

Carmichael, J. W. (1962). Viability of mold cultures stored at —20°C. *Mycologia* **54**: 432–436.

Chambers, R., and H. P. Hale. (1932). The formation of ice in protoplasm. *Proc. Roy. Soc.* **B110**: 336–352.

Cochrane, V. W. (1958). "Physiology of Fungi," p. 426. Wiley, New York.

Conway, E. J., and W. McD. Armstrong. (1961). The total intracellular concentration of solutes in yeast and other plant cells and the distensibility of the plant-cell wall. *Biochem. J.* **81**: 631–639.

Davis, E. E., F. A. Hodges, and R. D. Goos. (1966). Effect of suspending media on the survival of *Puccinia graminis* urediospores during freezing. *Phytopathology* **56**: 1432–1433.

Davis, R. J. (1963). Viability and behavior of lyophilized cultures after storage for twenty-one years. *J. Bacteriol.* **85**: 486–487.

Devik, O., and J. A. Ulrich. (1948–1949). Investigation of changes in foods during storage in the frozen condition. *Hormel Inst., Univ. Minn., Ann. Rept.* pp. 40–45.

di Menna, M. E. (1966). Yeasts in antarctic soils. *Antonie van Leeuwenhoek, J. Microbiol. Serol.* **32**: 29–38.

Doebbler, G. F., and A. P. Rinfret. (1963). Survival of microorganisms after ultra-rapid freezing and thawing. *J. Bacteriol.* **85**: 485.

Ebbutt, L. I. K. (1961). The relationship between activity and cell wall permeability in dried Baker's yeast. *J. Gen. Microbiol.* **25**: 87–95.

Farrant, J. (1965). Mechanism of cell damage during freezing and thawing and its prevention. *Nature* **205**: 1284–1287.

Faull, A. (1929). On the resistance of *Neurospora crassa*. *Mycologia* **21**: 288–303.

Fennell, D. I. (1960). Conservation of fungous cultures. *Botan. Rev.* **26**: 79–141.

Fennell, D. I., K. B. Raper, and M. H. Flickinger. (1950). Further investigations on the preservation of mold cultures. *Mycologia* **42**: 135–137.

Flor, H. H. (1954). Longevity of uredospores of flax rust. *Phytopathology* **44**: 469–471.

Foulkes, E. C. (1954). Citrate metabolism and cell permeability. *J. Bacteriol.* **68**: 505.

Fry, R. M. (1954). The preservation of bacteria. *In* "Biological Applications of Freezing and Drying" (R. J. C. Harris, ed.), pp. 215–252. Academic Press, New York.

Fry, R. M. (1966). Freezing and drying of bacteria. *In* "Cryobiology" (H. T. Meryman, ed.), pp. 665–696. Academic Press, New York.

Fry, R. M., and R. I. N. Greaves. (1951). The survival of bacteria during and after drying. *J. Hyg.* **49**: 220–246.

Gerhardt, P., and S. H. Black. (1960). Permeability of bacterial spores. *In* "Spores II" (H. O. Halvorson, ed.), pp. 218–228. Burgess, Minneapolis, Minnesota.

Goos, R. D., E. E. Davis, and W. Butterfield. (1967). Effect of warming rates on the viability of frozen fungous spores. *Mycologia* **59**: 58–66.

Gorrill, R. H., and E. M. McNeil. (1960). The effect of cold diluent on the viable count of *Pseudomonas pyocyanea*. *J. Gen. Microbiol.* **22**: 437–442.

Graham, S. O. (1956). Germination responses of *Ustilago tritici* (Pers.) *Rostr.* teliospores in relation to lyophilization. I. Some factors affecting mortality before and after sublimation. *Res. Studies State Univ. Wash.* **24**: 307–317.

Greaves, R. I. N. (1944). Centrifugal vacuum freezing. *Nature* **153**: 485–487.

Greaves, R. I. N. (1960). Some factors which influence the stability of freeze-dried cultures. *In* "Recent Research in Freezing and Drying" (A. S. Parkes and A. U. Smith, eds.), pp. 203–215. Blackwell, Oxford.

Greaves, R. I. N., and J. D. Davies. (1965). Separate effects of freezing, thawing, and drying living cells. *Ann. N.Y. Acad. Sci.* **125**: 548–558.

Guibert, L., and P. Bréchot. (1955). La lyophilisation des levures. *Ann. Inst. Pasteur* **88**: 750–768.

Gunderson, M. F. (1962). Mold problem in frozen foods. *Proc. Low Temp. Microbiol. Symp. Camden, N.J., 1961* pp. 299–312. Campbell Soup Co., Camden, New Jersey.

Hagen, P. O., and A. H. Rose. (1961). A psychrophilic cryptococcus. *Can. J. Microbiol.* **7**: 287–294.

Haines, R. B. (1938). The effect of freezing on bacteria. *Proc. Roy. Soc.* **B124**: 451–463.

Hamilton, J. M., and L. O. Weaver. (1943). Freezing preservation of fungi and fungus spores. *Phytopathology* **33**: 612–613.

Hansen, I. A., and P. M. Nossal. (1955). Morphological and biochemical effects of freezing on yeast cells. *Biochem. Biophys. Acta* **16**: 502–512.

Harrison, A. P., Jr., and M. J. Pelczar. (1963). Damage and survival of bacteria during freeze-drying and during storage over a ten-year period. *J. Gen. Microbiol.* **30**: 395–400.

Harrison, J. S., and W. E. Trevelyan. (1963). Phospholipid breakdown in baker's yeast during drying. *Nature* **200**: 1189–1190.

Harter, L. L., and W. J. Zaumeyer. (1941). Differentiation of physiologic races of *Uromyces phaseoli* typica on bean. *J. Agr. Res.* **62**: 717–731.

Haskins, R. H. (1957). Factors affecting survival of lyophilized fungal spores and cells. *Can. J. Microbiol.* **3**: 477–485.

Haskins, R. H., and J. Anastasiou. (1953). Comparisons of the survival of *Aspergillus niger* spores lyophilized by various methods. *Mycologia* **45**: 523–532.

Hawker, L. E. (1957). Ecological factors and the survival of fungi. *In* "Microbial Ecology" (R. E. O. Williams and C. C. Spicer eds.), pp. 238–258. Cambridge Univ. Press, London and New York.

Heckly, R. J. (1961). Preservation of bacteria by lyophilization. *Advan. Appl. Microbiol.* **3**: 1–76.

Heckly, R. J., R. L. Dimmick, and J. J. Windle. (1963). Free radical formation and survival of lyophilized microorganisms. *J. Bacteriol.* **85**: 961–966.

Herrera, T., W. H. Peterson, E. J. Cooper, and H. J. Peppler. (1956). Loss of cell constituents on reconstitution of active dry yeast. *Arch. Biochem. Biophys.* **63**: 131–143.

Hesseltine, C. W., B. J. Bradle, and C. R. Benjamin. (1960). Further investigations on the preservation of molds. *Mycologia* **52**: 762–774.

Hill, A. V. (1962). Longevity of conidia of *Peronospora tabacina* Adam. *Nature* **195**: 827–828.

Hutton, R. S., R. J. Hilmoe, and J. L. Roberts. (1951). Some physical factors that influence the survival of *Brucella abortus* during freeze-drying. *J. Bacteriol.* **61**: 309–319.

Hwang, S. W. (1960). Effects of ultra-low temperatures on the viability of selected fungus strains. *Mycologia* **52**: 527–529.

Hwang, S. W. (1966). Long-term preservation of fungus cultures with liquid nitrogen refrigeration. *Appl. Microbiol.* **14**: 784–788.

Jones, A. H., and F. W. Fabian. (1952). The viability of microorganisms isolated from fruits and vegetables when frozen in different menstrua. *Michigan State Univ., Agr. Expt. Sta., Tech. Bull.* **229**: 1–42.

Kiovsky, T. E., and R. E. Pincock. (1966). The mutarotation of glucose in frozen aqueous solutions. *J. Am. Chem. Soc.* **88**: 4704–4710.

Kirsop, B. (1955). Maintenance of yeasts by freeze-drying. *J. Inst. Brewing* **61**: 466–471.

Klingmüller, W. (1963). A damaging effect of drying on *Neurospora crassa* conidia and its reversibility. *Z. Naturforsch.* **18b**: 55–60.

Koga, S., A. Echigo, and K. Nunomura. (1966). Physical properties of cell water in partially dried *Saccharomyces cerevisiae. Biophys. J.* **6**: 665–674.

Kramer, C. L., and A. J. Mix. (1957). Deep freeze storage of fungus cultures. *Trans. Kansas Acad. Sci.* **60**: 58–64.

Kupletskaya, M. B. (1961). Lyophilization of saprophytic microorganisms. *Mikrobiologiya* **30**: 717–721.

Leibo, S. P., and P. Mazur. (1966). Effect of osmotic shock and low salt concentration on survival and density of bacteriophages T_4B and T_4Bo_1. *Biophys. J.* **6**: 747–772.

Lewis, J. C., N. S. Snell, and H. K. Burr. (1960). Water permeability of bacterial spores and the concept of a contractile cortex. *Science* **132**: 544–545.

Lion, M. B. (1963). Quantitative aspects of the protection of freeze-dried *Escherichia coli* against the toxic effect of oxygen. *J. Gen. Microbiol.* **32**: 321–329.

Lion, M. B., J. S. Kirby-Smith, and M. L. Randolph. (1961). Electronspin resonance signals from lyophilized bacterial cells exposed to oxygen. *Nature* **192**: 34–36.

Loegering, W. Q., and D. L. Harmon. (1962). Effect of thawing temperature on urediospores of *Puccinia graminis* f. sp. *tritici* frozen in liquid nitrogen. *Plant Disease Reptr.* **46**: 299–302.

Lund, A. J. (1951–1952). Investigation of changes that take place in foods during storage in the frozen condition. *Hormel Inst., Univ. Minn., Ann. Rept.* pp. 70–79.

Lund, A. J., and W. O. Lundberg. (1949–1950). Investigation of changes in foods during storage in the frozen condition. *Hormel Inst., Univ. Minn., Ann. Rept.* pp. 47–51.

Luyet, B. J. (1966). Anatomy of the freezing process in physical systems. *In* "Cryobiology" (H. T. Meryman, ed.), pp. 115–138. Academic Press, New York.

Luyet, B. J., and P. M. Gehenio. (1940). "Life and Death at Low Temperatures." Biodynamica, Normandy, Missouri.

Luyet, B. J., G. L. Rapatz, and P. M. Gehenio. (1963). On the mode of action of rapid cooling in the preservation of erythrocytes in frozen blood. *Biodynamica* **9**: 95–124.

McFarlane, V. H. (1941). Behavior of microorganisms at subfreezing temperatures. III. Influence of sucrose and hydrogen-ion concentrations. *Food Res.* **6**: 481–492.

McFarlane, V. H., and H. E. Goresline. (1943). Microbial destruction in buffered water and in buffered sugar sirups stored at −17.8°C (0°F). *Food Res.* **8**: 67–77.

Mallett, G. E., G. W. Monk, P. A. McCaffrey, and M. S. Davis. (1959). The mechanism of killing by the critical water content in *Serratia marcescens*. *Proc. 1st Natl. Biophys. Confer., Columbus, Ohio, 1957* pp. 202–206. Yale Univ. Press, New Haven, Connecticut.

Mazur, P. (1953). Studies of the effects of low temperatures and dehydration on the viability of fungous spores. Ph.D. Thesis, Harvard University.

Mazur, P. (1956). Studies on the effects of subzero temperatures on the viability of spores of *Aspergillus flavus*. I. The effect of rate of warming. *J. Gen. Physiol.* **39**: 869–888.

Mazur, P. (1960a). The effects of subzero temperatures on microorganisms. *In* "Recent Research in Freezing and Drying" (A. S. Parkes and A. U. Smith, eds.), pp. 65–77. Blackwell, Oxford.

Mazur, P. (1960b). Physical factors implicated in the death of microorganisms at subzero temperatures. *Ann. N.Y. Acad. Sci.* **85**: 610–629.

Mazur, P. (1961a). Physical and temporal factors involved in the death of yeast at subzero temperatures. *Biophys. J.* **1**: 247–264.

Mazur, P. (1961b). Manifestations of injury in yeast cells exposed to subzero temperatures. I. Morphological changes in freeze-substituted and in "frozen-thawed" cells. *J. Bacteriol.* **82**: 662–672.

Mazur, P. (1961c). Manifestations of injury in yeast cells exposed to subzero temperatures. II. Changes in specific gravity and in the concentration and quantity of cell solids. *J. Bacteriol.* **82**: 673–684.

Mazur, P. (1963a). Studies on rapidly frozen suspensions of yeast cells by differential thermal analysis and conductometry. *Biophys. J.* **3**: 323–353.

Mazur, P. (1963b). Kinetics of water loss from cells at subzero temperatures and the likelihood of intracellular freezing. *J. Gen. Physiol.* **47**: 347–369.

Mazur, P. (1963c). Mechanisms of injury in frozen and frozen-dried cells. *In* "Culture Collections: Perspectives and Problems" (S. M. Martin, ed.), pp. 59–70. Univ. of Toronto Press, Toronto.

Mazur, P. (1965a). Causes of injury in frozen and thawed cells. *Federation Proc.* **24**: Suppl. 15, S175–S182.

Mazur, P. (1965b). The role of cell membranes in the freezing of yeast and other single cells. *Ann. N.Y. Acad. Sci.* **125**: 658–676.

Mazur, P. (1966). Physical and chemical basis of injury in single-celled microorganisms subjected to freezing and thawing. *In* "Cryobiology" (H. T. Meryman, ed.), pp. 213–315. Academic Press, New York.

Mazur, P. (1967a). Physical chemical basis of injury from intracellular freezing in yeast. *In* "Cellular Injury and Resistance in Freezing Organisms" (E. Asahina, ed.), pp. 171–189. Inst. Low Temperature Sci., Hokkaido Univ., Sapporo, Japan.

Mazur, P. (1967b). Physical and chemical changes during freezing and thawing of cells, with special reference to blood cells. *Proc. 11th Congr. Intern. Soc. Blood Transfusion*. Karger, Basel, Switzerland (in press).

Mazur, P., and J. J. Schmidt. (1966). Unpublished data.

Mazur, P., and W. H. Weston, Jr. (1953). Unpublished data.

Mazur, P., and W. H. Weston, Jr. (1956). The effects of spray-drying on the viability of fungous spores. *J. Bacteriol.* **71**: 257–266.

Mazur, P., M. A. Rhian, and B. G. Mahlandt. (1957a). Survival of *Pasteurella tularensis* in gelatin-saline afttr cooling and warming at subzero temperatures. *Arch. Biochem. Biophys.* **71**: 31–51.

Mazur, P., M. A. Rhian, and B. G. Mahlandt. (1957b). Survival of *Pasteurella tularensis* in sugar solutions after cooling and warming at subzero temperatures. *J. Bacteriol.* **73**: 394–397.

Melander, L. W. (1935). Effect of temperature and light on development of the uredial stage of *Puccinia graminis*. *J. Agr. Res.* **50**: 861–880.

Meryman, H. T. (1957). Physical limitations of the rapid freezing method. *Proc. Roy. Soc.* **B147**: 452–459.

Meryman, H. T., ed. (1966). "Cryobiology." Academic Press, New York.

Meyer, E. (1955). The preservation of dermatophytes at sub-freezing temperatures. *Mycologia* **47**: 664–668.

Meyer, G. H., M. B. Morrow, and O. Wyss. (1962). Viable microorganisms in a fifty-year-old yeast preparation in Antarctica. *Nature* **196**: 598.

Meyer, G. H., M. B. Morrow, and O. Wyss. (1963). Viable organisms from feces and foodstuffs from early Antarctic expeditions. *Can. J. Microbiol.* **9**: 163–167.

Meynell, G. G. (1958). The effect of sudden chilling on *Escherichia coli*. *J. Gen. Microbiol.* **19**: 380–389.

Michener, H. D., and R. P. Elliott. (1964). Minimum growth temperatures for food-poisoning, fecal-indicator, and psychrophilic microorganisms. *Advan. Food Res.* **13**: 349–396.

Miner, C. S., and N. N. Dalton. (1953). "Glycerol," Monograph Ser. Am. Chem. Soc. 117, p. 271. Reinhold, New York.

Mitchell, J. H., Jr., and J. J. Enright. (1957). Effect of low moisture levels on the thermostability of active dry yeast. *Food Technol.* **11**: 359–362.

Monk, G. W., and P. A. McCaffrey. (1957). Effect of sorbed water on the death rate of washed *Serratia marcescens*. *J. Bacteriol.* **73**: 85–88.

Monk, G. W., M. L. Elbert, C. L. Stevens, and P. A. McCaffrey. (1956). Effect of water on the death rate of *Serratia marcescens*. *J. Bacteriol.* **72**: 368–372.

Moor, H., and K. Mühlethaler. (1963). Fine structure in frozen-etched yeast cells. *J. Cell Biol.* **17**: 609–628.

Morelli, F., F. P. Fehlner, and C. H. Stembridge. (1962). Effect of ultra-high vacuum on *Bacillus subtilis* var. *niger*. *Nature* **196**: 106–107.

Murrell, W. G. (1960). Discussion after paper by Gerhardt and Black (1960, pp. 229–236).

Naylor, H. B., and P. A. Smith. (1946). Factors affecting the viability of *Serratia marcescens* during dehydration and storage. *J. Bacteriol.* **52**: 565–573.

Nei, T. (1960). Effects of freezing and freeze-drying on microorganisms. *In* "Recent Research in Freezing and Drying" (A. S. Parkes and A. U. Smith, eds.), pp. 78–86. Blackwell, Oxford.

Nei, T., T. Ogawa, S. Kanehira, and H. Akimoto. (1954). Effects of low temperature on the functions of yeast cells. *J. Agr. Chem. Soc. Japan* **28**: 94–98.

Nei, T., H. Souzu, N. Hanafusa, and T. Araki. (1961). Mechanism of drying during freeze-drying. VIII. Relationship between water content and survival of cells at different parts of material during the drying process (Report 2). *Low Temp. Sci.* (*Sapporo*) **B19**: 59–72.

Nei, T., T. Araki, and H. Souzu. (1965). Studies of the effect of drying conditions on residual moisture content and cell viability in the freeze-drying of microorganisms. *Cryobiology* **2**: 68–73.

Ogawa, T. (1953). Effects of low temperature on yeast catalase. I. Effects of low temperature on catalase in living yeast cells. *Low Temp. Sci.* (*Sapporo*) **B10**: 175–185.

Ostroukhova, Z. A. (1961). Preservation of the properties of wine yeasts by the freeze-drying method. *Mikrobiologiya* **30**: 341–345.

Pedersen, T. A. (1965). Factors affecting viable cell counts of freeze-dried *Cryptococcus terricolus* cells. *Antonie van Leeuwenhoek, J. Microbiol. Serol.* **31**: 232–240.

Perkins, D. D. (1962). Preservation of *Neurospora* stock cultures with anhydrous silica gel. *Can. J. Microbiol.* **8**: 591–594.

Portner, D., D. R. Spiner, R. K. Hoffman, and C. R. Phillips. (1961). Effect of ultrahigh vacuum on viability of microorganisms. *Science* **134**: 2047.

Rapatz, G. L., and B. J. Luyet. (1963). Electron microscope study of the formation of ice in bacteria upon freezing of their suspensions. *Abstr. Papers, 7th Ann. Meeting Biophys. Soc., New York* p. WE 11.

Raper, K. B. (1963). General methods for preserving cultures. *In* "Culture Collections: Perspectives and Problems" (S. M. Martin, ed.), pp. 81–93. Univ. of Toronto Press, Toronto.

Raper, K. B., and D. F. Alexander. (1945). Preservation of molds by the lyophil process. *Mycologia* **37**: 499–525.

Record, B. R., R. Taylor, and D. S. Miller. (1962). The survival of *Escherichia coli* on drying and rehydration. *J. Gen. Microbiol.* **28**: 585–598.

Rey, L. R. (1960). Thermal analysis of eutectics in freezing solutions. *Ann. N.Y. Acad. Sci.* **85**: 510–534.

Rhoades, H. E. (1958). The effect of storage on viability of lyophilized cultures of bacteria, viruses, yeasts and molds. *Am. J. Vet. Res.* **19**: 765–768.

Rhodes, M. (1950). Preservation of yeasts and fungi by desiccation. *Brit. Mycol. Soc. Trans.* **33**: 35–39.

Rowell, J. B. (1956). Rehydration injury of dried urediospores of *Puccinia graminis* var. *tritici*. *Phytopathology* **46**: 25.

Sackston, W. E. (1960). Studies on sunflower rust. II. Longevity of urediospores of *Puccinia helianthi*. *Can. J. Botany* **38**: 883–889.

Sakagami, Y. (1959). Effects of freezing and thawing on growth and metabolism of yeast cells. *Low Temp. Sci.* (*Sapporo*) **B17**: 105–124.

Sakai, A. (1961). The mechanism of the frost injury in plant cells. I. Effect of medium against frost injury. *Low Temp. Sci.* (*Sapporo*) **B19**: 1–16.

Sakai, A. (1962). Mechanism of the protective action of sugars against frost injury in plant cells. *Nature* **193**: 89–90.

Sakurada, K. (1958). Studies on the comparison of freeze-drying and liquid-drying of microorganisms. *Low Temp. Sci.* (*Sapporo*) **B16**: 91–105.

Sant, R. K., and W. H. Peterson. (1958). Factors affecting loss of nitrogen and fermenting power of rehydrated active dry yeast. *Food Technol.* **12**: 359–362.

Schein, R. D. (1962). Storage viability of bean rust uredospores. *Phytopathology* **52**: 653–657.

Schwinghamer, E. A. (1958). The relation of survival to radiation dose in rust fungi. *Radiation Res.* **8**: 329–343.

Scott, W. J. (1957). Water relations of food spoilage microorganisms. *Advan. Food Res.* **7**: 83–127.

Scott, W. J. (1960). A mechanism causing death during storage of dried microorganisms. *In* "Recent Research in Freezing and Drying" (A. S. Parkes and A. U. Smith, eds.), pp. 188–202. Blackwell, Oxford.

Sharp, E. L., and F. G. Smith. (1952). Preservation of *Puccinia* uredospores by lyophilization. *Phytopathology* **42**: 263–264.

Sharp, E. L., and F. G. Smith. (1957). Further study of the preservation of *Puccinia* uredospores. *Phytopathology* **47**: 423–429.

Sherman, J. K. (1962). Preservation of bull and human spermatozoa by freezing in liquid nitrogen vapour. *Nature* **194**: 1291–1292.

Silverman, G. J., and S. A. Goldblith. (1965). The microbiology of freeze-dried foods. *Advan. Appl. Microbiol.* **7**: 305–334.

Simmons, E. G. (1963). Fungus cultures: Conservation and taxonomic responsibility. *In* "Culture Collections: Perspectives and Problems" (S. M. Martin, ed.), pp. 100–110. Univ. Toronto Press, Toronto.

Sinclair, N. A., and J. L. Stokes. (1965). Obligately psychrophilic yeasts from the polar regions. *Can. J. Microbiol.* **11**: 259–269.

Smith, A. U. (1961). "Biological Effects of Freezing and Supercooling," Monographs of the Physiol. Soc., No. **9**: p. 101. Williams & Wilkins, Baltimore, Maryland.

Smith, A. U., and J. Smiles. (1953). Microscopic studies of mammalian tissues during cooling to and rewarming from −79°C. *J. Roy. Microscop. Soc.* [3] **73**: 134–139.

Smith, A. U., C. Polge, and J. Smiles. (1951). Microscopic observation of living cells during freezing and thawing. *J. Roy. Microscop. Soc.* [3] **71**: 186–195.

Somers, E., and J. G. Horsfall. (1966). The water content of powdery mildew conidia. *Phytopathology* **56**: 1031–1035.

Souzu, H. (1964). Freezing injury in yeast cells. The mechanism of degradation of some phosphorus compounds of yeast cells resulting from freezing and thawing. *Low Temp. Sci.* (*Sapporo*) **B22**: 109–118.

Souzu, H. (1965). Freezing injury in yeast cells. Outbreak of phosphatase activity by freeze-thawing. *Low Temp. Sci.* (*Sapporo*) **B23**: 85–96.

Souzu, H., and T. Araki. (1962). Injury on nucleic acids synthesis due to the freezing and thawing of yeast cells. *Low Temp. Sci.* (*Sapporo*) **B20**: 69–79.

Souzu, H., T. Nei, and M. Bito. (1961). Water of microorganisms and its freezing. With special reference to the relation between water content and viability of yeast and coli cells. *Low Temp. Sci.* (*Sapporo*) **B19**: 49–57.

Stapleton, G. E., and A. Hollaender. (1952). Mechanism of lethal and mutagenic action of ionizing radiations on *Aspergillus terreus*. *J. Cellular Comp. Physiol.* **39**: Suppl. 1, 101–113.

Stille, B. (1950). Untersuchungen über den Kältetod von Mikroorganismen. *Arch. Mikrobiol.* **14**: 554–587.

Straka, R. P., and J. L. Stokes. (1959). Metabolic injury to bacteria at low temperatures. *J. Bacteriol.* **78**: 181–185.

Straka, R. P., and J. L. Stokes. (1960). Psychrophilic bacteria from Antarctica. *J. Bacteriol.* **80**: 622–625.

Strange, R. E., and F. A. Dark. (1962). Effect of chilling on *Aerobacter aerogenes* in aqueous suspension. *J. Gen. Microbiol.* **29**: 719–730.

Strange, R. E., and A. G. Ness. (1963). Effect of chilling on bacteria in aqueous suspension. *Nature* **197**: 819.

Sussman, A. S. (1961). The role of trehalose in the activation of dormant ascospores of *Neurospora*. *Quart. Rev. Biol.* **36**: 109–116.

Sussman, M. V., and L. Chin. (1966). Liquid water in frozen tissue: Study by nuclear magnetic resonance. *Science* **151**: 324–325.

Tanguay, A. E. (1959). Preservation of microbiological assay organisms by direct freezing. *Appl. Microbiol.* **7**: 84–88.

Tanner, F. W., and B. W. Williamson. (1928). The effect of freezing on yeasts. *Proc. Soc. Exptl. Biol. Med.* **25:** 377–381.

Tappel, A. L. (1966). Effects of low temperatures and freezing on enzymes and enzyme systems. *In* "Cryobiology" (H. T. Meryman, ed.), pp. 163–177. Academic Press, New York.

Thimann, K. V. (1963). "The Life of Bacteria," 2nd ed., p. 127. Macmillan, New York.

Tonino, G. J. M., and E. P. Steyn-Parvé. (1963). Localization of some phosphatases in yeast. *Biochim. Biophys. Acta* **67:** 453–469.

Ulrich, J. A., and H. O. Halvorson. (1946–1947). Investigation of changes in foods during storage in the frozen condition. *Horm. Inst., Univ. Minn., Ann. Rept.* pp. 44–46.

Ungar, J., P. Farmer, and P. W. Muggleton. (1956). Freeze-dried B.C.G. vaccine. *Brit. Med. J.* **II:** 568–571

von Hippel, P. H., and K. Y. Wong. (1964). Neutral salts: The generality of their effects on the stability of macromolecular conformations. *Science* **145:** 577–580.

Wallace, G. I., and F. W. Tanner. (1935). Microbiology of frozen foods. III. Longevity of pure cultures of microorganisms frozen in various menstra. *Fruit Prod. J.* **14:** 235–237.

Webb, S. J. (1965). "Bound Water in Biological Integrity." Thomas, Springfield, Illinois.

Wellman, A. M., and D. B. Walden. (1964). Qualitative and quantitative estimates of viability for some fungi after periods of storage in liquid nitrogen. *Can. J. Microbiol.* **10:** 585–593.

Weston, W. H., Jr. (1949). Influence of the several steps of the lyophile process on survival of fungous spores. *Am. J. Botany* **36:** 816–817.

Weston, W. H., Jr., C. B. Buell, and P. Mazur. (1949). Unpublished data.

Wickerham, L. J., and A. A. Andreasen. (1942). The lyophil process—its use in the preservation of yeasts. *Wallerstein Lab. Commun.* **5:** 165–169.

Wickerham, L. J., and M. H. Flickinger. (1946). The lyophil process. *Brewers Dig.* **21:** 55–60.

Wood, T. H., and A. M. Rosenberg. (1957). Freezing in yeast cells. *Biochim. Biophys. Acta* **25:** 78–87.

Wood, T. H., and A. L. Taylor. (1957). X-ray inactivation of yeast at freezing temperatures. *Radiation Res.* **7:** 99–106.

Woodburn, M. J., and D. H. Strong. (1960). Survival of *Salmonella typhimurium, Staphylococcus aureus,* and *Streptococcus faecalis* frozen in simplified food substrates. *Appl. Microbiol.* **8:** 109–113.

Woodward, V. W., and V. Swarup. (1956). The influence of water on the UV-sensitivity of *Neurospora* conidia. *Microbial Genet. Bull.* **13:** 36–37.

Yarwood, C. E. (1950). Water content of fungus spores. *Am. J. Botany* **37:** 636–639.

Zentner, R. J. (1966). Physical and chemical stresses of aerosolization. *Bacteriol. Rev.* **30:** 551–557.

CHAPTER 15

Genetical Adjustment of Fungi to Their Environment

CLAYTON PERSON[1]

Department of Genetics
University of Alberta
Edmonton, Canada

I. INTRODUCTION

This chapter will attempt to deal with some of the short-term micro-evolutionary events that lead to better genetic adjustment of fungi to their environment. In principle, the adaptation process is not expected to be any different for the fungi than for other organisms. However, as was shown in Volume II, Chapters 15–20, the fungi do display a number of genetic innovations that are not known in other groups, and where these are important in maintaining genetic variability they may also be expected to play an important role in adaptation.

Among the factors that play a part in the adaptation process, those of most significance are mutation, recombination, and selection. Mutation, which may be considered the ultimate source of variability, provides a constant flow of new genes into a population. Recombination, usually achieved through the sexual process in higher organisms, reassorts the new genes and the old in all their many possible genotypic combinations. The genotypic combinations so provided are, however, not of equal value to their possessors. Normally, some members within the population are much better suited than are others for survival and reproduction under the conditions that then exist. These more reproductive members of the population therefore make a relatively greater genetic contribution to the succeeding generation than do those which leave fewer offspring. As a consequence of this differential in reproductivity the genetic composition of the following population is somewhat changed; there has been a selec-

[1] *Present address:* Department of Botany, University of British Columbia, Vancouver, Canada.

tion in favor of genes and genotypes that best suit individuals for survival and reproduction. Selection therefore has its basis in the genetic variability that normally exists within a population, and has the effect of favoring those genes and gene combinations that increase survival and reproductivity in a given environment. Environment is not normally static, however, and the gene or genotype that is favored under one set of conditions may lose favor when these conditions are altered. The environment, therefore, plays a primary role in determining which of the many genes and gene combinations within a population will be selectively favored during the adaptation process.

The general subject of adaptation is treated much more adequately in any of several textbooks, including those of Dobzhansky (1951), Falconer (1960), Mayr (1963), and Sheppard (1958), to mention only a few.

II. ADAPTATION IN FUNGI

A. Adaptive Mechanisms in Fungi

For organisms in which reproduction is invariably sexual it is probable that no two individuals within a population are genotypically identical (Mayr, 1963). In many of the fungi, however, sexual reproduction is not known to occur, and for many of those in which it does occur the occurrence is sporadic rather than regular. An important mechanism for achieving genetic variability is therefore absent, or relatively unimportant, in most fungal populations. Also there is the additional fact that for most fungi in which sexual reproduction is known, fertilization and genetic recombination are followed by an extended haploid phase. The capacity to store genetic variability, so important in organisms with predominantly diploid life cycles, is therefore limited in the fungi. Although alternative mechanisms, including heterokaryosis, mitotic recombination, and extranuclear inheritance (see Volume II, Chapter 19), are known to operate in some fungi, their effectiveness as substitutes in providing and in storing genetic variability is difficult to assess. Pontecorvo (1958), in considering this point, estimated that in *Aspergillus nidulans,* where meiotic and mitotic recombination both occur, the amount of recombination occurring through the sexual cycle is about 500 times greater than that through the parasexual cycle. In *A. niger* and *Penicillium chrysogenum,* where sexual reproduction is not known, genetic recombination through parasexual processes seemed to occur more frequently than in *A. nidulans.* Pontecorvo concluded that where the sexual cycle does not occur it can be replaced by the parasexual cycle. He also pointed out, as had Beadle and Coonradt (1944), that the storage of genetic variability, made possible through heterozygosity in diploid organisms, can be accomplished through alternative mechanisms in the fungi. Heterokaryosis in itself can preserve genes and gene combinations by sheltering nuclei that would not otherwise survive in homokaryons. Upon fusion within the heterokaryon of genetically dissimilar nuclei, genetic variability can also be stored in diploid, heterozygous nuclei as in higher organisms. Another mechanism, resembling heterokaryosis in its effects but involving cytoplasmic rather than nuclear elements, is also known in the fungi (Jinks, 1959; see also Volume II, Chapter 19); many of the properties usually attributed to unlike nuclei within a heterokaryon are also explainable in terms of unlike cytoplasmic determinants within a heteroplasmon. Still another mechanism, leading to the preservation of genetic variability in the fungi, occurs when two genetically different strains each incapable of independent survival are able to live syntrophically, with each supplying the other's needs. Genetic variability can therefore be provided and maintained through a number of different mechanisms that are known to operate, together with mutation, in fungal populations. Much remains to be learned before it will be possible to put forward any general statement as to the relative importance of any of these mechanisms in the adaptation process.

The microevolutionary events that lead to better genetic adjustment of fungi to their environment have yet to be studied from the viewpoint of population genetics. Certain of the fundamental concepts have yet to be clarified before the analytical methods of population genetics can be properly applied to fungal populations. The use of the term "population" itself may be taken as an illustrative example. Ideally, a population comprises a group of randomly interbreeding individuals who share a common gene-pool. In most fungi the situations that are or will be encountered are even further from this ideal than is usually the case with other organisms, and for those fungi in which sexual reproduction is not known, the correspondence between the real and the ideal is likely to be even more remote. Until the fungi have been further examined, applying appropriately adjusted methods of population genetics, no satisfactory interpretation of the microevolutionary events that lead to their adaptation can be formulated.

B. *Saprobic Adaptation*

The distribution of most of the saprobic fungi is world wide. Following the considerations put forward by Stanier (1953), the reason for cosmopolitan distribution lies in the fact that saprobic fungi occupy micro- rather than macroenvironments, and that any particular type of microenvironment is as likely to occur in one geographical area as in another. A second feature is that microenvironments in nature are usually occupied by groups of organisms, whose combined activities cause conditions within the microenvironment to change. Microenvironments are therefore discontinuous both in space and in time. The habitats of saprobic fungi have been extensively treated in Chapter 1 of this volume, and Hawker (1957), in an earlier review, and Sussman (Chapter 17) have considered ecological factors and their relation to survival of fungi. The capacities for rapid growth and quick exploitation of available resources, for generous production and efficient dispersal of spores—these and other general characteristics of saprobic fungi are understandable in terms of selection directed toward survival under the short-term labile conditions that exist in microenvironments (Stanier, 1953).

Certain genetic mechanisms in fungi, in addition to those referred to in the last section, undoubtedly play a significant role in fitting saprobic fungi for survival in a changing microenvironment. As Beadle and Coonradt (1944) have shown, the relative proportions of the different nuclei within a *Neurospora* heterokaryon are not mechanically fixed. This allows for the adjustment of nuclear ratios to give maximum growth as an adaptive response to external conditions. Jinks (1952) has studied heterokaryons of *Penicillium* found in nature and shown that nuclear ratios do adjust in response to environmental changes. The evolutionary significance of this mechanism hinges on whether, in the absence of sexual reproduction, alternative means exist for the regular dispersal and propagation of the heterokaryon; Jinks found evidence for this in *Penicillium*. Induced adaptive changes, involving cytoplasmic rather than nuclear elements, are also known, and their transmissibility has been demonstrated (Jinks, 1957, 1958). Other processes by which the phenotype may undergo adaptive change in response to a changed environment include the formation of induced enzymes, the altering of vegetative cells, spore types, and other characters. Many saprobic fungi also have the ability to alter the microenvironment in a direction unfavorable to other competing organisms (Brian, 1957; see also preceding chapters of this volume). In all such cases the evolutionary value of the response will depend on the efficiency with which the capacity to make the response is transmitted to offspring, as well as on the survival value of the response itself.

Finally, for those saprobic fungi that reproduce sexually the incompatibility systems, where they occur, are of undoubted importance in maintaining genetic variability. These are described in Volume II, Chapter 20.

Considering the number and variety of mechanisms, most of them recently discovered, that may play a role in the microevolution of saprobic fungi, and considering also the peculiar characteristics of the saprobial microenvironment, it is perhaps not surprising that much is yet to be learned about adaptation in saprobic fungi.

C. Symbiotic Adaptation

The term symbiosis denotes the living together of dissimilar organisms. Three classes of symbiotic relationship are usually distinguished: (1) mutualism, in which both partners of the association appear to benefit; (2) parasitism, in which one partner benefits at the other's expense; and (3) commensalism, in which there is no apparent harm or benefit to either partner, or in which one partner benefits while the other remains unaffected.

Quispel (1951), in considering some of the theoretical aspects of symbiosis, asserted that "two organisms don't enter into symbiosis to give something to the partner, but in order to take as much advantage of the partner as possible." He developed the view that distinctions between mutualism, commensalism, and parasitism are generally difficult to recognize. A partnership in which each member is nutritionally dependent on the other may also be thought of in terms of reciprocal parasitism. He pointed out that this may account for the frequent disagreement among biologists in classifying symbiotic associations. Caullery (1952) stated that even in the lichens there is a conflict between the alga and the fungus. He concluded that the idea of a purely mutualistic association with equivalent reciprocal benefits must be abandoned, and stated (page 285) that "Commensalism, parasitism and symbiosis are only categories created by us and as soon as they are thoroughly analysed it is impossible to delimit them."

In spite of the evident analytical difficulties, considerable progress has been made in genetic studies of symbiotic partnerships that involve parasitic fungi (see below). Fungi that take part in mutualism and commensalism seem not to have been studied genetically. Where the relationship with a symbiotic partner is an essential condition, it follows that making contact with the partner is an event of major importance in the life cycle. The largest factor influencing the environment, and selection, may very well be the symbiotic partner, providing contact has been made.

Person *et al.* (1962) have enquired whether mutualism, which emphasizes the idea of reciprocal benefits, can be explained in terms of mutation and selection. In their opinion, selection cannot favor a gene whose *only* effect is to benefit another organism. Selection can favor a mutant gene only if it increases survival and reproductivity of the organism in which the mutation has occurred. A gene that is being selected for in one partner may have the effect of improving the total symbiotic relationship, but in such a case the other partner, which does not possess the gene and therefore benefits accidentally, plays no role in the selection process. It is conceivable, however, that a mutation in one partner may have its primary effect in improving the nutrition of the other and that, as a secondary effect arising through improvement in the other's nutrition, its own nutrition is also improved. While the secondary effect could provide a basis for the selection of the gene, the selection would have its origin in reciprocal benefits; this would again introduce the question of reciprocal parasitism.

An aspect of selection that appears not to have received attention concerns the way in which the symbiotic partners reproduce, and the effect that this may have on the adaptation process. Where the symbiotic association is truly mutualistic it may be expected that selection, acting through differential reproductivity in both organisms, will favor a continuation of the relationship. The relationship can be continued with greatest certainty when the partnership itself is propagated during reproduction, as it is in the lichens. Where symbiotic reproduction takes this pattern, with the partners no longer reproducing independently of one another, independent selection is no longer possible in either partner. Both partners will be affected by selection as though they were a *single* organism. Their identity as individuals in the adaptation process will have vanished. Selective forces, now acting on the complex that has been formed through the fusion of previously separated genetic systems, may be expected to lead to improved interaction and better integration of all genes present within the symbiotic complex, and thus to provide a new genetic basis for adaptation in the mutualistic association.

D. *Parasitic Adaptation*

In parasitism one symbiotic partner profits at the other's expense. This being so, any step in the adaptation process that favors one partner will automatically work to the disadvantage of the other; the relation between the partners is one of mutual antagonism. This is most evident when the dependence of the parasitic partner on the host partner is complete, as with obligate parasites which cannot live apart from their hosts. In this type of parasitic relationship, exemplified in fungi by the rusts, the environment of the parasite is completely provided by the host and, more importantly, is under the genetic control of the host. From the standpoint of the host, the presence of the parasite must be considered a not insignificant factor in its environment; this factor of the host environment is under the genetic control of the parasite. Microevolutionary events in this kind of symbiotic relationship will therefore have their basis, to a very large extent, in the interplay between the genetic systems of host and parasite.

Cases are known in which parasitic reproduction is tied to that of the host and where it might be proposed that, as in the lichens, independent selection is no longer possible in either partner. A distinguishing feature, in parasitic systems, is that a fraction of the host population is usually free of the disease, and that selection in the host population is among diseased and healthy individuals. In mutualism, as exemplified by the lichens, the situation is not comparable. This raises the interesting possibility that the origin of mutualism out of parasitism—proposed by numerous authors—had its basis in changes in selection at that point in the past when the parasite became universally successful.

Most of the concepts that are needed for interpreting adaptation in parasitic fungi have arisen out of genetic studies with the rusts (for reviews, see Johnson, 1953; Flor, 1956). The rusts are obligate parasites. They are diploid (dikaryotic) for the greater part of their life cycle, and, although there is very little morphological variability, the members within any rust group exhibit a surprising degree of variability in their parasitic specificity to varieties of the host (see Johnson, Chapter 21 of this volume). The pathogenic range of a single isolate is frequently confined to a small group of varieties within the host species. Classification of rust isolates, based on their interactions with a standard group of tester varieties, results in the recognition of scores, occasionally hundreds, of discrete "physiologic races." Genetic studies, made possible through Craigie's investigations of the sexual stages revealed that different cultures of a single race, that were equivalent pathogenically, were not necessarily alike genetically. The physiologic race was shown to be a collection of different genotypes. Further investigation showed that Mendelian segregations, not generally observable in terms of interactions with the test varieties taken as a group, were obtained on *individual* host varieties. Both one- and two-factor segregations were revealed within a single F_2 rust population, depending on the individual host variety to which the cultures were tested; other varieties were either resistant or susceptible to all F_2 cultures. For the host it had been shown much earlier that resistance and susceptibility segregated according to Mendel's laws. It is evident that genetic systems in both the host and the parasite play a role in determining the nature of their interactions. Flor (1956), in a series of classical studies with flax and its rust, came to the conclusion that the disease interactions have their basis in specific genetic interrelationships between genes in the host that govern its resistance to the rust and genes in the rust that govern its virulence to the host. Flor's hypothesis of "gene-for-gene" relationships—that for each locus conditioning rust reaction in the host there is a specific, related locus conditioning virulence and avirulence in the rust—is perhaps the most important single step yet taken toward the understanding of genetic interrelationships between host and parasite. Brief summaries of this part of the development of concepts in rust genetics have been presented earlier (Person, 1958; Johnson, 1961; also Chapter 21).

Flor's hypothesis was based on the observation that the genes for resistance possessed by flax varieties and the genes for virulence possessed by their attacking rust races were numerically equal. A difficulty in accepting this as satisfactory evidence lay in the fact that specific genes in either partner were identifiable only through their interaction with their specifically related counterparts in the other member of the association. This procedure of discovering gene-for-gene relationships seemed to require presupposition of the kind of information that was being sought. Person (1959) used Flor's hypothesis predictively, and showed that where gene-for-gene relationships are operating in parasitic systems, they will generate a number of characteristic properties that would otherwise not occur. These properties were then searched for. It was found that they had been conspicuously revealed in the earlier, published data relating to potatoes and the late blight fungus, and they were also found to be in evidence when certain of Flor's data were reanalyzed. It was concluded that Flor's hypothesis of gene-for-gene relationships had been validated.

The operation of gene-for-gene specificities has since been demonstrated or proposed in a number of other parasitic systems, including those that involve *Hordeum* and *Erysiphe* (Moseman, 1959), *Malus* and *Venturia* (Day, 1960), *Triticum* and *Erysiphe* (Powers and Sando, 1960), *Triticum* and *Puccinia* (Zadoks, 1961), *Triticum* and *Tilletia* (Metzger and Trione, 1962), *Lycopersicon* and *Cladosporium* (Fincham and Day, 1963), and *Triticum* and *Ustilago* (Oort, 1963, who in this paper refers to his earlier work, published in 1944, in which the gene-for-gene relationship was suggested). Flor's hypothesis of gene-for-gene relationships has thus provided a most useful basis for genetic interpretation of the interactions between parasitic fungi and their hosts.

Flor's hypothesis also provided the basis for Person's (1959) interpretation of microevolution within parasitic systems, where it was pointed out that selection would be expected to favor mutations in the host that place the parasite at a relative disadvantage, as well as those in the parasite that place the host at a relative disadvantage. Mutations in the host, favoring the parasite but not the host, and those in the parasite, favoring the host but not the parasite, were considered to be of very limited evolutionary significance. The point was also made that mutations conferring greater resistance on the host are of advantage only in host populations in which the parasite prevails; in the absence of the parasite, genes for resistance in the host, being nonoperative, are superfluous. Where the parasite is present the frequency of resistance genes in any host population may then be expected to increase so long as part of the population remains susceptible. The end point, if it is ever reached, will result in universal host resistance, a situation obviously inimical to parasitic survival. The spread of a gene for resistance throughout the host population exerts profound changes in the environment of the parasite; initially congenial, the environment of the parasite is now unsuited for survival. The unsuitability of the environment, and hence the pressure favoring the selection and spread of new genes in the parasitic population, is a direct function of the changing proportions of individuals within the host population that possess the resistance gene. Consider now the parasitic population, in which selection is expected to favor increased virulence toward the host. Here, if it may be imagined that genes for virulence have spread throughout the entire population of the parasite, further evolution in the parasite will then be expected to lead to a condition of optimal virulence, that is, to the point beyond which any advantage to the parasite in increasing its virulence is more than offset by attending disadvantages to the host, on which it ultimately depends. The extreme case, just imagined, is also one in which the environmental forces favoring selection and spread of new genes, this time in the host population, are maximal; as before, the degree to which the selective forces are operative is a function of the proportion of the host population that is infected. Selection is minimal in the host, and maximal in the parasite, when only a few individuals of the host population are susceptible to, and carry, the disease; under these conditions the probability of contact between the parasite and resistant individuals of the host population is greatest, and the screening of genes for virulence in the parasite is most rigorous. On the other hand, selection is maximal in the host, and minimal in the parasite, when only a few individuals of the host population are resistant to, and free of, the disease; under these conditions there is selection, among all the many individuals within the host population that come in contact with the parasite, in favor of those that carry genes for resistance to the disease. These considerations lead to the conclusion that systems involving parasitism are inherently unstable, with each microevolutionary step containing causal ingredients for the step which follows. As Pimentel (1961) has demonstrated in his studies of the house fly (*Musca domestica*) and the parasitic wasp (*Mormoniella vitripennis*) that feeds on house fly pupae, the relevant factors function together as a feedback system, operating through the dynamics of density pressure, selective pressure, and genetic changes within the interacting populations. Although genetic feedback mechanisms of this kind may also play a role in other biological systems, as proposed by Pimentel *et al.* (1961), it is from parasitic systems involving fungi, in which gene-for-gene relationships have been demonstrated, that the feedback hypothesis receives its strongest genetical support.

The general feature that emerges is that parasitic systems are expected to be unstable and changing. The changes are expected to be cyclical, alternating from the one extreme in which the host population is largely resistant to the disease, to the other extreme in which the host population is largely infected by the parasite and carrying the disease. These features have in fact been observed many times over; the records of "breakdown" of resistance in the host, and of the appearance of more virulent races of the pathogen following release of new, more resistant host varieties are numerous. Some of these are referred to by Johnson (1961).

Person (1959) in discussing the origin of gene-for-gene relationships also suggested that the existence within the host population of a single effective gene for resistance will have two effects: (1) the removal of selective forces acting on other loci in the host capable of supplying resistance genes, and (2) the imposition of selective forces at all loci in the parasite capable of supplying an effective gene for virulence. There is no reason to suppose that a mutation for increased virulence in the parasite is limited to any specific locus. But when at any locus an effective gene for virulence does appear, its action will be related to the specific gene in the host whose effect is now overcome. If this is accepted as the general process by which gene-for-gene relationships originate, it is then permissible to conclude that gene-for-gene relationships are to be expected, as a general rule, in parasitic systems. However, certain exceptions to the general rule may be expected: a mutant gene may modify the effects of an existing gene, or the advantage conferred by a genetic change in one population may be too small to evoke a related response in the other population (i.e., selection pressure is also a function of the level of effectiveness of the gene that is exerting the pressure) or, finally, independent genes at two loci may be selected for in response to a genetic change involving a single locus in the other population. Leaving these aside it is then possible to consider the evolutionary fate of the single genes in the host and parasite that comprise the gene-for-gene relationship. An effective gene for resistance may be expected to spread throughout the entire host population. The related gene for virulence, which overcomes the beneficial effects conferred by the resistance gene, now begins to spread and may ultimately be possessed by all members of the parasite population. Possession of the resistance gene is then no longer an advantage to the host, which is now susceptible. The frequency in the host population of the gene for resistance may now be expected to decrease (a process that will be much hastened if it is being displaced by a new allele at the same locus for improved resistance). Elimination of the resistance gene from the host population will at the same time make possible the departure of the related gene for virulence in the parasite population. Because the benefits conferred in their respective populations by genes for resistance in the host and their related genes for virulence in the parasite are expected to be short-term benefits, a constant turnover of related gene pairs within the parasitic system is to be expected. So far as the author is aware there is no good evidence that this actually occurs in parasitic systems. It is known, however, that other organisms, resistant to the action of chemicals, can lose their resistance when grown in the absence of the chemical. Past experiences with genetic changes in parasitic systems have largely been with diseases of agricultural crops. Although these experiences leave no doubt that the introduction of a new gene for resistance in the host is in fact followed by a responsive change in the parasite, it has not been the custom to withdraw previously useful but now ineffective genes for resistance from the host population. In breeding for disease resistance in agricultural crops where microevolution is man-guided and where there is a clear risk of encouraging "super" races of the pathogen (Johnson, 1961), the possibility of cycling genes for resistance in the host seems not to have been considered.

Although microevolution within parasitic systems may be in some respects unique, most of the individual, contributing events are of general occurrence. Person *et al.* (1962) pointed out the similarity to systems involving mimicry, where the genes for color and pattern that are to be of selective value to the mimic are predetermined by those genes for color and pattern that have become established in the organism which is mimicked. Pimentel (1961) proposed genetic feedback as a general concept, applicable to herbivore-plant and predator-prey as well as to host-parasite relationships. However, the gene-for-gene concept in its original meaning and in its subsequent usage has been applied only to parasitic systems. An attempt to define the gene-for-gene concept in such a way that its original meaning will be preserved has resulted in the following statement: "A gene-for-gene relationship exists when the presence of a gene in one population is contingent on the continued presence of a gene in another population, and where the interaction between the two genes leads to a single phenotypic expression by which the presence or absence of the relevant gene in either organism may be recognized" (Person *et al.*, 1962).

A striking feature in genetic studies of parasitism is the number of reports of multiple allelism at loci for resistance in the host. Flor (1956) in reviewing his own and earlier work reported that at least twenty-five different genes controlling reaction to rust had been identified in flax, and he postulated that these occurred as multiple alleles over five different loci. Multiple alleles in barley (*Hordeum*) for resistance to mildew (*Erysiphe graminis* f. sp. *hordei*) have been reported by Schaller and Briggs (1955) and by Luig *et al.* (1958); in addition, multiple alleles for resistance of corn (*Zea*) to corn-rust (*Puccinia sorghi*) have been reported by Hooker and Russell (1962). Some of the tactical problems encountered in identifying alleles for resistance have been referred to by Person (1959); the definition of the concept of allelism and its application to parasitic systems have been carefully examined by Shepherd (1963). Mode (1958) has examined the evolutionary significance of allelism and of gene-for-gene relationships in parasitic systems. He constructed a mathematical model, based on data of Flor (1956) and of Schaller and Briggs (1955), which showed that host-pathogen systems based on gene-for-gene specificities will eventually reach a state of stable equilibrium, providing certain conditions are met; if allelism of resistance genes was also considered to operate, again under certain conditions the system would be expected to reach a state of equilibrium. Mode (1958) concluded that the systems studied by Flor (1956) and by Schaller and Briggs (1955) were relicts of ancient systems of balanced polymorphism. The general occurrence of multiple alleles and their significance in polymorphic populations have been reviewed by Sheppard (1958) and by Mayr (1963), among others. The advantages of polymorphism to the host would stand out more clearly in parasitic systems in which the host is cross-fertilizing. As Mode (1958) has pointed out, the hosts in which allelic resistance genes have been discovered are self-fertilizing.

A second striking feature in genetic studies of parasitism is that genes for virulence in the parasite are commonly recessive and show no evidence of allelism. This contrasts sharply with the finding that resistance genes in the host are commonly dominant and allelic. The mathematical model proposed by Mode (1958) has been extended and modified to accommodate the results just referred to, together with specific gene-for-gene interactions, to provide a more detailed model of genetic polymorphism in parasitic systems. In this proposal (Person, 1966) it is pointed out that the interaction between a resistance gene and its related virulence gene is such that a continued increase in the frequency of either one of them will lead to a breakdown in the selective mechanism that initiated the increase. At the same time, each change from susceptibility to resistance in the host population calls for an adaptive response at a new locus for virulence that is not then contributing to parasitic survival on the existing host population. With these mechanisms operating the model would predict oscillating states of resistance and susceptibility in host populations, together with the cyclic, or repeating patterns of selection pressures that would serve to maintain balanced polymorphisms in the two interacting populations over long periods of time. Whether or not this proposed model proves helpful in coming to a better understanding of the problem, it is difficult not to agree with Mode's earlier suggestion that some such mechanism of self-regulation is a necessary condition for the continued co-evolution of hosts and their parasites.

With the parasitic fungi, as with other fungi, very few experimental studies of evolution appear to have been made. In fungi that are obligately parasitic there can be little doubt that the environment provided by the host is the largest single factor influencing their survival. Data given by Stakman *et al.* (1943) on the changing proportions, within the total population, of wheat stem-rust biotypes are representative of many similar reports. While minor fluctuations in relatively unimportant biotypes remain generally unexplained, it is widely accepted that the major fluctuations are determined by changes in the varieties that are grown. Johnson (1961) has pointed out that such changes are the result of human intervention. The recorded changes may therefore be unrepresentative of parasitism as it occurs in nature, where systems may be less complex, and changes less rapid. Because the same or similar resistance genes have been incorporated into wheat varieties grown from Mexico to Canada, the absolute size of the fungal population affected by the change may also be unnaturally large. Pimentel (1961), in discussing the regulating role of genetic feedback mechanisms, developed a mathematical model which showed that genetic changes, acting as a "damper" within a system, could have the long-term effect of decreasing the amplitude of the cyclic fluctuations so that a stable system would ultimately be achieved (cf. Mode, 1958). In his long-term experiment with interacting populations Pimentel *et al.* (1961) observed a decline in the amplitude of the cyclic fluctuations which he attributed to genetic changes in both populations. The apparent instability in systems involving agricultural crops may thus be a result of human interference, which may be keeping them out of balance. On the other hand, whether natural systems are, in fact, more stable seems not to have been investigated.

The persistence, in small proportions, of relatively innocuous biotypes, shown in the data of Stakman *et al.* (1943), indicates that genetic variability is being maintained. Loegering (1951) studied the changes that occur when wheat varieties are inoculated with controlled mixtures of biotypes. He concluded that the observed changes were not entirely explainable on the basis of selection by the host, and considered that other, unidentified, factors of the environment may have played a selective role.

Some of the data given by Cherewick (1958), who carried out extensive studies directed to the establishment of homogeneous cultures in several smut (*Ustilago*) species, also illustrate the effects of selection by host varieties on field collections of the pathogen. The data chosen for illustration (see Table I) are from experiments involving cultivated oats (*Avena*) and *U. avenae,* which causes loose smut; they record the changes in infectivity that occurred during eight generations, with inoculum for each generation taken from the oat variety Monarch. The data show that eight generations of selection in the environment provided by the one

TABLE I

PERCENTAGES OF SMUT-INFECTED PLANTS IN TWELVE VARIETIES OF OATS (*Avena sativa*) DURING EIGHT GENERATIONS OF SELECTION OF THE PATHOGEN (*Ustilago avenae*) ON THE OAT VARIETY MONARCH[a]

Oat variety	Year and percentage infection								
	1948[b]	1949	1950	1951	1952	1953	1954	1955	1956
Monarch	8	12	26	58	60	68	60	99	92
Anthony	65	10	19	32	44	48	53	71	85
Mabel	64	10	14	58	73	57	72	83	82
Beacon	38	12	31	61	62	55	51	49	80
Black Diamond	10	3	9	21	35	26	15	38	74
Victory	14	2	10	28	19	26	33	39	50
Gothland	15	1	1	13	28	13	7	27	25
Fulghum	1	0	1	3	3	8	0	10	9
Black Mesdag	0	0	0	1	0	0	0	0	1
Camas	0	0	0	0	0	0	3	4	0
Nicol	0	0	1	8	11	5	0	6	4
Atlantic	0	0	2	13	0	0	0	3	0

[a] Data from Cherewick (1958).

[b] The original field collection was tested in 1948; inoculum in all other years was produced in preceding year on variety Monarch.

variety, Monarch, have resulted in an increase in infectivity, from 8% to more than 90%, on this host. The changes in pathogenicity on the remaining varieties, which did not take part in selection, are instructive. These eleven host varieties, together with Monarch, are used to differentiate "biotypes" of the pathogen. Each of these, in effect, presents a different environmental challenge to the parasite. The data for 1949 show that one generation of culture on the variety Monarch has resulted in a screening out of those genotypes that had been previously successful on other varieties; infection percentages recorded for Anthony and five other varieties have dropped very considerably. Following this initial selective change, the data for 1950 and onward to 1956 show that continued selection by the variety Monarch through a further seven generations has provided two quite different results. On five varieties (Anthony, Mabel, Beacon, Black Diamond, and Victory) that had shown most clearly the effects of one generation of screening by the variety Monarch, a steady increase in the percentages of infected plants was recorded; the increase in these five varieties, which played no part in the selection process, parallels the increase that was recorded for Monarch. The interpretation of these data must be that the environment provided by each of the five varieties is similar to that provided by Monarch; they must, in fact, possess one or more genes for resistance in common with those possessed by

Monarch. No parallel increase was recorded on the remaining six varieties (data for the variety Gothland being somewhat ambiguous). The data indicate that genes for pathogenicity toward these varieties were not present in any effective number in the original culture. Fluctuations in pathogenicity on the variety Gothland and, at lower levels, on Nicol and Atlantic may be interpreted in terms of "genetic drift" [defined by Dobzhansky (1951) as "random fluctuations in gene frequencies in effectively small populations"]. The apparent absence of selection lends support to this interpretation. Cherewick (1958) carried out a large number of similar studies, using other host-parasite combinations, and found it very difficult to develop cultures through selection that remained constant in their pathogenic properties. Pathogenic variability had been maintained in spite of selection against it.

Some of the smuts appear to be well suited for population studies. Because they are diploid and sexually reproducing the problem of the population and the gene-pool is simplified; the same initial population can be studied in a number of different environments; relatively large populations can be handled; changes associated with parasitic adaptation can be measured quantitatively; species with both dipolar and tetrapolar mating systems are available; some species are known to be highly mutable; a number of different interspecific crosses can be made; quite different methods of spore dispersal occur; and finally, their biology is fairly well understood (Fischer and Holton, 1957). As was mentioned earlier, the list of parasitic systems in which gene-for-gene relationships have been reported includes one (Oort, 1963) in which the parasite is a smut. Species belonging to this group appear to offer good opportunities for arriving at a better understanding of adaptation in parasitic fungi.

Many fungi that are parasitic also have the ability to live as saprophytes. The distinction between parasites of this group (facultative parasites) and the obligate parasites is made on the basis of whether or not the parasite can live apart from the host organism. It is a distinction that relates to the nutrition of the parasite and, consequently, on how well the nutrition of the parasite is understood. Among this group of parasitic fungi are a number that produce toxins, as well as some that induce toxin production in their hosts. In one or two cases the toxin produced by the pathogen is equally as selective in its effects on the host as is the pathogen itself; for example, the toxin "victorin," produced by *Helminthosporium victoriae* which is pathogenic to varieties of oats (*Avena*) of Victoria lineage, produces its effects only in tissues of Victoria and its derivatives. In the majority of cases in which toxins are produced, however, there is little or no relation between toxin production and pathogenicity; at the same time, most facultative parasites are much less specific in their pathogenicity than is *H. victoriae* (for general review, see Wheeler and Luke, 1963). An interesting case, described by Turner (1961), involves the production by the pathogen (*Ophiobolus graminis* var. *avenae*) of a specific enzyme, avenacinase, which destroys the biological activity of a toxin, avenacin, produced by the host (*Avena sativa*). Turner (1961) has pointed out that a mutation of this kind, which overcomes the resistance of the host, would clearly be of great survival value. Person *et al.* (1962) have suggested that it is in interactions like this, in which the host and parasite produce substances whose interaction is specific, that the gene-for-gene relationship may have its basis. As Turner's results show, the possibilities of forming inhibitor-inactivating enzyme complexes are not limited to systems involving obligate parasites. It follows that micro-evolutionary processes comparable to those that occur with obligate parasites may also be expected in parasitic systems in which the parasite is facultative.

Oort (1963) has discussed, briefly, the applicability of the gene-for-gene concept to systems involving nonobligate parasites. While recognizing that a gene-for-gene relationship may exist in the case described by Turner (1961), he also points out that field resistance in potatoes (*Solanum*) to "late blight" caused by *Phytophthora,* is due to a non-specific mechanism. He emphasized the fact that, for the majority of cases, the facultative parasite in nature must survive in competition with other microorganisms, and that the competition would be keenest when the host was not present. He concluded that survival in facultative parasites would be governed to a greater extent by factors not of a gene-for-gene nature, and pointed out that development of resistance mechanisms in the host may similarly involve gene-for-gene relationships more rarely. In looking at this question from the viewpoint of adaptation, in which environment is considered to play the dominant selective role, one comes to the conclusion that the extent to which either the host or the parasite is in control of the other's environment should be a measure of the extent to which either is in control of the other's evolution. Where engagement with the host is not a prerequisite for survival, the host-created environment is unessential, and may be dispensed with. In the absence of the host, selection and adaptation within the fungus population will be determined by, and directed to, other factors within the microenvironment. With the host present and available, selection—working through differential reproductivity—will result in adaptation toward greater parasitic effectiveness only if the population, or some members of it, have the capacity to parasitize the host and, further, only if there is a reproductive differential favoring the parasitic variant. In this extreme case we may imagine the switch to parasitism to be fortuitous. Removal of the host, through death, microbial activity or other means, should result in deadaptation, and readaptation to the changed conditions of the microenvironment. For populations not containing variants that have a reproductive advantage in parasitizing the host (a likelihood that is increased if the host is resistant), an adaptive change to parasitism may be imagined not to occur. If it may be assumed, however, that the parasitic capacity of the species is in itself of selective value, it follows that selection will have favored the incorporation of mechanisms that preserve this capacity over those periods in which the host is not present. The excretion of toxins, whose effect is to convert the microenvironment in the direction favoring parasitism, may be such a preserving mechanism; if such is the case the nonspecific toxin produced by the nonspecific pathogen will play a most effective role. For pathogens that are in fact dependent on the host for their long-term survival (for completing their life cycle, or for any other reason) it has been assumed earlier that when contact with the host is made, it is with an attending disadvantage to the host. Selection in the host, tending to reduce the disadvantage, will change the environment of the parasite. All gradations in relative importance—of the parasite as a factor regulating adaptation in the host, and of the host as a factor regulating adaptation in the fungus—may be visualized. All effective mechanisms—in the host for improving resistance and in the parasite for improving virulence—may be considered to have selective value, and to play a part in determining environment, reproductive differential, selection and adaptation in the symbiotic partner; selection cannot be expected to favor any one kind of mechanism, physical or chemical, over any other kind of mechanism on any other basis than its adaptive value. All gradations in effectiveness, and in degree of their specificities, may be imagined. These general considerations lead to the conclusion that the range between the saprobic habit on the one hand, and the obligately parasitic habit on the other will be fully occupied. They also lead to agreement with Oort's (1963) conclusion that survival of facultative parasites will be governed to a greater extent by factors not of a gene-for-gene nature.

Blank (cited by Griffiths, 1958) has reported that *Phymatotrichum omnivorum* is able to attack some 2000 species of dicotyledons whereas at the other extreme some biotypes of *Puccinia graminis* f. sp. *tritici* are restricted to only a few varieties (genotypes within a single species of *Triticum*). Data have been presented here (Table I) to support the interpretation that the separate environments provided by six oat varieties, in which the oat-smut pathogen flourished, were similar environments, and that the similarity had its basis in genotypic similarities among the host varieties. In the same way, it must be accepted that the environments encountered by *Phymatotrichum omnivorum* in its interactions with 2000 different species involve similar environments, but in this case it is more difficult, in fact impossible, to accept the interpretation that the basis for their similarity is genetic. As suggested earlier, where the similarity is induced by the fungus—possibly through production of a nonspecific toxin with a wide-range capacity for killing plant tissue—the apparent lack of specificity in environmental preference is explained. While there may be relatively complete control by the host of the fungus environment in one parasitic system, there may also be relatively little control by the host in another. One extreme is represented by systems in which the parasite is obligate, highly specialized and highly specific; the other by systems in which the parasite is facultative, unspecialized and nonspecific. This also leads to the conclusion that no clear-cut distinctions between the two extremes, in the genetic mechanisms that contribute to the adaptation process, are likely to emerge.

Griffiths (1958) has presented evidence in support of the view that specificity in host-parasite relations is dependent upon the ability of both partners to perpetuate their particular genotypes indefinitely—through vegetative reproduction, as in the rusts, or through inbreeding, as in most cereals. While recognizing the value of outcrossing as a means of maintaining genetic variability within both interacting populations, it does not follow that, with outcrossing, interactions between specific genes in the two populations is prevented. The persistence in these interacting populations of genes for resistance or for virulence should depend to a greater extent on their selective value to individuals, and to a lesser extent on the reproductive mechanisms through which individuals receive them.

Other genetic mechanisms—heterokaryosis, mitotic recombination, mutation and cytoplasmic variation—that have been demonstrated in parasitic fungi are reviewed by Fincham and Day (1963). An interesting phenomenon, termed "delayed segregation," has been reviewed by Fischer and Holton (1957). Delayed segregation refers to the frequently recorded observation that in *Ustilago* species successively produced sporidia, isolated from a single promycelial cell, can give rise to phenotypically different, presumably haploid, cultures. This phenomenon may be attributable to the diluting out, in successive divisions of the stem cell, of cytoplasmic determinants.

In the parasitic fungi, as in other groups considered earlier, it is not possible to assess the relative importance of any particular genetic mechanism in the microevolutionary process. However, if the foregoing interpretations are correct, adaptation in parasitic fungi will be greatly influenced by the extent to which their environment is controlled by genes within the host. For obligate parasites, whose environment is largely host determined, specific interactions based on gene-for-gene relationships are to be expected. The operation of gene-for-gene relationships, together with feedback mechanisms, should lead to unstable systems in which gene frequencies undergo cyclic fluctuations which tend to equilibrium values. At this point, if it is ever reached, coadaptation between the interacting partners will have been achieved. For facultative parasites, adaptation should present a mixture of characteristics shown by obligately parasitic fungi at the one extreme, and by saprobic fungi at the other. The relative position of facultative parasites in the range between the two extremes should be largely a measure of the extent to which their environment is under the control of genes in their respective hosts.

REFERENCES

Beadle, G. W., and V. L. Coonradt. (1944). Heterokaryons in *Neurospora crassa*. *Genetics* **29**: 291–308.

Brian, P. W. (1957). The ecological significance of antibiotic production. *Symp. Soc. Gen. Microbiol.* **7**: 168–188.

Caullery, M. (1952). "Parasitism and Symbiosis" (transl. by A. M. Lysaght), 340 pp. Sidgwick & Jackson, London.

Cherewick, W. J. (1958). Cereal smut races and their variability. *Can. J. Plant Sci.* **38**: 481–489.

Day, P. R. (1960). Variation in phytopathogenic fungi. *Ann. Rev. Microbiol.* **14**: 1–16.

Dobzhansky, T. (1951). "Genetics and the Origin of Species," 3rd ed., 364 pp. Columbia Univ. Press, New York.

Falconer, D. S. (1960). "Introduction to Quantitative Genetics," 365 pp. Oliver & Boyd, Edinburgh and London.

Fincham, J. R. S., and P. R. Day. (1963). "Fungal Genetics," 300 pp. Blackwell, Oxford.

Fischer, G. W., and C. S. Holton. (1957). "Biology and Control of the Smut Fungi," 622 pp. Ronald Press, New York.

Flor, H. H. (1956). The complementary genic systems in flax and flax rust. *Advan. Genet.* **8**: 29–54.

Griffiths, E. (1958). Sexual reproduction and variation in *Gloeotinia temulenta* (Prill. & Delacr.) Wilson & Gray. *Brit. Mycol. Soc. Trans.* **41**: 461–482.

Hawker, L. E. (1957). Ecological factors and the survival of fungi. *Symp. Soc. Gen. Microbiol.* **7**: 238–258.

Hooker, A. L., and W. A. Russell. (1962). Inheritance of resistance to *Puccinia sorghi* in six corn inbred lines. *Phytopathology* **52**: 122–128.

Jinks, J. L. (1952). Heterocaryosis in wild *Penicillium*. *Heredity* **6**: 77–87.

Jinks, J. L. (1957). Selection for cytoplasmic differences. *Proc. Roy. Soc.* **B146**: 527–540.

Jinks, J. L. (1958). Cytoplasmic differentiation in fungi. *Proc. Roy. Soc.* **B148**: 314–321.

Jinks, J. L. (1959). The genetic basis of "duality" in imperfect fungi. *Heredity* **13**: 525–527.

Johnson, T. (1953). Variation in the rusts of cereals. *Biol. Rev.* **28**: 105–157.

Johnson, T. (1961). Man-guided evolution in plant rusts. *Science* **133**: 357–362.

Loegering, W. Q. (1951). Survival of races of wheat and stem rust in mixtures. *Phytopathology* **41**: 56–65.
Luig, N. H., K. S. McWhirter, and E. P. Baker. (1958). Mode of inheritance of resistance to powdery mildew in barley and evidence for an allelic series conditioning reaction. *Proc. Linnean Soc. N. S. Wales* **83**: 340–362.
Mayr, E. (1963). "Animal Species and Evolution," 797 pp. Belknap Press of Harvard Univ. Press, Cambridge, Massachusetts.
Metzger, R. J., and E. J. Trione. (1962). Application of the gene-for-gene relationship hypothesis to the *Triticum–Tilletia* system. *Phytopathology* **52**: 363 (abstr.).
Mode, C. J. (1958). A mathematical model for the co-evolution of obligate parasites and their hosts. *Evolution* **12**: 158–165.
Moseman, J. G. (1959). Host-pathogen interaction of the genes for resistance in *Hordeum vulgare* and for pathogenicity in *Erysiphe graminis* f. sp. *hordei*. *Phytopathology* **49**: 469–472.
Oort, A. J. P. (1963). A gene-for-gene relationship in the *Triticum–Ustilago* system, and some remarks on host–pathogen combinations in general. *Neth. J. Plant Pathol.* **69**: 104–109.
Person, C. O. (1958). Development of concepts in rust genetics. *Proc. Genet. Soc. Can.* **3**: 25–29.
Person, C. O. (1959). Gene-for-gene relationships in host:parasite systems. *Can. J. Botany* **37**: 1101–1130.
Person, C. O. (1966). Genetic polymorphism in parasitic systems. *Nature* **212**: 266–267.
Person, C. O., D. J. Samborski, and R. Rohringer. (1962). The gene-for-gene concept. *Nature* **194**: 561–562.
Pimentel, D. (1961). Animal population regulation by the genetic feed-back mechanism. *Am. Naturalist* **95**: 65–79.
Pimentel, D., R. Al-Hafidh, E. H. Feinberg, J. L. Madden, W. P. Nagel, N. J. Parker, and F. A. Streams. (1961). Self-regulation in natural communities. *Cornell Plantations* **17**: 51–55.
Pontecorvo, G. (1958). "Trends in Genetic Analysis," 145 pp. Columbia Univ. Press, New York.
Powers, H. R., Jr., and W. J. Sando. (1960). Genetic control of the host-parasite relationship in wheat powdery mildew. *Phytopathology* **50**: 454–457.
Quispel, A. (1951). Some theoretical aspects of symbiosis. *Antonie van Leeuwenhoek, J. Microbiol. Serol.* **17**: 69–80.
Schaller, C. W., and F. N. Briggs. (1955). Inheritance of resistance to mildew, *Erysiphe graminis hordei,* in the barley variety Black Russian. *Genetics* **41**: 421–428.
Shepherd, K. W. (1963). Studies of the genetics of host-pathogen interactions, with flax and its rust. Ph.D. Thesis, University of Adelaide, Adelaide, Australia.
Sheppard, P. M. (1958). "Natural Selection and Heredity," 212 pp. Hutchinson, London.
Stakman, E. C., W. Q. Loegering, R. C. Cassell, and L. Hines. (1943). Population trends of physiologic races of *Puccinia graminis tritici* in the United States for the period 1930 to 1941. *Phytopathology* **33**: 884–898.
Stanier, R. Y. (1953). Adaptation, evolutionary and physiological; or Darwinism among the micro-organisms. *Symp. Soc. Gen. Microbiol.* **3**: 1–22.

Turner, E. M. C. (1961). An enzymic basis for pathogenic specificity in *Ophiobolus graminis*. *J. Exptl. Botany* **12:** 169–175.
Wheeler, H. E., and H. H. Luke. (1963). Microbial toxins in plant disease. *Ann. Rev. Microbiol.* **17:** 223–242.
Zadoks, J. C. (1961). Yellow rust on wheat; studies in epidemiology and physiologic specialization. *Tijdschr. Plantenziekten* **67:** 69–256.

Ecology

RESULTS OF ADJUSTMENT IN NATURE

CHAPTER 16

Effects of Adjustment to the Environment on Fungal Form

PETER K. C. AUSTWICK

Central Veterinary Laboratory
Ministry of Agriculture, Fisheries and Food
Weybridge, Surrey, England

I. INTRODUCTION

The influence of the different components of the environment on the growth and reproduction of fungi has been the theme of several chapters in the first two volumes of this treatise. In this chapter it is the turn of the individual fungal thallus, from unicell to colony, to be examined for its ability to adjust to changes in its environment which occur during development. This adjustment is of great importance, for behind it operate environmental pressures in geological time, shaping the evolution of the organism and fitting it into its habitat, sometimes giving such apparently perfect examples of adaption as the insect-inhabiting Laboulbeniales. Corner (1964) has looked back briefly on fungal evolution and suggested the derivation of the agaric from the clavarioid fruit body as a protection for the developing basidiospores from the disaster of rain: then, when this risk is diminished in a dry region, the agaric form, e.g., *Galerina,* might possibly have lost its exposed gills and become a stalked puffball, such as *Galeropsis desertorum,* more closely related to agaric ancestors than to the gasteromycetes proper (Kotlaba and Pouzar, 1959).

Paradoxically, although it is the environmental influence over a long period which fosters genetic change, it is genetic constitution which governs the potentiality of an individual fungus to respond to immediate environmental change. Despite an unparalleled capacity for polymorphism, the range of this response in any fungal species is still limited, and it is these limitations which keep the individual physically in its place in nature.

Cytoplasmic changes may also occur under environmental influence and be inherited during cell division (Jinks, 1966), sometimes profoundly altering the appearance of the fungus such as in the sectoring of cultures, but the morphological effects considered here are never passed on. They are perhaps the Lamarckian echoes which have resounded loudly in taxonomic mycology since descriptions of higher fungi were drawn up, for many specific, and even some generic, characters based on color, texture, size, and shape, and in use since before the time of Elias Fries, are phenotypic and demonstrably mutable by such agencies as wind, rain, frost, and the nature of the substrate.

In the introductory sections I have first discussed the role of the environment in stimulating deviation of fungal development from that giving the ideal type of growth, i.e., the ultimate "normal" form as it exists in nature. Then the limitations imposed on response are mentioned, and finally the sites at which adjustment takes place are considered. Under the last heading it was found convenient to classify the different types of adjustment according to the place at which they occurred, so that the three subsequent sections are linked through the common factor of their nutrient substrates.

A. Role of the Environment

In mediating a morphological change in a fungus, the environment can play two roles; a passive one in which the changes that occur are by the influence of the fungus on its own surroundings, e.g., by the production of staling substances in culture; and an active one in which the physical, chemical, and biotic changes in the environment impose their effect independently of the fungus itself. In addition, because filamentous fungi almost always grow centrifugally, there are occasions when the hyphae grow out from a virtually static environment, in which few changes other than those of temperature and humidity associated with diurnal and seasonal fluctuations occur, into one which is dynamic, e.g., moving air or water, in which there are constant and rapid changes. The fungus must adjust to each change accordingly until the nature of the change exceeds the limits to which it can respond.

This rate of change of the environment plays a major role in adjustment. The slow, inexorable seasonal changes are closely bound with fungal life cycles and hence are almost parts of the taxa. Diurnal change is perhaps too short a cycle for this type of involvement, but it elicits a characteristic response in the form of the zonation of cultures and fruiting bodies. Multiple sequential changes in the type of reaction surrounding fungal cells invading animal tissues are again countered by a regular morphological response, e.g., a change from the filamentous to the yeast phase of growth. Similarly changes in living plant tissue may also be followed by changes in the morphology of the invading fungal elements. Sudden variations in the environment may have a dramatic effect on morphology, such as the killing of the surface layers of polypore fruit bodies by frost or desiccation, followed by rapid regeneration of the original form. Changes in orientation of the substrate, such as when a tree falls, are equally important in the stimulation of geotropic response, sometimes involving complete hyphal rearrangement.

B. Limits of Adjustment

The limits set on the morphological development of a fungus by its genetic constitution are basically the means by which taxa are distinguished from each other and are really the result of natural selection, i.e., environmental pressures on an evolutionary time scale. Thus despite "optimum" conditions for growth and a potential plasticity of form unsurpassed in other living organisms, no fungus can overstep the limitations imposed by the capacity of its genetic material to instruct the cellular components to synthesize protoplasm in a specific manner. Thus, outside the environment of the fungus, lie conditions which are inimical to the growth of the individual species.

This genetical influence is seen most clearly by comparing the growth of different fungi under "optimum" conditions (conditions allowing the fastest and most typical growth). Given unlimited nutrients and no impediment to growth, then fungi fall into two categories: viz. those in which vegetative reproduction will continue indefinitely, e.g., most filamentous fungi and yeasts; and those in which the thallus on reaching a given size, cannot continue activity without reproducing, e.g., the Chytridiales and Blastocladiales. These latter fungi of limited growth, which are invariably water molds, are of interest in that the chief morphogenetic influence arises from a conditioning of the environment (actually the substrate) by the growth of the fungus itself (see Cantino, 1966).

In those fungi of unlimited growth potential from a single thallus, continuous activity in budding and hyphal elongation is rarely achieved for any length of time because environmental effects almost always intervene to stimulate a morphological or reproductive change. Freedom of growth in all directions theoretically would allow a spherical colony to form, as in a shaken culture, but in nature it is only perhaps in the soil or in heartwood of large trees that fungi find conditions favorable enough to remain in the active vegetative state for many years. A limitation imposed, even in one of these immense habitats, is the size of the substrate, for many lignicolous basidiomycetes seem to require a certain volume of mycelial development before fruit-body initials will form. If the substrate is not large enough, then either fruiting fails or the fruit bodies are small. When nutrition is restricted, then the effectiveness of other environmental influences may be correspondingly diminished, partly because the time available for their effect to be felt is reduced by a rapid depletion of the substrate. Physical factors also introduce limitations on fungal growth, such as its cessation or reduction by a sudden fall in temperature, especially one accompanied by frost. An impenetrable mechanical barrier may equally impose restriction of growth and yet induce morphological changes or stimulate reproduction, and growth limitation by restriction of oxygen supply is well enough known. Within such limits the influence of other environmental factors on the normal course of development may be to effect a complete change in morphology.

C. *Sites of Adjustment*

Surprisingly little is known about the sites of action of environmental factors, but external morphological changes must necessarily be preceded by micromorphological ones. Changes in hyphal shape in turn must be preceded by the even less-studied submicronic changes in cell wall structure which themselves depend on the molecular rearrangements of metabolic processes. This sequence of events has already been discussed from many viewpoints in preceding chapters of this treatise (Volume I, Chapters 3 and 26; Volume II, Chapters 7–12), but the place at which the initial effect takes place still remains obscure. Recent work on the responses of hyphal tips to changes in the medium by Robertson (1965) has done much to elucidate this problem, and in the fungi pathogenic to animals the experimental control of morphology *in vitro* has already been of great help in the study of the pathogenesis of mycoses. It is the nature of the environmental changes at these sites which holds the clue to the morphological adjustment.

A problem arises here in assessing the importance of the site of change to the "individual fungus," because it is almost impossible to define such a term except in the simple forms such as the Chytridiales. An "individual fungus" can be a single yeast cell or the expanding "fairy ring" of a basidiomycete, including its fruiting bodies. Environmental effect on a large filamentous colony is really a matter of multiplying that effect on an individual hyphal tip many thousands of times. Moreover fungal organs may have similar functions but very different origins and structures, so that it is hardly right to compare environmental effects on the rhizoidal development of a chytrid with that on *Phallus impudicus*. The influence of the weather on the development of the basidiomycete fruit body is also relevant here, but because the concept of anatomical structure of these organs only began to be understood with the work of Corner (1932, 1950) little progress has been made in the study of the induced variations mentioned earlier. The developing fungal fruiting body is a delicate structure, generally tuned to stable surroundings, and whenever the rate or degree of environmental change reaches a level which upsets this stability, then adjustment must begin. Microscopically the response will be seen to range from a swelling or a narrowing of the hyphal tip to hyphal collapse and subsequent death, with all manner of behavior in between, including changes in the direction of growth, in the thickness of the wall, and even of the functional type of the hypha.

The site of the morphological change on the fungal thallus is important, but the site of the change in relation to the substrate must also be considered. It seems probable that it is at the interface of the substrate with the medium which circulates about it, i.e., at the surface of a solid exposed to air or water, that the most important morphogenic influences of the environment are initiated, a principle which must apply on both a micro- and a macroscale. The surface of a decaying leaf in water is as important to the conidiophore of the water mold *Tetracladium marchalianum* as is the upper layer of the leaf litter to a *Marasmius dryophilus* fruit body, and a surface exposed to the air is a vital but often unappreciated necessity for hyphomycetal sporulation. There is little fungal nutrient in air and not much in clean water, so that the shock of emergence from a medium affording both an abundance of food and protection is one which needs a rapid and fundamental adjustment in order that sporulation, fruit-body formation, and exploratory vegetative growth can continue or be initiated with the minimum of disturbance. The change from the trophic to the reproductive function brings with it diverse problems from the forward conduction of nutrients to the emerging hyphae, to their protection from desiccation, light, and predators until the reproductive phase is successfully completed. Growth of filamentous fungi within the substrate may be equally influenced if there are physical or chemical barriers to growth, e.g., in the form of other fungal colonies or, in the fungi which invade the living tissues of plants and animals, the presence of an active or a passive host resistance. Changes also occur in the passage of a hypha from a nutrient to a nonnutrient substrate of a similar consistency.

In seeking a suitable basis on which to examine the relationship of environment and form, the use of many promising criteria has been ruled out by lack of adequate information, especially of observations on the fungi in their natural habitats. Thus classification on the type of morphological response, i.e., the production of hyphal swellings, sclerotia, color change, and the direction and speed of growth, gave a confusing range of variations which seemed to be ontogenically unrelated in different species. Restriction to changes in shape was equally unrewarding, and so more attention has been paid to the environment itself. The one common feature in all these selected examples of adjustment to environment is that the fungus requires a nutrient substrate on which to grow, so that by considering the effect of the environment on the fungus within the substrate, on its surface and above its surface, it is possible to position all morphological changes even though this sometimes has resulted in one species appearing in more than one category.

II. ADJUSTMENT WITHIN THE SUBSTRATE

The substrate from which the fungus derives its nutrients is probably the most important part of the fungal environment, but because the growth within it is vegetative, then it might appear that any adjustments need be only minimal. This is not so, and the extremes of vegetative form shown by several of the fungi pathogenic for animals are examples of adjustment to what must be one of the most antagonistic environments known. Within the substrate the influences of temperature and humidity are generally of less morphogenic importance than they are outside, and correspondingly the other factors assume a greater role in determining fungal form. These factors, operating at a cellular level, influence the behavior of the hyphal tip or the rate of division of the yeast cell, and may also exert an overall effect on the mycelium, which, as in many basidiomycetes, may need to maintain its growth and reach a certain volume before fruit-body formation can begin.

The influence of the environment can perhaps best be judged by comparing the growth made under the most favorable conditions of pure culture with that found in the natural substrate, bearing in mind that in nature the fungus may occasionally grow faster than in culture and that this may be the wrong basis for comparison. For the moment it is necessary to regard optimum growth of a filamentous fungus as producing a spherical colony in which hyphae extend unimpeded in all directions. The external pressures responsible for any change in this situation are many, and among them the physical nature of the substrate will impose several conditions depending on its degree of heterogeneity. Liquids and solids, such as agar, offer little restriction to growth while dead plant material and soil present a series of different microhabitats, some favorable, others not. Living tissues vary greatly in their physical nature and chemical composition and introduce the factor of an active resistance to the growth of the fungus, which will vary in degree according to the site of attack. Resistance is a form of competition comparable with that from other microorganisms, which in a given substrate determine which fungi can grow, and subsequently which morphological and biochemical adjustments are necessary to enable growth to continue. The substrate thus ranges from a sterile medium to a living tissue, in neither of which are there other microorganisms present, to one harboring a vast population of bacteria, microanimals, plants, and other fungi, e.g., soil and dung.

A. Homogeneous Substrates

The physically simplest substrates of fungi are the liquids and solids used for pure culture studies. They present little resistance to growth, but colonies within agar or in shake cultures can show morphological changes. Burkholder and Sinnott (1945) considered that the macroscopical variation in colonial form of submerged and shaken cultures was attributable to mechanical contact of the colonies with the sides of the culture vessel and with other colonies and also to the lack of other orienting influences, such as gravity and chemical gradients. At the microscopical level Duckworth and Harris (1949), however, found the influence of the fungus on the medium itself to be the most important factor. They described morphological changes in the hyphae of *Penicillium chrysogenum* during growth in shaken cultures, and suggested that these were related to depletion of oxygen in the medium during the succession of growth cycles which was detected. Normally a progressive narrowing of the hyphae occurs over the first 48 hours of a fermentation, followed by their subsequent death. Resumption of growth occurs from wide, spherical hyphal cells originally derived from late germinating spores in the inoculum. Another effect of the fungus on its substrate is in the production of a "staling substance," which Park (1961) studied in *Fusarium oxysporum*. This labile substance accumulates as growth proceeds, and its presence leads to a progressive narrowing of the hyphae, cessation of growth, chlamydospore formation and eventually to lysis of the cells. Renewal of growth occurred after the concentration of the labile substance had decreased following the earlier cessation of growth.

Naturally occurring pure cultures are rare, except of course when a living body forms the substrate, but one notable example is the growth of fungi, especially *Aspergillus fumigatus,* in the amniotic fluid of the fetus in a proportion of cases of bovine mycotic abortion (Austwick and Venn, 1957). The fluid is a complex, protein-containing, oxygenated medium enclosed in a vessel which is constantly in motion so that the hyphal growth comes closely to resemble that in an *in vitro* shaken culture, consisting of small colonies of narrow hyphae with no signs of the morphological changes which mark the same fungi when they are growing in living tissue.

Substrates such as wood, which act as though they were homogeneous to the mycelium of an invading fungus, allow a generous freedom of hyphal growth, but their cellular nature makes them heterogeneous at the hyphal level. Wood-rotting fungi differ widely in their nutritional requirements and decompose their substrates by different enzyme systems (Cartwright and Findlay, 1958). In a fallen log, growth generally proceeds through the wood in all directions, and large sections can sometimes be seen to have the same type of rot, indicating the probability of invasion by one organism. In some logs, especially those of beech (*Fagus sylvaticus*) and elm (*Ulmus* spp.), clearly delimited black zones appear in the decaying wood, and on inspection these are found to consist of areas where the vessels are blocked by swollen and colored fungal cells surrounded by a black pigment which diffuses out into the surrounding wood. According to Campbell (1933a,b) and Campbell and Munson (1936), these zones probably represent the margins of individual mycelia in the wood and are formed when two colonies meet. The zones are really plates of sclerotized fungal cells and were studied in *Polyporus squamosus, Xylaria polymorpha,* and *Armillaria mellea,* and in each case the structure was similar. Initially hyaline hyphae aggregate, begin to swell, and become closely septate, filling all the spaces within and around the host xylem cells, and then produce a dark pigment which diffuses out after the collapse of the hyphae and permeates the surrounding wood. This black plate is virtually impermeable and persists long after the original wood has decayed. Campbell showed that identical zones also could be produced by placing wood blocks on agar cultures and subjecting them to slow desiccation, when the marginal hyphae went through the same changes to produce a zone beneath the surface. Investigation of rotting logs showed that the individual mycelia were mostly lens-shaped in the wood, arranged about an apparent point of entry in the bark, and the whole structure was termed a "pseudosclerotium" consisting of host tissue permeated by hyphae and compared in function with that of a true sclerotium, a reserve of nutrients required for fruit-body formation when external conditions are suitable. A comparable pseudosclerotium of limited size is formed by *Macrophomina phaseoli,* the cause of black nut disease of groundnuts (peanuts) (*Arachis hypogaea*), in which the cotyledons are invaded and a black sclerotic rind is formed beneath the testa.

B. *Heterogeneous Substrates*

1. Soil

The soil constitutes one of the most complex of microbial habitats and one in which many fungi complete their entire life cycle (see Burges, 1958). Growing hyphae are subjected to all manner of chemical and physical antagonism from actinomycetes, bacteria, animals, and other fungi, but some, notably those of basidiomycetes, seem little affected and produce immense colonies. Few examples of adjustment to conditions *in terram* are known, for few direct studies of soil fungi have ever been made. It is generally assumed that the structures observed in cultures of soil fungi, e.g., chlamydospores, gemmae, and sclerotia, are all at times produced in soil under the requisite conditions. Sclerotia are perhaps the triumph over adversity of the soil-inhabiting larger fungi, for they act as collecting foci for nutrients obtained by far-reaching hyphae and allow a protected period of grace before the fungus gathers the momentum to form a fruiting body. Unoriented toward surface or by gravity, they are also resistant to desiccation and microbial attack. Warcup and Talbot (1962) found that six of the twenty species of basidiomycetes they isolated and identified from wheat-field soil occurred as sclerotia in the soil and that four of these were agarics, in which the fruiting conditions are much more critical than in the resupinate species found. As yet we know little of the stimuli initiating sclerotium formation in the soil (Townsend, 1957; Sörgel, 1967), but the study by Townsend and Willetts (1954) shows clearly that there are several different developmental patterns. In those higher fungi which complete their life cycle entirely beneath the surface of the soil, the hypogeous species, the only morphological change noted seems to be the lobing distortion mentioned by Hawker (1954) in fruit bodies formed against an obstruction such as a root or stone. She also observed that the formation of fruit bodies occurred against the hard pan of subsoil or the edge of a woodland path, which perhaps represent the phase changes outlined in the next section.

2. *Living Tissue*

The internal tissues of plants and animals provide substrates in which relatively few fungi can grow. Those that can, must first be able to penetrate to the tissue and, secondly, survive attempts at suppression and exclusion by the host's reaction. There is little difference in the result whether penetration is directly by hyphal growth or passively by phagocytosis; in both cases the host cell generally resists by all the metabolic means at its disposal, until it overcomes the invading fungus or dies in the attempt. In these activities it exerts a profound influence on the morphology of the fungus within its cytoplasm, and this effect becomes graded according to the fungal species and its destructive ability.

a. Plants. The simplest fungal thalli to invade cells are those of the holocarpic chytridiaceous fungi, e.g., *Olpidium,* in which the germ tube from the motile zoospore penetrates the host cell wall and enlarges steadily to form the sporangium. There is little room for morphological effects of environmental pressures on such a thallus, but any departure from the spherical shape of the sporangium might be taken to indicate that formative influences may be operating in the death throes of the cell, especially in

Petersenia, in which the degree of lobing of the sporangium may well be influenced by the cell content of its host (Sparrow, 1960).

Penetration into the interior of higher plant cells is a characteristic of many plant pathogenic fungi and those forming endophytic mycorrhizas. In both processes, one often lethal and the other essentially symbiotic, the tip of the penetrating hypha may remain small and peglike, or swell to form a vesicle, branch in a variety of ways, or develop the "arbuscular" finely divided type of branching seen in certain root cells. The factors governing the size and shape of these structures within plant cells are not well known, but according to Fraymouth (1956) the availability of food supply may be important in the Peronosporales. She observed that although the haustoria in leaf cells were often simple and few in number, those in the pith or cortex of the host stem had filamentous lobes. In no case did the haustoria penetrate the cytoplasmic membrane but only indented it, so that the haustorium was never within the host cytoplasm itself, a fact which may have some bearing on the production of the dimorphic forms in animal pathogens with their more intimate contact with the contents of the host cell. Haustoria are also produced by other plant pathogens, especially the rusts, smuts, and powdery mildews, accompanied in many instances by widespread intercellular mycelium which rarely shows any special adjustment to the environment except in following the cellular structure of the tissue (see Butler and Jones, 1949). Whether the intracellular structures of the mycorrhizal species (now frequently shown to be species of *Pythium* and *Endogone*) are also extracytoplasmic is not known, but in each case it seems that the form of the haustorium is governed more by genetic than by environmental factors. This is despite the fact that extracts of roots and bulbs of mycorrhizal plants inhibit the fungi isolated from their cells (Hawker *et al.,* 1957).

b. Animals. Comparison of the pathogenesis of the fungal diseases of plants with those of animals is inevitable, for the principles of pathogenicity are the same. The plant is essentially a static structure with resistance mechanisms of several different types ranging from the production of a mechanical barrier such as cork, to the formation of diffusible substances which inhibit or kill the invading fungus. The metazoan animal poses a dynamic cellular organization in which foreign bodies are set upon and disposed of by the action of phagocytes and other tissue cells. Ingestion by a phagocyte is in fact a prerequisite for pathogenesis in many systemically invasive fungi. Its effect on the spore or yeast cell is to provide a microhabitat which necessitates the rapid growth or "conversion" into the *in vivo* or "dimorphic" form. The conditions which lead to this change of form have been delimited for the majority of species pathogenic to animals, and most have now been grown *in vitro* in their intracellular form. Reduced oxygen tension, increased temperature, and decreased carbohydrates are among the many factors that have been found to be responsible separately or together for these changes, which are constant for a given species. The phenomenon of dimorphism is fully described by Romano (1966), who discusses the important part played by investigations of the pathogens of animals in determining the biochemical basis of the yeast ⇌ mycelium transformations. These adjustments to the environment take on more significance when it is realized that fungi are really only incidentally pathogenic to animals, for all but a few species have been shown to have a separate existence in soil or on vegetation (Ainsworth, 1952).

Whether entry into the living animal body is by ingestion or inhalation, phagocytosis probably occurs at an early stage, so that the propagule soon becomes subjected to all the available intracellular enzyme systems aimed at its destruction and disposal. Within the tissues it may also become the target of the action of specific antibodies. The fungus adjusts by what appears to be characteristic of successful parasitism, i.e., by the rounding off of its cells to form a yeast or a spherical or swollen hyphal form as the first step in proliferation within the ingesting cell and subsequently in the tissue (see Mariat, 1964).

(1) *Unicellular phases.* The intracellular yeast-phase cells of *Histoplasma capsulatum* are generally 1–3 by 1–2 μ and continue to bud until the host cell membrane is so distended that it ruptures, freeing the cells into the surrounding tissue fluid, whence they are ingested by other phagocytes. Of the other fungi which occur as intracellular yeast cells, *Cryptococcus neoformans* shows a very distinctive feature in living tissues by the production of a wide, mucopolysaccharide capsule which is greatly reduced in pure culture. The factors responsible for this characteristic feature are not known, for it occurs both in the presence of little reaction, such as in the nervous system, and where there is a marked infiltration of tissues, as in the lung.

Rapid adjustment to the intracellular habitat also takes place in *Coccidioides immitis* when the inhaled arthrospore is phagocytized and itself turns into a spherule directly and then undergoes endosporulation. Succeeding generations of spherules may appear extracellularly, and on very rare occasions, in old lung lesions, hyphae and arthrospores may be produced (at an aerial surface). Spherule formation with endosporulation is also a feature of *Rhinosporidium seeberi,* which occupies an enigmatic position among pathogenic fungi in never having been cultured. However, no endosporulation has been found in *Emmonsia* spp., in which the inhaled aleuriospores simply increase in size almost a thousand times, reaching 900 μ in diameter and having a wall up to 50 μ thick. This is simply an adjustment to temperature, for aleuriospores placed on a nutrient agar at 37°C swell similarly whereas those placed at 25°C germinate in the normal way to produce hyphae. Yet another growth form of adaptation has been seen in the pathogenic *Penicillium marneffei* when the phagocytized conidium produces cuboidal arthrospores, which may be yet another economical shape.

(2) *Filamentous phases*. Whereas the formation of a distinct vegetative spore is a feature of certain pathogenic fungi, the pathogenic phycomycetes and aspergilli show fewer changes when invading living tissue, retaining their hyphal form even though it may show marked adjustment to the environment. One of the simplest adjustments in animal tissue has been described by Götz (1960), who found hyphae of *Trichophyton rubrum* in the 600 μ-thick stratum corneum of the sole of the foot to be approximately half the diameter of those in the 30 μ-thick stratum corneum of the inguinal region. In *Aspergillus fumigatus* the spores swell considerably on inhalation and phagocytosis (which may occur within 1 hour), and then form short, wide hyphal branches (5–10 μ wide) which eventually give rise to more typical hyphae (3–5 μ wide). These then branch in a characteristic fashion to form the "actinomycetoid" branches found in chronic aspergillotic lesions. This change in shape may be related to the changing pattern of the tissue reaction during the course of the infection (Austwick, 1965), and requires further investigation to discover, for instance, the part played by antibodies in determining form. It has been particularly noted that in animals in the terminal stages of the disease, the hyphae suddenly become typical of the vegetative type seen in culture, possibly indicating that the resistance of the tissue has been finally overcome.

The early stages of natural phycomycetic infections have not been studied, but it is likely that swelling of the spores may also occur, and between this stage and the development of the wide, branching aseptate hyphae there are intermediates corresponding to those seen in aspergillosis. One feature of phycomycetic granulomata is the complexity of their structure and the occurrence of frequent swellings and irregular internal wall thickenings ("pegs") in the hyphae. Some hyphae may reach 100 μ in diameter, when they appear to die and become invaded by narrower hyphae of the same organism. From this it may be deduced that the original hyphae adjusted to the antagonistic environment by swelling, whereas secondary hyphae, although growing in precisely the same place, were protected and hence grew normally. Occasional cross walls may develop in mucoraceous hyphae *in vivo,* which cut off dead sections of the hyphae and, in one gastric ulcer in a pig, chlamydospores of *Rhizopus microsporus* (Gitter and Austwick, 1959) were seen. Restriction of fungal growth by the body reaction seems to reach its ultimate development in the formation of a lobed eosinophilic sheath around the invading cells. The nature of the sheath has been investigated for *Actinomyces bovis* and found to be chiefly polysaccharide, originating from the activity of both host and pathogen (Pine and Overman, 1963). In some mycoses, such as sporotrichosis (caused by *Sporothrix schenckii*), not all the cells are encapsulated. In *A. fumigatus* the "asteroids," as they are called, occur regularly in the lungs of healthy dairy cows, and consist of the swollen celled hyphae arising from inhaled spores surrounded by a firm capsule covered by fingerlike projections. There is evidence that this sheath is instrumental in containing the fungus which eventually dies and disintegrates.

(3) *Madurella mycetoma.* Perhaps the most striking effect of the animal body on an invading monomorphic, filamentous fungus is seen in the disease known as *Madurella* mycetoma, maduromycosis, or Madura foot. All the 8 fungi and the 5 actinomycetes known to cause this disfiguring and progressive disease of the soft tissues of the limbs form small granular colonies, often with pronounced eosinophilic hyphal sheaths, which lie in the mass of infiltrating leukocytes forming the characteristic pus. This microhabitat differs greatly from that in which *Aspergillus fumigatus* becomes established in the lungs after inhalation, or the intracellular one of the dimorphic pathogens, principally by virtue of its mobility, for it is really a semiliquid culture medium in which the nutrients can be obtained only against an active resistance. The factors contributing to this antagonism perhaps range from phagocytosis and antibody reaction to nutritional deficiency and, in combination, induce the very characteristic growth form which has yet to be reproduced *in vitro*. The development of these colonies has therefore never been followed closely. Initial infection has been shown in the two cases described by Basset *et al.* (1965) to arise from the introduction into the subcutaneous tissues of a propagule of the ascomycete *Leptosphaeria senegalensis* borne on a plant thorn. The nature of this propagule was not known, but it provided a focus from which growth occurred in a centrifugal fashion. It seems possible that later environmental pressures cause the colony to become lobed and therefore more likely to fragment in the mobile substrate, and this fragmentation is probably the key to the spread of the fungus within the tissues. The color and structure of the "grains" varies according to the species of fungus concerned, although environmental factors probably play an important part in determining the "grain" morphology and hyphal form. Thus *Madurella mycetomi* forms black grains up to 5 mm in diameter which have filamentous hyphae within but a peripheral layer of swollen cells up to 30 μ across. *Allescheria boydii* has whitish grains, up to 2 mm in diameter, composed of closely bound hyphae which produce swellings at the surface (Mackinnon, 1954; Langeron, 1945). It is difficult to ascertain from the literature the relationship of age to the structure of the individual

grains, and it is not known whether the swelling and the sclerotization of the outside hyphae represent cessation of their growth or simply a stage in which growth is reduced, followed by one in which growth is resumed later after fragmentation. An analogous situation is sometimes seen in *Aspergillus fumigatus* colonies in animal lungs when a zone of swollen cells, similar to those found in the initial infection, is followed by a resumption of the actinomycetoid branching characteristically seen in the chronic progressing lesion.

III. ADJUSTMENT AT THE SUBSTRATE SURFACE

The growth of the fungus within its substrate was earlier described as the most important part of the life history of the organism, enabling it to build up its thallus for subsequent reproduction and survival. The morphological modifications dictated by this environment have therefore been related to the nature of the substrate and its mechanical and biological resistance to the growth of the fungus within it. The changes observed within the substrate must now be viewed as the background to the adjustments which take place when the fungus emerges onto the surface. Some of the same environmental pressures may still apply in modified form, for example, reduced competition, but supplementary ones appear, increasing the rate of change of the environment and operating on a much larger scale than previously experienced. Thus the movement of air and water, rapid fluctuations in temperature, and even the browsing of animals have to be taken into account, most factors increasing in their effect with increasing distance of the fungal structure from its source of nutrient.

The surface of its substrate often presents the vegetative stage of a growing fungus with its first major change of environment and immediate adjustment is generally necessary. This normally takes the form of the development of the reproductive phase under the stimulation of the many external factors discussed by Hawker (1966), but before this phase proceeds several morphological changes may occur which have been attributed to the loss both of the physical support of the substrate and of the protection from desiccation it offers. Morton (1961) has upset such simple deductions by his investigation of the factors influencing the sporulation of *Penicillium griseofulvum* and *P. chrysogenum*. He found that the emerging hypha is little affected by low humidity of the air at the substrate surface, but that it nevertheless undergoes a sharp physiological change within a few seconds of emergence. The mechanism of this change is as yet unknown but may prove fundamental to the morphogenesis of the hypha. Morton's suggestion that surface-active substances may play a role in these changes urgently needs examination.

The consequence of hyphal emergence, whether from the substrate or the spore, will depend on whether this is into a medium of liquid or gaseous phase. In a previous chapter Cantino (1966) summarized the extensive knowledge of morphogenesis in aquatic phycomycetes and discussed the significance of the various environmental factors facing a fungal structure emerging into a liquid. There is a similar field of investigation awaiting those interested in aquatic fungi imperfecti, especially in species of *Helicodendron* and related genera in which aerial spores are produced by hyphae originating in a submerged substrate (Glenn-Bott, 1955). Assuming, too, that emergence ultimately leads to fructification, situations can be cited ranging from the direct formation of a single spore on the tip of the emerging hypha to the development of a complex fruiting body at a point distant from that of emergence. Between these, many different types of structure directly related to the substrate surface may be formed, some for survival through adverse conditions, e.g., sclerotia, some to support conidiophores, and others to ensure the continued attachment of the fungus to the surface.

In order to classify these adjustments the substrate surface has been interpreted as a band on either side of the actual interface, with the changes observed grouped in positions below, within, or on the surface.

A. *Beneath the Substrate Surface*

Fairy Rings

The growth of a fungal mycelium within the soil is undoubtedly influenced by its relationship with the surface. In the terricolous agarics and other surface-fruiting fungi, this influence is the more pronounced and the whole life of the organism depends on the relationship of its thallus with the ground surface above. The classical example of the agaric mycelium is the circular form revealed as the grassland "fairy ring" which might perhaps be regarded as a culture in unsterilized soil. Superficial growth is generally minimal, possibly because of the drying-out on the surface, and no great penetration of the soil beneath takes place. During their well-known studies of fairy rings Schantz and Piemeisel (1917) never found mycelium nearer than 8 cm from the surface in most species and similarly found little penetration below the humus layer, possibly owing to the lack of nutrients or to the poor aeration. Behind the advancing edge of the ring perhaps a staling substance contributes to the destruction of the mycelium, which on decomposition may be responsible for the stimulation of growth of the grass in the region. The mycelium of the fairy ring is thus shaped above and below by the available nutrients and moisture in the environment, but within certain limits these factors seem to have little effect on the centrifugal growth, which is interrupted only when physical obstructions, e.g., stones, or other fairy rings, are encountered. The shape the mycelium assumes is thus probably that of a thick-rimmed plate which soon disintegrates in the center but continues to extend its periphery into a ringlike colony sometimes reaching immense size (up to 200 meters across) and great calculated age (up to 600 years).

B. *Within the Surface Layers*

1. *Frondose Hyphae*

Hyphae emerging from the substrate may well give rise to the extensive type of radiating colony seen on the surface of solid culture media. Similarly germination of a spore on a surface or the arrival of a hypha on it from elsewhere may produce unspecialized radial growth in one plane. If, however, restrictions to the spread of the hyphae are present, a characteristic growth form often develops. This is the frondose hypha or palmette, named from its resemblance to the palmelloid growth type in algae. Hyphae of this type have been figured in *Fusicladium* on apple leaves by Ducomet (1907, see Langeron, 1945) and recently by English (1963, 1965) in her excellent accounts of the invasion of keratinaceous substrates (hair and nail) by both keratinophilic and nonkeratinophilic fungi. In the latter the frondose hypha develops from a hyphal branch which penetrates beneath the cuticle of the hair and grows on in the horizontal, arrow-shaped space it creates by its own growth, but is completely restricted above and below. The hyphal cells are irregularly shaped with deep convolutions and frequent cross walls, but are still orientated in a particular direction generally away from the point of penetration. The hyphal fronds tend to elongate distally, but it is not clear whether the individual cells continue to increase in size and branch or whether growth is, as in normal hyphae, purely apical but from the lobes of each cell. Recent work on the colonization of cellulose film buried in soil also indicates that invasion takes place between the fibrillar layers of the film, thus creating a space which the fungus progressively fills with frondose mycelium (Tribe, 1957).

Similar frondose hyphae are found in leaf-inhabiting fungi belonging to the Microthyriaceae and related forms. Despite illustrations depicting surface development, it seems that much of the characteristic asterinoid growth of these fungi takes place between the epidermal cells and the lifted leaf cuticle, which sloughs off before the fructification is fully developed. In *Stigmatea robertianum* the mycelium is apparently entirely subcuticular and other "Asterineae" form various types of frondose hyphae with haustorial connections into the cells of the leaf, or hyphal masses in the intercellular spaces.

The roles of the different environmental factors involved in the production of frondose hyphae, and the related asterinoid thalli are still not clear. Arnaud's explanation that the high humidity in the regions in which the leaf-inhabiting fungi are commonly found enables them to have the epiphyllous habit, as in many bryophytes, and Langeron's opinion (1945) that their growth type is essentially xeromorphic, require reinvestigation at a microlevel, taking into account the special relations of the fungus to the host tissue and the physical nature of the habitat. Fischman's observation (1965) that the asterinoid hair-inhabiting ascomycete *Piedria hortai* only occurs frequently in the Amazonian region, where there is a fairly constant temperature of 26°C and a relative humidity rarely below 85%, seem to indicate a special requirement of this type.

2. *Subperidermal Hyphae*

On a macroscale the formation of a mycelium in a space restricted above and below may on the contrary produce a very rapidly growing colony identical to that on the surface of an agar plate. Such circumstances arise when a wood-rotting fungus emerges from the woody tissue of a log at one point and grows away radially between the wood and the inner surface of the bark. If such a space is wide then conditions are generally extremely favorable to vegetative growth, so that few morphological changes ensue. In some species this space may become filled with densely packed hyphae forming a subperidermal subiculum. These hyphal masses certainly vary in size and shape according to the substrate, but their form and structure have never been studied. They seem to provide a collecting base for nutrients later to be used for the production of fruit bodies.

C. *On the Substrate Surface*

1. *Zonation at the Surface*

The formation of differently colored or textured zones in agar cultures is one of the common visual effects of environmental factors on the growth of fungi. The relationship of illumination to these zones has already received attention in these volumes by Jerebzoff (1965) and Hawker (1966), and although response to light stimuli is chiefly concerned in initiating, enhancing, or depressing spore production, the formation of the concentric rings is not always due to reproductive changes. This chapter is, however, concerned with adjustments in vegetative morphology, and some of these are associated with zones in culture, others as discussed later, with those in fruit bodies.

Stephens and Hall (1909) observed zonation in cultures of *Ascochyta* which consisted of alternating aggregations and segregations of hyphae; the authors suggested that the zonation could be explained either by the depletion of nutrients because of dense hyphal growth or by the production of an inhibiting substance, both being followed by colonization of the next zone of medium by relatively few hyphae. Whether the work of Park (1961) on *Fusarium oxysporum* provides sufficient evidence to support the latter suggestion has not yet been determined, but in this species it seems that gradual recovery of growth occurs on removal of the staling substance. Endogenous rhythmic zonation of this type cannot be the result of direct environmental influence, actuated through external physical factors, and closer observations of the morphology of hyphae in the zones might reveal differences such as those between the juvenile and mature hyphae which Park describes in zones of centrifugal and meandering hyphal orientation. The formation of vegetative structures such as sclerotia also seems to be influenced by the same factors that affect conidiophore production, e.g., in *Aspergillus* spp.

2. *Attaching Organs*

As well as the closely packed frondose hyphae, many leaf fungi also develop a loose, truly superficial mycelium which adheres to the epidermis by means of special cells known as hyphopodia (Hansford, 1946). These are apparently produced following a thigmatropic stimulus and are generally unicellular, variously shaped, and often cover the site of a subsequent penetration of the leaf cuticle by a fine penetrating organ. The rhizoidal systems of those mucoraceous fungi which attack the hyphae of other Mucorales function in the same way, and the multicellular appressoria of certain plant parasites (e.g., *Sclerotinia*) also function this way and ensure against the separation of the host and parasite at the crucial stage of penetration. Of a slightly different function, although morphologically comparable, are the adhesive and labyrinthoid traps of the nematode-catching fungi, and in this case Pramer and Stoll (1959) have actually demonstrated that a substance they named nemin, obtained from cultures of nematodes, stimulated the formation of the latter organs in *Arthrobotrys conoides*.

3. *Supporting Organs*

Adequate anchorage to the surface of the substrate is equally important in enabling the cantilever spore- and seta-bearing structures of certain fungi to remain erect, and Pirozynski (1963) has illustrated well the elaborate peripheral lobing of such single basal cells of setae in *Beltrania*. These cells would seem to be endowed with the ability of maintaining growth to keep pace with the upward growth of the seta, although it is by no means certain that the cells of the similar frondose hyphae continue to grow behind the advancing tip of the system. The bizarre shape may be perhaps accounted for by considering them as swollen hyphae which, because of the surrounding restrictive pressures, can only develop distal lobes as if about to produce a branch and not round off as in a chlamydospore.

4. Penetrating and Perforating Organs

The extent to which a fungus will develop its vegetative system in the pursuit of nutrients depends on the species. Whereas most saprobic fungi have an unmodified but efficient mycelium, many types of morphological adjustment may be required of the pathogenic fungi. Penetration into the tissues of a plant host is a situation requiring the development of specialized structures, which are also paralleled in certain saprobes attacking resistant substrates such as the keratin of hair. The organs developed vary in size and shape, and mechanical force and lysis may both be necessary for their action. In their simplest form a very fine, possibly protoplastic, hypha is produced which enables many plant pathogens to penetrate the cuticle and epidermal cell walls of leaves, for example, in the powdery mildews of the genus *Erysiphe*. Contrasting with these are, firstly the boring hyphae of many saprobes, well illustrated by English (1965) as narrow but even-diametered and penetrating the substrate extensively. Secondly there are the perforating organs produced by certain dermatophytes when growing saprobically on hair. These are wide, septate hyphae with pointed tips, which lie within wide cone-shaped cavities produced in the cortex of the hair. All three types of penetrating organ arise from superficial hyphae which first produce some form of attaching organ, a hyphopodium, appressorium or a frondose hypha and then beneath form the new hypha. It is likely that the main formative stimulus is contact with a firm surface and the initial penetration is mechanical, soon to be followed by enzyme action as growth proceeds. These organs are certainly formed under the influence of unknown environmental stimuli, but in the saprobic invasion of dead hair and the parasitic attack on living hair in ringworm lesions the dermatophytes provide a rare example of different adjustments in one substrate under different environmental conditions.

IV. ADJUSTMENT ABOVE THE SUBSTRATE SURFACE

A. Macroscopical Adjustments

The efficiency of the nutrient transporting system of a fungus often determines whether it will be able to capitalize on its reserves of energy directly upon emergence from the substrate, or whether a further distribution of the thallus by, for example, the development of rhizomorphs will benefit subsequent dissemination of the spores. Apart from the obvious genetic characteristics which dictate the basic form of the thallus, we know little of the factors which initiate and mold the aerial organs of fungi. The atmosphere is inimical to growth by virtue of its lack of nutrients and its fluctuating moisture levels, and it undergoes such rapid physical changes that few fungi can adjust and survive in the time available. It is therefore small wonder that most fungi flourish in the dank and dark corners of the world, only appearing in order to fructify when the atmospheric conditions allow.

In the two previous sections, the factors influencing the reproduction of fungi are only briefly mentioned because they have been dealt with fully in several of the preceding chapters. The most noticeable organs of the fungi which occur above the substrate are, however, the fruiting bodies of the higher fungi, and although these are well adapted to their subaerial environment, with all its vagaries, they show clearly the effects of environmental change in both their macro- and micromorphology.

1. Natural

a. Size and Shape of the Fruiting Body. Because of its speed of development, the agaric fruiting body would seem to be a useful tool for observing the effect of rapid environmental changes on morphology, but little attention has been paid to it in this respect. Regulated by a mechanical relationship, *i.e,* the smaller the pileus the narrower and longer the stipe, which has been discussed by Ingold (1946), agaric sporophores appearing under adverse conditions of low temperature or lack of moisture, may be reduced in size but consistent in shape according to the species. There are few data to confirm this view, but the relatively small sizes of the fruit bodies of familiar species collected in arctic regions, give an indication that some size-regulating mechanism may be operating through temperature (Kobayashi *et al.,* 1967). The climate certainly has an important effect on the other aspects of the appearance of fruit bodies, and this is felt throughout their development. The persistence of the universal veil in *Amanita* spp., and the surface texture of polypores, are examples of important features governed by the weather at the time of fruit body formation.

Under the optimal conditions of a regular diurnal light cycle and equable limits of humidity and temperature, most soft-fleshed fruit bodies grow at an even pace and mature in a characteristic form with little delay. Various other environmental factors can influence this development in nature. Agarics in their expanding phase may become caught in vegetation and distorted on one side, mycetophilous dipterous larvae may appear very early and apparently halt fruit-body enlargement, and parasitic fungi may induce morphological changes in the sporophore, e.g., *Mycogone perniciosa* in *Agaricus bisporus*. One well-known phenomenon, now at least partially attributable to environmental factors, is the appearance of tremelloid outgrowths on the surfaces of pilei, which consist chiefly of fertile, proliferated, hymenial tissue. These outgrowths have been observed in many species of agarics but especially in *Collybia dryophila* (Ramsbottom, 1933), and were induced by Keyworth (1942) in *Coprinus ephemerus,* by passing a current of sterile air over developing fruiting bodies in petri dishes.

The complete absence of light may give rise to bizarre changes in the sporophore, e.g., the antler-like form of *Lenzites lepideus* seen on mine timbers, and it is possible that the response to light is one of the reasons why the stipes of log-inhabiting agarics may become greatly elongated upward, when the primordia originate on the underside of the log. Gravity too may also play some part in this adjustment, but it clearly has a dominant role in the changes which occur in the woody fruiting bodies of polypores when an upright trunk bearing them falls to the ground through 90 degrees. On such occasions the brackets of *Ganoderma applanatum* have been seen to resume growth at the margin but with a turn of 90 degrees to correspond to the new orientation of the substrate. Lohwag (1938) made experiments on this phenomenon and found that the response to a changed orientation is not necessarily the same in different species and that it depends on the anatomy of the bracket.

b. Zonation of the Fruiting Body. The short-lived fruiting body of the agaric, which grows "overnight" by means of its inflating hyphae, has little time to be influenced by changes of weather except on its surface and hence few induced internal changes are found in these structures. In contrast fruiting-bodies with uninflating hyphae which grow steadily by accretion of marginal hyphae for weeks and sometimes for years, have their meristematic region almost fully exposed to all manner of atmospheric and substrate changes. These are reflected particularly in the form of the fruit body, the same fungus forming a thick structure under some conditions and a thin one in others, or in its coloration. Thus zonation of the cap, especially in the bracket fungi, can give much information on the suitability of the weather for rapid or for slow growth during the period of development. Generally under conditions of high humidity and mild temperatures, growth occurs rapidly, but may cease abruptly under dry, frosty, or excessively wet conditions. Colored zones depend particularly on this speed of growth, for any slowing up of hyphal elongation tends to accumulate protoplasm in the hyphal tips, where pigment (especially that showing on hyphal death) is likewise concentrated. Similarly woolly, matte, or shining zones may be the result of upright, supine, or agglutinated hyphae, oriented by the influence of changes in the atmosphere surrounding the growing hyphal tips of surface and margin. Bayliss (1908) grew *Polystictus versicolor* fruit bodies in pure culture and noted that removal of the cover from a fruiting culture for 1 hour was sufficient to produce a marked surface zone. She was also able to correlate zones observed in the field with the occurrence of periods of drought. Lohwag (1940) examined the structure of the surface of many other polypore species and showed the specificity of this character, but the exact relationship of environmental factors to zonal type is not yet known.

2. *Experimental*

It is mostly due to the work of Plunkett (1956) that there is now a useful background of knowledge on the effect of individual components of the environment on the development of fruit bodies, and also on how they may sometimes operate in combination. He used a lignicolous agaric, *Collybia velutipes,* and a polypore, *Polyporus brumalis,* grown in pure culture in an ingeniously designed apparatus, in which conditions could be controlled with regard to nutrients, humidity, temperature, substrate pH, gaseous content and eventually light, and was able to induce consistent morphological changes. After a study of these effects, some of the abnormalities observed in pilei from the natural habitat could be reproduced in culture on a basis of the physical environment during growth. The wide differences in the effect of evaporating conditions on these two fungi, with the polypore being clearly xerophytic, indicate especially that adjustment to the environment may be a highly specific process and that generalizations on the responses to changed conditions are to be avoided at present. Red light, humidity, airflow, and atmospheric composition were among the most important factors inducing morphological change, and the bizarre and often sterile forms resulting from an imbalance of these are a testimony to their influence in evolution.

B. *Microscopical Adjustments*

Zonation of the Fruit-Body Tissue

Although more attention has been paid recently to the construction of fruit bodies of the higher fungi, little information is available on the internal effects of environmental factors. Zonation of the flesh is one of the most consistent characters found in polypores, which appears to be related to the environment, and is often mentioned as a taxonomic character. Few anatomical observations have ever been made on fruit body zones however, but even a brief study has shown that several different anatomical arrangements of hyphae may give rise to macroscopically identical zones. In polypore tissue, zones may be defined as regions differing in color and texture, which represent the positions of the margin at different times during the growth of the fruit body, thus reflecting the suitability of the environmental conditions for growth. Two main types of zonation have been observed, the regular (usually diurnal) and the irregular.

Corner (1932) studied zonation in the fruit bodies of *Fomes lamaensis* and *F. noxius,* and related the dark zones occurring at intervals of 0.3–0.8 mm to the diurnal variation of humidity in the Malaysian climate. The maximum growth rate occurred in the early hours of the morning and was associated with the development of a lax and pale type of construction whereas the dark zones of densely intertwining, agglutinating generative hyphae were the result of slower growth during the longer, but drier, part of the day. Similar regularly occurring zones have been seen in the fruit bodies of *Tyromyces lacteus,* but these are 2.0–5.0 mm wide, consisting of loosely bound hyphae alternating with closely aggregated ones. The result is seen as alternating light-colored and waterlogged zones, the former sometimes drying out to form prominent lacunae.

Irregular zones are more difficult to account for in terms of environmental influence, unless accurate observations of humidity, rainfall, temperature, etc., have been kept during the development of the fruit body, and as yet this does not seem to have been done. At last six different anatomical arrangements of hyphae of two main types were observed in eight species of the genus *Tyromyces* in a limited study (Austwick, unpublished), and all apparently depended, first, on the nature of the effect of environmental change on the marginal hyphal tips and, second, on the response of the growing region to this change. Most frequently, marginal and surface hyphal tips would agglutinate and die, probably as a result of sudden drying. In this case either the new growth would be resumed by lateral branches behind, growing forward between the groups of dead hyphal tips, or else, because agglutination was complete and an impervious layer was presented, new growth would arise from the pore field and extend up and over the old surface to form a new margin. Occasionally the marginal hyphal tips temporarily collapsed, but later recovered and regained their momentum but at a lower level on the margin, leaving a zone of geotropically inclined hyphae in the flesh. The other main type of irregular zone consisted of the proliferation of different types of hypha followed by resumption of the normal fruit-body construction. Such zones might consist of simultaneous intensive branching of generative hyphae at clamps, or an extensive development of skeletal or binding hyphae for a short period.

V. CONCLUSIONS

Fungal thalli are probably one of the most plastic forms of life. They occur wherever there is suitable organic nutrient in dead or living substrates, and it is therefore small wonder that adjustment to the environment is an essential part of fungal life and that the physiological, biochemical, and genetical means by which this is effected are necessities for survival. In this chapter the morphological results of this adjustment have been discussed, showing how wide a variation there is in the response to the environment and how this in itself precludes the use of a biological basis for classifying these morphological features. Too few of the mechanisms involved have yet been elucidated for this approach to be used successfully, and so it was found convenient to divide the topic on the basis of the relationship of the site of adjustment to the substrate. In following this arrangement, the underlying feature that has become apparent is that the type and extent of the morphological change are determined in a matter of seconds or minutes rather than hours or days. The effects of an environmental influence may thus first be noticed a long time after the initiating stimulus has disappeared, so that it is often exceedingly difficult to establish the origin of a particular change. Further complexity arises from the fact that the environment of an individual fungal thallus (however this is interpreted) is always changing, either by the activity of the thallus itself or by changes in external factors, and the rate of this change is of paramount importance in determining the morphological path taken by the fungus.

The net result of environmental activity is to mold the whole fungus to its surroundings, producing certain morphological adjustments clearly attributable to specific factors and others which, at present, defy interpretation on any basis. The study of fungal morphogenesis is thus still in its infancy and has great potential in the fields of biochemistry, genetics, and pharmacology, concerned, as they are, with the understanding of living processes and their control. But beyond these applications is the fact that adjustment to the environment is the basis for survival in all living things, and only by ecological studies embracing all habitats and all organisms can we too find the key to the survival of our world.

REFERENCES

Ainsworth, G. C. (1952). "Medical Mycology. An Introduction to Its Problems." Pitman, New York.

Austwick, P. K. C. (1965). Pathogenicity. *In* "The Genus *Aspergillus*" (by K. B. Raper and D. I. Fennell), Chapter 7, pp. 82–126. Williams & Wilkins, Baltimore, Maryland.

Austwick, P. K. C., and J. A. J. Venn. (1957). Routine investigations into mycotic abortion. *Vet. Record* **69**: 688–691.

Basset, A., R. Camain, R. Baylet, and D. Lambert. (1965). Rôle des épines de Mimosacées dans l'inoculation des mycetomes (à propos de deux observations). *Bull. Soc. Pathol. Exotique* **58**: 22–24.

Bayliss, J. S. (1908). The biology of *Polystictus versicolor* (Fries). *J. Econ. Biol.* **3**: 1–24.

Burges, N. A. (1958). "Micro-organisms in the Soil." Hutchinson, London.

Burkholder, P. R., and E. W. Sinnott. (1945). Morphogenesis of fungus colonies in submerged shaken cultures. *Am. J. Botany* **32**: 424–431.

Butler, E. J., and S. G. Jones. (1949). "Plant Pathology." Macmillan, New York.

Campbell, A. H. (1933a). Zone lines in plant tissues. I. The black lines formed by *Xylaria polymorpha* (Pers.) Grev. in hardwoods. *Ann. Appl. Biol.* **20**: 123–145.

Campbell, A. H. (1933b). Zones lines in plant tissues. II. The black lines formed by *Armillaria mellea* (Vahl) Quél. *Ann. Appl. Biol.* **21**: 1–22.

Campbell, A. H., and R. G. Munson. (1936). Zones lines in plant tissue. III. The black lines formed by *Polyporus squamosus* (Huds.) Fr. *Ann. Appl. Biol.* **23**: 453–464.

Cantino, E. C. (1966). Morphogenesis in aquatic fungi. *In* "The Fungi" (G. C. Ainsworth and A. S. Sussman, eds.), Vol. 2, pp. 283–337. Academic Press, New York.

Cartwright, K. St. G., and W. P. K. Findlay. (1958). "Decay of Timber and its Prevention," 2nd. ed. H. M. Stationery Office, London.

Corner, E. J. H. (1932). The fruit-body of *Polystrictus xanthopus* Fr. *Ann. Botany (London)* [N.S.] **46**: 71–111.

Corner, E. J. H. (1950). A monograph of *Clavaria* and allied genera. *Ann. Botany Mem.* **1**, 1–740.

Corner, E. J. H. (1964). "The Life of Plants." Weidenfeld & Nicolson, London.

Duckworth, R. B., and G. C. M. Harris. (1949). The morphology of *Penicillium chrysogenum* in submerged fermentations. *Brit. Mycol. Soc. Trans.* **32**: 224–235.

Ducomet, V. (1907). "Recherches sur le développement de quelques champignons parasites à thalle subcuticulaire." Thesis, Fac. Sci. Paris (cited from Langeron, 1945).

English, M. P. (1963). The saprophytic growth of keratinophilic fungi on keratin. *Sabouraudia* **2**: 115–130.

English, M. P. (1965). The saprophytic growth of non-keratinophilic fungi on keratinized substrata, and a comparison with keratinophilic fungi. *Brit. Mycol. Soc. Trans.* **48**: 219–235.

Fischman, O. (1965). Black piedra in Brazil. A contribution to its study in Manaus. (State of Amazonas.) *Mycopathol. Mycol. Appl.* **25**: 201–204.

Fraymouth, J. (1956). Haustoria of the Peronosporales. *Brit. Mycol. Soc. Trans.* **39**: 79–107.

Gitter, M., and P. K. C. Austwick. (1959). Mucormycosis and moniliasis in a litter of sucking pigs. *Vet. Record* **71**: 6–11.

Glenn-Bott, J. I. (1955). On *Helicodendron tubulosum* and some similar species. *Brit. Mycol. Soc. Trans.* **38**: 17–30.

Götz, H. (1960). Zur morphologie der Pilzelemente in Stratum Corneum bei Tinea (Epidermophytia) pedis, manus et inguinalis. *Mycopathol. Mycol. Appl.* **12**: 124–140.

Hansford, C. G. (1946). The foliicolous ascomycetes, their parasites and associated fungi. *Mycol. Papers* **15**: 1–240.

Hawker, L. E. (1954). British hypogenous fungi. *Phil. Trans. Roy. Soc. London* **B237**: 429–546.

Hawker, L. E. (1966). Environmental influences on reproduction. *In* "The Fungi" (G. C. Ainsworth and A. S. Sussman, eds.), Vol. 2, pp. 435–469. Academic Press, New York.

Hawker, L. E., R. W. Harrison, V. O. Nicholls, and A. M. Ham. (1957). Studies on vesicular arbuscular endophytes. I. A strain of *Pythium ultimum* Trow, in roots of *Allium ursinum* L. and other plants. *Brit. Mycol. Soc. Trans.* **40**: 375–390.

Ingold, C. T. (1946). Size and form in agarics. *Brit. Mycol. Soc. Trans.* **29**: 108–113.

Jerebzoff, S. (1965). Growth rhythms. *In* "The Fungi" (G. C. Ainsworth and A. S. Sussman, eds.), Vol. 1, pp. 625–645. Academic Press, New York.

Jinks, J. L. (1966). Mechanisms of inheritance. Extranuclear inheritance. *In* "The Fungi" (G. C. Ainsworth and A. S. Sussman, eds.), Vol. 2, pp. 619–660. Academic Press, New York.

Keyworth, W. G. (1942). The occurrence in artificial culture of tremelloid outgrowths on the pilei of *Coprinus ephemerus*. *Brit. Mycol. Soc. Trans.* **35**: 307–310.

Kobayasi, Y., N. Hiratsuka, R. P. Korf, K. Tubaki, K. Aoshima, M. Soneda, and J. Sugiyama. (1967). Mycological studies of the Alaskan Arctic. *Ann. Rept. Inst. Ferment., Osaka* **3**: 1–138.

Kotlaba, F., and Z. Pouzar. (1959). Nový nález vzácne houby špičatičky stepní-*Galeropsis desertorum* Velen. et Dvoř. e v. Ceskoslovensku a poznámky k rodu *Galeropsis* Velen. *Česk. Mykol.* **13**: 200–211.

Langeron, M. (1945). "Précis de mycologie." Masson, Paris.

Lohwag, K. (1938). Verwachsungsversuche an Fruchtkörpern von Polyporaceen. 1. *Biol. Generalis* **14**: 432–445.

Lohwag, K. (1940). Zur Anatomie des Deckgeflechtes der Polyporaceen. *Ann. Mycol.* **38**: 401–452.

Mackinnon, J. E. (1954). A contribution to the study of the causal organisms of maduromycosis. *Trans. Roy. Soc. Trop. Med. Hyg.* **48**: 470–480.

Mariat, F. (1964). Saprophytic and parasitic morphology of pathogenic fungi. *Symp. Soc. Gen. Microbiol.* **14**: 85–111.

Morton, A. G. (1961). The induction of sporulation in mould fungi. *Proc. Roy. Soc.* **B153**: 548–569.

Park, D. (1961). Morphogenesis, fungistasis and cultural staling in *Fusarium oxysporum* Snyder & Hansen. *Brit. Mycol. Soc. Trans.* **44**: 377–390.

Pine, L., and J. R. Overman. (1963). Determination of the structure of the sulphur granules of *Actinomyces bovis*. *J. Gen. Microbiol.* **32**: 209–223.

Pirozynski, K. A. (1963). *Beltrania* and related genera. *Mycol. Papers* **90**: 1–37.

Plunkett, B. E. (1956). The influence of factors of the aeration complex and light upon fruit-body form in pure cultures of an agaric and a polypore. *Ann. Botany* (*London*) [N.S.] **20**: 561–586.

Pramer, D., and N. R. Stoll. (1959). Nemin: A morphogenic substance causing trap formation by predaceous fungi. *Science* **129**: 966–967.

Ramsbottom, J. (1933). *Tremella mycetophila* Peck. *Brit. Mycol. Soc. Trans.* **18**: 253–256.

Robertson, N. F. (1965). The mechanism of cellular extension and branching. *In*

"The Fungi" (G. C. Ainsworth and A. S. Sussman, eds.), Vol. 1, pp. 613–623 Academic Press, New York.

Romano, A. H. (1966). Dimorphism. *In* "The Fungi" (G. C. Ainsworth and A. S. Sussman, eds.), Vol. 2, pp. 181–209. Academic Press, New York.

Schantz, H. L., and R. L. Piemeisel. (1917). Fungus fairy rings in Eastern Colorado and their effect on vegetation. *J. Agr. Res.* **11**: 191–245.

Sörgel, G. (1967). Vegetative Fortplanzung bei Pilzen. *In* "Handbuch der Pflanzenphysiologie" (W. Ruhland, ed.), Vol. 18, pp. 777–786. Springer, Berlin.

Sparrow, F. K., Jr. (1960). "Aquatic Phycomycetes," 2nd ed. Univ. of Michigan Press, Ann Arbor, Michigan.

Stephens, F. L., and J. G. Hall. (1909). Variation of fungi due to environment. *Botan. Gaz.* **48**: 1–30.

Townsend, B. B. (1957). Nutritional factors influencing the production of sclerotia by certain fungi. *Ann. Botany* (*London*) [N.S.] **21**: 153–166.

Townsend, B. B., and H. J. Willetts. (1954). The development of sclerotia of certain fungi. *Brit. Mycol. Soc. Trans.* **37**: 213–221.

Tribe, H. T. (1957). Ecology of micro-organisms in soils as observed during their development on buried cellulose film. *Symp. Soc. Gen. Microbiol.* **7**: 287–298.

Warcup, J. H., and P. H. B. Talbot. (1962). Ecology and identity of mycelia isolated from soil. *Brit. Mycol. Soc. Trans.* **45**: 495–518.

CHAPTER 17

Longevity and Survivability of Fungi

A. S. SUSSMAN

Department of Botany
University of Michigan
Ann Arbor, Michigan

I. LONGEVITY

A. Longevity in Nature

Although many data exist for the limits of survival of microorganisms in pure or mixed cultures under laboratory conditions, many fewer are available on survival under natural conditions (Tables I and II). Of course, laboratory studies are very important in isolating and identifying the effects of environmental factors, but field observations must accompany these if a full understanding of longevity in nature is to be achieved. Recent reviews of aspects of the survival of fungi include those of Wahl (1961), Hawker (1957a), Menzies (1963), Park (1965), Barton (1965), Sussman (1965a), and Mazur (Chapter 15).

But even when experimenters have worked from nature they have encountered technical difficulties such as those in accurately assessing the proportion of spores and vegetative cells occurring in soils. This question has been reviewed elsewhere (Warcup, 1957; S. T. Williams *et al.*, 1964) so it will merely be noted that such data should be accepted with reserve. Nevertheless, several pathogenic fusaria are claimed to be maintained as the "wild types" due to survival as dormant propagules (McKeen and Wensley, 1961). Moreover, Borut (1960) provides excellent evidence that spores are preeminent in determining the survival of fungi in desert soils. She found that most of the fungi isolated from such habitats sporulate intensely, or possess resting structures of other kinds. Also, the optimum for sporulation in all the species tested was 4–10°C higher than for growth, which may explain why a selective advantage lies with sporulating fungi in such hot environments. Soil steaming also reveals a preponderance

TABLE I
LONGEVITY OF FUNGUS SPORES AND THE CONDITIONS UNDER WHICH THEY SURVIVE

Organism	Stage	Longevity	Conditions of storage	Reference
Physarum cinereum, Fuligo septica, Hemitrichia clavata, Stemonitis ferruginea, Didymium squamulosum, Diachea leucopoda	Spores	>30 yr	Herbarium coll'n	Smith (1929)
Trichia scabra, T. lateritia	Spores	>27 yr	Herbarium coll'n	Smith (1929)
Trichia botrytis, Badhamia panicea, Lepidoderma tigrinum, Physarum staminipes	Spores	>26 yr	Herbarium coll'n	Smith (1929)
Phytophthora infestans	Conidia	1 month (57% survival)	Dry	de Bruyn (1926)
P. infestans	Sporangium	9–10 weeks	Soil	Kaung (1956)
	Zoospores, mycelium	<9–10 weeks	Soil	
Mucor sp.	Conidia	>2 yr 8 months	7°C, on agar	Hesseltine (1947)
Mucor sp.	Conidia	8–10 yr	Unsealed test tubes	McCrea (1931)
Phycomyces sp.	Conidia	>2 yr 8 months	7°C, on agar	Hesseltine (1947)
Phycomyces sp.	Conidia	>317 days	On agar	Robbins *et. al.* (1942)
Rhizopus sp.	Conidia	>2 yr 8 months	7°C, on agar	Hesseltine (1947)
Rhizopus nigricans [*R. stolonifer*]	Conidia	22 yr	Dried in sealed tubes	McCrea (1923)
Peronospora nicotinae	Oospores	4–7 days (1%)	—	Wolf *et al.* (1934)
P. schleideni [*P. destructor*]	Oospores	3–4 yr	Dry	McKay (1935)
P. destructor	Oospores	>8 yr	In soil	McKay (1939)

Synchytrium endobioticum	Resting spores	>10 yr	Field plots	McKay (1935)
Aphanomyces euteiches	Oospores	10 yr	In soil	Linford and Vaughn (1925)
Plasmodiophora brassicae	Resting spores	>10 yr	Field plots	J. C. Walker (1952)
Empusa [*Entomophthora*]*muscae*	Conidia	3–5 days	—	Schweizer (1947)
	Azygospores, zygospores	>1 yr	—	Schweizer (1947)
Erysiphe graminis, *E. cichoracearum*, *Podosphaera leucotricha*, *Sphaerotheca pannosa*, *S. fuligenea*	Conidia	Avg., 5 species:		Yarwood *et al.* (1954)
		40 days	−10 to 0°C	
		20 days	0 to 10°C	
		8 days	10 to 20°C	
		4 days	20 to 30°C	
		1 day	30 to 40°C	
Erysiphe graminis	Perithecia	>2 yr	On plant	Cherewick (1944)
Claviceps purpurea	Conidia	3 months	2–4°C	Glaz (1955)
Pestalotia psidii	Conidia	1 yr	—	Patel *et al.* (1950)
Endoconidiophora fagacearum	Endoconidia	<16 days	30°C	McLaughlin and True (1952)
		111 days	20°C	McLaughlin and True (1952)
		173 days	10°C	McLaughlin and True (1952)
E. fagacearum	Ascospores	232 days	24°C, 10% R.H.	Merek and Fergus (1954)
	Endoconidia	173 days	3–9°C	Merek and Fergus (1954)
Endothia parasitica	Ascospores	1 yr	Dried in bark	Anderson and Rankin (1914)
	Ascospores	<5 months	Removed from bark	Anderson and Rankin (1914)
	Conidia	1 yr	Dry spore horns	Anderson and Rankin (1914)
	Conidia	<1 month	Separate, dry	Anderson and Rankin (1914)

(*Continued*)

TABLE I (*Continued*)

Organism	Stage	Longevity	Conditions of storage	Reference
Pyrenophora bromi	Conidia	11 days	Laboratory temp.	Chamberlain and Allison (1945)
	Ascospores	7 months	Inside perithecium	Chamberlain and Allison, 1945
Chaetomium sp.	Conidia	2 yr 8 months	7°C, on agar	Hesseltine (1947)
Neurospora crassa	Conidia	2–3 yr	5°C, on agar	Mitchell (1960)
	Ascospores	>10 yr	5°C, on agar	Mitchell (1960)
Cronartium ribicola	Basidiospores	10 min	Room temp., 90% R.H.	Spaulding (1922)
	Aeciospores	8 weeks	—	Spaulding (1922)
C. ribicola	Sporidia (basidiospores)	5–6 days	Air-dried	Spaulding and Rathbun-Gravatt (1926)
C. fusiforme	Aeciospores	7 months	Below 10°C	Siggers (1947)
	Uredospores	>223 days	4–10°C	Siggers (1947)
	Teliospores	>2 months	—	Siggers (1947)
Melampsora lini	Uredospores	11 weeks	7°C, 60% R.H.	Hart (1926)
	Teliospores	Several months	Out-of-doors	Hart (1926)
Puccinia amorphae	Uredospores	89 days	Dry	Maneval (1924)
P. sorghi	Uredospores	168–180 days	Dry	Maneval (1924)
P. coronata	Uredospores	<100 days	5, 10°C; and O, 75, or 90% R.H.	Rosen and Weetman (1940)
P. coronata	Uredospores	301 days	5°C, 25–50% R.H.	Rosen and Weetman (1940)
P. triticina [*P. recondita*]	Teliospores	<1 yr	Room temp. or in nature	Prasada (1948)
P. triticina [*P. recondita*]	Teliospores	2 yr	5–7°C	Prasada (1948)
P. glumarum [*P. striiformis*]	Teliospores	3 months	0–5°C, 40% R.H.	Manners (1951)

P. glumarum [*P. striiformis*]	Teliospores	1 yr	5–7°C	Prasada (1948)
P. graminis f.sp. *tritici*	Teliospores	<6.5 months	10–20°C	Prasada (1948)
P. graminis f.sp. *tritici*	Teliospores	6 yr 9 months	7.5 months freezing, remainder at 10°C	T. Johnson (1941)
Uromyces striatus	Uredospores	173–178 days	Dry	Maneval (1924)
U. caryophyllum	Uredospores	185 days	Dry	Maneval (1924)
U. setariae	Uredospores	<15 days	28–30°C	Ramakrishnan (1949)
Coleosporium solidaginis	Aeciospores	143 days	8°C over $CaCl_2$	Fergus (1959)
	Aeciospores	103 days	8°C over H_2O	Fergus (1959)
	Uredospores	120 days	8°C over $CaCl_2$	Fergus (1959)
	Uredospores	40 days	8°C over H_2O	Fergus (1959)
Sphaerobolus stellatus	Basidiospores	10 yr	Dry, in gleba	Buller (1933)
Tilletia caries	Chlamydospores	>18 yr	In herbarium	Fischer (1936)
T. foetida	Chlamydospores	>25 yr	In herbarium	Fischer (1936)
T. caries	Chlamydospores	>12 yr	In laboratory	Woolman and Humphrey (1924)
T. caries, *T. foetida*	Chlamydospores	>11 yr	—	Lowther (1950)
T. tritici, [*T. caries*], *T. levis* [*T. foetida*]	Chlamydospores	>3 yr	—	Hahne (1925)
T. contraversa	Chlamydospores	>2 yr	In soil	Brefeld (1895)
Ustilago nuda	Chlamydospores	8 months	Dry	Stakman (1913)
U. tritici [*U. nuda*]	Chlamydospores	5 months	Dry	Stakman (1913)
U. striiformis	Chlamydospores	332 days	—	W. H. Davis (1924)
Urocystis tritici [*U. agropyri*]	Chlamydospores	10 yr	13–31°C, 33.5% R.H.	Noble (1934)
Stereum hirsutum	Basidiospores	56–64 days	Room temp., dry	Harrison (1942)
S. rugisporum	Basidiospores	46–66 days	Room temp., dry	Harrison (1942)
S. sanguinolentum	Basidiospores	131–137 days	Room temp., dry	Harrison (1942)
Polyporus schweinitzii	Basidiospores	162–170 days	Room temp., dry	Harrison (1942)
Trametes pini	Basidiospores	>65 days	Room temp., dry	Harrison (1942)
Coniophora sistrotremoides	Basidiospores	46–68 days	Room temp., dry	Harrison (1942)

(*Continued*)

TABLE I (*Continued*)

Organism	Stage	Longevity	Conditions of storage	Reference
Fomes igniarius	Basidiospores	91–99 days	Room temp., dry	Harrison (1942)
F. pinicola	Basidiospores	>173 days	Room temp., dry	Harrison (1942)
F. annosus	Basidiospores	>18 months	On bark, in soil	Evans (1965)
		<18 months	Without bark, in soil	Evans (1965)
F. igniarius	Basidiospores	>10 days to <80 days	Open field lab	Good and Spanis (1958)
Lycoperdon umbrinum	Basidiospores	22 months	—	Fries (1941)
Psilocybe mutans	Basidiospores	>9 yr	Herbarium, dry	McKnight (1960)
Schizophyllum commune	Fruit body and basidiospores	—	0.1 mm Hg and 3 weeks at −190°C	Ainsworth (1962)
Aspergillus niger	Conidia	>2 yr 8 months	7°C, on agar	Hesseltine (1947)
A. niger	Conidia	>12 yr	Covered test tubes, room temp.	Roberg (1948)
A. wentii	Conidia	>2 yr 8 months	7°C, on agar	Hesseltine (1947)
A. flavus	Conidia	>12 yr	Covered test tubes, room temp.	Roberg (1948)
A. flavus-oryzae	Conidia	>2 yr 8 months	7°C, on agar	Hesseltine (1947)
A. oryzae	Conidia	>22 yr	Dry, in sealed test tube	McCrea (1923)
A. fumigatus	Conidia	>2 yr 8 months	7°C, on agar	Hesseltine (1947)
A. fumigatus	Conidia	>15 yr	Covered test tubes, room temp.	Roberg (1948)
A. fischeri	Conidia	>2 yr 8 months	7°C, on agar	Hesseltine (1947)

A. fischeri	Conidia	>10 yr	Covered test tubes, room temp.	Roberg (1948)
A. versicolor	Conidia	>2 yr 8 months	7°C, on agar	Hesseltine (1947)
A. ficuum	Conidia	>12 yr	Covered test tubes, room temp.	Roberg (1948)
A. glaucus	Conidia	>15 yr	Covered test tubes, room temp.	Roberg (1948)
A. nidulans	Conidia	>12 yr	Covered test tubes, room temp.	Roberg (1948)
Aspergillus sp., *Penicillium* sp., *Fusarium* sp.	Conidia	8–10 yr	Unsealed test tubes	McCrea (1931)
Helminthosporium oryzae	Conidia	>6 months	2°C, 20% R.H.	Page *et al.* (1947)
H. sativum [*Cochliobolus sativus*]	Conidia	>20 months	Soil in field	Chinn and Ledingham (1958)
	Conidia	>9 months	Soil: 18% water holding capac.	Chinn and Ledingham (1958)
	Conidia	<9 months	Soil: 88% water holding, capac.	Chinn and Ledingham (1958)
H. sativum [*C. sativus*]	Conidia	>1 yr	Soil in field	Henry (1931)
Penicillium sp.	Conidia	>2 yr 8 months	7°C, on agar	Hesseltine (1947)
P. brevicaule, *P. luteum*, *P. camemberti*	Conidia	<12 yr	Covered test tubes, room temp.	Roberg (1948)
Trichoderma sp.	Conidia	2 yr 8 months	7°C, on agar	Hesseltine (1947)
Fusarium sp.	Conidia	>2 yr 8 months	7°C, on agar	Hesseltine (1947)
Alternaria sp.	Conidia	>2 yr 8 months	7°C, on agar	Hesseltine (1947)
Dematium pullulans [*Aureobasidium pullulans*]	Chlamydospores	2 yr	Moist agar cultures	Bennett (1928)

TABLE II
LONGEVITY OF SCLEROTIA AND VEGETATIVE STRUCTURES

Organism	Stage	Longevity	Conditions of storage	Reference
Myxomycete (unknown species)	Sclerotium	20 yr	Laboratory	Leveillé (1843)
Badhamia utricularis	Sclerotium	3 yr	Dry, *in vacuo*	Lister (1888)
Physarum polycephalum	Sclerotium	>13 months		Hodapp (1942)
P. polycephalum	Sclerotium	Several years		Seifriz and Russell (1936)
Candida albicans	Vegetative	21 yr	10°C	Miller and Simons (1962)
Ophiobolus graminis	Vegetative	Few months to 2 yr	In host in soil	Fellows (1941)
O. graminis	Vegetative	Up to 1 yr	In host	Butler (1953, 1959)
Gibberella saubinettii	Vegetative	27 months	Barley seeds	Shands (1937)
Helminthosporium sativum [*Cochliobolus sativus*]	Vegetative	>15 yr	Wheat seeds	Russell (1958)
H. sativum [*C. sativus*]	Vegetative	2 yr	In host	Butler (1953, 1959)
Alternaria tenuis	Vegetative	>7 yr	Wheat seeds	Russell (1958)
Leptosphaeria salvinii	Sclerotium	6 yr	Uncultivated rice soils	Tullis and Gralley (1941)
Cercosporella herpotrichoides	Vegetative	3 yr	In host	Macer (1961)
Claviceps purpurea	Sclerotium	2 yr	Soil	Heald (1937)
Omphalia flavida	Gemma	>26 hr	Dry air	Buller (1934)
Sclerotinia sclerotiorum	Sclerotium	8 hr	Soil	Pape (1937)
S. trifoliorum	Sclerotium	5 hr	Dry, laboratory	Wadham (1925)
Rhizoctonia solani [*Corticium solani*]	Sclerotium	6 yr	Dry, laboratory	Gadd and Bertus (1928)
Verticillium alboatrum	Micro-sclerotium	13 yr	In field or test tubes	Wilhelm (1955)

V. dahliae	Sclerotium	14 yr	Soil	Wilhelm (1955)
Phymatotrichum omnivorum	Sclerotium	1¼ hr	Dry, laboratory	King *et al.* (1931)
P. omnivorum	Sclerotium	10–12 yr	Soil	Rogers (1942)
Sclerotium rolfsii	Sclerotium	<1 month	Soil	G. H. Williams and Western (1965)
S. rolfsii	Sclerotium	>5 yr	Soil	Leach and Davey (1938)
S. delphinii	Sclerotium	>2 yr	Soil	G. H. Williams and Western (1965)
S. cepivorum	Sclerotium	>4 yr	Soil	Coley-Smith (1959)
S. cepivorum	Sclerotium	>2 yr	Dry, laboratory	Coley-Smith (1959)
Ustilago nuda	Mycelium	>11 yr	In barley seed	Porter (1955)
Armillaria mellea	Mycelium	>6 yr	Citrus roots	Garrett (1956)
Melampsorella caryophyllacearum	Mycelium	60 yr	*Abies* roots	Gäumann (1950)

of spore formers among the survivors (Warcup, 1957), thereby suggesting again that spores have an advantage under these conditions. Nevertheless, as we shall see, the evidence from nature is far from complete and is contradictory in part, for there are habitats, such as the Arctic, in which mycelial stages are very persistent. Moreover, even soils from temperate regions yield fungi which have appeared to survive by means of vegetative structures (Park, 1965).

The information that is available suggests that the most frequent means whereby survival of fungi in nature is ensured is through the formation of special resistant bodies (Hawker, 1957a; Park, 1965; Sussman, 1965a). These may be relatively simple modifications of hyphal elements such as chlamydospores, or various types of spores and fruiting bodies, as well as aggregates of hyphae such as sclerotia and rhizomorphs. Thus, the resting spores of *Plasmodiophora brassicae* survived for more than 10 years in the field plots studied by J. C. Walker (1952) and those of *Synchytrium endobioticum* for over 7 years (McKay, 1935). And the oospores of *Aphanomyces euteiches* (Linford and Vaughn, 1925) and of *Peronospora destructor* (McKay, 1939) were alive after 10 and 8 years, respectively. Using case histories of onion land in the Connecticut Valley, Thaxter (1890) concluded that teliospores of *Urocystis colchici* probably remain viable for up to 25 years but he did not rule out the possibility that mycelium might have been responsible for the parasite's great longevity. However, very recently, Tachibana and Duran (1966) have ascertained "that mycelia [of *U. colchici*] are not important infective agents in nature."

Types of propagules other than spores often are of great longevity, such as sclerotia which, in the case of *Verticillium dahliae,* persist for 14 years in soil and those of *V. alboatrum* are almost as long-lived (Wilhelm, 1955). Other examples of sclerotia of great longevity are provided in Table II, and by Garrett (1956).

Also, the ascocarp itself in many parasitic ascomycetes may adopt the function of tiding the fungus over bad times, as in the Erysiphales and other organisms described in Chapter 7 of this volume.

Mycelium of surprising persistence has been reported as well (Table II and page 197). For example, Russell (1958) showed that the hyphae of *Helminthosporium sativum* [*Cochliobolus sativus*] survived more than 15 years in wheat seeds and those of *Alternaria tenuis* more than 7 years in the same plant. Enduring mycelium is not exceptional because some powdery mildews can overwinter in this way in buds of host plants (Yarwood, 1954), as can rusts (Zimmerman, 1925; Porter, 1955; Hawker, 1957a). In the severest sections of the Arctic, which have a very short and cold summer, most of the obligate parasites have a persistent mycelium which remains in the crown of the host. In fact, according to Savile (1963) a perennial mycelium often is required for survival. Even among saprophytes of the Arctic, the predominance of the Pyrenomycetes may be due to their ability to survive despite taking two to three years to form mature ascocarps. Discussions of other parasites which survive in seeds and other plant materials appear in Wahl's (1961) and Barton's (1965) reviews, and in Chapter 7 of this volume.

That evanescent spores and other stages occur also is clear from the data in Tables I and II. Among these are sporidia of rusts (Spaulding and Rathbun-Gravatt, 1926), conidia of *Phytophthora infestans* (de Bruyn, 1926), and basidiospores of *Fomes annosus* when free of bark (Evans, 1965).

The microenvironment of the fungus in nature is of great importance to its longevity, as is evident from the range of survival times listed for sclerotia of *Phymatotrichum omnivorum* and *Sclerotium rolfsii* in Table II. Such is also the case for basidiospores of *Fomes annosus* which survive more than 18 months when on bark in soil but which die much sooner when free in this environment (Evans, 1965).

B. Longevity in the Laboratory

In contrast to the data from nature, those from laboratory experiments strongly suggest that spores usually are the stage of fungal development which survives best. Thus, Hesseltine *et al.* (1960) have demonstrated that more than half of the cultures that did not survive lyophilization had no spores when lyophilized. They conclude, "Spores, or mycelial structures functioning as spores must be present before lyophilization, especially in the Fungi Imperfecti." On the other hand, Wellman and Walden (1964) have shown that 9 of the 11 species without spores that they exposed to liquid nitrogen survived 12 hours, so hyphae often are resistant to rigorous environmental conditions. The conditions under which fungus cultures can be stored and the criteria used in judging survival have been reviewed by Fennell (1960) and Mazur (Chapter 15).

Many slime molds can survive 10–20 years or longer in herbarium collections, and some smuts have been shown to do as well under similar conditions (Table I). Agar cultures of several of the Fungi Imperfecti and of *Neurospora crassa* survive more than 10 years although most of the other fungi studied have survived somewhat more than 2 years under these circumstances.

Spore types within a single organism often differ in their longevity. For example, the teliospores of rusts usually are the most resistant of the several types of spores formed by these fungi. Also, ascospores of *Neurospora crassa* are much more durable than conidia, and the azygospores and zygospores of *Entomophthora muscae* are much more long-lived than its conidia.

The maximum time that microorganisms can survive was studied by Sneath (1962). Because there are few data on the kinetics of survival over long time periods, Sneath determined the number of microorganisms present in the dried soil from plants in the collections of the Royal Botanical Gardens, Kew, and the British Museum (Natural History). Although few fungi and actinomycetes survived over 50 years, various species of *Bacillus* were found in older samples. From these data Sneath estimated that about 90% of the microorganisms died every 50 years initially or every 100 years in the more resistant fraction. Using this figure and commercial standards for sterilization, he calculated that a kilogram of soil would be sterilized after about 1000 years. The survey by Sussman and Halvorson (1966) of the longevity of bacteria reveals that spore formers have been recorded to survive more than 100 years, and it is not uncommon to find nonspore formers which are viable in storage for more than 20 years.

Seeds of *Nelumbium nucifera,* the sacred lotus of China, set the standard for the longevity of living things for they have been successfully germinated after 800 years, according to ^{14}C-dating (Chaney, 1951; Arnold and Libby, 1951). The longevity of other seeds is reviewed by Barton (1965), of cryptogams other than fungi by Sussman (1965b), and of animals and other organisms by Keilin (1959). Finally, survival after exposure to extreme environmental conditions is reviewed in the book by Mamukinian and Briggs (1965).

II. SURVIVABILITY

A. Factors in Survivability

Fungi can survive in many different conditions in soil, about which more is known than most habitats. Park (1965) divides the modes of survival into *active* types in which the organism continues to grow as a parasite, commensal, or saprophyte, or *inactive* types, as in structures in which dormancy is exogenously imposed or constitutive (Sussman, 1965b). Examples of each of these modes of survival are provided by Park and in Tables I and II.

As Garrett (1956) has pointed out, survivability is the result of many interacting variables. These have been discussed by Garrett (1956), Park (1965), Sussman (1965b), and Sussman and Halvorson (1966) and are listed below.

1. Resistance to deleterious agents
2. "Competitive saprophytic ability" (Garrett, 1956)

3. Disseminability
4. Responsiveness (timing)
5. Mutational capacity

Not all these factors are of equal importance to the survival of all organisms, but an appropriate combination probably is required. Each of the factors will be considered in turn and, whenever possible, an attempt will be made to evaluate the role in survival of the different stages in the life history of fungi. However, as has been noted above, these conclusions are subject to the uncertainties in quantitatively assessing these stages in natural environments.

B. Resistance to Deleterious Agents

Detailed examinations of the effects upon fungi of environmental factors have been provided in other sections of this book. These include chapters on the effects of ionizing radiations (Pomper, Volume I, Chapter 24), pressure (Morita, Volume I, Chapter 22), chemicals (Byrde, Volume I, Chapter 20), visible light (Page, Volume I, Chapter 23), and temperature (Deverall, Chapter 5, Mazur, Chapter 15 of this volume). Therefore, these subjects will not be reviewed in detail here. Other reviews of the resistance of fungi to environmental variables can be found in Garrett (1956), Burges (1958), Mamukinian and Briggs (1965), and Sussman and Halvorson (1966).

1. *Temperature*

Although fungus spores often are more resistant than vegetative stages, there are instances where vegetative stages are remarkably resistant to extremes of temperature. The thermophilic fungi described by Cooney and Emerson (1964) and by Emerson (Chapter 4 of this volume) are examples of this kind. But even the mycelium of mesophilic organisms like *Colletotricum lini* survives 3–4 hours at 55°C (Tochinai, 1926), and those of *Lenzites sepiara, L. lepideus, Trametes scialis,* and *T. carnea* survive 2 hours in wood at 55°C (Snell, 1923). As was suggested in the section on longevity, where spores are not produced survival may be attributed to the mycelium, or to specialized parts of the mycelium like arthrospores or sclerotia. Thus, the microsclerotia of *Verticillium albo-atrum* survive for 40 minutes at 47°C whereas hyphae and conidia tolerate this temperature for only 10 minutes (Nelson and Wilhelm, 1958).

Studies of the fungi of desert soils have revealed that most sporulate intensely, or form resistant stages of other kinds (Borut, 1960). It is significant that the optimum for the sporulation of all the species tested was 4–10°C higher than that for growth, suggesting adaptation to the hot arid environment of the desert. *Rhizoctonia* and *Sclerotium* also were found so that vegetative structures survive as well. Spore-forming bacteria were found to constitute a high percentage of the total microbial flora around desert plants, as compared with fertile Egyptian soils (Mahmoud *et al.,* 1964). As in many other studies, the rhizosphere flora was much more extensive than that in the surrounding soil.

Studies of the semideserts of the American southwest, including the Nevada Test Site and Death Valley, have yielded 41 fungal taxa from the former and 14 from the latter (Durrell and Shields, 1960). All the species isolated were common soil fungi, and four taxa were recovered in 40–80% of the samples, including *Stemphylium ilicis, Fusarium* sp., *Phoma* sp., and *Penicillium oxalicum.* It was noted in this work, and in that of Nicot (1960) on desert fungi, that a high percentage of dark-spored species occurred in soils collected from both localities. Although, as will be noted later, Durrell and Shields (1964), L. F. Johnson and Osborne (1964), and others suggest that the black pigments provide selective advantage against ultraviolet light and other radiations, the fluxes reaching even desert soils do not seem large enough to require that spores be protected. Rather, it may be that such spores and melanized hyphae are better able to withstand the dehydrating effects of visible light in such environments, but this is only conjecture at the moment.

Soil-steaming, in order to partially sterilize soil, has been widely used in agriculture and has provided data on the survival of microorganisms after such treatment (Warcup, 1951a). Increased numbers of spore formers have been reported after heating, while the total fungal flora of an old forest nursery soil was markedly reduced. A high proportion of ascomycetes, which appear to form heat-resistant ascospores, was found and many of the species were recorded only rarely from untreated soils. These results may be interpreted to mean that heat breaks the dormancy of the ascospores of these species so that they germinate only after such treatment; alternatively, their growth may be suppressed by competing microorganisms, which do not survive after being heated. It will be noted later that almost the same group of fungi can be isolated from soil if treated with ethanol instead of heat (Warcup, 1962), but the explanation of these effects still remains to be worked out.

But, again, fungi which do not form ascospores, including *Aspergillus versicolor. Penicillium purpurogenum,* and *Fusarium oxysporum* survived 6 minutes of steaming; *Trichoderma viride* tolerated 4 minutes of such treatment, thereby supporting the observation of Tam and Clark (1943) that this fungus is very thermoresistant.

Little is known about the survival of fungi in cold environments like the Arctic and Antarctic. Some recent data bearing on this subject are reviewed on page 129, and in the papers by Elliott and Michener (1965) and Stokes (1963). Psychrophilic organisms have been studied in natural soils where they represent 0.5–86% of the bacterial population and 25% of the fungi according to Stokes and Redmond (1966). Psychrophiles also are major fractions of the bacterial flora of fresh waters, although fungi are a much smaller component of this environment. Meats, milk, and ice cream contained few, if any, psychrophilic fungi but, again, psychrophilic bacteria were a conspicuous part of the flora. However, thousands of psychrophilic molds are present per gram of fresh pastries (Kuehn and Gunderson, 1962, 1963) so some foods do contain large amounts of these organisms. But such technical details as the temperature at which the isolates are incubated, and the kinds of isolation media used, influence the results markedly, so much remains to be learned about the fungi from environments with extremes of temperature.

2. *Chemicals*

Toxic compounds of various kinds have been introduced into natural environments with increasing frequency as a result of the use of fungicides, insecticides, and other types of chemicals. Although breakdown renders many of these substances innocuous, others may persist for long periods of time. Even chemicals like hormonal weed killers, which usually disappear within a few weeks after application, may last for up to a year under dry conditions but do not seem to affect microorganisms very greatly in the concentrations found in soil (Burges, 1958).

Increased fertility and relief from pathogens often result from the partial sterilization of soil by steaming or chemical treatment. As a result of fumigation with methyl bromide, propane-propene, and ethylene dibromide, Wensley (1953) found that several ascomycetes, whose development usually is suppressed by penicillia and aspergilli, could be recovered from soil. Ascosporic species of *Penicillum. Aspergillus, Chaetomium,* and *Thielavia* are very resistant to carbon disulfide, as well as to the above substances. Sterilization of soil with formalin (Warcup, 1951b) killed fungi to a depth of 12 cm, and 18 months after treatment only about half the species originally present had returned, *Trichoderma viride* being the principal recolonizer.

Trichoderma viride is the predominant species found after carbon disulfide treatment as well even though Saksena (1960) has found that, of 15 other species tested, fully 9 were more tolerant of this chemical, results that were confirmed by Moubasher (1963). Therefore, it is likely that this fungus owes its success as a colonizer to a combination of its adequate tolerance to fumigation and rapid rate of growth.

Some data suggest that spores are more resistant to toxic chemicals than are vegetative stages, and this is clearly the case for bacteria (Sussman and Halvorson, 1966). As for the fungi, conidia of *Aspergillus niger* have been shown to be more resistant to pentachlorophenol, dehydroacetic acid, sorbic acid, phenylthiobenzoate, butylthio-1,4-naphthoquinone, mycelin, and eurocydin (Yanagita and Yamagishi, 1958). Moreover, the growing mycelium of *Venturia* spp. is more sensitive to *o*-coumaric acid than are spores (Flood and Kirkham, 1960), and vegetative cells of baker's yeast likewise are killed by lower concentrations of ethanol than are vegetative cell (Sawada, 1959).

However, the reverse often is true. Thus, spore germination in *Fusarium oxysporum* f. sp. *lycopersici* and *F. roseum* is completely inhibited by less than 5 ppm of Phygon (3,3-dichloro-1,4-naphthoquinone) whereas mycelial growth occurs at 100-fold greater concentrations (Deep and Corden, 1961). Also, Actidione is ten times more effective against spores of *Myrothecium verrucaria* than against its mycelium (A. T. Walker and Smith, 1952), and mycelial fragments of *Verticillium* are much less sensitive to chlorogenic acid than are spores (McLean *et al.,* 1961). Very striking results of this kind are those of Domsch (1958), who found that spores of *Pythium* sp., *Rhizoctonia solani* [*Corticium solani*], and *Fusarium culmorum* were 100-fold more sensitive to certain fungicides than is their mycelium. Finally, certain fungi which do not form resistant spores are well adapted to survive treatment with chemicals. Such is the case with *Trichoderma viride,* which, as was noted above, survives fumigation of soil remarkably well and can recolonize sterilized soil. Moreover, even sterile fungi were recovered from fumigated soils by Wensley (1953).

Therefore, no generalization can be made about the relative sensitivity of the spores and mycelium of fungi to chemicals. Even closely related chemicals differ in their effect upon different stages, as in the case of cinnamic and *o*-coumaric acids (Flood and Kirkham, 1960). Moreover, the type of spore is a factor that must be considered in view of data which show that ascospores of *Neurospora* are much more resistant to toxic cations than are conidia of the same organism (Sussman, 1965a).

Lytic factors of natural origin are another aspect of resistance to chemicals and are briefly reviewed in a recent paper (Lloyd *et al.,* 1965). For example, conidia of *Glomerella cingulata, Penicillium frequentans,* and *Fusarium oxysporum* are soon destroyed when in contact with raw soil but survive for a long time in autoclaved soil (B. T. Lingappa and Lockwood, 1961). Similar results have been reported by Subramanian (1950) and Park (1955), and mycelium also is subject to lysis in soil (Chinn, 1953; Carter and Lockwood, 1957; Lockwood, 1959, 1960; Acha *et al.,* 1965). Antibiotics (Carter and Lockwood, 1957; Lockwood, 1959) or enzymes (Leal and Villanueva, 1962) may be involved. Therefore, survivability in some instances may depend upon resistance to lytic factors.

Thus, Iichinska (1960) suggests that spore formation may protect bacilli against their own autolytic enzymes because some asporogenous mutants are unstable and undergo lysis very readily. Moreover, yeast spores may be resistant to autolysis on the basis of their presence in the outer autolyzed layer of old yeast colonies (Lindegren and Hamilton, 1944). Ascospores of *Neurospora* are very resistant to breakdown in soil (unpublished results of the author) so it may be that one function of melanized walls is to aid in resisting lysis.

That resistance to lysis may be engendered by melanins is suggested by the dark hyphae of *Helminthosporium sativum* [*Cochliobolus sativus*] and *Alternaria solani* which resist lysis more effectively than their hyaline hyphae (Lockwood, 1960). And, albino chlamydospores of *Thielaviopsis bascicola* are not resistant to lysis whereas dark ones are (Linderman and Tousson, 1966). Similar observations have been made with melanin-containing sclerotia of *Sclerotium rolfsii* and conidia of *Aspergillus phoenicis* whose hyaline vegetative stages, and the spicule-free conidia of the latter species, are readily lysed (Bloomfield and Alexander, 1967). A relation between the melanin content of walls of the hyphae of several fungi and their resistance to enzymatic degradation was noted by Potgieter and Alexander (1966), and quantitative studies in melanin-containing and melanin-free strains of *Aspergillus nidulans* have confirmed this relationship (Kuo and Alexander, 1967). In these studies it was found that a synthetic melanin inhibited a glucanase, chitinase, and proteinase *in vitro* and that such a melanin may be very resistant to microbial degradation in soil. So, melanins probably have an ecological role in conferring survivability upon certain microorganisms by protecting them against the effects of lytic enzymes released in natural environments. However, the data are not complete because studies with natural melanin-wall complexes subjected to natural conditions in soil have not been reported.

In summary, survival of fungi would seem to be abetted by resistance to toxic chemicals. The mechanisms through which such resistance is engendered are not known but might involve permeability, the possession of insensitive enzyme systems, or means of detoxification, or a combination of these. In the case of lytic enzymes, cell walls and membranes which resist lysis could be added to these mechanisms of defense, but very few data exist which bear upon these.

3. *Radiations*

The spectral distribution of sunlight at the surface of the earth reveals that the lower wavelength limit in the ultraviolet is at about 290 mμ (Moon, 1941; Blum, 1961; Gates, 1966), due to the absorption of shorter wavelengths by ozone. Considerable infrared radiation reaches the earth with a small amount extending beyond 2.0 μ. Many, if not most, of the effects of the infrared radiations are probably due to high temperature and have been covered in a previous section. Therefore, resistance to ultraviolet light and ionizing radiations will be stressed herein.

As Pomper (Volume I, Chapter 24) has concluded, there is a close correlation between the activity of ultraviolet light upon fungi and the peaks corresponding to those of nucleic acid absorption. The single exception among the many studied is *Chaetomium globosum* in which the maximum production of mutations was at about 280 mμ (McAulay and Ford, 1947). The fact that the maximum effect upon fungi is by wavelengths around 260 mμ, which probably are totally absorbed by the ozone layer, provokes the question, "Is ultraviolet light a significant factor in the survival of fungi in nature?" Unfortunately, a satisfactory answer cannot be provided at this time. Thus, measurements of the amount of light of wavelengths below 290 mμ which reach the earth have not been entirely satisfactory and must be considered in relation to air mass and concentrations of aerosol, ozone, and water vapor (Gates, 1966). But even if it is assumed that none of the short wavelengths do reach the surface of the earth, the effects of long wavelength ultraviolet need further exploration. Phototropic and other responses are known to be elicited by wavelengths near 280 mμ (Page, 1965), in addition to the effect noted above for *Chaetomium,* so that the wavelengths in the long ultraviolet which reach the earth may be found to have considerable significance to the development of fungi, thereby influencing their survival indirectly. Another uncertainty in this field is the effect of chronic exposures to low levels of such radiations. It might be expected that fungi are irradiated continuously during their dispersal in air, or *in situ* in exposed environments like the Arctic and deserts so that, if cumulative effects can be engendered, almost any wavelength of light might affect survival.

Although the effects of ionizing radiations upon fungi *in vitro* have been studied intensively, much less is known about their effect upon survival in nature. Soil samples from the Nevada Test Site were exposed to gamma radiation from a ^{60}Co source by Shields *et al.* (1961), and five taxa of fungi developed following 640 kr total dosage. These results agreed with those of Stotzky and Mortensen (1959), who found that the fungal flora is increasingly inhibited by dosages from 8 to 250 kr. Similar work was performed and reviewed by L. F. Johnson and Osborne (1964), who found that 28 species of fungi survived 250 kr irradiation by gamma rays from a ^{60}Co source. Many of these species had not previously been isolated from untreated soil. Furthermore, it was found that the resistance of certain of the fungi found was related directly to their rate of growth in pure culture under sublethal levels of continuous irradiation. These workers also note that the Dematiaceae were the most resistant fungal group that was recovered, as did Shields *et al.*

Numerous questions are raised by these studies. For example, is the correlation between growth rate under chronic irradiation and resistance to high levels generally true? Why are species not encountered in untreated soil found after irradiation? This finding is reminiscent of the results of heat treatment of soil which were reviewed before (page 460; Warcup and Baker, 1963). The role of fungus spores in determining survival under irradiation also is not well understood. Although there is clear evidence that bacterial spores are much more resistant than are vegetative cells (Sussman and Halvorson, 1966), the data are incomplete for the fungi.

And are melanized species more resistant to radiations than are hyaline ones? This was first studied in detail by Fulton and Coblentz (1929), who found that of the 27 species they exposed to ultraviolet irradiation, the dark-walled ones were most resistant. Also, Weston (1931) showed that dark uredospores of *Puccinia graminis* f. sp. *tritici* survived such treatment best. Similar results have been obtained with conidia of *Ophiostoma* (Fries, 1946), *Glomerella cingulata* (Markert, 1953), and *Cochliobolus sativus* (Tinline *et al.,* 1960). A detailed examination of dark, thick-walled conidia, as well as olivaceous and hyaline types revealed that their sensitivity to ultraviolet light diminished as the intensity of their pigmentation increased (Rabinovitz-Sereni, 1932; English and Gerhardt, 1946). Therefore, support is lent Buller's (1934) suggestion that the black wall of coprophilous fungi which are in exposed positions on vegetation serves as protection against excessive insolation.

Inasmuch as the pigment usually involved is probably a melanin, Durrell's experiments (1966) with synthetic materials of this kind are pertinent. Such pigments prevented damage to unpigmented spores of *Gliocladium roseum* when they were interposed between the spores and an ultraviolet light source. Other pigments may protect against photodynamic killing including the carotenoids of *Dacryopinax spathularia* (Goldstrohm and Lilly, 1965) and the brown one in the ascospores of *Caliciopsis* (Funk, 1963). By contrast, the nonmelanoid pigment in conidia of *Aspergillus niger* does not protect against ultraviolet irradiation (Durrell and Shields, 1960), so each system must be studied individually.

Perhaps, a model to illustrate one mechanism for phenotypic adaptation to environments with high incident light intensity is to be found in the work of Y. Lingappa *et al.* (1963) and Sussman *et al.* (1963). These workers showed that light induces melanization in *Pullularia* [*Aureobasidium*] and *Cladosporium,* which are frequently encountered in air (Gregory, 1961) and in desert soils (Borut, 1960).

But the question raised above still remains. Granted that melanins and other pigments protect against ultraviolet and deleterious effects of other wavelengths in the laboratory, how significant is this effect in nature? Very little of the most toxic wavelengths reach the surface of the earth, so the chronic effects of those that do at significant levels must be studied before conclusions can be drawn.

4. Desiccation

That effects attributed to one environmental variable are not clearly distinguishable from those induced by others is often the case when moisture is involved. Thus, the effect of high temperature may be the result of drought injury as well (Levitt, 1956), and frost injury and the effect of desiccation may both stem from a rise in salt concentration (see Chapter 14 of this volume). Other cases include the desiccation which results when anoxia is imposed under high vacuums and the effect of humidity upon radiation damage (Webb *et al.,* 1964). Accordingly, many of the phenomena to be discussed below may be the result of the interaction of two or more environmental variables.

The superiority of wet sterilization over dry is a well-established phenomenon and suggests that lowering the water content of organisms ameliorates the lethal effects of high temperature. Furthermore, the utility of the lyophil technique is a parallel effect which bears upon survival at low temperatures (Hesseltine *et al.,* 1960). Other data suggest that organisms with low water content survive for longer times than do those with more water (Table III).

But some fungi are sensitive to dehydration, like the uredospores of *Puccinia glumarum* [*P. striiformis*] which survive best at 40% relative humidity between 0 and 5°C (Manners, 1951). Similar relative humidities are optimal for sclerotia of *Phymatotrichum omnivorum* (Taubenhaus and Ezekiel, 1936), uredospores of *Puccinia coronata* (Rosen and Weetman, 1940), conidia of *Helminthosporium oryzae* (Page *et al.,* 1947) and spores of *Uromyces setariae* (Ramakrishnan, 1949). Moreover, the viability of some fungi is best preserved in wet conditions as in the case of conidia of *Erysiphe graminis* (Metzger, 1942), *E. polygoni* (Yarwood *et al.,* 1954), and *Oidium heveae* (Corner, 1935), basidiospores of *Tilletia tritici* [*T. caries*] (Buller, 1933), and gemmae of *Omphalia flavida* (Buller, 1934).

Even more perplexing is the observation that intermediate relative humidities may be more damaging to survival than either extreme. Thus, bimodal survival curves have been reported which suggest a definite minimum between 50 and 70% relative humidity (Hart, 1926; Page *et al.,* 1947; Teitell, 1958; Clerk and Madelin, 1965). Perhaps this effect is

TABLE III

COMPARISON OF THE WATER CONTENT AND LONGEVITY OF PROPAGULES[a]

Organism	Stage	Water content (% dry weight)	Reference	Longevity	Reference
Erysiphe graminis	Conidia	75	Yarwood (1950)	78 days (−2°C)	Metzger (1942)
E. cichoracearum	Conidia	52	Yarwood (1950)	25 days (7°C)	Yarwood (1954)
E. polygoni	Conidia	52–74	Yarwood (1950)	12 days (7°C)	Yarwood (1954)
Claviceps purpurea	Conidia	71	Glaz (1955)	3 months	Glaz (1955)
Neurospora tetrasperma	Ascospores	5	Y. Lingappa and Sussman (1959)	>3 years	Sussman (1960)
Tilletia levis [*T. foetida*]	Chlamydospores	7.9	Zellner (1911)	>3 years	Hahne (1925)
T. tritici [*T. caries*]	Chlamydospores	8.0	Zellner (1911)	>3 years	Hahne (1925)
Aspergillus oryzae	Conidia	17.4	Sumi (1928)	>22 years	McCrea (1923)
A. fumigatus	Conidia	7	Zöbl (1950)	>15 years	Roberg (1948)

[a] Taken from Sussman and Halvorson (1966).

related to the dramatic change in the stability of *Escherichia coli* which occurs below 60% relative humidity, at about the same point when structural water bound to macromolecules like DNA is removed (Falk *et al.*, 1963). Webb *et al.* (1964) and Webb (1965) have presented evidence to suggest that a physical change in an essential macromolecule occurs when water is removed, and that substances which protect cells during drying replace water as a stabilizer. Perhaps one of the roles that is played by substances that appear in high concentrations in spores, such as dipicolinic acid in bacteria, and trehalose and mannitol in fungi, is as protection against drought injury.

C. *Competitive Saprophytic Ability*

1. *Factors Involved*

The success of *Trichoderma viride* in recolonizing soils treated with carbon disulfide and formaldehyde, although it is only moderately resistant to these agents, suggests that passive factors alone do not suffice to ensure survival. Among the active modes of survival can be included "competitive saprophytic ability." Although dormant stages may survive for long periods their life is limited by their maximum longevity, which is defined by their potential viability as modified by the environment. Thus, unfavorable ecological conditions may reduce survivability drastically. But organisms that can exist as active saprophytes can survive indefinitely under the right conditions (Park, 1965).

The term "competitive saprophytic ability" was first introduced by Garrett (1951, 1956) and includes the following: (a) high growth rate, and rapid spore germination; (b) good enzymatic complement and potential; (c) capacity for production of antibiotics; and (d) tolerance to antibiotics produced by competitors. It is defined by Garrett ". . . as the summation of physiological characteristics that make for success in competitive colonization of dead organic substrates." Ability to utilize substrates in pure culture is not meant; what is meant instead is the potential of an organism to colonize in a competitive natural situation.

Many saprophytes can germinate and grow very rapidly when substrate is near. Such rapid exploitation of the resources of an environment can spell the difference between success and failure in highly competitive microbial societies for, as Garrett (1963) has said, starvation is the commonest cause of death in soil, and it is probably true for other habitats as well. Opportunities to develop are fleeting when antibiotic producers are in the vicinity, or when substrate is preempted by a more rapid grower. Although it cannot be assumed uncritically that antibiotics are always produced and are effective in soil, failure to find measurable amounts in soil is not a conclusive argument against their presence (Brian, 1949; Garrett, 1956; Jackson, 1965).

Parasites also may benefit from high growth rates which ensure infection before resistance is engendered in the maturing host. On the other hand, the successful parasite cannot be overaggressive, lest too rapid growth, enzymatic lysis, or toxin formation put a precocious end to a source of food.

As Hawker (1957a) has argued, colonization of unusual habitats may aid the survival of some fungi. There are numerous microenvironments which may vary in their physical or chemical aspects, and in the degree to which they can serve to sustain a microflora. To this extent, the enzymatic capacity of an organism is a determinant of its survivability under conditions where food is limiting or competition keen. The range of substrates that is available to microorganisms and techniques used in their study are reviewed by Burges (1958), Warcup (1965), Park (1965), and in Chapter 13.

Although prototrophy often is an advantage to organisms, metabolic incapacities sometimes confer advantages in survival. For example, in *Ophiostoma multiannulatum*, conidia of deficient mutants are more viable than are those of unmutated strains under some circumstances (Fries, 1948). Also, spores of a biotin-requiring mutant of *Aspergillus nidulans* died rapidly in a biotin-deficient medium, but the introduction of a second nutritional requirement greatly increased survival in minimal media (MacDonald and Pontecorvo, 1953). Similar effects in inositolless strains of *Neurospora*, whose longevity on deficient media was extended seventyfold if a tryptophan requirement was added, have led to a useful technique for the selection of auxotrophic mutants (Lester and Gross, 1959). Such data have led to the suggestion (Sussman and Halvorson, 1966) that antibiotics may extend the life of some organisms, as in the case of ethionine which prolongs the life of conidia of inositolless strains of *Neurospora* (Strauss, 1958).

Mention of the inositolless strains of *Neurospora* and the biotin-deficient ones of *Aspergillus*, which "commit suicide" on unsupplemented media, is a reminder that a partially deficient medium may be more detrimental to survival than a completely depauperate one. However, only a few "suicide" strains have been described from laboratory experiments alone, so their occurrence and role in nature are largely unknown; the recent work of Garrett (1966) with cereal foot-rot fungi suggests, however, that excess nitrogen may shorten survival under certain conditions in nature.

2. *Relation to Inoculum Potential*

Despite the fact that *Ophiobolus graminis, Cochliobolus sativus,* and *Cercosporella herpotrichoides* are poor competitive saprophytes and are not remarkably resistant to deleterious environmental conditions, they manage to thrive and survive in soils which teem with antagonistic and parasitic neighbors (Garrett, 1963). Apparently, survival is accomplished in these fungi when their "inoculum potential" at the surface of available substrates is higher than those of its competitors. Garrett (1956) defines inoculum potential as "the energy of growth of a fungus (or other micro-organism) available for colonization of a substrate at the surface of the substrate to be colonized."

It is easy to see how an antibiotic producer might gain advantage by the release of its toxin from a concentrated mass of fungal material, but the effect of inoculum potential in the cases mentioned above, and others cited by Garrett (1956), is more difficult to interpret. One possibility is that considerable energy must be expended during the initial breakdown of poorly available carbon sources like lignin. The experiments of Gottlieb *et al.* (1950) suggest that very small amounts of glucose will suffice to initiate and sustain lignin degradation, so Garrett has suggested that an autocatalytic process like induced enzyme biosynthesis may explain the effect of high inoculum potential. Norkrans (1950) has explained the effect of "start-glucose" on cellobiose, lichenin, and cellulose degradation by *Tricholoma* in a similar way.

Another explanation advanced by Garrett (1963) involves the inability of *Cercosporella herpotrichoides* to use even so readily available a source of cellulose as carboxymethylcellulose, despite its ability to survive for 3 years in buried infected wheat straw (Table II; Macer, 1961). Thus it is possible that the colonization of wheat straw by cellulose decomposers coming in after *C. herpotrichoides* is controlled and limited by prior utilization of the more easily available food materials by the latter.

Therefore, the inoculum potentials of competing saprophytes often will determine their survival, not only in virgin substrates, but in already colonized ones as well. And, it is possible to speculate on the manner in which high inoculum potential will ensure antibiotic-producers a foothold in available substrates, which determines the concentration of the antibiotic that can be brought to bear during further exploitation of the environment. Yet, convincing proof that these models represent the realities of microbial interactions in nature remains to be provided.

D. *Disseminability*

Dispersal of organisms is required to avoid, or overcome, crowding so that geographic extension serves an important function in the history of species. But even individuals within their circumscribed ranges must find their way to habitats where their development can be furthered. And, finally, adjustment to a fickle environment requires the capacity for genetic change, which is fostered by dispersal in the ways discussed on page 475. Therefore, disseminability is vital to the survival of fungi and is treated in detail in the books of Gregory (1961) and Ingold (1965) and in Volume II, Chapters 21 and 22.

A large number of devices have been evolved by fungi to assist in the release and take-off of propagules (cf. Ingold, Volume II, Chapter 21). Often parallel mechanisms are developed by taxonomically diverse fungi, such as the coprophiles, which form spore guns which can be trained phototropically on a target area like surrounding grass. Or, taxonomically related organisms like the mucors can establish diverse methods of dissemination, despite their apparent phylogenetic similarities. So, coping with problems of dispersal has resulted in the development of structures which characterize whole groups of fungi, or which help to distinguish between them. Of course, "incidental" mechanisms often aid in dispersal but are probably less important than the "specialized" mechanisms that have been evolved by fungi (cf. Gregory, Volume II, Chapter 22).

Although spores are the most important units of dispersal, the data reviewed by Gregory (1961) suggest that yeasts often are widely disseminated and other vegetative structures sometimes are. Ingold points out that during dissemination natural selection can operate on any, or all, of the critical phases of a propagule's existence, including liberation, transport, arrival and arrest on a substratum, and germination. Thus, adaptive significance may derive from any or all features of propagules which affect dispersal, such as size, shape, color, contents, arrangement, and their role must have ". . . had a great impact on the structure of fungi and, therefore, in trying to understand structure, its relationship to spore dispersal should be constantly in mind" (Ingold, 1965).

For example, the size of spores is an important determinant of the distance of dispersal, larger spores, or spore-aggregates, being shot to greater distances, both horizontally and vertically. On the other hand, this advantage must be balanced against the greater tendency of such spores to fall. The ways in which spore structures such as walls can affect survival include restricting metabolism, thereby enforcing dormancy, and protection against desiccation and other deleterious influences like radiations and chemicals. So it is thought by some that melanized spores gain survival advantage by absorbing otherwise toxic radiations (Sussman and Halvorson, 1966), although the paucity of ultraviolet light on earth might make this role somewhat unlikely. Shape of spores may have great selective effects among aquatic fungi, where the tetraradiate form appears to be useful as an anchor (Ingold, 1959), and in those ascomycetes whose ascospores have blunt anterior ends and tapered posterior ones (Ingold, 1954).

A frequent means through which the environment and organisms interact is in the rhythms of fruiting and spore discharge. As will be noted in the next section (page 475), such rhythms are manifestations of the ability of many organisms to respond to environmental cues, and fungi are no exception. That dispersal rhythms are common in fungi can be seen in Table IV in which some of these are summarized. They range in period from annually (*Cladosporium*) to daily, the latter being by far the most frequent. The peaks of discharge among fungi with diurnal rhythms can occur at any time of the day or night and sometimes peaks at both times may be displayed, as in the rusts studied by Pady *et al.* (1965). Temperature may determine such rhythms, as in *Pilobolus sphaerosporus* (Uebelmesser, 1954), but most often discharge can be related to humidity and light. The majority of fruiting rhythms are determined by light although temperature may also induce zoning (Hafiz, 1951). Moreover, endogenous rhythms exist (circadian and others) which seem not to require external pacemakers, although they may have to be set by light (see Volume I, Chapter 27).

The biological role of such timing devices often may be guessed, for survival value could attach, for example, to daytime peaks for wind-dispersed fungi because of the development of thermal turbulence which results in relatively great wind velocities. Also, nocturnally discharged spores might benefit if they depend upon droplets for infection or if they lose their viability quickly when exposed to the relatively drier atmospheres and warmer temperatures of daylight.

However, the phenology of organisms is selected for as a result of the interaction of many environmental variables, so the biological significance of an adaptation may be difficult to evaluate. This is the case with *Sphaerobolus stellatus,* which discharges its glebal masses diurnally when grown under alternating light and dark conditions. But not only is light absolutely necessary for the initiation of fruit bodies, but for their further development as well; and the very last stage of their development appears to be retarded by light (Alasoadura, 1963). Moreover, no fruiting occurs unless cultures are held below 25°C, and there is a diurnal rhythm of discharge which seems to be unrelated to the previous period of illumination (Engel and Friederichsen, 1964), when cultures are kept in darkness. So, although *S. stellatus* appears to discharge only during daylight hours under some circumstances, it will do so in the dark under others. To further complicate matters, this fungus displays a discharge rhythm with a period of 10–12 days when kept in constant light and temperature (Alasoadura, 1963). So, the patterns of spore discharge in relation to the environ-

TABLE IV
TYPES OF DISSEMINATION RHYTHMS DISPLAYED BY FUNGI

Organism	Stage	Peak of discharge	Environmental conditions	Period	Reference
Phytophthora infestans	Spores	Forenoon	Agric. land	24 hr	Hirst (1953)
Peronospora tabacina	Conidia	Early A.M.	Tobacco fields	24 hr	Waggoner and Taylor (1958)
Sporobolomyces sp.	Spores	Night	Island estuary	24 hr	Gregory and Sreeramulu (1958)
Ustilago nuda	Spores	Noon	Agric. land	24 hr	Sreeramulu (1962)
Puccinia polysora	Uredospores	9 A.M.	Agric. land (dry season)	24 hr	Cammack (1955)
P. polysora	Uredospores	1 P.M.	Agric. land (wet season)	24 hr	Cammack (1955)
P. recondita	Uredospores	4–5 P.M.	Agric. land	24 hr	Pady *et al.* (1965)
P. recondita (minor peak)	Uredospores	10 P.M.–2 A.M.	Agric. land	24 hr	Pady *et al.* (1965)
Cordana musae and *Deightoniella torulosa*	Conidia	6–8 A.M.	Banana plantation	24 hr	Meredith (1961, 1962)
Cladosporium herbarum	Conidia	Afternoon	Agric. land	24 hr	Hirst (1953)
C. herbarum	Conidia	Summer	Agric. land	Annual	Hyde and Williams (1953)
Sphaerobolus stellatus	Gleba	—	Constant light and temperature	10–12 days	Alasoadura (1963)
S. stellatus	Gleba	Light	12L:12D[a]	24 hr	Friederichsen and Engel (1960)
S. stellatus	Gleba	Dark	Constant dark	24 hr	Engel and Friederichsen (1964)

[a] 12 hours light and 12 hours dark.

ment can be very complex and their role in nature becomes, correspondingly, more difficult to understand.

E. Responsiveness (Timing)

Survivability is enhanced when an organism can respond to environmental stimuli at a time when it is propitious to do so. This response may involve the beginning of active vegetative growth, or its cessation, with or without the formation of propagules or other morphologically different stages. Thus, environmental cues must be recognized and the necessary changes effected, if survival is to be maximal.

Spore formation and dormancy often are timed responses which serve this function and are discussed in this connection in Volume II, Chapter 23 and by Sussman and Halvorson (1966). Thus, the induction of sporulation by the variety of environmental variables described by Hawker (1957b), Cochrane (1958), and Ingold (1965) may often have survival value. Borut's (1960) work provides an example from nature, in that the optimum for sporulation of all the desert fungi she tested was 4–10°C higher than for growth, suggesting that selective advantage is conferred on those organisms that fruit before the advent of unfavorable weather.

A case where a cue stimulates germination in nature is that of basidiospores of *Flammula alnicola,* which causes decay of conifers in Canada. These spores are activated by a temperature that occurs in that latitude coincidentally with the start of growth of its host (Denyer, 1960). Other instances can be provided such as the activation of spores by exudates from hosts (Sussman, 1965b) and, possibly, the reversal of the widespread soil fungistasis by glucose and other substrates (Garrett, 1956).

On the other hand, the suppression of activity often may be of advantage to fungi, as with resting spores of *Plasmodiophora brassicae* whose survival is enhanced by the presence of endogenous inhibitors (Macfarlane, 1952). Similar results have been obtained with spores of *Cochliobolus sativus* kept in soil (Chinn and Tinline, 1964). Perhaps the fungistatic principle in soil imposes a type of dormancy upon spores which derive survival value through this means. Self-inhibitors are widely distributed among the fungi (Volume II, Chapter 23) and help to prevent the germination of spores at the place where they are produced. Thus, it is a common observation that ascospores often do not germinate within the ascus, despite the suitability of conditions for their development, and many other examples could be cited. Thereby, dissemination to new environments and subsequent mixing of gene pools may be engendered.

Biological clocks are a form of timing device used by many organisms, including fungi (Volume I, Chapter 27). Circadian as well as noncircadian rhythms (Neurath and Berliner, 1964; Sussman *et al.,* 1965) have been described for vegetative growth, spore discharge (see page 472) and fruiting, a familiar example of the latter being fairy rings. The period of these ranges from hours to days, with varying dependence upon the medium, temperature, or light, depending upon the type of rhythm. Although much is known about the physiology of such rhythms, only their function in spore discharge can be guessed at in those cases where dissemination is favored by release at certain times of the day (Ingold, 1965). However, sometimes there are discrepancies in the data, such as extra peaks in the occurrence of spores, and the possibility of periodicities in wind turbulence. As for the other types of rhythms, much less is known of their role in nature, if any, so that more information is needed.

F. *Mutational Capacity*

Because the gene pool is the ultimate source of all inherited variation and controls processes like protein synthesis as well, the mutational capacity of an organism is a vital determinant of adaptability and, hence, of survivability.

In the fungi, genetic recombination usually is closely associated with sporulation (Gregory, 1952; Bonner, 1958), and often with the formation of resistant spores or sporangia. Therefore, such spores are of very variable genetic constitution, affording the organism the advantage that resistant and disseminable structures are the site of variations that may be adapted to new or changed environmental or geographic situations.

Exceptions to this rule occur, but often they are more apparent than real. For example, meiosis in the mucors probably occurs when a resistant zygospore germinates to form an abbreviated mycelium from which an asexual sporangium is formed. Asexual spores are then released from the secondary resistant spore which forms within this sporangium. Thus, in this case, recombinant nuclei are not distributed until after the secondary resistant spore is formed. The teliospores of rusts are another exception in that they are resting spores which, upon germination, form a promycelium in which meiosis occurs. Basidiospores, which form on the promycelium, distribute the recombinant nuclei. Thus, although the site of meiosis may be removed from that where the recombinant nuclei are formed into spores, recombination usually is carried out in a resistant stage. Rusts, in which evanescent basidiospores are produced, may be a true exception to this rule.

Imperfect fungi which form resistant stages are a valid extension of the rule. Thus, new heterokaryons of different genetic constitution are formed in macroconidia of several species. Furthermore, new combinations of nuclei result upon the germination of uninucleate spores (microconidia), therefore, asexually as well as sexually formed spores may be the site of new recombinations.

Heterogeneity of the genome and maintenance of mutant nuclei are assured by the coexistence of numerous nuclei in the same mycelium (Lindegren, 1942; and Volume II, Chapter 15). Heterokaryons permit the survival of mutant genomes even under conditions where such nuclei are selected against by growth on deficient media (R. H. Davis, 1959). Survivability is, of course, enhanced by the maintenance of such genetic heterogeneity, which is a reservoir of variability when new environments are to be exploited. On the other hand, the accumulation of disadvantageous mutations may reduce survivability, whether the deleterious genetic elements are nuclear or cytoplasmic (Volume II, Chapter 15). Therefore, there may be selective advantage in the periodic isolation of the components of a heterokaryotic organism, such as occurs in the formation of microconidia and certain other types of spores. The formation of new heterokaryons, or the occurrence of new mutations, after spore germination, assures further variability.

Somatic recombination also occurs in fungi and is another means through which variation, and thereby survivability, is engendered (Volume II, Chapter 15).

III. CONCLUSION

The fact that survival, especially in nature, depends upon the interaction of numerous interacting environmental and organismal elements, means that studies of the effects of single isolated variables oversimplify the issues. Furthermore, conclusions derived from laboratory cultures must be tempered by recognition of the extreme heterogeneity of microbial populations and, as was discussed in the previous section, their mutability. Consequently, the accuracy of extrapolations from such studies to natural situations is difficult to evaluate. Nevertheless, under any circumstances there is the biological equivalent of the "uncertainty principle" such that any manipulation is likely to disturb a natural situation. Therefore, such upsets must be reckoned with as part of biological research, and it is through laboratory studies in combination with those in the field that an understanding of survival of fungi in nature will be obtained.

REFERENCES

Acha, I. G., J. A. Leal, and J. R. Villanueva. (1965). Lysis of uredospore germ tubes of rusts by species of *Verticillium*. *Phytopathology* **55**: 40–42.

Ainsworth, G. C. (1962). Longevity of *Schizophyllum commune*. II. *Nature* **9**: 1120–1121.

Alasoadura, S. O. (1963). Fruiting in *Sphaerobolus* with special reference to light. *Ann. Botany* (*London*) [N.S.] **27**: 125–145.

Anderson, P. J., and W. H. Rankin. (1914). Endothia canker of chestnut. *Cornell Univ., Agr. Expt. Sta. Bull.* **347**: 661–668.

Arnold, J. R., and W. F. Libby. (1951). Radiocarbon dates. *Science* **113**: 111–120.

Barton, L. V. (1965). Longevity in seeds and in the propagules of fungi. *In* "Handbuch der Pflanzenphysiologie" (A. Lang, ed.), Vol. 15, Part 2, pp. 1058–1085. Springer, Berlin.

Bennett, F. T. (1928). On *Dematium pullulans* DeB. and its ascigerous stage. *Ann. Appl. Biol.* **15**: 371–391.

Bloomfield, B. J., and M. Alexander. (1967). Melanins and resistance of fungi to lysis. *J. Bacteriol.* **93**: 1276–1280.

Blum, H. F. (1961). Does the melanin pigment of human skin have adaptive value? *Quart. Rev. Biol.* **36**: 50–63.

Bonner, J. T. (1958). The relation of spore formation to recombination. *Am. Midland Naturalist* **92**: 193–200.

Borut, S. Y. (1960). An ecological and physiological study of soil fungi of the northern Negev (Israel). *Bull. Res. Council Israel* **D8**: 65–80.

Brefeld, O. (1895). "Mykologie," No. xii. Hemibasidii, Muenster.

Brian, P. W. (1949). The production of antibiotics by microorganisms in relation to biological equilibria in soil. *Symp. Soc. Exptl. Biol.* **3**: 357–372.

Buller, A. H. R. (1933). "Researches on Fungi," Vol. V. Longmans, Green, New York.

Buller, A. H. R. (1934). "Researches on Fungi," Vol. VI. Longmans, Green, New York.

Burges, N. A. (1958). "Microorganisms in the Soil." Hutchinson, London.

Butler, F. C. (1953). Saprophytic behavior of some cereal rotting fungi. III. Saprophytic survival in wheat strains buried in soil. *Ann. Appl. Biol.* **40**: 305–311.

Butler, F. C. (1959). Saprophytic behaviour of some cereal root-rot fungi. IV. Saprophytic survival in soils of high and low fertility. *Ann. Appl. Biol.* **47**: 28–36.

Cammack, R. H. (1955). Saesonal changes in three common constituents of the air spora of southern Nigeria. *Nature* **176**: 1270–1272.

Carter, H. P., and J. L. Lockwood. (1957). Lysis of fungi by soil microorganisms and fungicides including antibiotics. *Phytopathology* **47**: 154–158.

Chamberlain, D. W., and J. L. Allison. (1945). The brown leaf spot on *Bromus inermis* caused by *Pyrenophora bromi*. *Phytopathology* **35**: 241–248.

Chaney, R. W. (1951). How old are Manchurian lotus seeds? *Garden J., N. Y. Botan. Gardens* **1**: 137.

Cherewick, W. J. (1944). Studies on the biology of *Erysiphe graminis* D. C. *Can. J. Res.* **C22**: 52–86.

Chinn, S. H. F. (1953). A slide technique for the study of fungi and actinomycetes in soil with special reference to *Helminthosporium sativum*. *Can. J. Botany* **31**: 718–724.

Chinn, S. H. F., and R. J. Ledingham. (1958). Applications of a new laboratory method for the determination of the survival of *Helminthosporium sativum* spores in the soil. *Can. J. Botany* **36**: 289–295.

Chinn, S. H. F., and R. D. Tinline. (1964). Inherent germinability and survival of spores of *Cochliobolus sativus*. *Phytopathology* **54**: 349–352.

Clerk, G. C., and M. F. Madelin. (1965). The longevity of conidia of three insect-parasitizing hyphomycetes. *Brit. Mycol. Soc. Trans.* **48**: 193–209.

Cochrane, V. W. (1958). "Physiology of Fungi." Wiley, New York.

Coley-Smith, J. R. (1959). Studies of the biology of *Sclerotium cepivorum* Berk. III. Host range; persistence and viability of sclerotia. *Ann. Appl. Biol.* **47**: 511–518.

Cooney, D. G., and R. Emerson. (1964). "Thermophilic Fungi." Freeman, San Francisco, California.

Corner, E. J. H. (1935). Observations on resistance to powdery mildews. *New Phytologist* **34**: 180–200.

Davis, R. H. (1959). Asexual selection in *Neurospora crassa. Genetics* **44**: 1291–1308.

Davis, W. H. (1924). Spore germination of *Ustilago striaeformis. Phytopathology* **14**: 251–267.

de Bruyn, H. L. G. (1926). The overwintering of *Phytophthora infestans* (Mont.) DeBy. *Phytopathology* **16**: 121–140.

Deep, I. W., and M. E. Corden. (1961). Relative sensitivity of fungus spores and mycelium to toxic agents. *In* "Biological Investigations for Secondary School Students," pp. 103–105. Am. Inst. Biol. Sci. Curriculum Study, Boulder, Colorado.

Denyer, W. B. G. (1960). Cultural studies of *Flammula alnicola* (Fr.) Kummer and *Flammula conissans* (Fr.) Gillet. *Can. J. Botany* **38**: 909–920.

Domsch, K. H. (1958). Die Prüfung von Bodenfungiciden. I. Pilz-substrat-Fungicid-Kombinationen. *Plant Soil* **10**: 114–131.

Durrell, L. W. (1966). Personal communication.

Durrell, L. W., and L. M. Shields. (1960). Fungi isolated in culture from soils of the Nevada Test Site. *Mycologia* **52**: 636–641.

Elliott, R. P., and H. D. Michener. (1965). Factors affecting the growth of psychrophilic microorganisms in foods—a review. *U.S. Dept. Agr. Tech. Bull.* **1320**.

Engel, H., and I. Friederichsen. (1964). Der Abschuss der Sporangiolen von *Sphaerobolus stellatus* (Thode) Pers. in kontinuierlicher Dunkelheit. *Planta* **61**: 361–370.

English, H., and F. Gerhardt. (1946). The effect of ultraviolet radiation on the viability of fungous spores and on the development of decay in sweet cherries. *Phytopathology* **36**: 100–111.

Evans, E. (1965). Survival of *Fomes annosus* in infected roots in soil. *Nature* **207**: 318–319.

Falk, M., K. A. Hartman, and R. C. Lord. (1963). Hydration of deoxyribonucleic acid. III. A spectroscopic study of the effect of hydration on the structure of deoxyribonucleic acid. *J. Am. Chem. Soc.* **85**: 391–394.

Fellows, H. (1941). Effect of certain environmental conditions on the prevalence of *Ophiobolus graminis* in the soil. *J. Agr. Res.* **63**: 715–726.

Fennell, D. I. (1960). Conservation of fungous cultures. *Botan. Rev.* **26**: 79–141.

Fergus, C. L. (1959). The influence of environment upon germination and longevity of aeciospores and urediospores of *Coleosporium solidaginis. Mycologia* **51**: 44–48.

Fischer, G. W. (1936). The longevity of smut spores in herbarium specimens. *Phytopathology* **26**: 1118–1127.

Flood, A. E., and D. S. Kirkham. (1960). The effect of some phenolic compounds on the growth and sporulation of two *Venturia* species. *In* "Phenolics in Plants in Health and Disease" (J. B. Pridham, ed.), pp. 81–85. Pergamon Press, Oxford.

Friederichsen, I., and H. Engel. (1960). Der Abschussrhythmus der Fruchtkörper von *Sphaerobolus stellatus* (Thode) Pers. *Planta* **55:** 313–326.

Fries, N. (1941). Über die Sporenkeimung bei einigen Gasteromyceten und mykorrhizabildenden Hymenomyceten. *Arch. Mikrobiol.* **12:** 266–284.

Fries, N. (1946). X-ray induced parathiotrophy in *Ophiostoma. Svensk Botan. Tidskr.* **40:** 127–140.

Fries, N. (1948). Viability and resistance of spontaneous mutations in *Ophiostoma* representing different degrees of heterotrophy. *Physiol. Plantarum* **1:** 330–341.

Fulton, H. R., and W. W. Coblentz. (1929). The fungicidal action of ultraviolet irradiation. *J. Agr. Res.* **38:** 159–168.

Funk, A. (1963). Studies in the genus *Caliciopsis. Can. J. Botany* **41:** 503–543.

Gadd, C. H., and L. S. Bertus. (1928). *Corticium vagum* B. and C. the cause of a disease of *Vigna oligosperma* and other plants in Ceylon. *Ann. Roy. Botan. Garden Peradeniya* **11:** 27–49.

Gäumann, E. A. (1950). *In* "Principles of Plant Infection" (W. B. Brierley, ed.). Crosby Lockwood, London.

Garrett, S. D. (1951). Ecology of the root-inhabiting fungi. *Biol. Rev.* **25:** 220–254.

Garrett, S. D. (1956). "Biology of Root-Infecting Fungi." Cambridge Univ. Press, London and New York.

Garrett, S. D. (1963). "Soil Fungi and Soil Fertility." Pergamon Press, Oxford.

Garrett, S. D. (1966). Cellulose-decomposing ability of some cereal foot-rot fungi in relation to their saprophytic survival. *Brit. Mycol. Soc. Trans.* **49:** 57–68.

Gates, D. M. (1966). Spectral distribution of solar radiation at the earth's surface. *Science* **151:** 523–529.

Glaz, E. T. (1955). Researches about the viability and preservation of ergot conidia of *Claviceps purpurea* (Fr.) Tul. grown in submerged culture. *Acta Microbiol. Acad. Sci. (Hung.)* **2:** 315–325.

Goldstrohm, D. D., and V. G. Lilly. (1965). The effect of light on the survival of pigmented and nonpigmented cells of *Dacryopinax spathularia. Mycologia* **57:** 612–623.

Good, H. M., and W. Spanis. (1958). Some factors affecting the germination of spores of *Fomes igniarus* var. *populinus* (Neuman) Campbell, and the significance of these factors in infection. *Can. J. Botany* **36:** 421–437.

Gottlieb, S., W. C. Day, and M. J. Pelczar. (1950). The biological degradation of lignin. II. The adaptation of white-rot fungi to growth on lignin media. *Phytopathology* **40:** 926–935.

Gregory, P. H. (1952). Fungus spores. *Brit. Mycol. Soc. Trans.* **35:** 1–18.

Gregory, P. H. (1961). "The Microbiology of the Atmosphere." Wiley (Interscience), New York.

Gregory, P. H., and T. Sreeramulu. (1958). Air spora of an estuary. *Brit. Mycol. Soc. Trans.* **41:** 145–156.

Hafiz, A. (1951). Cultural studies of *Ascochyta rabiei* with special reference to zonation. *Brit. Mycol. Soc. Trans.* **34:** 259–269.

Hahne, J. (1925). Untersuchungen über die Keimungsbedingungen von *Tilletia* sporen. *Kuhn.-Arch.* **9:** 224–226.

Harrison, C. H. (1942). Longevity of the spores of some wood-destroying hymenomycetes. *Phytopathology* **32:** 1096–1097.

Hart, H. (1926). Factors affecting the development of flax rust, *Melampsora lini* (Pers.) Lév. *Phytopathology* **16:** 185–205.

Hawker, L. E. (1957a). Ecological factors and the survival of fungi. *Symp. Soc. Gen. Microbiol.* **7**: 238–258.

Hawker, L. E. (1957b). "The Physiology of Reproduction in Fungi." Cambridge Univ. Press, London and New York.

Heald, F. D. (1937). "Introduction to Plant Pathology." McGraw-Hill, New York.

Henry, A. W. (1931). The natural microflora of the soil in relation to the foot-rot problem in wheat. *Can. J. Res.* **C4**: 69–77.

Hesseltine, C. W. (1947). Viability of some mold cultures. *Mycologia* **39**: 126–128.

Hesseltine, C. W., B. J. Bradle, and C. R. Benjamin. (1960). Further investigations on the preservation of molds. *Mycologia* **52**: 762–774.

Hirst, J. M. (1953). Changes in atmospheric spore content: diurnal periodicity and the effects of weather. *Brit. Mycol. Soc. Trans.* **36**: 375–393.

Hodapp, E. L. (1942). Some factors inducing sclerotization in Mycetozoa. *Biodynamica* **4**: 33–46.

Hyde, H. A., and D. A. Williams. (1953). The incidence of *Cladosporium herbarum* in the outdoor air at Cardiff, 1949–50. *Brit. Mycol. Soc. Trans.* **36**: 260–266.

Iichinska, E. (1960). Some physiological features of asporogenous mutants of bacilli. *Microbiology* (*USSR*) (*English Transl.*) **29**: 147–150.

Ingold, C. T. (1954). Ascospore form. *Brit. Mycol. Soc. Trans.* **37**: 19–21.

Ingold, C. T. (1959). Submerged aquatic Hyphomycetes. *J. Quekett Microscop. Club* [4] **5**: 115–130.

Ingold, C. T. (1965). "Spore Liberation." Oxford Univ. Press (Clarendon), London and New York.

Jackson, R. M. (1965). Antibiosis and fungistasis of soil microorganisms. *In* "Ecology of Soil-borne Plant Pathogens—Prelude to Biological Control" (K. F. Baker and W. C. Snyder, eds.), pp. 363–369. Univ. of California Press, Berkeley, California.

Johnson, L. F., and T. S. Osborne. (1964). Survival of fungi in soil exposed to gamma radiation. *Can. J. Botany* **42**: 105–113.

Johnson, T. (1941). Longevity of teliospores of *Puccinia graminis* under laboratory conditions. *Phytopathology* **31**: 197–198.

Kaung, Z. (1956). Persistence and movement of *Phytophthora infestans* in soil. *Brit. Mycol. Soc. Trans.* **39**: 385.

Keilin, D. (1959). The Leeuwenhoek lecture. The problem of anabiosis or latent life: History and current concept. *Proc. Roy. Soc.* **B150**: 149–192.

King, C. J., H. F. Loomis, and C. Hope. (1931). Studies on sclerotia and mycelial strands of the cotton root rot fungus. *J. Agr. Res.* **42**: 827–840.

Kuehn, H. H., and M. F. Gunderson. (1962). Psychrophilic and mesophilic fungi in fruit-filled pastries. *Appl. Microbiol.* **10**: 354–358.

Kuehn, H. H., and M. F. Gunderson. (1963). Psychrophilic and mesophilic fungi in frozen food products. *Appl. Microbiol.* **11**: 352–356.

Kuo, M.-J., and M. Alexander. (1967). Inhibition of the lysis of fungi by melanins. *J. Bacteriol.* **94**: 624–629.

Leach, L. D., and A. E. Davey. (1938). Determining the sclerotial population of *Sclerotium rolfsii* by soil analysis and predicting losses of sugar beets on the basis of the analysis. *J. Agr. Res.* **56**: 619–631.

Leal, J. A., and J. R. Villanueva. (1962). Fungilytic activity of a species of *Verticillium*. *Science* **136**: 715–716.

Lester, H. E., and S. R. Gross. (1959). Efficient method for selection of auxotrophic mutants of Neurospora. *Science* **129**: 572.

Leveillé, J. H. (1843). Mémoire sur le genre *Sclerotium*. *Ann. Sci. Nat.: Botan.* [2] **20**: 218–248.

Levitt, J. (1956). "The Hardiness of Plants." Academic Press, New York.

Lindegren, C. C. (1942). The use of fungi in modern genetic analysis. *Iowa State J. Sci.* **16**: 271–290.

Lindegren, C. C., and E. Hamilton. (1944). Autolysis and sporulation in the yeast colony. *Botan. Gaz.* **105**: 316–321.

Linderman, R. G., and T. A. Tousson. (1966). Behavior of albino chlamydospores of *Thielaviopsis basicola*. *Phytopathology* **56**: 887.

Linford, M. B., and R. E. Vaughn. (1925). Root disease of peas. Some ways to avoid it. *Ext. Circ. Wisconsin Coll. Agr.* **188**.

Lingappa, B. T., and J. L. Lockwood. (1961). The nature of the widespread soil fungistasis. *J. Gen. Microbiol.* **26**: 473–485.

Lingappa, Y., and A. S. Sussman. (1959). Changes in the heat-resistance of ascospores of *Neurospora* upon germination. *Am. J. Botany* **46**: 671–678.

Lingappa, Y., A. S. Sussman, and I. A. Bernstein. (1963). Effect of light and media upon growth and melanin formation in *Aureobasidium pullulans* (De By.) Arn. (=*Pullularia pullulans*). *Mycopathol. Mycol. Appl.* **20**: 109–128.

Lister, A. (1888). Notes on the plasmodium of *Badhamia utricularias* and *Brefeldia maxima*. *Ann. Botany* (*London*) **2**: 1–24.

Lloyd, A. B., R. L. Noveroske, and J. L. Lockwood. (1965). Lysis of fungal mycelium by *Streptomyces* spp. and their chitinase systems. *Phytopathology* **55**: 871–875.

Lockwood, J. L. (1959). Streptomyces spp. as a cause of natural fungitoxicity in soils. *Phytopathology* **49**: 327–331.

Lockwood, J. L. (1960). Lysis of mycelium of plant pathogenic fungi by natural soil. *Phytopathology* **50**: 787–789.

Lowther, C. (1950). Chlamydospore germination in physiologic races of *Tilletia caries* and *Tilletia foetida*. *Phytopathology* **40**: 590–603.

McAulay, A. L., and J. M. Ford. (1947). Saltant production in the fungus *Chaetomium globosum* by ultra-violet light, and its relation to absorption processes. *Heredity* **1**: 247–257.

McCrea, A. (1923). Longevity of spores of *Aspergillus oryzae* and *Rhizopus nigricans*. *Science* **58**: 426.

McCrea, A. (1931). Longevity of conidia of common fungi under laboratory conditions. *Papers Mich. Acad. Sci.* **13**: 165–166.

MacDonald, K. D., and G. Pontecorvo. (1953). The genetics of *Aspergillus nidulans*. *Advan. Genet.* **5**: 142–238.

Macer, R. C. F. (1961). The survival of *Cercosporella herpotrichoides* Fron in wheat straw. *Ann. Appl. Biol.* **49**: 165–172.

MacFarlane, I. (1952). Factors affecting the survival of *Plasmodiophora brassicae* Wor. in the soil and its assessment by a host test. *Ann. Appl. Biol.* **39**: 239–256.

McKay, R. (1935). Germination of resting spores of onion mildew (*Peronospora schleideni*). *Nature* **135**: 306–307.

McKay, R. (1939). Observations on onion downy mildew caused by the fungus *Peronospora schleideniana* W. G. Sm. *J. Roy. Hort. Soc.* **64**: 272–285.

McKeen, C. D., and R. N. Wensley. (1961)). Longevity of *Fusarium oxysporum* in soil tube culture. *Science* **134**: 1528–1529.

McKnight, K. (1960). Personal communication.

McLaughlin, W. D., and R. P. True. (1952). The effects of temperature and

humidity on the longevity of conidia of *Chalara quercina*. *Phytopathology* **42**: 470.
McLean, J. G., D. J. Le Tourneau, and J. W. Guthrie. (1961). Relation of histochemical tests for phenols to *Verticillium* wilt resistance of potatoes. *Phytopathology* **51**: 84–89.
Mahmoud, S. A. Z., M. Abou El-Fadl, and M. Kh. Elmofty. (1964). Studies on the rhizosphere microflora of a desert plant. *Folia Microbiol.* **9**: 1–8.
Mamukinian, G., and M. H. Briggs. (1965). "Current Aspects of Exobiology." Pergamon Press, Oxford.
Maneval, W. E. (1924). The viability of uredospores. *Phytopathology* **14**: 403–407.
Manners, J. G. (1951). The establishment and maintenance of pure cultures of rust fungi. *Indian Phytopathol.* **4**: 21–24.
Markert, C. L. (1953). Lethal and mutagenic effects of ultraviolet radiation on *Glomerella* conidia. *Exptl. Cell Res.* **4**: 427–435.
Menzies, J. D. (1963). Survival of microbial plant pathogens in soil. *Botan. Rev.* **29**: 79–122.
Meredith, D. S. (1961). Fruit-spot ("speckle") of Jamaican bananas caused by *Deightoniella torulosa* (Syd.) Ellis. IV. Further observations on spore dispersal. *Ann. Appl. Biol.* **49**: 488–496.
Meredith, D. S. (1962). Dispersal of conidia of *Cordana musae* (Zimm.) Höhnel in Jamaican banana plantations. *Ann. Appl. Biol.* **50**: 263–267.
Merek, E. L., and C. L. Fergus. (1954). The effect of temperature and relative humidity on the spores of the oak wilt fungus. *Phytopathology* **44**: 61–64.
Metzger, I. (1942). Versuche zur Aufbewahrung lebender Sporen von Weizen-und Gerstenmehlau. *Kuhn-Arch.* **56**: 163–172.
Miller, R. E., and L. A. Simons. (1962). Survival of bacteria after twenty-one years in the dried state. *J. Bacteriol.* **84**: 1111–1114.
Mitchell, M. (1960). Personal communication.
Moon, P. (1941). Proposed standard solar-radiation curves for engineering use. *J. Franklin Inst.* **230**: 583–617.
Moubasher, A. H. (1963). Selective effects of fumigation with carbon disulphide on the soil fungus flora. *Brit. Mycol. Soc. Trans.* **46**: 338–344.
Nelson, R. E., and S. Wilhelm. (1958). Thermal death range of *Verticillium albo-atrum*. *Phytopathology* **48**: 613–616.
Neurath, P. W., and M. D. Berliner. (1964). Biological rhythms: A new type in strains of a mutant of *Neurospora crassa*. *Science* **146**: 646–647.
Nicot, J. (1960). Some characteristics of the microflora in desert sands. *In* "The Ecology of Soil Fungi" (D. Parkinson and J. S. Waid, eds.), pp. 94–97. Univ. of Liverpool Press, Liverpool.
Noble, R. J. (1934). Note on the longevity of the spores of the fungus *Urocystis tritici* Kern. *J. Proc. Roy. Soc. N. S. Wales* **67**: 403–410.
Norkrans, B. (1950). Studies in growth and cellulolytic enzymes of *Tricholoma*. *Symbolae Botan. Upsalienses* **11**: Part 1, 1–126.
Pady, S. M., C. L. Kramer, V. K. Pathak, F. L. Morgan, and M. A. Bhatti. (1965). Periodicity in airborne cereal rust urediospores. *Phytopathology* **55**: 132–134.
Page, R. M. (1965). The physical environment for fungal growth. *In* "The Fungi" (G. C. Ainsworth and A. S. Sussman, eds.), Vol. 1, pp. 559–574. Academic Press, New York.
Page, R. M., A. F. Sherf, and T. L. Morgan. (1947). The effect of temperature and

relative humidity on the longevity of the conidia of *Helminthosporium oryzae*. *Mycologia* **39**: 158–164.
Pape, H. (1937). Beiträge zur Biologie und Bekämpfung des Kleekrebses (*Sclerotinia trifoliorum* Erikss.). *Arb. Biol. Reichsanstalt Land Forstwirtsch., Berlin-Dahlem* **22**: 159–247.
Park, D. (1955). Experimental studies on the ecology of fungi in soil. *Brit. Mycol. Soc. Trans.* **38**: 130–142.
Park, D. (1965). Survival of microorganisms in soil. *In* "Ecology of Soil-Borne Pathogens—Prelude to Biological Control" (K. F. Baker and W. C. Snyder, eds.), pp. 82–97. Univ. of California Press, Berkeley, California.
Patel, M. K., M. N. Kamat, and G. M. Hingorami. (1950). *Pestalotia psidii* Pat. on Guava. *Indian Phytopathol.* **3**: 165–176.
Porter, R. H. (1955). Longevity of loose smut *Ustilago nuda* (Jens) Kostr. in barley seed. *Phytopathology* **45**: 637–638.
Potgieter, H. J., and M. Alexander. (1966). Susceptibility and resistance of several fungi to microbial lysis. *J. Bacteriol.* **91**: 1526–1532.
Prasada, R. (1948). Studies of the formation and germination of teliospores of rusts. *Indian Phytopathol.* **1**: 119–126.
Rabinovitz-Sereni, D. (1932). Il grado di resistenza di alcuni funghi all'azione de raggi ultravioletti. *Boll. Regia Staz. Patol. Vegetale* [N. S.] **12**: 115–144.
Ramakrishnan, K. (1949). Investigations of general rusts. II. *Uromyces setariae italicae* (Diet.) Yoshino. *Indian Phytopathol.* **2**: 31–34.
Robbins, W. J., V. W. Kavanagh, and F. Kavanagh. (1942). Growth substances and dormancy of spores of *Phycomyces*. *Botan. Gaz.* **104**: 224–242.
Roberg, M. (1948). Über die Lebensdauer von *Aspergillus* Kulturen. *Arch. Mikrobiol.* **14**: 1–11.
Rogers, C. H. (1942). Cotton root rot·studies with special reference to sclerotia, cover crops, rotations, tillage, seeding rates, soil fungicides and effects on seed quality. *Texas Agr. Expt. Sta., Bull.* **614**.
Rosen, H. R., and L. M. Weetman. (1940). Longevity of urediospores of crown rust of oats. *Arkansas Univ. (Fayetteville), Agr. Expt. Sta., Bull.* **391**: 3–20.
Russell, R. C. (1958). Longevity studies with wheat seed and certain seed-borne fungi. *Can. J. Plant Sci.* **38**: 29–33.
Saksena, S. B. (1960). Effect of carbon disulphide fumigation on *Trichoderma viride* and other soil fungi. *Brit. Mycol. Soc. Trans.* **43**: 111–116.
Savile, D. B. O. (1963). Mycology in the Canadian arctic. *J. Arctic Inst. North Am.* **16**: 17–25.
Sawada, S. (1959). Resistance of the spore of a baker's yeast to ethyl alcohol. *Ecol. Rev.* **15**: 23–25.
Schweizer, G. (1947). Über die Kultur von *Empusa muscae* Cohn. und anderen Entomophthoracean auf kalt sterilisierten Nährböden. *Planta* **35**: 132–176.
Seifriz, W., and M. A. Russell. (1936). The fruiting of Myxomycetes. *New Phytologist* **35**: 472–478.
Shands, E. G. (1937). Longevity of *Gibberella saubinetii* and other fungi in barley kernels and its relation to the emetic effect. *Phytopathology* **27**: 749–762.
Shields, L. M., L. W. Durrell, and A. H. Sparrow. (1961). Preliminary observations on radiosensitivity of algae and fungi from soils of the Nevada Test Site. *Ecology* **42**: 440–441.
Siggers, P. V. (1947). Temperature requirements for germination of spores of *Cronartium ribicola*. *Phytopathology* **37**: 855–864.

Smith, E. C. (1929). Longevity of myxomycete spores. *Mycologia* **21**: 321–323.
Sneath, P. H. A. (1962). Longevity of microorganisms. *Nature* **195**: 643–646.
Snell, W. H. (1923). The effect of heat upon the mycelium of certain structural-timber-destroying fungi. *Am. J. Botany* **10**: 399–411.
Spaulding, P. (1922). Investigations of the white pine blister rust. *U.S. Dept. Agr., Tech. Bull.* **957.**
Spaulding, P., and A. Rathbun-Gravatt. (1926). The influence of physical factors on the viability of sporidia of *Cronartium ribicola* Fischer. *J. Agr. Res.* **33**: 397–433.
Sreeramulu, T. (1962). Aerial dissemination of barley loose smut (*Ustilago nuda*). *Brit. Mycol. Soc. Trans.* **45**: 373–384.
Stakman, E. C. (1913). Spore germination of cereal smuts. *Minn., Univ., Agr. Expt. Sta., Tech. Bull.* **133.**
Stokes, J. L. (1963). General biology and nomenclature of psychrophilic micro-organisms. *Proc. 8th Intern. Congr. Microbiol., Montreal, 1962* pp. 187–192. Univ. of Toronto Press, Toronto.
Stokes, J. L., and M. L. Redmond. (1966). Quantitative ecology of psychrophilic microorganisms. *Appl. Microbiol.* **14**: 74–78.
Stotzky, G., and J. L. Mortensen. (1959). Effect of gamma radiation on growth and metabolism of microorganisms in an organic soil. *Soil Sci. Soc. Am. Proc.* **23**: 125–127.
Strauss, B. S. (1958). Cell death and "unbalanced growth" in *Neurospora. J. Gen. Microbiol.* **18**: 658–669.
Subramanian, C. V. (1950). Soil conditions and wilt disease in plants with special reference to *Fusarium vasinfectum* on cotton. *Proc. Indian Acad. Sci.* **B31**: 67–71.
Sumi, M. (1928). Über die chemischen Bestandteile der Sporen von *Aspergillus oryzae. Biochem. Z.* **195**: 161–174.
Sussman, A. S. (1960). Activation of dormant ascospores of *Neurospora. Anat. Record* **137**: 396–397 (abstr.).
Sussman, A. S. (1965a). Dormancy of soil microorganisms in relation to survival. *In* "Ecology of Soil-Borne Pathogens—Prelude to Biological Control" (K. F. Baker and W. C. Snyder, eds.), pp. 99–109. Univ. of California Press, Berkeley, California.
Sussman, A. S. (1965b). Physiology of dormancy and germination in the propagules of cryptogamic plants. *In* "Handbuch der Pflanzenphysiologie" (A. Lang, ed.), Vol. 15, Part 2, pp. 933–1025. Springer, Berlin.
Sussman, A. S. (1966). Unpublished results.
Sussman, A. S., and H. O. Halvorson. (1966). "Spores: Their Dormancy and Germination." Harper, New York.
Sussman, A. S., Y. Lingappa, and I. A. Bernstein. (1963). Effect of light and media upon growth and melanin formation in *Cladosporium mansonii. Mycopathol. Mycol. Appl.* **20**: 307–314.
Sussman, A. S., T. L. Durkee, and R. J. Lowry. (1965). A model for rhythmic and temperature-independent growth in "clock" mutants of *Neurospora. Mycopathol. Mycol. Appl.* **25**: 381–396.
Tachibana, H., and R. Duran. (1966). Comparative survival of teliospores and mycelia of the onion smut fungus in soil. *Phytopathology* **56**: 136–137.
Tam, R. K., and H. E. Clark. (1943). Effect of chloropicrin and other soil disinfectants on the nitrogen nutrition of the pineapple plant. *Soil Sci.* **56**: 245–261.

Taubenhaus, J. J., and W. N. Ezekiel. (1936). Longevity of sclerotia of *Phymatotrichum omnivorum* in moist soil in the laboratory. *Am. J. Botany* **23**: 10–12.

Teitell, L. (1958). Effects of relative humidity on viability of conidia of aspergilli. *Am. J. Botany* **45**: 748–753.

Thaxter, R. (1890). The smut of onions (*Urocystis cepulae* Frost). *Conn. Agr. Expt. Sta., New Haven, Ann. Rept.* pp. 127–154.

Tinline, R. D., J. F. Stauffer, and J. G. Dickson. (1960). *Cochliobolus sativus.* III. Effect of ultraviolet radiation. *Can. J. Botany* **38**: 275–282.

Tochinai, Y. (1926). Comparative studies on the physiology of *Fusarium lini* and *Colletotrichum lini. J. Coll. Agr., Hokkaido Imp. Univ.* **14**: 171–236.

Tullis, E. C., and E. M. Gralley. (1941). Longevity of sclerotia of the stem-rot fungus *Leptosphaeria salvinii. Phytopathology* **31**: 279–281.

Uebelmesser, E. R. (1954). Über den endonomen Tagesrhythmus der Sporangienträgerbildung von Pilobolus. *Arch. Mikrobiol.* **20**: 1–33.

Wadham, S. M. (1925). Observations on clover rot (*Sclerotinia trifoliorum* Eriks.). *New Phytologist* **24**: 50–56.

Waggoner, P. E., and G. S. Taylor. (1958). Dissemination by atmospheric turbulence: Spores of *Peronospora tabacina. Phytopathology* **48**: 46–51.

Wahl, I. (1961). Hypobiotic phenomena in fungi and their significance in plant pathology. *In* "Cryptobiotic Stages in Biological Systems, 5th Biology Conference 'Oholo, 1960'" (N. Grossowicz, S. Hestrin, and A. Keynan, eds.), pp. 107–119. Elsevier, Amsterdam.

Walker, A. T., and F. G. Smith. (1952). Effect of actidione on growth and respiration of *Myrothecium verrucaria. Proc. Soc. Exptl. Biol. Med.* **81**: 556–559.

Walker, J. C. (1952). "Diseases of Vegetable Crops." McGraw-Hill, New York.

Warcup, J. H. (1951a). Soil steaming: A selective method for the isolation of ascomycetes from soil. *Brit. Mycol. Soc. Trans.* **34**: 515–518.

Warcup, J. H. (1951b). Studies in the growth of basidiomycetes in soil. *Ann. Botany* (*London*) [N. S.] **15**: 305–318.

Warcup, J. H. (1957). Chemical and biological aspects of soil sterilization. *Soils Fertilizers* **20**: 1–5.

Warcup, J. H. (1962). Personal communication.

Warcup, J. H. (1965). Growth and reproduction of soil microorganisms in relation to substrate. *In* "Ecology of Soil-Borne Pathogens—Prelude to Biological Control" (K. F. Baker and W. C. Snyder, eds.), pp. 52–67. Univ. of California Press, Berkeley, California.

Warcup, J. H., and K. F. Baker. (1963). Occurrence of dormant ascospores in soil. *Nature* **197**: 1317–1318.

Webb, S. J. (1965). "Bound Water in Biological Integrity." Thomas, Springfield, Illinois.

Webb, S. J., D. V. Cormack, and H. G. Morrison. (1964). Relative humidity, inositol and the effect of radiations on air-dried microorganisms. *Nature* **201**: 1103–1105.

Wellman, A. M., and D. B. Walden. (1964). Qualitative and quantitative estimates of viability for some fungi after periods of storage in liquid nitrogen. *Can. J. Microbiol.* **10**: 585–593.

Wensley, R. N. (1953). Microbiological studies of the action of some selected soil fumigants. *Can. J. Botany* **31**: 277–308.

Weston, W. A. R. Dillon. (1931). The effect of ultra-violet radiation on the urediniospores of some physiologic forms of *P. graminis tritici. Sci. Agr.* **12:** 81–87.

Wilhelm, S. (1955). Longevity of the *Verticillium* wilt fungus in the laboratory and field. *Phytopathology* **45:** 180–181.

Williams, G. H., and J. H. Western. (1965). The biology of *Sclerotinia trifoliorum* Erikss. and other species of scuerotium-forming fungi. II. The survival of sclerotia in soil. *Ann. Appl. Biol.* **56:** 261–268.

Williams, S. T., D. Parkinson, and N. A. Burges. (1964). An examination of the soil washing technique and its application to several soils. *Plant Soil* **22:** 167–186.

Wolf, F. A., L. F. Dixon, R. McLean, and F. R. Darkis. (1934). Downy mildew of tobacco. *Phytopathology* **24:** 337–363.

Woolman, H. W., and H. B. Humphrey. (1924). Studies in the physiology and control of bunt, or stinking smut, of wheat. *U.S. Dept. of Agr., Bull.* **1239.**

Yanagita, T., and S. Yamagishi. (1958). Comparative and quantitative studies of fungitoxicity against fungal spores and mycelia. *Appl. Microbiol.* **6:** 375–381.

Yarwood, C. E. (1950). Water content of fungus spores. *Am. J. Botany* **37:** 636–639.

Yarwood, C. E. (1954). Mechanism of acquired immunity to a plant rust. *Proc. Natl. Acad. Sci. U.S.* **40:** 374–377.

Yarwood, C. E., S. Sidky, M. Cohen, and V. Santilli. (1954). Temperature relations of powdery mildews. *Hilgardia* **22:** 603–622.

Zellner, J. (1911). Zur Chemie der höheren Pilze. VIII. Mitt. Über den Weizenbrand (*Tilletia levis* Kühn und *tritici* Winter). *Monatsh. Chem.* **32:** 1065–1074.

Zimmerman, A. (1925). Sammelreferate über die Beziehungen zwischen Parasit und Wirtepflanze. *Zentr. Bacteriol., Parasitenk., Abt. II* **65:** 311–418.

Zöbl, K. (1950). Über die Beziehungen zwischen chemischer Zusammensetzung von Pilzsporen und ihrem Verhalten gegen Erhitzen. *Sydowia Ann. Mycol.* **4:** 175–184.

CHAPTER 18

Geographical Distribution of Fungi

K. A. PIROZYNSKI[1]

Commonwealth Mycological Institute
Kew, Surrey, England

I. INTRODUCTION

To write an essay on the geographical distribution of fungi is, as Ajello (1960) remarked for dermatophytes, to "attempt to accomplish an impossible task." "Vast portions of earth's surface remain completely unexplored for fungi" (Wolf and Wolf, 1947). "Scanty knowledge of marine fungus distribution is manifestly the result of the limited search for them" (Johnson and Sparrow, 1961), and "our knowledge of the terrestrial air-spora is fragmentary in the extreme" (Gregory, 1961).

These quotations taken from authors who have considered the distribution of fungi, well illustrate the dilemma facing anyone attempting to review the subject.

The ecology of fungi as the basis for study of geographical distribution, unlike that of phanerogams, has not been widely investigated. There are at least twice as many flowering plants described as fungi (Bisby, 1933, 1943), though in mycologically investigated areas the number of species of fungi exceeds that of phanerogams (p. 512) The same is probably true in other localities where little mycological work has been done and where the recorded distribution of certain fungi often coincides with the distribution of mycological collectors.

The subject of geographical distribution can be considered from several viewpoints. In dealing with the problem on a worldwide basis the commonly adopted approach is either to outline the occurrence of some better known members of different fungal groups, or alternatively, to discuss the effect of various physical and biological factors on the distribution of particular fungi. In view of the scanty and incomplete records for most fungi, the latter approach seems to be more rational and is the one

[1] *Present address:* Plant Research Institute, Ottawa, Canada.

adopted in this chapter. One can speculate, in more general terms, on what effect different factors have on the distribution of different types of fungi in different habitats, bearing in mind, however, that these factors are interrelated and interdependent, and that it is their cumulative effect that governs the geographical distribution.

II. DISTRIBUTION IN WATER

Water constitutes a uniform, specialized habitat with a characteristic flora of adapted forms. Though in constant motion, water supports the vegetative growth of organisms so that their distribution is controlled primarily by edaphic or nutritional factors, and to some extent by temperature, particularly where the amount of water is small.

A. Marine Fungi

Our knowledge of marine fungi and their distribution, summarized in Johnson and Sparrow (1961) and Chapter 3 is relatively recent, and consequently incomplete. Most species known are from intertidal and eulittoral zones, and waters adjacent to land masses. Little is known of the distribution of fungi inhabiting greater depths, recovered from sediments at 3245 m, or waters at 4610 m.

1. Edaphic Factors

It is convenient to divide aquatic fungi into saprobic and parasitic forms, and this division is further elaborated when other habitats are dealt with.

Generally speaking saprobes are more widely distributed since they rarely show preference for one particular nutritional source, and substrata on which they can grow are likely to be widely distributed. Nonspecific saprobes on driftwood and other floating dead organic matter, as well as a number of free-living yeasts and actinomycetes, have a changing distribution and appear to be cosmopolitan. Marine and brackish water ascomycetes and fungi imperfecti on submerged wood and dead animal and vegetable matter are geographically more limited. *Lulworthia opaca* and *Ceriosporiopsis halima* are widely distributed in coastal waters. Species of *Mucor, Aspergillus,* and *Penicillium* are widely distributed in eulittoral sediments and particularly in estuaries, where the water is richer in organic matter.

Parasites, particularly obligate parasites, being more selective in their nutritional requirements, tend to be geographically more limited. Those parasitizing plankton, like *Ectrogella* on diatoms and *Coenomyces consuens* and *Phyllachorella oceanica* on free floating algae, have a changing distribution. Similarly the distribution of fungi pathogenic for animals is limited by the distribution of their hosts. Some, such as *Ichthyosporidium hoferi* on fish, are widely distributed; others which attack more sedentary animals and sponges, for example, *Dermocystidium marinum* on oysters, are more localized. Still more limited is the distribution of fungi parasitizing sedentary plants. The species of *Labyrinthula* occurring on attached algae and vascular plants are restricted by the distribution of their hosts, to intertidal and eulittoral zones. The more specialized a parasite, the more limited its distribution to a habitat peculiar to its host, though not necessarily to any particular geographical region. Even such specialized fungi as *Plasmodiophora bicaudata,* apparently confined to *Zostera nana,* are probably widely distributed.

2. *Other Factors*

Some fungi are curiously limited in their distribution or appear to be more common in certain geographical regions. *Eurychasma dicksonii,* widespread in coastal waters of Europe, has only once been found in the western hemisphere. *Olpidiopsis andreei,* apparently common in the north polar and temperate regions, has not yet been recorded from the southern hemisphere. Such examples indicate that other factors, apart from edaphic, may have a limiting effect on the distribution of certain marine fungi. Evidence exists that salinity, for instance, controls establishment of some phycomycetes, those less tolerant being able to colonize the estuaries only. Temperature too may have an effect as is demonstrated by *Dermocystidium marinum,* which parasitizes oysters only in warm waters. This evidence, however, is far from conclusive, as it is based on too few records and collections. Very often, no sooner does a search for marine fungi begin in a new locality, than fungi previously thought to be confined to remote parts of the globe are recovered. Interest in the marine fungus flora is on the increase, and with the establishment of marine research stations which at present are few and far between, and improved sampling methods, marine mycologists may soon be able to undertake more accurate studies on distribution. When this comes about, no doubt many fungi which at present appear to be geographically localized will be shown to have continuous distribution.

B. *Freshwater Fungi*

In general, many of the observations made on marine fungi are applicable also to freshwater fungi. Knowledge of their geographical distribution is equally fragmentary (Chapter 2).

Most freshwater fungi are phycomycetes. They occur on a wide variety of substrata and, according to Sparrow (1960), are probably limited in distribution only by inimical physical conditions and lack of suitable substrata.

1. Edaphic Factors

Saprobic members of the Chytridiales, Leptomitales, and Saprolegniales, which are able to utilize a variety of substrata such as dead vegetable and animal remains, are ubiquitous. So are the parasitic members of the Chytridiales on aquatic algae, fungi, and animals. As facultative parasites these can also exist saprobically on the remains of their hosts. Lagenidiales, primary parasites of freshwater plankton, have a changing and therefore equally wide distribution. Only a few freshwater fungi, members of the Plasmodiophorales, are obligate parasites of aquatic and semiaquatic angiosperms and are limited in their distribution by that of the host.

2. Other Factors

For truly freshwater fungi, oceans and seas should represent barriers. This, however, is rarely the case. Most species seem to be cosmopolitan. An example often quoted is that of *Allomyces arbuscula,* a semiaquatic phycomycete, which does not tolerate salinity, yet is found in waterlogged soils throughout the world.

Freshwater reservoirs because of their comparatively small size are affected by outside temperature, and this probably influences the distribution of certain fungi. Complete lack of records from large areas of the globe prevents us, however, from assessing to what extent this is so. Some evidence is presented in the work of Harder (1954), who has established that the number and frequency of occurrence of species decreases as one progresses northward from the Equator. A picture of more definite latitudinal zonation is provided by the geographical distribution of species of *Monoblepharis* and *Allomyces.* Members of both genera colonize similar substrata, submerged plant debris, but species of *Monoblepharis* tend to predominate in the cooler waters of the temperate zones, while *Allomyces* is confined to tropical and subtropical regions (Emerson, 1941).

Intensive studies on the freshwater hyphomycete flora, initiated by Ingold twenty-five years ago, have led to an accumulation of a considerable amount of information. This information was recently summarized by Nilsson (1964), who, discussing aspects of geographical distribution, classified known species into three groups. In the first, Nilsson included species which are on the whole worldwide and which are little, or not at all localized geographically. In this group, which contains the commonest genera and species, some species tend to be, however, either more frequently encountered in cooler regions or appear to have their main distribution in the tropics. The second category comprised species, such as

Clavatospora stellata, which appear to be climatically restricted to temperate and cold regions; and the third group, species which are geographically very localized. Significantly perhaps, the distribution data for the last-mentioned fungi are often based on a single collection, or the fungi involved are of uncertain taxonomic standing.

In general, the majority of freshwater hyphomycetes are cosmopolitan. Considering how specialized and discontinuous is their habitat, this may, at first, seem rather surprising. However, since the dispersal of freshwater hyphomycetes over large distances overland can be effected through contaminated organic matter, by animals, or by airborne spores of pycnidial or ascigerous states which may well exist, their wide distribution can be easily accounted for.

Local fluctuations in the distribution of freshwater hyphomycetes are known to occur. Seasonal increase in organic substrates, for instance, can bring about an increase in the fungal population. In smaller reservoirs, in spite of adequate supply of suitable substrates, increased water temperature with associated reduction of oxygen content and increased competition between microorganisms may have a limiting effect on the composition and distribution of fungal populations. That the temperature may have similar effects on a continental scale is suggested by the geographical distribution of the species which Nilsson listed in his second group.

III. DISTRIBUTION IN SOIL

Fungal populations in soil can be classified conveniently into two categories (Garret, 1956): (A) soil-inhabiting fungi, the obligate soil saprobes and unspecialized root parasites which colonize dead organic material; and (B) root-inhabiting fungi, including root parasites and mycorrhizal fungi invading living tissues.

The occurrence of fungi in soil is almost entirely limited to the top 20 cm. Waksman (1917) calculated that there are up to a million fungal spores, two million actinomycetes, and fifteen million bacteria in a gram of dry soil. Soil, therefore, represents a very crowded habitat, a microhabitat where organisms are affected by a number of closely interrelated factors. Fierce competition for food, biological interactions between antagonistic organisms, surface vegetation, physicochemical properties, and the microclimate of soil will all influence the distribution of fungi although their effect is local rather than continental.

A. Soil-Inhabiting Fungi

Different soils have specific fungus floras, but the majority of species found in them are cosmopolitan (Chapter 1). Unfortunately records of the occurrence of soil fungi are usually based on their ability to produce fructifications. Many species isolated from soil do not readily sporulate.

1. Edaphic Factors

Fungi capable of utilizing a variety of organic substrata, whether lignin or polysaccharides, find such substrata in all suitable soils. Their distribution will, therefore, vary locally with the type of soil. Similarly the inorganic composition of soil either directly or indirectly favors some fungi and prohibits establishment of others. Certain myxomycetes, e.g., *Badhamia,* which incorporate lime granules in their thalli are prevalent in limestone districts but are relatively poorly represented in sandstone soils. Among basidiomycetes similar distribution patterns are shown by species such as the calciphilic *Boletus satanas* and the calcifugic *B. bovinus.*

2. Climatic Factors

The soil microclimate, which is related to the physical structure of soil, has considerable influence on fungal populations though the effect on their distribution is strictly local. Moisture, particularly rainfall, affects the distribution of a number of fungi: many myxomycetes and phycomycetes of semiarid regions are more common at higher altitudes where rainfall is higher. High temperature, low moisture content, and increased ultraviolet radiation are the factors that govern the distribution of fungi in desert soils inhabited by specialized populations with large proportions of strongly pigmented phragmo- and dictyosporous hyphomycetes and coelomycetes with carbonaceous pycnidia (Nicot, 1960). The effect of temperature, though not clearly defined, also appears to influence the distribution of fungi on a continental scale. Similar floras inhabit similar soils in Canada, Denmark, and Siberia. Aspergilli, many of which tolerate low humidity and have high optimum temperatures, predominate in tropical and subtropical soils, whereas penicillia are more commonly recovered from temperate soils. Most eubasidiomycetes tolerate a wide thermal range, though few are limited to, or predominate in, well-defined climatic zones. Species of *Amanita,* particularly *A. caesarea,* are confined to temperate regions, while species of *Marasmius* appear to be predominantly tropical.

3. Geographical Barriers

The majority of soil-inhabiting fungi are probably cosmopolitan and widely distributed at least in their climatic zones. Many, e.g., *Mucor racemosus,* have been isolated from different types of soils throughout the world; a few, repeatedly isolated from European soils but not American, and vice versa, indicate the existence of geographical barriers.

An interesting example of a soil-inhabiting fungus with a limited distribution is *Coccidioides immitis*. The distribution of this fungus in certain arid regions of North and South America can be safely inferred from the incidence of the disease, coccidioidomycosis, which it causes in man and in domesticated and farm animals. Once only recognized as a rare and usually fatal infection, coccidioidomycosis is now known to be typically mild or subclinical, and millions of individuals resident in areas where *C. immitis* is endemic have, following infection, become serologically marked for life and give a positive reaction to skin testing with an antigen prepared from the fungus. *Histoplasma capsulatum* provides a parallel example, but in this case the endemic areas are more widely distributed and tend to be warm and humid (Ainsworth, 1957).

B. Root-Inhabiting Fungi

1. Edaphic Factors

Generally speaking root-inhabiting fungi which are capable of attacking a variety of plants are widely distributed. *Armillaria mellea* is ubiquitous. Fungi which are more selective in their nutritional preferences are often limited to the geographical range of their host plants. *Fomes annosus,* which parasitizes conifers and certain deciduous trees, is restricted by the distribution of these hosts to temperate climates. Many specialized root-inhabiting fungi affecting plants with continuous distribution are coextensive with their hosts. *Plasmodiophora brassicae* follows its plant host, *Brassica,* throughout the temperate and subtropical regions of both hemispheres; *Oospora citri* attacks *Citrus* everywhere in its subtropical and tropical distribution zone; and *Fusarium oxysporum* f. sp. *cubense* has been isolated in all banana-growing regions throughout the tropics. Specific parasites of rare or localized plants are often similarly limited. *F. albedinis* parasitic on date palm has so far been reported only from northern Africa, and *Thecaphora solani* attacks the andean potato found only in the northern Andes. Many higher basidiomycetes forming mycorrhizal association with roots of certain trees are frequently geographically localized. An agaric, *Descolea,* appears to be limited to the southern hemisphere by the distribution of antarctic beech with which it is associated.

2. Climatic Factors

Temperature is probably the most important single climatic factor influencing geographical distribution of root-inhabiting fungi. It operates either directly by affecting the pathogen itself, or indirectly by limiting its host to definite climatic zones as already noted in the preceding section. The direct effect on the pathogen can be illustrated by the notorious

Phymatotrichum omnivorum which, though capable of attacking some 1700 species of flowering plants, is restricted to the southern United States. This fungus, given suitable conditions can survive in its sclerotial form up to eight years, yet is unable to withstand desiccation for more than 1¼ hours, or temperatures below −13°C (Hawker, 1950). *Fusarium bulbigenum* parasitic on narcissus bulbs can be serious on the continent of Europe but is rarely troublesome in Britain. The reason given is that the pathogen cannot penetrate bulbs at temperatures below 20°C (Hawker, 1950). Judging by its widespread occurrence *Synchytrium endobioticum,* the pathogen of the wart disease of potatoes, tolerates a wide range of climatic conditions. On the other hand, *Oospora pullulans* attacks the same host only in temperate climates.

3. *Geographical Barriers*

Many root-inhabiting fungi are important pathogens of economic plants and their geographical distribution is, therefore, better known. From the available evidence it appears that at least the oceans present a barrier which some well-known root parasites cannot cross unless aided by man. Thus, oceans prevent longitudinal spread of *Phymatotrichum omnivorum,* protect South American rubber trees from Afro-Asian *Fomes noxius,* and keep *Omphalia flavida* confined to South American coffee. *Synchytrium endobioticum,* helped by man, has invaded all continents except Australia, where southern potato fields are protected not only by oceans and seas but also by a waterless desert and by legislation.

IV. DISTRIBUTION ON LAND

Terrestrial fungi represent by far the largest group, and their distribution, particularly that of economically important parasites, is relatively well known.

Terrestrial fungi also can conveniently be classified into plurivorous, and usually widely distributed, saprobes, and specialized parasites often strictly host-specific and consequently, geographically more localized. However, the division into the two categories is anything but clear cut. Fungi referred to as saprobes occur predominantly on dead organic matter and are not capable of attacking vigorously growing plants, but they often follow a primary parasite or pest. Life histories of relatively few saprobes have been fully investigated. Some, like *Cladosporium herbarum,* will attack healthy plants given suitable conditions; others, which regularly appear on one particular kind of dead substratum may be active parasites which produce recognizable structures only after the death of their hosts.

Nevertheless, fungi generally accepted and classified as saprobes are treated in a separate section.

A. Obligate Saprobes and Secondary Invaders

Relatively few saprobes are geographically restricted, and their distribution is governed by factors discussed below.

1. Edaphic Factors

Since the majority of these fungi are able to colonize many different substrata, nutritional habits are of little importance as limiting factors. For example, *Periconia byssoides* colonizing dead plants and plant debris, and *Chaetomium globosum* occurring on dung, soil, plants, and man-made products are cosmopolitan. However, species showing preference for one type of substrata are often more limited geographically. The work of Miller (1961) on *Hypoxylon* and Wehmeyer (1961) on *Pleospora* provides examples illustrating some aspects of the geographical distribution of species belonging to these two genera. *H. rubiginosum* commonly occurs on wood of dicotyledons but is rarely found on monocotyledons and gymnosperms, and although it is not limited to climatic zones and is distributed from northern Canada to southern Argentina and from northern Sweden to the Cape, it is absent from, or rare in, the coniferous belt. Similarly the distribution of *H. sassafras* is worldwide but confined to wood of Lauraceae. As the geographical range of hosts decreases or as the hosts become more localized, so does the fungus. *H. cohaerens* occurs chiefly on wood of *Fagus* and with its host is restricted to the north temperate zone. *Biatorella disciformis* and *B. resinae* on resin of conifers are similarly limited to temperate regions.

2. Climatic Factors

Climate, especially temperature, is an important factor affecting the distribution of many well-known saprobes. Much work remains to be done, particularly in the tropics, but present evidence indicates that several fungi, and sometimes even families of fungi, are restricted to well-defined climatic zones. *Botryodiplodia theobromae,* occurring on a great variety of dead plants, including those which grow also in temperate regions, is commonly found in the tropics and subtropics but has never been collected in cooler zones. On the other hand, *Pleospora* and its allies are predominantly temperate and subarctic. *Pleospora vagans,* colonizing a number of different grasses and herbs, is widely distributed in both temperate zones but is absent from the tropical belt. *Pleospora ambigua* of the north temperate zone has not been able to cross the tropics to colonize the southern hemisphere. Another interesting plurivorous species, *P.*

chlamydospora, is limited in its distribution to subarctic climates of the mountainous regions of South America, Central Asia, and the Middle East, where it remains isolated by unsuitable climatic conditions in the lowlands. An interesting relationship between arctic and alpine fungus floras, which will be discussed later, may be briefly mentioned here. This relationship, based on the occurrence of identical species in both habitats, is illustrated by examples such as *Lophodermium tumidum* saprobic on dead leaves of *Sorbus aucuparia,* which has been found only in arctic and alpine habitats, though its host has a continuous distribution. Omnivorous fungi such as *Pleospora longispora* and *P. graminearum* are similarly restricted to arctic regions of Europe, Tierra del Fuego, and mountains of Europe and North America.

3. Geographical Barriers

Some evidence exists that oceans operate as barriers limiting distribution even of obligate plurivorous saprobes such as *Hypoxylon oodes.* This species is found in tropical and subtropical regions of the Americas and isolated Pacific Ocean Islands (Tahiti and the Marshall Islands), but is not present in the Old World. Equally plurivorous, *H. nucigenum* occurs in comparable climatic zones of Asia only. Deserts and mountain ranges may also act as geographical barriers. *Hypoxylon uniapiculatum,* distributed along the Pacific coast of North America, and *H. bartholomaei,* occurring in the northeastern part of the United States, have failed to spread across the continent. In South America *H. bovei,* found in Argentina, Chile, and Peru, has not yet been recorded from localities east of the Andes.

B. Parasitic Fungi

Most parasitic fungi known are those attacking plants. Relatively few attack terrestrial animals and man. The majority of parasites depend on one kind of nutrient substratum, therefore edaphic factors primarily determine their geographical distribution.

1. Edaphic Factors

The geographical range of a parasitic fungus largely depends on the degree of its specialization. Many nonspecialized parasites, such as *Bremia lactucae* or *Phyllactinia corylea,* the latter attacking at least 50 host genera belonging to 30 different families, are cosmopolitan. Similarly many specialized, host-specific parasites which attack plants with continuous distribution are global, e.g., *Alternaria solani* on Solanaceae. As the range of suitable hosts decreases or as the host plants become geographically localized, so likewise do the parasites. Thus *Nectria galligena* attacks apple and pear, with which it is coextensive, in both northern and southern temperate zones; *Elsinoe fawcettii* follows *Citrus* throughout tropical and subtropical regions; and *Cordana musae* is confined by the distribution of its host, the banana, to the tropics.

Among parasitic fungi, the powdery mildews, because of their economic importance, are a group which has been intensively investigated. Their host range and geographical distribution were recently reviewed by Hirata (1966). According to him, the powdery mildews parasitize 7187 species and varieties of plants scattered through 1289 genera belonging to 149 families and 44 orders. Of these host plants, 91% are dicotyledons. The remaining 9% are monocotyledons, predominantly members of the Gramineae, which are the hosts for one species only, *Erysiphe graminis*. *Sphaerotheca fuliginea* has a very wide host range scattered among many families which are not always closely related, and is, therefore, widely distributed. *Erysiphe graminis,* attacking 608 species of the Gramineae which are often taxonomically removed from each other, or *Uncinula salicis,* having many host plants in the Salicaceae, though nutritionally restricted to one host family, show such adaptability as to be cosmopolitan. However, even in this successful and widely distributed group, the species more particular in their nutritional requirements are inevitably geographically localized if their host plants have discontinuous distribution. *Sphaerotheca epilobii* and *Erysiphe tortilis* are found only on the predominantly north temperate genera *Epilobium* and *Cornus,* respectively. An extreme case is *Uncinula asteris* which occurs only on *Aster japonicus* and is apparently confined to Japan.

2. *Climatic Factors*

The distribution of many parasitic fungi follows well-defined climatic zonation. Plurivorous *Phytophthora parasitica* and *Sphaerostilbe repens* are widespread in the tropics but do not occur elsewhere. Similarly *Pyricularia oryzae,* which attacks various grasses, but mainly rice, is strictly tropical. Many host-specific parasites do not follow hosts throughout their geographical range. Certain species of *Balansia,* obligate on grasses in the tropics, die out when infected hosts are grown in cooler climates (Diehl, 1937). Only three species of *Ravenelia* occur north of 40°N latitude, and a large number of ascomycete genera or even families, such as the Microthyriaceae and Perisporiaceae, are almost entirely confined to the tropics. A similar state of affairs exists in temperate regions. *Phytophthora cactorum* and *Stereum purpureum* attack their hosts only in temperate zones. *Phytophthora hibernalis* occurs on *Citrus* only along its northernmost and southernmost boundaries. *Betula odorata,* which is evenly distributed over large areas of Europe, is attacked by *Taphrina lapponica* in northern Scandinavia only. Similarly, widespread *Chamaenerion angustifolium* is parasitized by *Puccinia gigantea* and *Dothidella adusta* in Lapland only (Lind, 1934).

Among the powdery mildews the limiting effect of climate is not as clearly defined as in other examples quoted, though generally speaking *Leveillula* appears to be commoner in hot and warm climates, and *Phyllactinia* favors cooler regions. Most of the species, however, overlap over large areas of the globe and seem to tolerate a wide range of climatic conditions except perhaps extreme cold. That this may be so is suggested by the distribution of *Sphaerotheca fuliginea*. This fungus, prevalent in tropical and temperate climates, is also most tolerant to cold conditions among the powdery mildews. Its range extends beyond the thermal barrier which bars other species from both subarctic and alpine habitats (Hirata, 1966).

Humidity also may play a part in geographical distribution. *Brooksia tropicalis* and *Grallomyces portoriensis,* members of a vast tropical assemblage of epiphytic fungi and lichens, occur on living leaves of a wide range of host plants, apparently without preference except for evergreen rather than deciduous plants, in the West Indies, tropical South America, West Africa, and Pacific Ocean Islands but are absent from certain areas, e.g., East Africa, in similar latitudes. From an analysis of climatic and biotic conditions associated with the geographical areas where they occur, it becomes apparent that both *Brooksia* and *Grallomyces* are restricted to the humid equatorial type of intertropical climate and are confined to and coextensive with areas where tropical evergreen hygrophilic forest is the natural vegetational climax.

3. *Geographical Barriers*

Ample evidence exists that oceans, and possibly mountain ranges and deserts, operate as barriers limiting the distribution of parasitic fungi. Although man has successfully operated to break these barriers in the past, many destructive parasites still remain isolated and every effort is now being made to prevent their spread, sometimes through cooperative regional legislation as in the case of the Inter-African Phytosanitary Commission for Africa. *Puccinia striiformis* has not yet succeeded in colonizing Australia. *Dibotryon morbosum* attacking *Prunus* is confined to North America, where it remains isolated by oceans from other continents in the same climatic zone, and from the south temperate belt by the tropical thermal zone and discontinuity of the host. *Puccinia rhytismoides* occurs only in the northernmost part of Fenno-Scandinavia although its host, *Thalictrum alpinum,* is widely distributed in the subarctic regions of Asia, Greenland, and North America (Lind, 1934).

Interesting examples of geographical barriers operating are found when one studies the frequency of occurrence, the ratio between species, and, particularly, the edaphic preferences of certain widely distributed fungi in widely separated localities. The occurrence of some fungi and their relative abundance may differ from year to year in any one locality, but the nutritional requirements, particularly of specialized obligate parasites such as powdery mildews, are usually specific. It seems therefore significant that *Rhus* should be affected by *Uncinula* in the Far East but only by *Sphaerotheca* and *Phyllactinia* in North America, that only *Sphaerotheca* occurs on *Euphorbia* in Asia, and only *Microsphaera* is found on the same host genus in the New World, and that *Vaccinium* is the host of *Microsphaera* in North America but of *Podosphaera* in Europe (Hirata, 1966).

V. DISTRIBUTION IN THE ATMOSPHERE

Air does not serve as a habitat, in the same way as water or soil. Only fungal fragments and spores, particularly air-borne conidia and ejected asco- and basidiospores adapted for aerial dispersal, all originating from terrestrial sources, constitute the air spora. Nutritional factors, which are of paramount importance in the distribution of growing fungi, play no part, the occurrence of fungal bodies in the atmosphere being governed by the physical properties of the air which is in constant motion. Aerobiology has recently been most ably summarized by Gregory (1961) and Chapter 22 of Volume II, and only aspects pertaining to geographical distribution are mentioned here.

Fungi in the atmosphere are mostly found in the troposphere extending up to 10 km, only rarely wandering into the stratosphere. In the lower strata the air spora is directly related to the ground flora, the type and concentration of fungi depending on season, time, weather, and human activity. Generally speaking, dry conidia of fungi such as *Cladosporium* and *Alternaria* predominate during daytime and in dry weather and are replaced by ascospores and basidiospores which require moisture for dispersal during the night and in damp weather. Above 1 km, these local fluctuations disappear as the spores, their concentration diluted, are reshuffled by convection currents and joined by "long distance travelers."

This, very briefly, is the picture of "vertical distribution." But is there any evidence of geographical distribution? It has been realized relatively recently that large air masses of uniform temperature and humidity are formed over extensive areas of the globe and are separated from each other by "fronts." These masses, basically classified as polar continental, polar maritime, tropical continental and tropical maritime, though in constant motion may carry air sporas specific to the land masses above which they are formed. The evidence, however, resulting from sporadic sampling is, at present, extremely scanty.

What factors, apart from physical properties of air, influence the distribution of suspended spores? Edaphic factors are nonexistent, as are competition for food and the biological effect of antagonistic organisms associated with nutrition. Low temperature, if anything, favors survival. Man, a most successful agent of dispersal on land, has not yet noticeably affected the air spora in the upper strata. Only geographical barriers, thousands of miles of oceans, or barren land which spores have to cross in viable condition, limit their distribution. Perhaps it is not so much the distances, which many spores can undoubtedly traverse, but the dispersal time, which is the limiting factor. During the time which a spore takes to cross these barriers, its life is shortened by alternating temperatures, periods of drought and humidity, cloud-induced germination, precipitation by rain, and, perhaps, increased ultraviolet radiation (cf. Volume I, Chapter 24). These factors may well explain why *Puccinia graminis,* known to be carried by air currents hundreds of miles across the North American continent and India and Russia have not yet succeeded in colonizing isolated areas of Australia, Central Asia, and South America.

VI. ENDEMISM AND ACTIVITY OF MAN

One of the most important single factors affecting the geographical distribution of fungi is man himself. "The natural ranges and habitats of fungi tend towards the establishment of stability and biological balance. Man has always upset this stability by intensive cultivation of a given species of host in a limited area, by constructing artificial environments in which to grow plants, by attempts to grow crops in new areas, and by introducing fungi into areas where the environment unfortunately has too frequently proved more favourable for the fungi than did their natural range" (Wolf and Wolf, 1947). The consequences of introducing fungi such as *Phytophthora infestans,* a native of Andes where it coexists with the local varieties of potato, into Europe or coffee rust into Ceylon, are well known and of historical interest. Some other cases of the introduction of similarly destructive fungi are noted below. Among phycomycetes, *Physoderma maydis,* endemic in southeastern United States, migrated with maize introduced to Central America, Africa, and Asia, finding in many areas ideal conditions. Another North American fungus, *Plasmopara viticola,* a destructive parasite of vines, was introduced into Europe with a pest-resistant variety and within a few years devastated European vineyards before spreading to northern Africa and Australia. *Peronospora tabacina,* a native of Australia, has received much publicity. Its recent devastating epidemic spread through the tobacco-growing regions of Europe is only too well known (Rayner and Hopkins, 1962). Among ascomycetes may be mentioned the notorious *Endothia parasitica* endemic in northern China, which in a short space of time almost eradicated chestnut trees from North America, and the European *Ceratocystis ulmi* which threatens to do the same for American elms.

Man has also played his part in dispersing human pathogenic fungi. *Microsporum audouinii,* the classical cause of head ringworm in children, has been a European export to many parts of the world, and although in North America the fungus is now endemic, in tropical countries its spread seems to be usually limited to Europeans. Similarly the establishment of a tropical dermatophyte, such as *Trichophyton rubrum* (a cause of ringworm of the feet), in temperate countries seems to be the exception rather than the rule. *Microsporum ferrugineum,* has frequently been introduced into Europe without ever initiating an epidemic (Ainsworth, 1957).

VII. DISCUSSION

Once a fungus reaches a new locality it can survive and establish itself only by finding a suitable ecological niche. Plurivorous fungi tolerating a wide range of climatic conditions become widespread and common; specialized parasites often remain geographically isolated.

Studies of the fungal population of the Krakatau group of islands have shown that the process of colonization is a rapid one. The world-famous volcanic eruption of 1883 left the islands mycologically sterile, yet botanical surveys during the following fifty years yielded no less than 310 species of fungi in spite of the fact that their arrival must have been preceded by their hosts according to the hypothesis postulating that "the number of lower plants is determined by that of the higher ones" (Boedijn, 1940).

Investigation of the north polar region by Lind (1934) shows that relatively few species occur in the Arctic, where severe climatic conditions and scarcity of suitable substrata prevent wider colonization. The fact that plurivorous species predominate indicates the greater limiting effect of the lack of variety of substrata. Since not one genus of fungi (or phanerogams) is indigenous to the north polar region, and since most fungi of that region occur also in comparable climatic and vegetational zones in the Alps, Pamirs, etc., Lind put forward a hypothesis that the arctic flora did not originate there, but that it followed the retreating glacier some 15,000 years ago. In spite of the long period of isolation, most of the fungi have not changed morphologically. However, Lind noticed a tendency for some of the species to split into two or more distinct taxa. *Mycosphaerella nebulosa,* common on *Solidago* but very rare on *Melandrium,* is undergoing this process of division, and *Metasphaeria sepalorum* and *M. junci* on glumes and stems of the same *Juncus* species each represent the completed process. Lind concluded that species with continuous distribution are "in their strength and prime," and species specializing geographically or physiologically show "sign of old age." On the other hand Bisby (1943) found that the geographical distribution of Uredinales fits Willis' "age and area" theory, which postulates, in general, that the commonest genera are the oldest rather than the best adapted, and that the older (and larger) a genus, the wider its distribution (Willis, 1922). Similarly Hirata (1966) working with the Erysiphaceae found that the genus *Erysiphe,* believed to be the most primitive member of the group, has the largest host range and widest distribution. Both the host range and geographical distribution are narrowed in genera such as *Leveillula, Sphaerotheca,* and *Microsphaera,* which are considered to be direct descendants from *Erysiphe;* they are still further narrowed in more distantly related genera, some of which, such as *Cystotheca* and *Typhulochaeta,* are extremely restricted. Hirata concluded that "the host range of the older genera is generally larger than that of the advanced." In Lind's work too, evidence can be found supporting Willis' theory. Most of the species represented in arctic regions belong to large genera such as *Leptosphaeria, Mycosphaerella,* and *Pleospora,* and Lind himself stated that polar fungi "which are able to thrive in these arid regions, most frequently have a wide geographical distribution."

Similar conclusions can also be drawn from Nilsson's (1964) work on aquatic hyphomycetes. However, it is also suggested in this work that an adaptation to a particular specialized habitat, in this case freshwater, plays an important role in the geographical distribution of freshwater hyphomycetes. Species with spores best adapted for aquatic dispersal, that is, those with the best-developed and simplified tetraradiate or sigmoid structure, are dominant and widespread.

The physical and biological affinities between widely separated continents of the southern hemisphere have for a long time fascinated scientists, who have put forward various theories and hypotheses explaining this phenomenon. The affinities between the floras, as illustrated by the distribution in the southern temperate zones of America and Australasia of *Nothofagus* and certain species of *Araucaria,* indicate that these plants may have had continuous distribution in the past. Recent work (Dennis, 1960, 1961) shows that similar relationships also exist between fungus floras and are demonstrated not only by parasitic fungi closely linked with hosts such as *Nothofagus,* but also by saprobes. The distribution of the genus *Cyttaria,* parasitic on and confined to the species of *Nothofagus* in the southern Andes, Tierra del Fuego, New Zealand, Tasmania, and Eastern Australia, is a classic example. A comparable case is presented by the agaric *Descolea,* believed to form a mycorrhizal association with *Nothofagus,* with which host, like *Cyttaria,* it has probably evolved. *Descolea,* originally described from Tierra del Fuego has recently been recognized in Victoria. Among saprobic fungi the relationship between South American and Australasian fungi can be seen to cover a wide range of similar conditions. *Mollisia subglobosa,* a distinctive Tasmanian fungus, has been found in Venezuela at an altitude of 4500 m, a climatic extension of the southern temperate zone along the Andes. Another discomycete, *Sorokina,* described from Venezuela was subsequently found in Tasmania.

East of the Andes the fungus flora shows some affinities with that of West Africa as illustrated by such distinctive genera as *Thamnomyces, Peltigeromyces,* and *Ionomydotis,* as yet unrecorded from tropical Asia or Australia. Recently a peculiar discomycete, *Polydiscidium martynii,* described from Trinidad has been also found in the Congo (Dennis, 1961).

Many cases of odd or erratic distributions, such as that of the genera *Milesina, Pucciniastrum,* and *Cronartium* in Australasia (the first but not the second represented in New Zealand, and only *Cronartium* in Australia), or the occurrence of a striking discomycete *Urnula geaster* recorded only from Japan and Texas, may find explanation as records accumulate and our knowledge of the distribution of fungi increases. More systematic collecting and mapping of records is needed, for, to quote Bisby (1933), one cannot look for principles governing distribution when "mycologists have been able to map with accuracy the geographical distribution of comparatively few fungi."

REFERENCES

Ainsworth, G. C. (1957). The dispersal of fungi pathogenic for man and animals. *In* "Biological Aspects of the Transmission of Disease" (C. Horton-Smith, ed.), pp. 1–5. Oliver & Boyd, Edinburgh and London.

Ajello, L. (1960). Geographic distribution and prevalence of the Dermatophytes. *Ann. N.Y. Acad. Sci.* **89**: 33–39.

Bisby, G. R. (1933). The distribution of fungi as compared with that of phanerogams. *Am. J. Sci.* **20**: 246–254.

Bisby, G. R. (1943). Geographical distribution of fungi. *Botan. Rev.* **9**: 466–482.

Boedijn, K. B. (1940). The mycetozoa, fungi and lichens of the Krakatau group. *Bull. Jardin Botan. Buitenzorg* **16**: 358–429.

Commonwealth Mycol. Inst. Distrib. Maps of Plant Diseases. 1–422.

Dennis, R. W. G. (1960). *Proc. Roy. Soc.* **B162**: 539.

Dennis, R. W. G. (1961). A collection of *Polydiscidium* from Africa. *Bull. Jardin Botan. Bruxelles* **31**: 155–157.

Diehl, W. W. (1937). A basis for mycogeography. *J. Wash. Acad. Sci.* **27**: 244–254.

Emerson, R. (1941). An experimental study of the life cycle and taxonomy of *Allomyces. Lloydia* **4**: 77–144.

Garret, S. D. (1956). "Biology of Root-infecting Fungi." Cambridge Univ. Press, London and New York.

Gregory, P. H. (1961). "The Microbiology of the Atmosphere." Wiley (Interscience), New York.

Harder, R. (1954). Über die arktische Vegetation nieder Phycomyceten. *Nachr. Akad. Wiss. Goettingen, Math.-Physik. Kl., IIa. Math.-Physik. Chem. Abt.* pp. 1–9.

Hawker, L. E. (1950). "Physiology of Fungi." Oxford Univ. Press (Univ. London), London and New York.

Hirata, K. (1966). "Host Range and Geographical Distribution of the Powdery Mildews." Niigata Univ., Niigata, Japan (mimeographed).

Johnson, T. W., Jr., and F. K. Sparrow, Jr. (1961). "Fungi in Oceans and Estuaries." Cramer, Weinheim.

Lind, J. (1934). Studies on the geographical distribution of Arctic circumpolar micromycetes. *Kgl. Danske Videnskab. Selskab, Biol. Medd.* **11**: 1–152.

Miller, J. H. (1961). "A Monograph of the World Species of *Hypoxylon*." Univ. of Georgia Press, Athens, Georgia.

Nicot, J. (1960). Some characteristics of the microflora in desert sands. *In* "Ecology of Soil Fungi" (D. Parkinson and J. S. Waid, eds.), pp. 94–97. Liverpool Univ. Press, Liverpool.

Nilsson, S. (1964). Freshwater hyphomycetes. *Symbolae Botan. Upsalienses* **18**: 2–130.

Rayner, R. W., and J. C. F. Hopkins. (1962). Blue mould of tobacco. *Commonwealth Mycol. Inst. Misc. Publ.* **16**: 1–16.

Sparrow, F. K., Jr. (1960). "Aquatic Phycomycetes." Univ. of Michigan Press, Ann Arbor, Michigan.

Waksman, S. A. (1917). Is there any fungus flora in the soil? *Soil Sci.* **3**: 565–589.

Wehmeyer, L. E. (1961). "A World Monograph of the Genus *Pleospora* and its Segregates." Univ. of Michigan Press, Ann Arbor, Michigan.

Willis, J. C. (1922). "Age and Area." Cambridge Univ. Press, London and New York.

Wolf, F. A., and F. F. Wolf. (1947). "The Fungi," Vol. II. Wiley, New York.

CHAPTER 19

The Number of Fungi

G. C. AINSWORTH

Commonwealth Mycological Institute
Kew, Surrey, England

I. INTRODUCTION

The question "How many fungi are there?" can be answered in two words, "Nobody knows." This fact does not, however, inhibit mycologists from making numerical statements. For example: "One gram of air-dried soil may contain up to 100,000 fungi"; "The number of yeasts in the rhizospheres exceeded that in the soil sometimes 20-fold"; "There are fewer fungi in air over oceans than over land masses"; "On average, 250 species are collected at an Autumn Foray of the British Mycological Society"; "There are 65 fusaria according to Wollenweber and Reinking, 500 in Saccardo"; "Perhaps half the 100,000 species of fungi which have been described are synonyms." All these statements would be accepted as meaningful in conversation, even if they should not all escape the editorial blue pencil. If looked at more closely some are decidedly peculiar. Although the British Mycological Society has been holding forays regularly for the past seventy years the number of species of larger fungi in the country has increased rather than decreased. Many of the "fungi" recorded in soil and air are merely spores (and is a spore a fungus?), while species is a taxonomic category and synonyms are different names for the same thing. A moment's thought shows that these semantic difficulties are mainly due to the failure to distinguish between individuals, kinds of individuals, and the names by which both individuals and kinds of individuals are designated. The problem of the number of fungi can perhaps best be approached by consideration in turn of individual fungi, kinds of fungi, and names of fungi.

II. INDIVIDUAL FUNGI

What is an individual among fungi? An individual mushroom can be held in the hand but not an individual of *Agaricus campestris,* for in gathering a fruit body the mycelial part of the individual has been left behind in the soil. Perhaps it would be as well to take a simpler example—a vegetative cell of *Schizosaccharomyces*. There seems no reason not to call that an individual. Under suitable conditions, in a matter of minutes, it elongates, develops a transverse wall, and splits into two independent cells (or individuals) which repeat the progress. With a cell of *Saccharomyces* there are added complications. The cell buds off a new individual but the mother cell can be distinguished and after repeating the process eventually declines into a much scarred old age. Also, the buds may remain attached to the parent cell and produce buds in their turn. What have we now; still an individual, or a rudimentary colony? As a final example, if one spore of *Penicillium* is sown at the center of a petri dish of malt agar the resulting colony with its conidiophores and spores is surely a satisfactory individual. Tap the petri dish and then incubate the plate again. In a few days the original colony is surrounded by smaller "daughter" colonies. Microscopic examination would show hyphal fusions between the daughter and parent colonies. Return it to the incubator for another period and when next examined (if staling products have not prevented intermingling of the colonies) the plate is completely overgrown. Has one individual become several and then one again?

In the field mycelia certainly persist as entities as everyone who has had to collect class material can confirm, and sometimes such mycelia reveal their presence as "fairy rings" in lawns and pastures. It is usual to make quantitative studies on larger fungi by counting sporophores, by assessing the crop as it were. Rarely, as on the Island of Skokholm off the coast of Wales (Parker-Rhodes, 1954), is an attempt made to count mycelia which gives a more accurate measure of the number of individuals in the population.

Although the longevity of fungi is dealt with in detail in Chapter 18 it is perhaps of interest here to comment on the longevity of individual fungi. At one extreme is an individual fission yeast which may have a lifetime measured in minutes. At the other are fairy rings of *Agaricus praerimosus* and *Calvatia cyathiformis* the age of which have been estimated at 250–400 years while some fragmentary rings may be 600 years old (Shantz and Piemeisel, 1917). Over the years the mycelia of such fairy rings anastomose and presumably engulf younger mycelia in their paths and hence over the years their genetical composition could change. However, Burnett and Evans (1966) recently made an experimental study of a series of rings of *Marasmius oreades* 3–7.5 meters in diameter and estimated them to be 100–150 years old. *M. oreades* is bipolar, and for no ring did they find more than two mating-type factors. This was taken as good presumptive evidence that each mycelium was genetically homogeneous.

To count individual fungi in soil samples in any meaningful sense is impossible, whether the counts are of cells seen visibly or of viable cells (spores or mycelial fragments) estimated by plating out highly diluted soil suspensions. This method is analogous to making deductions about an oak wood by taking litter samples and germinating the acorns when there would appear to be a few hundred oaks to the acre in early summer, millions to the acre in autumn. This does not mean that soil dilution plating which has been so widely practiced has not yielded results that are both interesting and valuable in elucidating the composition of the mycological flora of soil and of the effects of the environment or experimental treatments in the survival of fungi in soil. Also, if the technique used is standardized, as it was in the classical paper from Rothamsted by Brierley *et al.* (1927) which has been a starting point for much soil dilution plating work, quantitative comparisons are possible.

As for soil, sampling air and water has its problems regarding the meaning to be attached to the counts, which are frequently either of spores or viable units of dissemination—and Sernander (1927) coined the term *diaspore* for such parts which separate for propagation.

III. KINDS OF FUNGI

From the outset it must be remembered that the differentiation of one kind of fungus from another is largely based on considerations of convenience, tradition, and personal opinion. There are few objective criteria that can be applied, particularly at the specific level. For most people the black rust of wheat is one kind of fungus but a cereal pathologist recognizes more than 250 kinds of this particular pathogen. At which of these levels are kinds of fungi to be enumerated? It all depends on the purpose of the enumeration. Perhaps the question of the number of kinds of fungi can be more usefully approached by first considering some of the main factors which determine their recognition.

A. Effects of Mycologists

The most important factor is mycologists, their number, distribution, and temperament. This is not necessarily self-evident. The number of higher plants is much less dependent on the number of practising taxonomic phanerogamists, for all but a small fraction of the flowering plants have already been described. For fungi on the other hand, as will be suggested later in this chapter, most have still to be described. Their recorded number and distribution is closely correlated with the number and distribution of mycologists. If the type localities of the ringworm fungi described in

Sabouraud's "Les Teignes" (1910) are dotted by country into an outline map of the world and then the geographical distribution of the authors listed in the bibliography to that monograph are similarly treated the two maps look very alike. There are similar high incidences of the number of species and the number of mycologists in Western Europe, a result which has little relevance to the number and distribution of dermatophytes.

There are more taxonomic mycologists at work today than ever before, and the number of species of fungi described annually is on the increase. But the number described or the number recognized by any individual mycologists also depends on temperament. Some taxonomists are perhaps unduly impressed by small differences and so distinguish as different very similar or even morphologically indistinguishable fungi. These taxonomists are the "splitters." Others, the "lumpers," at the generic or specific levels at least, recognize far fewer kinds although the more broad-minded of them see no objections in the broadly based "kinds" they recognize being subdivided into smaller units whenever such a proceeding seems to be required.

B. *Effects of Parasitism*

During the past hundred and fifty years there have been marked changes of emphasis in the criteria used to differentiate one fungal species from another, and as Ainsworth (1962) pointed out some of these changes are reflected in the specific epithets, the second and often mainly descriptive terms of the Latin binomials used to designate species. In the early days mycologists made much use of morphological features. A random sampling of the specific epithets in Persoon's "Synopsis methodica fungorum" (1801), the main starting-point of modern taxonomic mycology, showed 40% of the epithets to be based on morphological features, 25% on color terminology, and 10% on the names of higher plants. Similar samples from the general index to the first eleven volumes of Saccardo's "Sylloge fungorum" (Volume 12, 1897) and of the first volume of the "Index of Fungi" covering new fungal names proposed during 1940–1949 showed the distribution of the categories of epithets to be approximately similar in these two works: between a quarter and a third are based on morphological features, approximately 10% on color, and 30% on the names of plants. The predominance of morphological terms in coining specific epithets (presumably to aid identification) is very apparent from these data. The greater use of color distinctions by early mycologists was certainly determined by their poor optical equipment and by the fewer forms they had to distinguish, while the increasing popularity of the host as a "spot" character is well brought out. This last usage could be emphasized even more by an examination of obligate parasites, such as rusts and powdery mildews, and of other genera composed entirely of plant pathogens in which 60–80% of the specific epithets may be derived from host names.

Parasitism as a differential character for fungi tends to the multiplication of the number of kinds and to the neglect of other determinable fungal characters. In other words, infection of a named host plant is the criterion by which a fungus in both differentiated from others and identified, and as not infrequently the approach has been nonexperimental neither end has been achieved. To take a well known and typical modern example, Chupp (1954) in his monograph on the genus *Cercospora* catalogued and described 1270 species in one series by host plants arranged in their turn alphabetically by families. *Cercospora* has a relatively complicated morphology and many named species can be distinguished on morphology, but the chances of identifying a species of *Cercospora* on an unnamed host or in culture is remote—which is humilating for a mycologist.

Sometimes genera or species are distinguished by the spatial relationship of the parasite to its host, by what Ciferri (1952) called ecological characteristics. The genera *Phoma* and *Phyllosticta* are differentiated by the occurrence of the former on the stems and the latter on the leaves of host plants, and an example of a similar spatial differentiation of species is the smut *Ustilago lygei* which was distinguished from the stem smut of grasses, *U. hypodytes,* because it attacks the inflorescence and not the culm.

Such examples of the effect of the parasitism on the differentiation of fungi could be multiplied. It may be of interest to recall that Ainsworth (1955) noted the general effect of parasitism in the Ascomycetes, in which class the average number of species per genus was 8.3, and for 11 of the 14 orders varied from 2.3 to 10.5. In the remaining three orders, the Laboulbeniales, Erysiphales, and Taphrinales, all orders in which host specificity has played an important part in speciation, the numbers of species per genus were 12.5, 16.7, and 20.8, respectively. For rusts (Uredinales) he found the number to be 36.

In concluding this section it may be noted that the wheel has turned full circle. It is again a "modern" approach to differentiate species on morphological grounds rather than on parasitic specialization. Fischer (1943) has consolidated many morphologically similar species of cereal and grass smuts, and Yerkes and Shaw (1959) list more than 80 synonyms of *Peronospora brassicae,* the downy mildew of brassicas, which Gäumann (1923) subdivided into no less than 54 species.

IV. NAMES OF FUNGI

Names surely mark a return to earth in providing items which are susceptible to unequivocal counting. By and large they do, although the laborious task of compiling all the scientific names which have been applied to fungi during the past 166 years (and during 214 for myxomycetes) is still unfinished. There are, however, difficulties. The coining and application of the names given to fungal taxa are (fungi having been traditionally included in the Plant Kingdom) governed by the provisions of the International Code of Botanical Nomenclature which determines which names may be legitimately used, and which must be rejected. A minor difficulty in determining the legitimacy of names is that over the years the Code itself undergoes changes as it evolves in successive editions, but the desirability of following internationally agreed rules for the use of names is generally accepted not only by mycologists but by all biologists.

The main principle underlying the choice of names is that of priority, an older name takes precedence over a younger one. This means that the Code lays down starting points for nomenclature: Linnaeus' "Species plantarum" (1753) for myxomycetes, Persoon's "Synopsis fungorum" (1801) for some fungi, Fries' "Systema mycologicum" (1821–1832) for others. Names published before these dates must be rejected, unless validated by subsequent publication. So must names unaccompanied by descriptions of the fungi designated (*nomina nuda*), the later use of one name applied to two different taxa (homonyms), and names used in so many senses as to become meaningless (*nomina confusa*).

Inasmuch as there are differences in opinion as to how fungi should be classified, the Code allows every taxonomist to use a correct name which reflects his current taxonomic opinion. For example, *Polystictus versicolor, Coriolus versicolor,* and *Trametes versicolor* are all names in line with the Code for one fungus, the particular name adopted being a matter of taxonomic opinion. The two names rejected by any author are synonyms and many of the names that have been proposed for fungi must be considered synonyms by every mycologist, even though some names considered synonymous by one worker are acceptable to another.

There is a further complication. The Code allows different names to be applied to the imperfect (asexual) and perfect (sexual) states of one fungus and there are many imperfect fungi for which no perfect state is known although for some of these the perfect state must already be described but its connection with the imperfect state is still unrecognized.

There are already more than 100,000 specific names in the literature. The author of every new name implies that the taxon to which the new name is given is without a designation. He is only too frequently mistaken. Common fungi of worldwide distribution are described as new and renamed many times and, if there are also uncertainties regarding taxonomic status, names are further multiplied. The thrush fungus (*Candida albicans*) has, according to Lodder and Kreger-van Rij (1952), been described as new 36 times and has 92 synonyms in 11 different genera. From such considerations as these it is apparent that the mere counting of names gives a very inadequate measure of the number of fungal taxa.

V. NUMBER OF SPECIES OF FUNGI

We are now in a position to consider the number of kinds of fungi at the specific level. Two estimates are possible. First, how many "good" species have already been described. In other words, of the specific names hitherto proposed, how many represent taxa acceptable as distinct on the basis of current speciation practice. Secondly, how many species of fungi have yet to be described?

A. Number of Described Species

The most detailed modern estimate of the number of species of fungi is that by Bisby and Ainsworth (1943). These authors compiled the numbers of genera and species recorded in the 25 volumes of Saccardo's "Sylloge fungorum" (1882–1931) and in various later works and then scaled the numbers down to those accepted in monographs by specialists on particular groups or to estimates based on their own judgment. They summarized their conclusions in a table setting out the numbers of "good" species for classes, orders, and some families. This tabulation, which is largely a compilation of the numbers cited in the first edition of Ainsworth and Bisby's "Dictionary of the Fungi" (1943), does not merit reproduction here. It can be consulted by anyone interested. A summary will suffice.

Saccardo's "Sylloge" contains 78,360 numbered specific entries, distributed approximately as follows: Myxomycetes, 750; Phycomycetes, 1500; Ascomycetes, 26,150; Basidiomycetes, 24,700; Fungi Imperfecti, 24,200. If to Saccardo's total new names are added at the rate of 1000 per year, up to 1943 at least 100,000 specific names had been proposed. This total was reduced to 37,500 specific names distributed through 3584 genera, while another 3503 generic names were treated as synonyms.

Of this total (after the exclusion of the Myxothallophyta) Bisby and Ainsworth wrote: "While the figure of 37,000 species of Eumycetes is fairly conservative, there are two respects in which it is too large: (1) it is probable that a third of the [10,500] Fungi Imperfecti have named perfect stages (proved or unproved, known or unknown); (2) many species of fungi are not based on morphology alone—the generally accepted criterion for specific distinction—but (as in *Meliola, Septoria, Ustilago*) on host as well. We estimate that about 3500 Fungi Imperfecti can be classified as 'host-species'. This indicates that there are about 34,000 species now known, of which not more than 25,000 are based on morphology."

These estimates are now nearly twenty-five years old. More and more new species are proposed and the current rate approximates to 1500 a year. Not all these will, of course, prove acceptable. Bisby and Ainsworth somewhat pessimistically estimated that "not more than one out of two new genera is 'good,' one out of three new species." If one makes the charitable assumption that taxonomists are now twice as successful as they were in proposing species, 1000 species a year can be added to the previous total. In other words, there are now 50,000 known species based on morphology, and well over 100,000 specific names.

B. *Number of Undescribed Species*

Every mycologist would agree that there are many more species of fungi still to be recognized and described. Bisby and Ainsworth (1943) suggested that about a third of the fungi were known and that in all there are approximately 100,000 species. This estimate is, as Martin (1951) pointed out, extremely conservative.

As a standard class exercise in Professor G. W. Martin's mycology course at the University of Iowa, 100 species of vascular plants were selected at random from the Seventh edition of "Gray's New Manual of Botany" (1908), divided into 10 series in such a way that each of 10 students compiled the fungi listed on every 10th host species in Seymour's "Host Index of the Fungi of North America" (1929). Of the 100 hosts in one particular trial 40 had no parasitic fungi listed as occurring on them while the numbers listed on the other 60 ranged from 1 to 89. Of the 423 parasitic fungi recorded on the 100 host plants 11 species were listed on two or more hosts a total of 31 times, thus reducing the total of fungi by 20 to 403. Even allowing for synonyms or possible synonyms, the number of valid species represented in this sample can scarcely be below 300. This result was in accord with other samplings which have resulted in totals for the fungi as approximately equal to or as high as five times the number of hosts.

Martin also cites as supplementary evidence a survey by Gilman and Archer of fungi of Iowa; 980 fungi were found to attack 1067 host species, and Bisby and Ainsworth (1943) estimated that the 6000 species of fungi had been recorded for Britain, for which the number of vascular plants, as listed in the "London Catalogue," was 2362.

Martin concludes from such findings that the total number of fungal species may be of the same order of magnitude as that of the vascular plants, which has been estimated at rather more than a quarter of a million (Jones, 1951).

This estimate is probably still on the conservative side for although specialization for plants may have multiplied fungal species, animals too are parasitized by fungi. Fungi are usually considered rarely to parasitize animals. However, as pointed out in Chapter 8 (page 211), there seem to be approximately the same number of pathogenic species per host for both plants and vertebrate animals. Many invertebrates too are parasitized by fungi, and it would seem reasonable to conclude that even when allowance is made for plurivorous species, synonymy, and host-species and the fact that many pathogens of both plants and animals are also saprobic, the number of species of fungi exceeds rather than equals the number of vascular plants.

In conclusion it may be noted that while the numbers of new genera and new species of fungi proposed each year fluctuate and though the numbers proposed per year are on the increase, since 1925 the ratio of the number of species to the number of genera proposed annually has been virtually constant at slightly below twenty (cf. Ainsworth, 1954). This regularity is what would be expected if the new fungal taxa proposed each year are a random sample from a large undescribed population and that there are generally accepted conventions for the differentiation of genera and species among taxonomic mycologists.

REFERENCES

Ainsworth, G. C. (1954). The pattern of mycological taxonomy. *Taxon* **3**: 77–79.

Ainsworth, G. C. (1955). Host-parasite relationships. *J. Gen. Microbiol.* **12**: 352–355.

Ainsworth, G. C. (1962). Pathogenicity and the taxonomy of fungi. *In* "Microbial Classification" (G. C. Ainsworth and P. H. A. Sneath, eds.), pp. 249–269. Cambridge Univ. Press, London and New York.

Bisby, G. R., and G. C. Ainsworth. (1943). The numbers of fungi. *Brit. Mycol. Soc. Trans.* **26**: 16–19.

Brierley, W. B., S. T. Jewson, and M. Brierley. (1927). A quantitative study of soil fungi. *Proc. Papers 1st Intern. Congr. Soil Sci., 1927.* Vol. 3, pp. 1–24.

Burnett, J. H., and E. J. Evans. (1966). Genetical homogeneity and stability of mating-type factors of "fairy rings" of *Marasmius oreades. Nature* **210**: 1368–1369.

Chupp, C. (1954). "A Monograph of the Fungus Genus *Cercospora,*" 667 pp. Privately printed, Ithaca, New York.

Ciferri, R. (1952). The criteria for the definition of species in mycology. *Ann. Mycol. (Berlin)* **30**: 122–136.

Fischer, G. W. (1943). Some evident synonymous relationships in certain graminicolous smut fungi. *Mycologia* **35**: 610–619.

Gäumann, E. A. (1923). Beiträge zu einer Monographie der Gattung *Peronospora* Corda. *Beitr. Kryptogamenflora Schweiz* **5**: 1–360.
Jones, G. N. (1951). On the number of species of plants. *Sci. Monthly* **72**: 289–295.
Lodder, J., and N. J. W. Kreger-van Rij. (1952). "The Yeasts: A Taxonomic Study," 713 pp. North-Holland Publ., Amsterdam.
Martin, G. W. (1951). The numbers of fungi. *Iowa Acad. Sci.* **58**: 175–178.
Parker-Rhodes, A. F. (1954). The basidiomycetes of Skokholm Island. I. Annotated species list. *Brit. Mycol. Soc. Trans.* **37**: 324–342.
Sernander, R. (1927). Zur Morphologie und Biologie der Diasporen. *Nova Acta Regiae Soc. Sci. Upsaliensis Vd. Extra Ord. Ed.*: 1–104.
Shantz, H. L., and R. L. Piemeisel. (1917). Fungus fairy rings in Eastern Colorado and their effect on vegetation. *J. Agr. Res.* **11**: 191–246.
Yerkes, W. D., and C. G. Shaw. (1959). The taxonomy of *Peronospora* species on Cruciferae and Chenopodiaceae. *Phytopathology* **49**: 499–507.

Taxonomy

TAXONOMIC CRITERIA

CHAPTER 20

Morphology as a Taxonomic Criterion

C. G. C. CHESTERS

Department of Botany
The University
Nottingham, England

I. INTRODUCTION

Mycologists who deal with the classification of fungi approach this topic from several aspects: two extremes may be recognized. At one end are the taxonomists who are concerned with the study and naming of fungal collections, either fresh or dried, and at the other are those concerned with assigning names to fungi in culture on agar media. Between these extremes are the fortunate taxonomists able to collect their material in the field, study it throughout its growth phases on its natural substrate, isolate it in pure culture, follow its development within the limits imposed by the techniques used, and assess the total morphological criteria accumulated from field and laboratory study. The modern taxonomic approach in mycology has constantly emphasized the importance of developmental criteria and the necessity of discovering the basic genotypic characteristics of the individual, recognizing both for obligate parasites and for unspecialized saprophytes that the kinds of substrate on which the fungus grows and the habitat conditions to which it is exposed result in different phenotypic expressions of the genotype. Emphasis has been placed on a search for those criteria less subject to pressures arising from differences in substrate or habitat. But the definition of valid taxa must take into account as wide a range of criteria as possible and the assessment of the degree of variation which may be expected of each criterion. That these criteria should be morphological for the vast majority of fungi cannot be disputed, but it must never be forgotten that the morphology of an individual is the ultimate expression of its growth processes, the final display of all its complex relationships with its normal habitat. In nature relatively few fungi live in a state of monoculture, and these are mainly obligate parasites having a close dependence on one or on a few host individuals. The majority of fungi live in communities of organisms exposed to competition pressures which of necessity have a limiting effect upon the degree of expression of their genotypic potentialities. For saprophytic fungi, particularly those easily cultivated on laboratory media, freedom from competition pressures allows the individual to express other aspects of its genotype, to display different morphological criteria or at least different degrees of already recognized criteria. This of itself demands of the taxonomist who must attempt to define taxa from laboratory cultures the greatest care in evaluating criteria, particularly with respect to assessing their range of variation. An agar medium not only differs from the majority of natural substrates in chemical composition, but also possesses entirely different physical properties, not the least of which is the surface resistance of the substrate to emerging spore-bearing organs. There is sound common-sense underlying the use by many mycologists of surface-sterilized host material as the final court of reference for their culture studies of fungi. While it was proper for Grove (1937, p. 367) to emphasize the state of "petripatellism" as: "The state of mind of a mycologist who studies his fungus in a laboratory, on agar-slants or *Petri dishes,* without paying equal regard to what the fungus can do out of doors in the wide and untrammelled field," modern mycologists have recognized the importance of combining the criteria displayed by the fungus in its "state of nature" with the criteria unfolded during development and during laboratory cultivation. But these criteria cannot stand alone as the hallmarks of taxa, particularly at the specific level; where possible they should be referred to a final court of appeal before a name is assigned, to the authentic herbarium material lodged by the author of a species name. Equally for new species, published descriptions, illustrations, and measurements should be supplemented by dried specimens lodged in permanent herbaria. Live cultures of fungi, properly named, have their uses as references, but a fungus relieved of the pressures of its native habitat often becomes attenuated, partly because of the unnatural conditions of pure culture, partly because of its intrinsic variability, and partly because of the hazards of transfer techniques.

II. CRITERIA

Morphological criteria may be selected from all stages of the life cycle of a fungus. Their value in the definition of taxa depends upon their constancy and upon the accuracy with which they can be described in qualitative and quantitative terms. In turn, these depend in some measure upon the conditions under which the observations have been made.

The morphology of the mycelium of a fungus within its host substrate may be entirely useless as a diagnostic criterion, not because it lacks characteristic features, but because these are difficult to display and to observe. If a fungus can be cultivated on laboratory media, the morphology of its mycelium, its branching, the degree and constancy of septation, and measurements of hyphal width, can all be obtained with precision and are valid for *that individual on that medium at that time*. They are valuable so long as it is realized that they refer to a particular individual under a defined set of culture conditions and their value increases with the accuracy of definition of these conditions and with comparative studies of their constancy under related conditions for the same individual and for closely related individuals.

Fungi growing in nature on highly decomposed substrates normally display in culture on laboratory media morphological characteristics closely approximating those on their natural substrates. Thus, members of the Mucoraceae and of the Gymnoascaceae generally produce mycelia and spore-bearing structures in culture which differ mainly in luxuriance from these features in their normal habitats—a result partially due to the conditions of monoculture. On the other hand, more complex fungi such as stromatic pyrenomycetes, may produce ascocarps in agar culture, but these differ radically from their counterparts in host tissues mainly because of differences in the physical and chemical properties of such laboratory media as contrasted with the host tissues, but the asci and ascospores and the development of perithecia are alike in nature and in culture.

The definition of fungal taxa depends upon the assessment of the sum of their morphological characteristics and upon the recognition of valid levels of differences in criteria selected as definitive. Not all criteria are of equal value at the same level of taxonomic separation. Spore producing members and the stages of development through which they pass, and the spores which they bear, are more constant than many of the characteristics of the mycelium that produced them.

The important requirements demanded of morphological criteria for taxonomic purposes may be stated as:

1. Criteria should show sufficient degrees of difference to allow effective separation of taxa.
2. Ranges of variation within a criterion should be known.
3. Within limits each criterion should be capable of being observed accurately.
4. Criteria used to separate higher taxa should possess a considerable measure of constancy.

Ideally, criteria should be obtained from the whole body structures of individuals but, because of the complexity of many life cycles, this is not always possible except for the majority of phycomycetes and the simpler ascomycetes and certain basidiomycetes. For some individuals, such as members of the Chytridiales, Monoblepharidales, and Blastocladiales, the whole thallus may be examined as a unit and over a period of time its sporing structures may be followed through the sequences of their development. Even individuals belonging to the Mucorales and certain members of the Peronosporales are amenable to direct and continued observation at all phases of the life cycle. For higher ascomycetes and basidiomycetes which grow over long periods in their substrates before sporulation, and which produce different kinds of spores at widely separated time intervals within the life cycle, the collection of a representative series of criteria from the whole, complete individual is extremely difficult. Hence, the recognition of taxa in such higher fungi has been based upon the characters of the perfect state. With these fungi, classical systems of separation of taxa have concentrated upon the external form of the sporophore, its consistency and color, its relationship to the substrate, and upon the morphology of spore-producing members and the spores which they carry. The advent of studies in life cycles initiated by the brothers L. R. and C. Tulasne, A. DeBary, O. Brefeldt and many others at the end of the nineteenth century and continued by workers in the present century, led directly to considerations of development, particularly that of spore-bearing structures. Some provided a fund of additional criteria, which could be used for the separation of taxa; others demonstrated that the final form of a structure may be arrived at by different patterns of development and that the pattern, not the final product, is of primary value in taxonomic separation.

While all mycologists faced with the identification of fungi must applaud the increase in morphological data that can be used to separate taxa, they must be constantly aware also of the frustration implicit in much of this new knowledge. In particular, the discontinuity which partly results from the wealth of material awaiting examination causes the real value of such studies to be underestimated. The classical systems of mycological taxonomy, both pre-Friesian and post-Friesian, and the compilations of species culminating in the publication of Saccardo's "Sylloge Fungorum," have been based upon criteria observed in materials collected in nature and upon mature spore-bearing organs. Many descriptions of species were restricted to external characters because detailed observations of the spore-bearing structures were at that time impossible. Admittedly many of the taxonomic systems were highly artificial, but, applied as their authors intended, names could be given to individuals collected in nature. That the same individual might appear at several points in the systems under different names was a trial but equally a logical consequence of the imposed necessity of using terminal structure as a basic criterion in the absence of a knowledge of developmental stages. To follow patterns of development sheds new light on interpretations of mature structure, but it is time consuming and often results in the accumulation of a plethora of detailed information about one or a few individuals. True, these individuals can be very clearly defined, but how are they to be compared or contrasted with apparently closely related individuals for which such detailed information is lacking? The sad fact is that this cannot be done until much more work on developmental patterns has been carried out and, equally, because apparently similar mature structures may arise by entirely different means.

At present, and as a consequence of studies of the development of individual fungi and of the reinvestigation of the anatomy and development of spore-bearing members, broad classes of individuals can be defined, monographic treatment of certain families and genera have been published, but complete taxonomic works embodying the new concepts are only slowly making their appearance. Taxonomy of living things cannot remain static as the frontier of knowledge continually expands, but the very rate of expansion brings problems in its wake because much of the new knowledge concerns individuals and can be accounted of real value only when the volume of it allows generalizations on a sound, firm base.

III. SOURCES OF MORPHOLOGICAL CRITERIA

It is customary to select morphological criteria from consideration of the several distinctive features of individuals. For fungi this should involve a consideration of the structure of the thallus and its several parts and of the way in which it reaches its mature form. It must also involve the consideration of any sporing structures which the thallus produces, their development and final anatomical structure, and the origin and morphology of the spores which they carry. While the thallus can show marked changes in relation to the environment, sporing structures remain remarkably constant for every individual included in a single species concept. The criteria derived from the morphology of the spore-producing members constitute the major factors for the separation of taxa at all levels.

A. The Thallus

The thallus of fungi exhibits considerable diversity of extent and development, ranging from a single cell through branched cells of limited extent to extensive mycelial systems consisting of complexly branched hyphae often aggregated in various ways into massive spore-producing structures. For simpler fungi (e.g., individuals belonging to the Chytridiales) characteristics of the thallus may be observed by examining the whole individual in or on its substrate or by developing new thalli on fresh substrates and following their progressive differentiation. Even at the level of the Blastocladiales and Monoblepharidales examination of the thallus as an entire unit is possible. This being so, and bearing in mind that the whole individual is displayed for inspection, it is understandable that criteria of value can be obtained from its shape, differentiation of its parts and its relationships with the substrate (whether mainly intramatrical or mainly extramatrical), and the precise degree to which the whole or parts of the thallus are involved in spore production.

With mycelial fungi the size of the thallus increases and the area over which it grows extends. These features impose difficulties in making use of mycelial characters, particularly from mycelia growing on natural substrates. Where an individual can be cultivated on laboratory media the difficulties inherent in the close relationship of the mycelial hyphae with the natural substrate are avoided and hyphal morphology can be examined on and in the medium. But, the value of mycelial data requires careful scrutiny, not only with respect to its precise taxonomic status but also with respect to the degree of accuracy with which such information can be conveyed to other investigators.

While it is possible to relate mycelial color and any pigment changes produced in the culture media to standard color charts, it is not always possible to ensure that two observers match color values with the same degree of accuracy. When it comes to the description of the gross appearance of a mycelium, difficulties are magnified because of a lack of precise terms to describe the form of a mycelium. Even photographs are of little help because of the difficulty of obtaining sufficiently accurate reproduction and of obtaining the requisite numbers of plates. The advent of color photography spread a ray of hope, but except for limited use the cost of reproduction has proved prohibitive. But, color reproductions have much to commend them where differences in gross mycelial characters are really essential for the definition of a taxon.

By contrast, recording of hyphal characters is on a different level of accuracy. Measurements of hyphal diameters, degrees of branching, angles of divergence of branches, and intervals between branches may be combined with information on the constancy and degree of septation, the occurrence of particular cell shapes, aggregations of specially differentiated cells, and constant features of cell protoplasts, and all can be accurately recorded and illustrated. Insofar as mycelia are concerned, it is the detail of their component parts which is more important than the gross characters of the whole, but even these criteria must be used with care and their use must be accompanied by detailed facts about the conditions under which they were observed.

B. *Spore-Producing Members*

The morphology of spore-producing members has provided the majority of criteria employed in the recognition of taxa. This is as it should be because such structures are genetically more stable than the thalloid systems which bear them. But in the more complex groups (e.g., Pyrenomycetes, Discomycetes, Hymenomycetes, and Sphaeropsidales), the spore-producing members consist in essence of two parts; the spore-forming structures—asci, basidia, conidiophores, and certain other closely related structures—and the protecting or carrying structures—ascocarps, carpophores, pycnidia, and the like. Environmental factors may bring about morphological changes in the protective or bearing structures which appear to have diagnostic value but which in reality are merely expressions of habitat pressures of varying degree. A case in point is the variability of the ostiolar neck of perithecia or of pycnidia developed in dry situations, where they are short, and in wet situations, where they are long. But recent studies have shown that the patterns of development of ascocarps and the basic construction of carpophores yield valid criteria for taxonomic separation despite differences in the external morphology of the mature structures. The accumulation of information on the development of spore-bearing members in all facets of their growth has brought a new outlook on fungal classification. The only sad feature is that so much remains to be done before a truly representative account of fungi becomes possible.

In most phycomycetes both imperfect sporangiospores and perfect resting spores of diverse kinds exist in each life cycle. The criteria to be obtained from the imperfect state include the method of development of the sporangium, its relationship to differentiated sporangiophores, the kinds of spores produced, whether flagellate or nonflagellate and, if the former, the number, size, and differences in insertion of the flagellum. In simple individuals (species of *Olpidium*) the whole thallus may be converted into a sporangium, whereas in eucarpic individuals (species of *Chytridium*) and in more complex individuals (species of *Monoblepharis*) only a portion of the thallus is involved in sporangial formation. The degree of differentiation of the sporangium and the way in which it is borne upon the mycelium is of significant importance in the Peronosporales, where the frequent absence of a precise sporangiophore, coupled with the successive development of sporangia in species of *Pythium* and *Phytophthora* serve to differentiate these at family level (Pythiaceae) from the Peronosporaceae, in which defined sporangiophores and caducous sporangia are the rule. Within the Mucorales arrangement of sporangia on sporangiophores of diverse degrees of branching, the structure of individual sporangia and their method of spore discharge, the presence or absence of a columella and its shape and size where present, the numbers and sizes of spores are morphological criteria of importance.

By contrast, the value of criteria from the perfect state varies with the order and family relationships of individuals. The process of conjugation of gametangia in zygomycetes is relatively constant within species of a genus and gives little assistance in the definition of taxa at species level, but the final morphology of zygospores may have validity in specific separations. Within the Oomycetes the process of formation of the resting spore is highly conservative, but valuable criteria can be obtained from consideration of the details of such processes and, in particular, relationships between the origin of or the insertion of the antheridium relative to the position of the oogonium, the number of antheridia per oogonium, the degree of differentiation within the oogonium, particularly the number of oospores and their differentiation from the oogonial plasm, and the number and size of the oospores and the degree of differentiation of their walls.

Within the Phycomycetes studies of development of mycelium, of sporangia and sporangiophores, and of resting spores (oospores and zygospores) has been pursued over many years and, since most individuals in the class can be cultivated, such studies have been a normal result of investigations into their life cycles. Thus the major criteria available to taxonomists have been known for many years and have been subjected to critical revision from time to time, and the recognition of taxa, while not universally accepted by all workers, is nonetheless in a relatively stable condition. However, this is not true for certain other classes of fungi, particularly at the level of the higher taxa. Thus separation of many members of the Ascomycetes, Basidiomycetes, and Fungi Imperfecti into generic and higher taxa still awaits an assessment of new information relating to the development of their spore-bearing members before entirely acceptable systems of classification can be achieved. Even the recognition of species limits is often in doubt, particularly in individuals with wide-ranging substrate relationships.

From each of these classes examples of how the new morphological information has been applied will be reviewed, starting with imperfect states in relation to attempts to define affinities in the Fungi Imperfecti.

IV. OF FUNGI IMPERFECTI

The separation of major taxa in this class has followed in general principles the classification used by Saccardo (1884) in the "Sylloge

Fungorum," which employed the arrangement of the conidiophores with respect to the mycelium or its substrate as primary criteria for the separation of the following large groups: Hyphomyceteae, with conidiophores and conidia distributed over the mycelium; Sphaeropsideae, with conidiophores and conidia protected by some form of pycnidial envelope; and Melanconieae, with conidiophores and conidia developed from a restricted formative layer of hyphae produced underneath the superficial tissues of the substrate. The first two groups were each separated into sections according to the precise arrangement of the conidiophores and their degree of aggregation, or upon the nature of the wall of the protecting structures. Within each of the sections spore septation and spore color along with the degree of definition of conidiophores were used to build up a highly artificial but nonetheless workable system. Grove (1935, p. xiii) separated the class into two divisions depending upon whether the spores were borne outside the matrix (Hyphomycetes) or within some cavity produced by the mycelium or by the matrix on which they developed (Coelomycetes).

The fungus–substrate relationship has been invoked to no mean degree within the Coelomycetes for the recognition of taxa at generic and specific levels, and many host-limited species exist. Reappraisal of taxa within this group is urgently required.

Attempts to formulate more logical systems were forced on mycologists by the increasing use of agar cultures, because it was no longer possible to differentiate between species that might have produced defined conidiophores on their natural substrates and species that might have lacked such conidiophores. On agar the type of conidiophore seen in nature was often absent. Pycnidia, if produced in culture, seldom resembled closely those of the individual in nature. The physical state of the substrate surface in nature could not be imitated on agar media.

In 1888, J. Constantin attempted to divide the Hyphomycetes on criteria based on the degree of branching and definition of conidiophores, on the type of insertion of the conidia or of conidial chains, and on the presence or absence of mucilage around the conidia. Whenever he could he grew his collections in artificial culture. Between 1910 and 1911, Vuillemin (see Mason, 1933) discussed the way in which certain hyphomycetes produced their spores and recognized two essentially different methods: those excised from their formative hyphae immediately after production (conidia vera) and those not immediately cut off from their formative hyphae and resembling these hyphae in diameter (thallospores). The latter could be formed by different growth processes. Where they arose by fragmentation of the parent hypha they were termed arthrospores, where by budding they were termed blastospores, and where by thickening of the parent cell they were termed chlamydospores. Terminal chlamydospores were later called aleuriospores when they showed a degree of differentiation from the parent hypha. Aleuriospores might closely resemble conidia vera but differed in not being immediately caducous, by retaining contact with their formative hyphae for longer periods. Vuillemin divided conidia vera into three categories, depending on their relationship with the parent hyphae: (a) those arising from normal mycelial hyphae; (b) those arising from differentiated hyphae or conidiophores, and (c) those produced from flask-shaped cells, or phialides.

Mason (1933) redefined phialides to include fusiform, truncate, or beaked, or acuminate hyphal units which, at their apex or within their apex, excised thin-walled conidia. Where the phialide produced only one spore, that was considered to be a *terminus* spore; and where a series were produced, the term *meristem* spores was suggested. *Radulospores* which might be considered as similar in genesis to phialospores were so called because they were produced over undifferentiated hyphal cells, without reference to the hyphal apex, from minute persistent sterigmata. He accepted Vuillemin's concept of thallospores and their differentiation into arthrospores (by fragmentation), blastospores (by budding), and chlamydospores (by cell modification).

Mason (1933) showed that in one and the same life cycle conidia of different genesis could occur—blastospores and phialospores (*Monilia cinerea*), aleuriospores and phialospores (*Trichothecium roseum*), radulospores and phialospores (*Botrytis cinerea*), terminus and meristem spores (*Echinobotryum atrum*). His aim was to draw attention to the fact that in the life cycles of some ascomycetes with imperfect states a phialospore form occurs in "form genera" based on other spore forms, and that, if the phialospore form is unknown, search should reveal its presence. However, his work focused attention on the genesis of conidia and pointed the way for a reappraisal of the criteria to be used in the separation of taxa in the Fungi Imperfecti.

Subsequently, Mason (1937), called attention to the fact that there were two ways in which conidia were presented for dispersal; as dry, essentially wind-dispersed conidia and as slimy, essentially water- or insect-dispersed conidia. Dry spores were released by shock: slimy spores required rain splash or animal contact to remove them. Wakefield and Bisby (1941, p. 50) used these distinctions within the Hyphomycetes to separate Xerosporae (dry spore types) from Gloiosporae (slimy spore types). They found that many "species" did not exactly conform to one class or the other, and although extremes were easy to recognize many "species" could not be placed with certainty in either section. It is too much to expect that this biological criterion can be fully exploited until much more information is available of the precise dispersal mechanisms in more "species." Existing descriptions of fungi imperfecti give little information on either the state of the conidia as such or how they appear to be dispersed.

Hughes (1953) stated: "I believe that there are only a limited number of methods whereby conidia can develop from other cells and that morphologically related imperfect states will only be brought together when precise methods of conidium origin take first place in the delimitation of the major groupings." The essential processes demonstrated by Hughes in his review of conidial formation and of the conidiophores which bear them may be regarded as processes of septation, budding, and fragmentation. If a hyphal cell becomes meristematic and in subsequent growth forms conidia by direct division of the cell, the formation of a wall produces a daughter cell with a broad basal wall: the cell may later increase in size and become rounded off and remain unicellular or develop septa. If the original mother cell remains meristematic and repeated divisions occur, either a series of conidia in chains or a series of apparently simple conidia result. However, a meristematic cell may proliferate by budding, producing a unit at first much smaller in diameter than itself which by subsequent growth increases in size to a diameter greater than the parent hypha. During this process the wall between the parent hypha and the daughter cell forms a minute isthmus. If the parent hypha retains its meristematic activity new buds may be formed below the original bud but, following sympodial growth of the parent cell, a series of conidia in acropetal sequence may be produced, or, lacking such sympodial extension, a cluster of conidia may be formed. Equally, the original bud may itself produce one or more buds and these in turn repeat the process to give a series of connected conidial chains either straight or branched in which varying degrees of septation can occur within the individual conidia. Cells of hyphae may undergo division, with subsequent increase in size of the daughter cells and modification of their wall structure to produce conidia standing in the same relationship to the parent hypha as its original cells. Such chains of conidia produced by fragmentation are in essence a series of chlamydospores.

Making use of these basic growth processes for conidial formation and the several permutations which can be related to the growth patterns of the conidium-bearing cells, Hughes recognized eight major sections in the Hyphomycetes. The commonest process of conidium formation was by budding of the "conidiophore," forming solitary conidia, or by budding of the initial conidium, producing chains of conidia.

In separating his sections Hughes pointed out that there were two methods of "conidiophore" growth, by apical extension which is shown by the majority of hyphomycetes, or by intercalary, and usually basal, meristematic division which occurs in a limited number of hyphomycetes.

The forms which he included in his first seven sections have conidiophores growing by apical extension, and in Section I to Section IV the conidia are produced by budding from fertile cells. Chains may be formed by subsequent budding of the initial conidium. In all these sections "conidiophores" may be simple or branched. Section I was divided into two subsections: 1A, having thin mycelial hyphae, thin "conidiophores" and, for the most part, conidia arising in acropetal and often branched chains from the first-formed conidium which might be modified as a "bearer" cell; and IB, having thick mycelial hyphae and "conidiophores," and conidia usually formed from slightly, or greatly swollen, cells either terminal or intercalary and often showing denticles after dispersal of the spores. In Section II growth of the "conidiophore" could be sympodial with longer or shorter internodes between the spores. When formation of conidia was localized, terminal swellings covered by densely crowded conidia could result.

Section III embraced individuals in which the first-formed conidium was followed by subsequent conidia produced by proliferation through the scar left by the excision of the earlier spore. These scars become apparent as annellations at the end of the formative cell, and Hughes suggested the term annellophore as appropriate. In representatives of all the above sections, dispersal of the conidium leaves a marked scar at the point of origin, but in Section VI where the growth process of the conidium is an extrusion of the wall—a budding—the outer wall of the formative hypha and of the conidium are continuous and remain continuous during the formative process, at excision a wide pore is left on the parent hypha and a similar pore is visible on the spore. Acropetal succession of conidium development from the initial conidium may give rise to spores in chains: when these break up the intermediate members of the chain have two, and sometimes more, pores, if the chains are branched. Section IV grouped together individuals producing phialides with growing points either within marked or minute collarettes which produced a series of phialospores. Conidia arising in basipetal succession by division and gradually differentiating from a basal meristematic cell were gathered together in Section V, whereas conidia arising by basipetal fragmentation of hyphae of determinate length were included in Section VII; here no meristematic zone was present. A distinct series in which the "conidiophore" increased in length by a basal meristem after the production of a single terminal conidium by budding, and subsequent formation of solitary or of clustered conidia from cells of the "conidiophore" was placed in Section VIII.

Following a series of "Studies on the Japanese Hyphomycetes" from 1954 onward, Tubaki (1958) reviewed the classification with particular reference to the scheme proposed by Hughes (see also Vol. II, Chapter 4).

He subdivided certain of Hughes' sections. In Section III he proposed three subsections based on differences in the behavior of the annellophore. In IIIA he placed what may be termed serial "annellospores" in which the terminal part of the initial cell bears a series of annellations. In IIIB are solitary "annellospores" which at excision leave a single frill round the apex of the initial cells. In IIIC, in which an intercalary cell is formed between the conidium and the initial cell, when excision occurs it is the wall of this intercalary cell which is ruptured so that both spore and initial have a part of it as a "frill." Phialospores (Section IV) were placed in two subsections differentiated by the way in which the spore was formed: in IVA by budding of a meristem enclosed within a small collar and in IVB by cell division and wall formation of a meristem in a tall collar. Section VII, which contains arthrospores, was considered to be divisible into subsection A containing exogenous arthrospores and subsection B containing endogenous arthrospores. Tubaki added Section XI to receive types in which the "conidiophore" produced a terminal conidium by septation and in which renewed growth immediately below this spore formed a secondary initial producing the second spore by septation, this spore becoming attached to the primary spore. This process being repeated gave a "head" of chains of spores which remained adherent or later became separate. Such a type of development is found in *Trichothecium roseum*.

These two proposed systems of segregating the major groups of Hyphomycetes are of importance because they place clear emphasis on the methods of conidium formation and show that it is possible to assemble forms with like spore genesis and that different methods of development of conidia can be clearly differentiated. Similar studies within the Coelomycetes are urgently needed. Equally, a clear definition of what is meant by the term "conidiophore" is long overdue. Hughes (1953, p. 646) pointed this out very cogently. One solution might be to use the term fertile hyphae for the assemblage of hyphae which bear the formative cells, to describe the systems of branching of these hyphae by descriptive terms, and to restrict the term conidiophore to the formative cell.

V. OF PYRENOMYCETES

It is still true that if a name for a pyrenomycete is being sought the usual works of reference which have to be consulted classify these fungi under schemes reflecting the treatment of Lindau in "Die Natürlichen Pflanzenfamilien" (1897) which separated suborders and families on the characters of ascocarps. Such characters included the relationship of simple perithecia or stromata containing groups of perithecia to host substrates, the color and consistency of the ascocarp or stroma, and the shape, color, and septation of the ascospores.

The name Pyrenomycetes was introduced by Fries (1823, p. 312), who regarded the possession of a perithecium containing asci as an essential character of the group. The flask-shaped perithecium consisted of a more or less spherical venter bearing a neck of variable length punctured at its apex by a dispersal pore or ostiole. Perithecia might sit singly upon or be immersed within the substrate (simple pyrenomycetes), or be organized into stromata containing several perithecia (complex pyrenomycetes), the stromata being formed either entirely of fungal tissue or of a mixture of substrate and fungal tissues. When closer examination of these stromatic pyrenomycetes was undertaken, it was found that in a proportion of them the stroma did not contain flask-shaped, determinate perithecia, but rather cavities in the general stromatic tissues, carrying basal groups of asci. Fries had seen this type of structure in *Dothidea,* and Lindau (1897) recognized the presence of such ascostromatic forms in which true perithecia were lacking. In the years up to 1928 other examples of this sort of structure were disclosed by various workers both in the simple and compound pyrenomycetes. Attempts were made to show that the perithecium with its clearly defined wall containing asci and determinate paraphyses in the center and opening to the exterior by a neck lined with periphyses, was a terminal product of the locular stroma in which the asci were not accompanied by definite paraphyses but by diverse kinds of hyphal threads which were apparently displaced stromatic tissues (F. von Hoehnel, F. Theissen and H. Sydow, F. Theissen, F. Petrak, and others).

Miller (1928) critically examined the structure and development of certain pyrenomycetes and demonstrated that there were two kinds of development in the group. The true perithecium with an organized wall enclosing asci and paraphyses, and the ascostroma arising from plectenchymatous hyphae by meristematic growth and developing one or more locules containing asci in fascicles and also hyphal threads which had grown down from the top of such locules and remained as pseudoparaphyses. Discussing the classification of the Ascomycetes, Nannfeldt (1932, pp. 13–56) reviewed earlier studies of the Pyrenomycetes and proposed the recognition of three series, Plectascales, Ascohymeniales, and Ascoloculares. The two latter sections included most pyrenomycetes; the Ascohymeniales embraced perithecial forms with an organized hymenium of asci and paraphyses enclosed in a determinate wall and also discomycetous forms. The Ascoloculares included ascostromatic forms with single or multiloculate stromata, each locule containing either asci alone or asci and pseudoparaphyses, but not being limited by a perithecial wall.

In considering certain stromatic pyrenomycetes, von Hoehnel (1907,

1917, 1918) emphasized the importance of the perithecial "nukleus," the central matrix of the perithecium, as a diagnostic feature. Modern studies have shown that the ways in which this centrum becomes organized and the structural features of its mature contents provide some of the most constant morphological criteria for the classification of pyrenomycetes. Of these criteria, the morphology of the ascus is of considerable importance. Ascus structure had already been employed by Lindau (1897) for the separation of certain families of the Pyrenomycetes. Both Nannfeldt (1932) and Miller (1949) made use of structural differences of asci in defining orders within the class, and Ingold (1933) demonstrated relationships between ascus structure and spore discharge processes. Luttrell (1951) reviewed ascus morphology and focused attention on differences between the bitunicate ascus on the one hand and the unitunicate on the other. In the former, well-defined outer and inner walls exist, and at dispersal these behave in quite distinct fashions: the outer wall is thin and inextensible and is ruptured at spore dispersal to release the thicker, extensible inner wall. Initially the whole wall is thick, but as the ascus grows it becomes thinner except for the apical region which remains as a cap either entire or containing a cylindrical channel within the thickness of the wall. At maturity the dual nature of the wall becomes visible and even more so when the outer wall ruptures at ascospore discharge. Although diversity in details of discharge has been observed, the general pattern is relatively constant, and this form of ascus occurs in large, and apparently natural, divisions of the Pyrenomycetes, namely, the Myriangiales, Dothideales, Hemisphaeriales, Pseudosphaeriales (Pleosporales; Luttrell, 1955) and in some species presently included in the Sphaeriales, among others. By contrast, the unitunicate ascus appears to have a single wall which for the most part is relatively thin in the mature ascus. It may be uniformly thin but is usually thickened at the apex. These apical thickenings assume various aspects which may be highly characteristic and of diagnostic value at the generic or even family level, so much so, that Miller (1949) emphasized their value as a diagnostic criterion and Luttrell (1951, pp. 29–32) distinguished between eight characteristic ascal types, including in the descriptions details of the apical structure. French mycologists have done much to extend our knowledge of ascus morphology particularly with respect to apical structure (Chadefaud, 1957, 1958; Chadefaud and Nicot, 1957; Doguet, 1960; Strikmann and Chadefaud, 1961; Schrantz, 1960). With increasing knowledge of ascus structure information of primary importance in separating taxa in the Pyrenomycetes is certain to emerge.

Ascus morphology is constant for any particular taxon, but the ascus is only a unit within the ascocarp. The manner of development of the ascocarp and the relationship of such processes to the mature structure can also provide criteria of significance. Wehmeyer (1926) suggested the term "centrum" to embrace all the structures that arise from the ascogonium or its equivalent structure. Since then numerous studies of development of centra in pyrenomycetes have appeared and Luttrell (1951) has reviewed pertinent examples of centrum development and has suggested eight major types that can be recognized.

Where the ascus is bitunicate, the ascogonia (or their equivalent structures) are formed within a mycelial stroma which is either plectenchymatous or pseudoparenchymatous and produce only ascogenous hyphae and asci. Three distinct lines of centrum development can be recognized. In the first (the *Dothidea* type) the central stromatic area distintegrates forming a locule in the base of which ascogenous hyphae produce fascicles of asci which eventually fill the locule. Depending upon whether there is a single or more than one ascogonium the stroma may be uniloculate or pluriloculate. Examples of this sort of development are found in species of *Dothidea, Plowrightia, Mycosphaerella,* and *Guignardia.*

The second line (the *Pleospora* type) differs from the first in that the mature centrum contains pseudoparaphyses as well as the asci. The stroma centrum becomes loculate because of pressure stresses resultant from the growth of a new series of hyphae attached both at the apex and the base of the central area (or incipient locule cavity); these hyphae constitute the pseudoparaphyses and persist. The steps by which this central cavity traversed by pseudoparaphyses arises varies in different individuals of the line, but all conform to the final picture. Ascogenous hyphae form a concave layer at the base of the locule and produce asci (generally in fascicles) which project among the pseudoparaphyses. Examples of this development may be found in species of *Pleospora, Melanomma,* and *Leptosphaeria.*

In the third line (the *Elsinoe* type) ascogenous hyphae penetrate through the tissues of the stroma initial, forming individual asci each within a separate cavity. These monoascal cavities are either in a single layer or are randomly distributed. In certain instances the ascal area may be clearly separated from the stromatic tissues. This sort of development may be found in species of *Elsinoe, Atichia,* and *Myriangium.*

Where the ascus is unitunicate, five lines of development can be recognized. The first three lines possess in common the fact that the ascogonia (or their equivalent structures) are either formed free on the mycelium or within a stroma. Hyphal branches from the ascogonial stalk or from adjacent mycelial hyphae, produce investing hyphae to form the perithecium initial. The outer layers of this initial forms the perithecial wall; the inner layers a pseudoparenchymatous centrum. Later growth in the apical region of the wall forms a perithecial neck in which schizogenous development in its central column produces a canal opening to the exterior through an ostiole.

In the first line (the *Diaporthe* type) the centrum tissues of the perithecial initial disintegrate to form a locule lined by developing ascogenous hyphae which produce asci whose stalks finally deliquesce, freeing them into the spherical ventral locule. This sort of development is to be found in species of *Diaporthe, Melanconis,* and *Gnomonia.*

The second line (the *Xylaria* type) differs from the first inasmuch as paraphyses arise as determinate branches from the inner wall layers of the perithecial initial and spread upward and outward. Pressures set up by their growth create a locule from the pseudoparenchymatous centrum. Their development continues along the sides of the perithecial neck canal as a lining of short periphyses. Ascogenous hyphae developing among the paraphyses produce an hymenium of asci with persistent stalks which lines the whole of the inner wall surface of the perithecium. Examples of this development are found in species of *Xylaria, Hypoxylon, Diatrype, Cordyceps,* and *Claviceps.*

In the third line (the *Nectria* type), hyphae growing down from the upper region of the centrum become vertically oriented, ultimately forming pseudoparaphyses stretching across a locule resulting from the pressure of their growth, and becoming attached to the base of this locule. Ascogenous hyphae spread over the base of the locule, forming a concave layer of asci (frequently in fascicles) which grow upward among the pseudoparaphyses. Such development is known to occur in species of *Sphaerostilbe* and *Thyronectria.* Jacobs (1958) has shown the presence of vertically oriented hyphae (or, as he called them, basitropic hyphae) in *Hypomyces aurantius, Hypocrea pulvinata, Nectria cinnabarina, N. peziza,* and *N. ochraleuca.*

The last two lines of development in the unitunicate ascus series share in common the fact that the ascogonium, whether with an accompanying antheridium or not, is formed free of investments upon the mycelium surface.

In the fourth line (the *Ophiostoma* [*Ceratocystis*] type), branches from the ascogonial stalk or from adjacent mycelial hyphae produce the perithecial initial which differentiates into wall layers and a pseudoparenchymatous centrum. Ascogenous hyphae develop chains of asci at all levels and, following the collapse of the centrum tissues, the asci mature from the base toward the apex of the ascogenous hyphae. Each ascus wall deliquesces and ascospores are dispersed in mucilage through the neck canal. This type of development is shown by species of *Ophiostoma* (*Ceratocystis*).

In the fifth line (the *Phyllactinia* type) branches from the ascogonial and antheridial stalks produce a sheathing wall: no neck is formed. The ascogonium divides into three cells, the central cell being binucleate and producing either a single ascus or ascogenous hyphae forming fascicles of asci. *Phyllactinia, Sphaerotheca,* and *Erysiphe* show this type of development.

Luttrell (1951, p. 71 *et seq.*) reviewing the evidence from the development of ascocarps suggested that within the Ascomycetes as a whole the occurrence of the unitunicate and bitunicate ascus could be regarded as a criterion of the first order in establishing a major division of such fungi. He placed in the Bitunicate Series the orders Myriangiales, Dothideales, Pseudosphaeriales, Hysteriales, and Trichothyriales. The Unitunicate Series embraced a larger number of Euascomycetes: such asci occur in Plectomycetes, Laboulbeniomycetes, Discomycetes, and Pyrenomycetes. He considered the Pyrenomycetes to be limited to such ascomycetes as formed a true perithecium enclosing fascicles of asci or an hymenial layer of asci (Miller, 1928).

The morphology of the perithecial centrum was used to separate the orders Xylariales, Hypocreales, Diaporthales, and Erysiphales. In a later contribution (Luttrell, 1955) he proposed the recognition of *Loculoascomycetes* as a subclass to accommodate the members of the Bitunicate Series and, in the main, the members of the Ascoloculares (Nannfeldt, 1932). He regarded this subclass as on a level with the Euascomycetes which included all unitunicate ascomycetes and embraced the Ascohymeniales of Nannfeldt (1932) as well as the Plectascales.

VI. OF BASIDIOMYCETES

The pileate members of the Basidiomycetes have attracted the interest not only of professional mycologists, but also of the public at large for several centuries. The traditional systems of classification have made use of features of the gross morphology of the carpophore as criteria for separating taxa. The relationships of stipe to pileus, the arrangement of the lamellae or gills, the kinds of velar structures where present, the occurrence of a volva, the colors of pileus and stipe, the colors of spore deposits, and prominent features of the anatomy of gills have all been employed for defining taxa. The Friesian system of separating the Hymenomycetes into sections based upon such of these features as could be determined visually without the aid of a microscope has stood the test of time. His sections of *Agaricus* elevated to generic rank by himself and by subsequent workers have been in accepted use for many years.

From the latter part of the nineteenth century and throughout the present century, the discovery of a wide range of hymenomycetes from the tropics and elsewhere which were not easily referable to Friesian genera stimulated an already growing interest in the stages of development and in the anatomy of the carpophore of hymenomycetes. While accepting that macroscopic characters are of importance in the designation of taxa at the specific level, it soon became evident that anatomical details of the carpophore provided additional and significant taxonomic criteria and that a knowledge of the development of the carpophore helped in a logical separation of higher taxa. In particular, details of the structure of the flesh of stipe and pileus, of the relationship of the stipe to the pileus, and of the way in which velar structures were formed and were later broken as the carpophore expanded, provided new and important taxonomic criteria.

Persoon (1801) separated larger basidiomycetes into the Angiocarpi, which released their spores from a closed fructification (*Lycoperdon*) and into the Gymnocarpi, which bore their spores over exposed surfaces (*Agaricus, Stereum*). Fries (1821) applied the name Gasteromycetes to the Angiocarpi and the name Hymenomycetes to the Gymnocarpi. The latter were divided into five series: the Auricularini and Tremellinei having gelatinous sporophores, the Agaricini containing gill fungi, the Polyporei embracing tube fungi and including both *Boletus* and *Polyporus,* the Hydnacei containing species with teeth, and the Clavarinei with hymenia on flat surfaces (*Clavaria, Stereum*). Simple and useful as a classification, it has been the basis of many more recent systems which have been used with varying degrees of confidence in the separation of taxa. Fries paid particular attention to the Agaricini and separated groups on spore color, either directly from gill color or from spore prints. These groups were the: Leucosporus (white spores: *Amanita, Lepiota, Armillaria, Russula*); Hyporhodium (pink spores: *Leptonia, Nolanea*); Cortinaria (ochraceous spores: *Inoloma, Dermocybe*); Derminus (ferruginous spores: *Naucoria, Pholiota, Hebeloma*); Protella (purple-violet spores: *Agaricus, Hypholoma*); Coprinus (black spores); Gomphidius (black spores).

Secondary characters were then used to separate tribes. Such characters included the position and character of the stipe, the presence and character of veils, and the arrangement and form of the lamellae or gills. Spore color is a difficult criterion to assess, and intergrading colors are not easy to place. With the rise in the study of carpophore ontogeny (Patouillard, 1900; Konrad and Maublanc, 1924–1936) and the recognition of the degrees of protection afforded by velar tissues, new approaches to criteria useful in classifying the hymenomycetes became the fashion. Some carpophores were found to have exposed hymenia from their initiation, and such gymnocarpic types differed significantly from the majority, the angiocarpic, which were found to possess veils of different kinds protecting the developing lamellae. Intermediate forms in which very young carpophores were found to possess a veil but in which this was destroyed before the basidia reached maturity were placed in the hemiangiocarpic types (Patouillard, 1900). Later studies have shown that many of the hemiangiocarpic forms are really gymnocarpic if one accepts as true angiocarps the type of development found in the Gasteromycetes. Much emphasis has been placed on the way in which, and the stage at which, the veil develops. Reijnders (1948) proposed a series of descriptive terms for the different types of development which he recognized, but the precise value to be placed on veil ontogeny in the Hymenomycetes as a whole still awaits final assessment because relatively few individuals have been adequately studied.

The carpophore is composed of dikaryotic hyphal systems which are homogeneous in the carpophore initial forming a mass of prosenchyma. Differentiation of the hyphae quickly becomes apparent as the hyphal systems of the mature carpophore develop. The majority of these hyphae are of wide diameter forming the *fundamental* hyphae or structural framework of the sporophore. Mixed with these are thinner and more delicate *connective* hyphae representing almost unchanged hyphae of the sporophore initial. The consistency of the flesh of carpophores is related to the relative occurrence of particular types of such hyphal systems and to the way in which areas of hyphae become modified during maturation. Brittle or grained flesh such as occurs in *Russula* or *Lactarius* is constructed of narrow and loosely interwoven hyphae along with hyphae of large isodiametric cells (sphaerocysts) which may form coherent groups. It is the heterogenity of such a tissue that produces the physical attributes of the flesh. Specialized laticiferous hyphae occur in species of several genera, particularly *Lactarius, Russula, Mycena, Naucoria, Collybia,* and *Boletus.*

Anatomy of the lamellae is of taxonomic value because several differences in structure occur within specific or generic limits. The central or tramal region of a lamella represents an extension of the tissues of the pileus. Tramal tissues may be irregular, lacking directional arrangement of the constituent hyphae, or regular, exhibiting a quite definite pattern. In the latter instance, sections may show rounded cells giving a vesciculose or cellular pattern. In *Amanita, Gomphidius,* and *Paxillus* the central area of the trama (the mediostratum) is thin and produces elongate elements which pass outward on each side and downward. In *Russula* the trama consists of isodiametric elements as well as of thin hyphae resembling the mixture in the flesh of the pileus.

Now that more is known of the range of structure of the subhymenial layers, valuable criteria are becoming apparent. Subhymenia may be regular and homogeneous or irregular and heterogeneous. They may consist of obvious filaments or of more or less cellular elements. Sometimes a layer of fine filaments separates the subhymenium from the hymenium: such a layer has been termed a hymenopodium.

The lamellar edge has long been recognized as an area of diagnostic importance. The hymenium may extend from each side of the lamella over its edge, which thus shows the characters of the hymenium and is termed homomorphic. However, it may consist of hairlike hyphae which are extensions of the central tramal hyphae, and is then termed heteromorphic. Development of the lamellae varies within the Hymenomycetes and has been studied by Atkinson (1906, 1916). Any discussion of the formation of lamellae and of their relationship to the stipe must necessarily involve consideration of the origin and nature of veil tissues.

For some time the anatomy of the hymenium has provided criteria of diagnostic importance. It is true that, for the most part, basidia are conservative in pattern, but sufficient differences occur in shape and in size to be valuable criteria at species level. Thus, use has been made of the ratio of length to width of the basidium contrasted with the length to width ratio of its basidiospores. Individuals with ellipsoid spores usually have basidia about as broad as the length of the spore, and their length usually varies between two and five times the length of the longer axis of the spore. In *Hygrophorus* this is exceeded and the extreme length of the basidium may be one of the factors responsible for the waxy character of the mature lamellae. Somewhat similar long basidia occur in some species of *Tricholoma, Mycena,* and *Amanita* without any waxy appearance in the mature gills. Gill thickness is not necessarily a function of the depth of the hymenium: it may be due to the depth of the trama, as in *Laccaria.* Thus, the gross morphological characters of mature gills may be due to differences in anatomy which, when more fully revealed, may be significant criteria in assisting the definition of taxa.

Besides basidia, most hymenia produce certain sterile cells whose morphology is sufficiently varied in many instances to be valuable as diagnostic criteria (see also Vol. II, Chapter 6). Some genera (*Collybia, Marasmius*) have hymenia bearing basidioles (sometimes called paraphyses), which are permanently juvenile basidia. Pseudoparaphyses, which are broad "empty" cells, are characteristic of the gill edge of species of *Coprinus* and of some members of the Bolbitaceae. In some species the arrangement of the pseudoparaphyses in hymenia is very regular. Cystidia are distinctive sterile cells dispersed in the hymenium or occurring elsewhere on the carpophore (e.g., on the pileus surface or stipe surface).

Within recent years careful examination of the microscopic structure of cystidia has given rise to their fuller use as diagnostic criteria. Buller

(1924, p.52) proposed a terminology for cystidia which was based upon the position in which they developed upon the carpophore, but precisely the same structure of cystidium may occur in the hymenium, on the edge of lamellae, or on the surface of the pileus. Equally, cystidia which differ morphologically may occur in identical positions on the carpophores of two different species. Some attention must be paid to the origin of these structures as well as to their mature morphology. Cystidia may arise either from the trama, from the subhymenium or from exactly the same level as the basidia, when they are termed cystidioles, and may then differ only in shape from the basidia.

Singer (1962, p. 41) points out that prolongations of the central tramal elements occur along the lamellar edges of the hymenophores of many *Russula* and *Lactarius* species. These are best considered as pseudocystidia. Entirely similar structures may be formed on the pileus and stipe by growth of the conducting elements of the context. Pseudocystidia differ in structure and in their cellular contents, this being reflected in their reactions to certain chemicals.

The search for criteria on which to base a natural classification of the Polyporales has in many respects run parallel to the explorations of microstructures in the Agaricales. The classical definition of generic lines was based upon the gross morphology of the carpophore, consideration being given to such features as its shape, the relationship of its attachment to the substratum, its consistency and color, any differentiation of the pore-bearing layer from the rest of the context, and the annual or perennial nature of the carpophore. Within comparatively recent times attention has been paid to the structural details of the carpophore, and searches for criteria of constant value have been based upon analyses of the methods of formation of the context, of its surface tissues, and of the layers of the hymenophore.

Under appropriate conditions the carpophore initial is formed from dikaryotic mycelium established in the substratum and all the tissues of the hymenophore are produced by changes in hyphal morphology. What modifications occur and how constant these are within a given genotype will determine their usefulness as taxonomic criteria. The microstructures of the carpophore and, in particular, any specialized and regularly produced hyphal elements of the context and of the pileus surface, as well as the basidia, cystidia, and setae of the hymenophore are all useful as taxonomic criteria. Different names have been applied to the basic, formative hyphae of the carpophore, but the term "generative hyphae" as employed by Corner (1932a), Cunningham (1954), and Teixeira (1962) has much to recommend it, because the tissues of the mature carpophore are developed from these hyphae by processes of differentiation. Generative hyphae are delicate, thin-walled, sometimes inflated, and of indefinite growth and similar morphology throughout all carpophores except in the presence or absence of clamp connections. The occurrence or the absence of clamp connections is a characteristic and permanent feature of all individuals within a species. It must be remembered that sometimes generative hyphae may show clamp connections interspersed with normal septa: this is shown in certain hymenomycetes. Differentiation due to changes in growth pattern produces branches of limited growth which are short and either straight, needlelike, terminally dendroid, vermiculiform, or complexly arachnoid. To modified generative hyphae which are unbranched, normally aseptate but have thickened walls and have unlimited growth, Corner (1932a) has applied the term skeletal hyphae; and to hyphae which are much branched, rarely septate and thick-walled, and have limited growth, he has applied the name binding hyphae. Often carpophores consist entirely of generative hyphae: such sporophores are considered by Corner (1953) to show monomitic structure. If one other system of hyphae is present in the carpophore, its structure is said to be dimitic: the additional elements may be either "skeletal" or "binding" hyphae. When "generative," "skeletal," and "binding" hyphae are present together, the carpophore is said to be trimitic.

It has been a character of most systems of classification of the Polyporales to use the mature appearance of the pileus surface as a diagnostic criterion, along with others, for the separation of taxonomic units. Most of the terms in use are descriptive and fail to indicate how the surface tissues have been produced. The final morphology of this layer is attained by diverse means. Patouillard (1887) discussed the formation of the surface layer and the ways in which hyphae of the context became modified to produce the "crust." But the idea that the ontogeny of the surface might disclose relatively stable criteria for taxonomic separation was tardily accepted by mycologists. Ames (1913) agreed that the formation of the crust represented almost the only differentiation shown by hyphae from the context, but considered that, when such modifications were fully understood, they would not rank higher than details of context structure. Corner (1932b) gave very precise details of the formation of the surface tissues of a species of *Fomes*. His work emphasized that ontogenetic detail rather than descriptive morphological terms for the final appearance of the surface layer was of paramount importance. Major contributions in this field have been made by K. Lohwag (1940) and H. Lohwag (1941), and the latter proposed a classification of surface layers based upon their ontogeny. He emphasized that surface hyphae of the context could grow anticlinally (at right angles to the surface) or periclinally (parallel to the surface). To the products of the former he applied the name derm; to those of the latter the name cutis. According to the extent of hyphal growth, the regularity of arrangement of the hyphae, the width of the hyphae and their degree of aggregation, he recognized four types of derm. Matting of periclinal hyphae, with or without cementing of the matted layers, served to distinguish two main types of cutis. Where the context became progressively denser without clear differentiation of an outer layer he applied the term cortex. Quite irrespective of the genesis of the surface layer and when the surface tissues are heavily encrusted he applied the term crust: such surfaces are always sharply contrasted from the context.

The number of types which have been examined remains small, and in many instances it is still uncertain how surface tissues arise from the generative hyphae or from their specialized branches. Equally, while terms are valuable if they can be precisely defined, experience shows that the adult surface of many pilei is based upon more than a single structural type. When it is possible to describe and illustrate the hyphae making up the surface tissues, to give details of their width, degree of septation and color, whether discrete or aggregated into bundles, the degree of deposition of materials on their walls, and particularly of how they are related to the hyphal systems of the context, much more use may be made of these features

It is becoming evident that, since carpophore structure and its ultimate gross morphology depends upon the interrelationships of its microstructures, analyses of these systems in a sufficiently wide range of individuals—and it must be a wide range—should provide reliable criteria for assessing the limits of taxa, the more so because the construction pattern appears to be constant within narrow limits for the lower taxa.

REFERENCES

Ames, A. (1913). A consideration of structure in relation to genera of the Polyporaceae. *Ann. Mycol. (Berlin)* **11**: 211–253.

Atkinson, G. F. (1906). The development of *Agaricus campestris*. *Botan. Gaz.* **42**: 241–264.

Atkinson, G. F. (1916). Origin and development of the lamellae in *Coprinus*. *Botan. Gaz.* **61**: 89–130.

Buller, A. H. R. (1924). "Researches on Fungi," Vol. III. Longmans, Green, New York.

Chadefaud, M. (1957). Les asques des Diatrypales. *Compt. Rend.* **244**: 1813–1815.

Chadefaud, M. (1958). Sur les asques de Nectriales, et l'existence de *Pleosporales nectrioides*. *Compt. Rend.* **247**: 1376–1379.

Chadefaud, M., and J. Nicot. (1957). Les asques des Sordariales. *Compt. Rend.* **244**: 2415–2418.

Corner, E. J. H. (1932a). The fruit-body of *Polystictus xanthopus* Fr. *Ann. Botany (London)* **46**: 71–111.

Corner, E. J. H. (1932b). A *Fomes* with two systems of hyphae. *Brit. Mycol. Soc. Trans.* **17**: 51–81.

Corner, E. J. H. (1953). The construction of polypores -1. *Introduction—Phytomorphology* **3**: 156–167.

Cunningham, G. H. (1954). Hyphal systems as aids in identification of species and genera of the polyporaceae. *Brit. Mycol. Soc. Trans.* **37**: 44–50.

Doguet, G. (1960). Étude du *Melogramma spiniferum* (Wallr.) de Notaris, Pyrenomycète Ascohyménié, Annellascé, Bitunique. *Rev. Mycol.* [N.S.] **25**: 13–36.

Fries, E. (1821, 1823). "Systema mycologicum," Vols. I and II. Berlingiana, Lund.

Grove, W. B. (1935, 1937). "British Stem- and Leaf-Fungi (Coelomycetes)," Vols. I and II. Cambridge Univ. Press, London and New York.

Hughes, S. J. (1953). Conidiophores, Conidia, and Classification. *Can. J. Botany* **31**: 577–659.

Ingold, C. T. (1933). Spore discharge in the Ascomycetes. I. Pyrenomycetes. *New Phytologist* **32**: 175–196.

Jacobs, L. (1958). Developmental studies in the Hypocreales (sensu Lindau). Thesis, University of Nottingham.

Konrad, P., and A. Maublanc. (1924–1936). "Icones selectae fungorum." P. Lechevalier, Paris.

Lindau, G. (1897). Pyrenomycetineae. *In* "Die Naturlichen Pflanzenfamilien" (A. Engler and K. Prantl, eds.), Abt. **II**: pp. 321–505. Engelmann, Leipzig.

Lohwag, H. (1941). "Anatomie der Asco- und Basidiomyceten." Berlin.

Lohwag, K. (1940). Zur Anatomie des Deckgeflechtes der Polyporaceen. *Ann. Mycol. (Berlin)* **38**: 401–432.

Luttrell, E. S. (1951). Taxonomy of the Pyrenomycetes. *Univ. Missouri Studies* **24**: 1–120.

Luttrell, E. S. (1955). The Ascostromatic Ascomycetes. *Mycologia* **47**: 511–532.

Mason, E. W. (1933). Annotated account of fungi received at the Imperial Bureau of Mycology. List II (Fascicle 2). *Mycol. Papers* No. 3.

Mason, E. W. (1937). Annotated account of fungi received at the Imperial Mycological Institute. List II (Fascicle 3—General Part). *Mycol. Papers* No. 4.

Miller, J. H. (1928). Biologic studies in the Sphaeriales. *Mycologia* **20**: 187–213 and 305–339.

Miller, J. H. (1949). A revision of the classification of the Ascomycetes with special emphasis on the Pyrenomycetes. *Mycologia* **41**: 99–127.

Nannfeldt, J. A. (1932). Studien über die morphologie und Systematik der Nicht-Lichenisierten Inoperculaten Discomyceten. *Nova Acta Regiae Soc. Sci. Upsaliensis* [4] **8**: 1–368.

Patouillard, N. (1887). "Les Hymenomycètes d'Europe." Klincksieck, Paris.

Patouillard, N. (1900). "Essai taxonomique sur les families et les genres de Hymenomycètes." Le Declume. Lons-le-Sannier, Jura, France.

Persoon, D. C. H. (1801). "Synopsis methodica fungorum." Springer, Berlin.

Reijnders, A. F. M. (1948). Études sur le développement et l'organization histologique des carpophores dans les Agricales. *Rev. trav. bot. Néerl.* **41**: 213–396.

Saccardo, P. A. (1884). "Sylloge Fungorum omnium hucusque cognitorum." Vols. III and IV. Pavia, Italy.

Schrantz, J. P. (1960). Récherches sur les Pyrenomycètes de l'Ordre des Diatrypales (sensu Chadefaud, 1957). *Bull. Soc. Mycol. France* **76**: 305–407.

Singer, R. (1962). "The Agaricales in Modern Taxonomy," pp. 1–134. Cramer, Weinheim.

Strikmann, E., and M. Chadefaud. (1961). Recherches sur les asques et les perithèces des *Nectria* et réflexions sur l'évolution des Ascomycètes. *Rev. Gen. Botan.* **68**: 725–770.

Teixeira, A. R. (1962). The taxonomy of the Polyporaceae. *Biol. Rev.* **37**: 51–81.

Tubaki, K. (1958). Studies on the Japanese Hyphomycetes. V. Leaf and stem group with a discussion of the Classification of Hyphomycetes and their perfect stages. *J. Hattori Botan. Lab.* **No. 20**: 142–238.

von Hoehnel, F. (1907). Fragmente zur Mykologie III. No. 128. *Wettsteinina* n.g. *Sitzber. Akad. Wiss. Wien, Math.-Naturw. Kl. Abt. I* **116**: 126–129.

von Hoehnel, F. (1917). System der Diaportheen. *Ber. Deut. Botan. Ges.* **35**: 631–638.

von Hoehnel, F. (1918). Mycologische Fragmente *CXCV*. Über die Gattung *Parodiopsis* Maublanc. *Ann. Mycol. (Berlin)* **16**: 40–41.

Wakefield, E. M., and G. R. Bisby. (1941). List of Hyphomycetes recorded for Britain. *Brit. Mycol. Soc. Trans.* **25**: 50–126.

Wehmeyer, L. E. (1926). A biologic and phylogenetic study of stromatic Sphaeriales. *Am. J. Botany* **13**: 574–645.

CHAPTER 21

Host Specialization as a Taxonomic Criterion

T. JOHNSON

Canada Department of Agriculture
Research Station
Winnipeg, Canada

I. INTRODUCTION

The question of specificity in fungi in relation to host cannot be considered entirely apart from other taxonomic criteria. The main practical purpose of taxonomy is to enable taxonomists to give specific identity to organisms they collect in nature. Species are commonly designated according to a binomial nomenclature, and any system of classification should be such as to enable a competent mycologist to give a specific name to a sample without the necessity of experimental research, except in cases where new species are being described.

Morphology, gross and microscopic, has, traditionally, been the main criterion of classification. This is apparently based on the assumption that organisms, regarded at the species level, have a shape and a structure that enable them to be distinguished from one another.

Parasitic fungi are limited as to substrate: they occur only on certain host plants or animals. This fact cannot be ignored in setting up a system of classification. And this means that there has to be some relationship between host classification and the classification of the parasites of the hosts. This relationship must be such as to lead to a workable method of classification of the parasitic fungi—that is, workable for the competent mycologist who cannot be expected to carry out an experimental investigation into host-parasite relations before he can give a specific name to the organism collected.

Regarded from the evolutionary point of view, it seems certain that taxonomic criteria, and especially specialization with respect to host, are not static. It is probable that this specialization has proceeded in the past, and is now proceeding, from the simpler to the more complex; that it is broadening out to a greater diversity that would correspond to any increase in the diversity of the hosts; and that this broadening out generally proceeds without radical morphological changes in the parasitic organism.

II. PLASTICITY OF PHYSIOLOGICAL CHARACTERS

The view that physiological traits are more plastic than morphological characters appears to be borne out by cultural and genetical studies with parasitic fungi. Such studies have often demonstrated a remarkable cultural, physiological and pathogenic variability that is not associated with any comparable variability in the morphological characters that have commonly been used for species description. Many supporting examples could be given. Brierley (1931) and Hansen and Smith (1932) record an enormous range of variation in cultural characteristics in *Botrytis cinerea,* the latter concluding that "the basic unit of the individual is the nucleus and not the cell, and that a multinucleate spore is, therefore, not an individual but, in reality, a colony and it can, therefore, not give rise to a genetically pure culture unless all its nuclei are genetically identical."

Snyder and Hansen (1940), in a study of the genus *Fusarium,* used single-spore cultures extensively and demonstrated that variation in cultural characteristics greatly overlapped the limits set by Wollenweber and Reinking for their species in the section *Elegans*. In consequence, Snyder and Hansen reduced the 10 species, 18 varieties, and 12 forms of Wollenweber and Reinking to the single morphological species *Fusarium oxysporum,* but they subdivided this species into 25 specialized forms on the basis of pathogenicity alone.

In obligate parasites, such as the rusts, smuts, powdery mildews, and downy mildrews, pathogenic specialization appears to have reached its greatest extremes. In these organisms, a morphological species may generally be subdivided into pathogenic entities adapted in their parasitism to particular host plants, but the narrowness of the adaptation—whether it is to family, tribe or genus—may differ in different organisms. The complexity of specialization also differs according to which organism is studied. In the well known example of the rust *Puccinia graminis,* often cited because it has been thoroughly studied, the specialized forms (formae speciales) created by Eriksson (1894) are similar but not morphologically identical in the uredial phase. The complexity of specialization within each forma is directly related to the variability in its hosts. The variation induced in the genus *Triticum* by nature and man provides the opportunity of demonstrating a corresponding variation in the rust. The numerous "physiologic races" that have been described within f. sp. *tritici* are relatively stable entities because of the dikaryotic condition of the uredial phase but may be genetically unstable when passed through the sexual phase. The type of specialization already demonstrated in *P. graminis* is probably applicable to other obligate parasites with deviations conditioned by the cytological and genetical constitutions of the different parasites.

The realization by many modern mycologists that parasitic organisms vary immensely in their pathogenic traits appears to be basic to the principle that pathogenic organisms should be classified, at the species level, mainly on morphological criteria and that physiological characteristics, such as pathogenicity, should be represented by specialized forms.

This does not imply that pathogenic, or other physiologic, specialization is relegated to a place of secondary significance. Rather, the principle elucidated above appears to be the most practical way of giving proper consideration to the phenomenon of specialization without confusing taxonomy. On this principle, the taxonomist does not have to force himself to give adequate consideration to the task—that would probably be impossible for him anyway—of solving the intricacies of specialization before he can give a specific name to his organism.

The conclusion that an organism may have many characteristics that should be reflected in a scheme for its classification, is by no means recent. This problem has been considered by many prominent taxonomists, and various solutions have been suggested. One of the well-known suggestions is that of Ciferri (1932), who proposed that species might be defined on several different bases—morphological, biological, cultural, etc.—and designated according to these categories, an abbreviation following the binomial indicating into which category the species fell. This proposal, though perhaps difficult to apply in practice, is noteworthy for its recognition of the diversity of the characteristics of an organism that may have to be taken into consideration in its classification.

III. IMPLICATIONS OF GENETICAL RESEARCH

In the last three decades, genetical research on the hosts of parasitic fungi, and on the fungi themselves, has thrown considerable light on the nature of the interaction of host and parasite. It has been known for more than half a century that Mendelian genes in the host plant conditioned the reaction of the host to the parasite. The demonstration by Johnson and Newton (1940) that hereditary factors in wheat stem rust governed pathogenicity according to Mendelian laws was one of the early proofs that pathogenicity in parasitic fungi was gene controlled. Shortly thereafter, Flor (1946, 1947) showed that in flax rust, *Melampsora lini* and its hosts, varieties of *Linum usitatissimum,* there was, in each host-parasite combination, an interaction between a particular gene or genes in the rust and a particular gene or genes in the host. These observations led to his gene-for-gene theory (Flor, 1959) which, judging by the investigations of Loegering and Powers (1962), is also applicable to the host-parasite interactions of wheat and wheat stem rust. Proof of a somewhat similar gene-controlled host-pathogen relationship now exists for the cereal smuts (Holton, 1959), apple scab, *Venturia inaequalis* (Keitt *et al.*, 1959), barley mildew (Moseman and Schaller, 1960), and corn rust, *Puccinia sorghi* (Flangas and Dickson, 1961) and undoubtedly for a number of other host-parasite combinations. In other parasitic fungi in which the genetics is less well understood, such as the downy mildews, there is evidence to indicate a similar type of host-parasite relationship. One of the best demonstrations of the intimate relations of host and pathogen is that of the potato and the late-blight organism (Gallegly and Niederhauser, 1959). The four resistance genes R_1, R_2, R_3, and R_4 studied by Black (1952) in *Solanum demissum* each conditioned resistance to a common physiologic race of *Phytophthora infestans*. Separately, and in all possible combinations, these genes made possible the identification of physiologic races corresponding in their pathogenicity to the genotypic combinations of R factors. Various mutations that took place in the races each showed a single-step extension of pathogenic range—that is, a step overcoming the resistance effect of a single R factor. This type of extension of pathogenic range by single mutational steps has been demonstrated experimentally by Flor (1956) in flax rust and is probably of common occurrence in the cereal rusts as judged by the frequent appearance of races differing from previously known races by ability to overcome the resistance effect of a single gene in a cultivated variety.

This pathogenic lability in parasitic fungi might suggest that a given fungus would eventually overcome the resistance effect of all existing host genes. Almost invariably, however, an extension of pathogenic range by a fungus has enabled investigators to discover hitherto unknown resistance genes in the host, or in related hosts: genes that, in fact, could not have been discovered had it not been for the change in the fungus. It must therefore be postulated that hosts contain a large reservoir of resistance genes whose mutation rate is similar to that of the genes of parasites; otherwise the reservoir of resistance genes in the host would be exhausted in a relatively short time.

It seems clear from present knowledge that neither host nor parasite is a static entity. Therefore nomenclature cannot be static either. If the argument is valid that physiological traits are more labile than the morphological traits on which binomial species have generally been founded, it would seem to follow that the taxonomist should not attempt a very rigid or permanent definition of the pathogenic limits of a given species. These limits may change with time and are primarily the concern of the experimentalist interested in particular host-parasite relationships.

IV. SPECIALIZED FORMS AS TAXA

Despite the physiological plasticity of parasitic fungi, their pathogenic traits are definite characteristics and must therefore be regarded as taxonomic criteria. It seems doubtful, however, that any fixed rules applicable to parasitic fungi in general can be established that would satisfy the requirements of both the plant pathologist concerned with experimental studies of a fungus and the taxonomist concerned with classification. Fungi differ so greatly in their host adaptations and cytogenetics that it would seem probable that any fixed rules laid down should be applicable only to a particular type of fungus. Thus rules applicable to the rusts might not be equally applicable to the somewhat closely related smuts, and even less so to more distantly related fungi such as Fungi Imperfecti or powdery and downy mildews.

In trying to assess host specificity in fungi as a taxonomic criterion, it is necessary to take into account the experience of those taxonomists who have attempted to relate host specificity to various other fungal characteristics that have taxonomic value. But, to be profitable, the discussion should be limited to those taxonomic studies that rest on a basis of adequate knowledge of the pathogenic range of the fungi concerned. All taxonomists recognize host specificity in parasitic fungi, but many studies, such as that of Chupp (1953) on *Cercospora,* lack "the necessary cross inoculations required for determining the host range of any species," to use his own comments on his monograph.

Snyder and Hansen (1954) stated that originally systematists looked "not so much for similarities between individuals of a species as for differences of any kind." Brierley (1931) stated that if one had isolates of only five or six races of *Botrytis cinerea,* their differences could be so great that one would call them species; but when hundreds of races are compared it would become clear that all these isolates are only members of the large cluster which is the species *B. cinerea.* The approach of Snyder and Hansen (1954) to the taxonomy of *Fusarium* was to determine the *extent* of variability. Their studies eventually made clear to them which characters were not suitable and which were stable enough to serve as taxonomic criteria.

These approaches to taxonomy are diametrically opposite to the much older attitude paraphrased by Brierley (1919): "The essential specific characters of an organism may be determined and evaluated by sight in one specimen of one generation." As Brierley emphasizes, the different individuals in a species are not identical but show similarities great enough to warrant grouping them together as a unit distinct from other groups of individuals.

If this attitude applies to the grouping of individuals into species, it applies equally to the grouping of individuals into specialized forms. The tendency of the investigator at the beginning of a study of the pathogenic specialization of an organism is to place the emphasis on any *differences* that are noted. Thus Stakman and Piemeisel (1917a,b) described the first pathogenic variant of *Puccinia graminis* f. sp. *tritici* as a new form, *P. graminis tritici-compacti,* because it was pathogenic to varieties of *Triticum compactum* but not to the varieties of *T. aestivum* that they tested. On further study they were impressed by the similarities of this specialized form to the form they had previously recognized as f. sp. *trtitici. T. compactum* and certain grasses were common hosts of the two. To this was added the discovery of further pathogenic variants. The logical conclusion at which they presently arrived was that f. sp. *tritici,* parasitic on wheat, was composed of many strains differing in pathogenicity which had in common the capacity to parasitize species of *Triticum* and could therefore be distinguished from other strains of *P. graminis,* such as those that appeared to be parasitically adapted to varieties of the genera *Secale* or *Avena.* But it must be recognized that these are man-made subdivisions of the species *P. graminis.* This species has its host range within the family Gramineae. The "special forms" *tritici* and *secalis* are recognized by their parasitic adaptation to the genera *Triticum* and *Secale,* respectively, but they have several common hosts including *Agropyron, Elymus, Hordeum,* and *Bromus.* Hence the host genus is not an adequate criterion of the specialization of the rust, although it is sometimes stated that specialization in *P. graminis* conforms to the host genus. Actually, the host ranges of the forms *tritici* and *secalis* fall, principally, within the tribe Hordeae, but individual collections of the rust can generally be determined as one form or the other by the reaction of suitable varieties of *Triticum* and *Secale.* Each specialized form has its characteristic adaptation. The range of adaptation of f. sp. *avenae* lies chiefly within the tribe Avenae but includes some genera of the Festuceae and Agrostideae.

The above details on host specificity in *P. graminis* have been given because they describe a host-parasite relationship that has been worked out in more detail than most others. Although the specialized forms are named according to the genus principally parasitized, their parasitism is not limited to that genus nor even confined entirely to the tribe to which it belongs. The man-made grouping of host genera into tribes is only partially reflected in the host selectivity of the fungus. For example, f. sp.

tritici confines its pathogenicity, in a large measure, within the tribe Hordeae but, for some unknown reason, finds suitable hosts in certain species of *Bromus*. In setting up the range of pathogenicity of a specialized form, it cannot be safely assumed that this is going to be limited to groups of host plants that appear to be closely related taxonomically.

Some further clarification of the forma specialis may perhaps be obtained by considering the individuals that constitute it. Wheat stem rust, *P. graminis* f. sp. *tritici*, is an assemblage of individuals that resemble one another more in pathogenicity than they resemble the individuals of other specialized forms. They all have in common the capacity to attack one or more species of *Triticum*, hence the inclusion of several of these species among the differential hosts used for identifying the physiologic races of wheat stem rust. Host adaptation among these races differs considerably. Some are best adapted to varieties of common wheat (*T. aestivum*), others to varieties of durum wheat (*T. durum*), a few are best adapted to *T. dicoccum* or *T. monococcum*, and some can attack all of these. At the periphery of this mass of races one finds, though more rarely, races that have only a limited ability to attack wheat. These are often better adapted to barley and may have some capacity to attack rye. They appear to blend the characteristics of wheat stem rust and rye stem rust and, since hybrids of these two rusts are sometimes of this type, they may be natural hybrids between *tritici* and *secalis* races. In nature, they are less common than typical *tritici* or *secalis* races, presumably because they lack adaptation to the main agricultural cereals necessary for their increase. Another reason for the scarcity of such races is the fact that there is a certain amount of sterility between the different formae speciales, which is another justification for their separation as distinct entities.

In the cereal rusts, a forma specialis is subdivided into physiologic races, and the physiologic race is generally considered the ultimate taxonomic unit despite the fact that physiologic races are, in some cases, further divided into subraces and biotypes. Stakman *et al.* (1962), in discussing *P. graminis* f. sp. *tritici*, state that the "physiologic race is the only taxon that is recognized." They define physiologic race as "a biotype or group of biotypes, within a species or lower taxon, which can be distinguished with reasonable facility and certainty from other biotypes or groups of biotypes by physiologic characters, including pathogenicity." The biotype, as they point out, cannot be granted a taxonomic status because it connotes a population of individuals of the same genotype, and taxonomy must necessarily confine itself to phenotypes.

In connection with physiologic races, it should not be overlooked that these are identified by the reaction of a particular assortment of host cultivars. Cultures of a physiologic race that by their infection types on standard differential hosts show minor, but repeatable, deviations from the generally accepted infection types of a race are sometimes regarded as subraces. This is a justifiable subdivision of a physiologic race. When, however, the standard differential hosts are supplemented by other cultivars a somewhat different situation arises. When many cultures of a given race are tested on a series of supplemental hosts, they do not necessarily all produce the same infection types. The supplemental hosts have then served to demonstrate that different cultures of the race are phenotypically alike only in those characteristics expressed on the standard differential hosts. The pathogenically distinct strains thus brought to light are subraces in quite a different sense from those differentiated by minor deviations from the usual infection types produced on the standard hosts, because they are based on characteristics other than those recognized in race differentiation. Supplemental hosts are, however, important to those concerned with classifying the pathogenic characters of rust strains, since new and economically important strains are frequently variants of well-known standard races produced, perhaps, by mutation at one particular locus. A single mutation may make all the difference between the success and failure of a strain to parasitize certain agricultural crops. Concerning such strains, Stakman *et al.* (1962) state that they accept strains differentiated by supplemental hosts as races because they fit the definition of a race, as given above, but add that "the term 'subrace' could be applied in a collective sense, to subdivisions of standard races . . . such as 59A, 59B, 15B, 15B-1, etc. If these terms are used, however, it should be understood that they do not necessarily connote superiority and inferiority in rank."

In the physiologic races of flax rust, as identified by Flor, the genic composition of the host becomes more nearly an index of the genic composition of the rust, owing to the fact that each of his differential hosts contains a single gene for resistance which presumably interacts with a complementary gene in the rust. But because pathogenicity is recessive, it is not possible to tell, in the case of an avirulent reaction, whether the race is homozygous or heterozygous for avirulence. It is only when a variety is susceptible to a race that the phenotype gives an exact indication of the genotype. That the procedure employed by Flor may be applied to race identification in the cereal rusts in the future is indicated by the work of Green *et al.* (1960) on wheat stem rust and Green *et al.* (1961) on oat stem rust.

In the foregoing, the discussion of rust taxa has been confined to the uredial phase. In the heteroecious rusts, the fact that the uredial and telial phases occur on one type of host and the pycnial and aecial phases on another has been responsible for some confusion in nomenclature, as pointed out by Dennis (1952). Klebahn's division of crown rust into the two species *Puccinia coronata* and *P. coronifera* according to whether the aecial phase occurred on *Rhamnus frangula* or *R. cathartica* created confusion and uncertainty in the nomenclature of the rust for many years until it was finally agreed by several investigators that certain of the formae speciales were harbored by both species of *Rhamnus*. It has seemed to some mycologists that when two or more specialized forms of a rust have their aecial phases on separate hosts, they should have different specific designations. If, however, the aecial phases do not differ morphologically, the host preferences should be regarded simply as physiologic characters and there would seem to be no good reason for separate species identity. Most North American mycologists have, in fact, considered gametophytic host preferences as merely another form of host specificity and have, in this respect, followed the 1925 recommendation of the Joint Committee on nomenclature of the American Phytopathological Society that the term forma "should be applied to a subdivision of a species or variety which is characterized and distinguished primarily by physiological instead of morphological characters."

It should, however, be noted that in many North American publications on rusts there has been considerable looseness in the use of the terms "variety" and "forma specialis." The specialized forms of *P. graminis* have been referred to as varieties and as formae speciales, even by the same writer. This confusion is perhaps mainly due to the fact that the investigator realizes that there are minor morphological differences between specialized forms distinguished from one another primarily by pathogenicity. Thus, for example, Fraser and Ledingham (1933) demonstrated some morphological differences between their four varieties of *Puccinia coronata* and called them varieties despite the fact that their chief differentiation was on a pathogenic basis.

The fact that there exist minor morphological differences, below the level of those commonly used for species differentiation, lends an element of confusion to taxonomy, simply because these minor differences tend to be so slight that statistical methods are often needed for their detection. The specialist working with a particular group of organisms, knowing that these are genuine differences, is tempted to set up one or more varieties on this basis and can justify this practice by the fact that he himself can consistently differentiate these taxa on a morphological basis, sometimes perhaps only with the assistance of statistics. There is, however, no assurance that the general taxonomist, or even another specialist, can employ his criteria with equal success.

V. DESCRIPTION AND PUBLICATION IN RELATION TO TAXA

Ainsworth (1962) has called attention to the fact that taxa based on pathogenicity, such as formae speciales and physiologic races, are not subject to the legislation of the international codes of nomenclature. There are no requirements laid down for their description or their recording at any central agency. The result is that each organization concerned with investigating these taxa formulates its own rules or decides that no rules need be observed. In Canada, it has been the practice of the Department of Agriculture to require, when a forma specialis is described, that a type specimen be deposited in the Mycological Herbarium, Ottawa, and the forma be described in English and Latin, in published form. This would seem to be a desirable practice because it makes the description generally available and enables any subsequent investigator to check the morphological characters of the type specimen.

For physiologic races no general regulations have been established; any rules employed have been derived from the investigators. Fortunately, practical considerations have enforced a certain degree of order. Races are described, in scientific or special publications, by use of the symbols generally employed for that purpose. Specialists in the study of a particular pathogenic organism maintain contact with one another and, when circumstances seem to demand it, make arrangements for reorganization of their systems of classification. Generally, the last thing they would wish is any regimentation that might hamper their freedom of action. This attitude is not unnatural in view of the fact that schemes of racial classification are liable to frequent revision in response to practical demands. Expediency is such an important factor that few classification schemes now in use can be considered to have any permanence. A possible exception is the racial classification for wheat stem rust based on the "standard" differential hosts so carefully selected by Stakman and his collaborators. These hosts are maintained as far as possible in their original genetical condition to serve as points of reference to determine changes in physiologic races that take place from time to time. Another differential host assortment that may have permanence is that established by Flor for the determination of races of flax rust, in which each variety contains a single resistance gene. Differential host assortments of the future are likely to be of this type. At present, most schemes for racial classification in the rusts are in such a state of flux that the workers concerned are generally not willing to commit themselves to any permanent system of classification.

VI. CONCLUSIONS

It would seem that the best guide to the use of host specificity in fungi as a taxonomic criterion is to be derived from the experience of those mycologists who, in the last twenty or thirty years, have applied to classification the increased knowledge emanating from various types of studies

—cultural, pathogenic, host range determinations, etc.—and have also taken into consideration the improved knowledge on the genetics of host and pathogen and, it might be added, have based their attempts at classification on the Botanical Code. Recommendation 4 of the International Code of Botanical Nomenclature, 1956, reads: "In classifying parasites, especially parasitic fungi, authors who do not give specific value to taxa characterized from a physiological standpoint but scarcely or not at all from a morphological standpoint should distinguish within the species special forms (formae speciales) characterized by their adaptation to different hosts."

In recent years, this statement has been a guidepost to most of those who have been concerned with the classification of parasitic fungi. Another guiding influence has been research on the range of variation in fungi, in which the single-spore culture has been an essential factor. In this respect, one of the early landmarks was the work of Hansen and Smith (1932) which found its natural outcome in Snyder and Hansen's paper, "The species concept in Fusarium" (1940). Perhaps the philosophical basis of this concept is nowhere better expressed than by Snyder and Hansen (1954).

Much the same theoretical concept has been employed in the classification of the smut fungi by Fischer and his collaborators. Fischer (1943) began to subdivide species into specialized varieties on the basis of host specificity and, later, Fischer and Shaw (1953) laid down an adequate statement of their species concept for the smut fungi based on "a practicable degree of morphological variation and on host specialization at the host family level."

The level at which host specificity is determined—whether at the host family, genus, species, etc.—will differ for different parasitic fungi and, in all probability, cannot be fixed even for a single species because fungi select their hosts on a physiological basis whereas the taxonomist classifies them on a morphological basis.

Present-day mycologists are trying to take this into account. Gustavsson (1959), who reconsidered the classification of the peronospores, rejected de Bary's principle of "one host family—one *Peronospora* species" and also rejected Gäumann's statistically based taxonomy, except where supported by cross inoculations, and concluded that "the biologic species concept should be based not on phanerogamic species delimitations but on the genetic relationship between parasite and host." But he admits that "the possible occurrence of different genes for resistance to *Peronospora* within the host material and different genes for infection in formae speciales and physiologic races of the parasite makes the problem extremely complicated."

In making this statement, Gustavsson is conforming to current trends of thought. Flor's work on flax rust and the work of Black and others on the late blight of potatoes have tended to direct the thinking and experimentation of plant pathologists toward establishing relationships between pathogenic races of a fungus and the host genes conditioning host reaction. It is further assumed by many that genetic studies with the fungus will reveal an interaction between pathogenicity genes in the fungus and resistance genes in the host. This is an important current trend, but only the future will reveal how intimate and how widespread such host-parasite relationships are or how useful they can be as a taxonomic basis.

One of the justifications for fungal taxonomy is its usefulness to applied mycology. The plant pathologist wants a taxonomy that will enable him readily to apply a specific epithet to a given fungal specimen. Furthermore, those plant pathologists who are not competent mycologists dislike the frequent nomenclatural changes brought about by the use in classification of fine morphological distinctions. The majority of these would welcome a stable specific nomenclature based on easily applied morphological characters. The use only of well-defined and reliable morphological traits would tend to reduce the establishment of numerous varieties which are too often based on morphological features influenced by environmental factors, or requiring the use of statistics. In a subspecific classification based mainly on host-parasite relations the plant pathologist would find scope for his experimental work which in any event is essential to the delimiting of specialized forms of any parasitic fungus. Thus the experimentalist would be contributing his share to taxonomy and, although it is not possible to foretell the future, it may well be that the physiologist may some day expose some of the reasons for the now inexplicable host preferences of parasitic fungi.

REFERENCES

Ainsworth, G. C. (1962). *Symp. Soc. Gen. Microbiol.* **12:** 249–269.

Black, W. (1952). A genetical basis for the classification of strains of *Phytophthora infestans. Proc. Roy. Soc. Edinburgh* **B65:** 36–51.

Brierley, W. B. (1919). Some concepts in mycology—an attempt at synthesis. *Brit. Mycol. Soc. Trans.* **6:** 204–235.

Brierley, W. B. (1931). Biological races in fungi and their significance in evolution. *Ann. Appl. Biol.* **18:** 420–434.

Chupp, C. (1953). "A Monograph of the Fungus Genus *Cercospora*," 667 pp. Ithaca, New York.

Ciferri, R. (1932). The criteria for the definition of species in mycology. *Ann. Mycol.* **30:** 122–136.

Dennis, R. W. G. (1952). Biological races and their taxonomic treatment by mycologists. *Proc. Linnean Soc. London* **163:** 47–53.

Eriksson, J. (1894). Ueber die Specialisierung des Parasitismus bei den Getreider-ostpilzen. *Ber. Deut. Botan. Ges.* **12:** 292–331.

Fischer, G. W. (1943). Some evident synonymous relationships in certain graminicolous smut fungi. *Mycologia* **35:** 610–619.

Fischer, G. W., and C. G. Shaw. (1953). A proposed species concept in the smut fungi, with application to North American species. *Phytopathology* **43:** 181–188.

Flangas, A. L., and J. G. Dickson. (1961). The genetic control of pathogenicity, serotypes and variability in *Puccinia sorghi. Am. J. Botany* **48:** 275–285.

Flor, H. H. (1946). Genetics of pathogenicity in *Melampsora lini. J. Agr. Res.* **73:** 335–357.

Flor, H. H. (1947). Inheritance of reaction to rust in flax. *J. Agr. Res.* **74:** 241–262.

Flor, H. H. (1956). Mutations in flax rust induced by ultraviolet radiation. *Science* **124:** 888–889.

Flor, H. H. (1959). Genetic controls of host-parasite interactions in rust diseases. *Plant Pathol., Probl. Progr., 1908–1958.* p. 137–144.

Fraser, W. P., and G. A. Ledingham. (1933). Studies of the crown rust, *Puccinia coronata* Corda. *Sci. Agr.* **13:** 313–323.

Gallegly, M. E., and J. S. Niederhauser. (1959). Genetic Controls of host–parasite interactions in the phytophthora late blight disease. *Plant Pathol., Probl. Progr., 1908–1958* pp. 168–182.

Green, G. J., D. R. Knott, I. A. Watson, and A. T. Pugsley. (1960). Seedling reactions to stem rust of lines of Marquis wheat with substituted genes for rust resistance. *Can. J. Plant Sci.* **40:** 524–538.

Green, G. J., T. Johnson, and J. N. Welsh. (1961). Physiologic specialization in oat stem rust in Canada from 1944 to 1959. *Can. J. Plant Sci.* **41:** 153–165.

Gustavsson, A. (1959). Studies on the nordic Peronosporas. II. General account. *Opera Botan.* 3(2): 1–61.

Hansen, H. N., and R. E. Smith. (1932). The mechanism of variation in imperfect fungi: *Botrytis cinerea. Phytopathology* **22:** 953–964.

Holton, C. S. (1959). Genetic controls of host–parasite interactions in smut diseases. *Plant Pathol., Probl. Progr., 1908–1958* pp. 145–156.

Johnson, T., and M. Newton. (1940). Mendelian inheritance of certain pathogenic characters of *Puccinia graminis tritici. Can. J. Res.* C18: 599–611.

Keitt, G. W., D. M. Boone, and J. R. Shay. (1959). Genetic and nutritional controls of host–parasite interactions in apple scab. *Plant Pathol., Probl. Progr., 1908–1958* pp. 157–167.

Loegering, W. Q., and H. R. Powers, Jr. (1962). Inheritance of pathogenicity in a cross of physiological races 111 and 36 of *Puccinia graminis* f. sp. *tritici. Phytopathology* **52:** 547–554.

Moseman, J. G., and C. W. Schaller. (1960). Genetics of the allelic series at the Ml_a locus in barley and cultures of *Erysiphe graminis* f. sp. *hordei* that differentiate these alleles. *Phytopathology* **50:** 736–741.

Snyder, W. C., and H. N. Hansen. (1940). The species concept in Fusarium. *Am. J. Botany* **27:** 64–67.

Snyder, W. C., and H. N. Hansen. (1954). Variation and speciation in the genus *Fusarium. Ann. N.Y. Acad. Sci.* **60:** 16–23.

Stakman, E. C., and F. J. Piemeisel. (1917a). A new strain of *Puccinia graminis. Phytopathology* **7**: 73 (abstr.).

Stakman, E. C., and F. J. Piemeisel. (1917b). Biologic forms of *Puccinia graminis* on cereals and grasses. *J. Agr. Res.* **10**: 429–495.

Stakman, E. C., D. M. Stewart, and W. Q. Loegering. (1962). Identification of physiologic races of *Puccinia graminis var. tritici. U.S. Dept. Agr., ARS* **E617**: 1–53 (revised 1962).

CHAPTER 22

Biochemical Differentiation of Taxa with Special Reference to the Yeasts

A Discussion of the Biochemical Basis of the Nutritional Tests Used for Classification

J. A. BARNETT[1]

King's College
Cambridge, England

I have not given specific names to these different yeasts, any more than to the other microscopic organisms that I have had occasion to study. This is not from indifference towards nomenclature, but rather that as I have been exclusively preoccupied with the physiological functions of these little beings, I have always been afraid of attaching too much importance to exterior characters. Many a time I have found that forms different in appearance, often belong to the same species and that similar forms can hide profound differences.

Translation from L. Pasteur, "Etudes sur la Bière," p. 147. Gauthier-Villars, Paris, 1876.

I. INTRODUCTION

The nutritional tests for classifying yeasts are a crude means of surveying the ability of the different organisms to use a variety of substrates. The results of such surveys evoke three questions which are discussed in this chapter. (1) Why are some yeasts unable to use certain substrates that are used by other yeasts? (2) To what extent do different yeasts use any given substrate by similar or different metabolic routes? (3) Why are the results of certain tests associated with those of others, so that most of the yeasts which can use substrate (A) can also use another (B)?

[1] *Present address:* Food Research Institute, Norwich, England.

II. THE NUTRITIONAL TESTS

The nutritional tests used in the first major taxonomic study of the yeasts (Stelling-Dekker, 1931) were chiefly of semi-anaerobic "fermentation," each with one of eight sugars. Lodder (1934) introduced aerobic growth tests with five fermentable sugars, in order to differentiate between entirely aerobic yeasts. In 1948, Wickerham and Burton proposed using a far wider range of test compounds for identifying yeasts, including organic acids, glucosides, hexoses, pentoses, and sugar alcohols (polyols).[1] Since that time, an increasing number of taxonomists have described the reactions of yeasts to these substrates (Table I).

TABLE I

SUBSTRATES USED IN AEROBIC GROWTH TESTS FOR CLASSIFYING YEASTS[a]

α-Glucosides	*β-Glucosides*	*α-Galactoside*	*β-Galactoside*
Raffinose	Cellobiose	Melibiose	Lactose
Melezitose	Arbutin		
Sucrose	Salicin		
Maltose			
Trehalose			
α-Methyl D-glucoside			
Hexoses	*Pentoses*	*Polyols*	*Acids*
D-Glucose	D-Ribose	Glycerol	Succinate
D-Galactose	D-Xylose	Erythritol	Citrate
L-Sorbose	D-Arabinose	Ribitol (adonitol)	Lactate
L-Rhamnose	L-Arabinose	D-Glucitol (sorbitol)	
		D-Mannitol	
		Galactitol (dulcitol)	
		Inositol	
Others			
Ethanol			
Inulin			

[a] Kreger-van Rij (1964).

Nearly all the nutritional tests used for identifying yeasts are intended to determine whether or not each yeast can utilize a single organic com-

[1] *Note on carbohydrate nomenclature*

Polyols. The names used for the polyols in this chapter have been those recommended by the International Committee on Carbohydrate Nomenclature (1952, 1962; Staněk *et al.*, 1963). Alternative names are given in parentheses: ribitol (adonitol), arabinitol (arabitol), D-glucitol (sorbitol), galactitol (dulcitol).

Sugars. Older names have been used for the sugars; some of the newer names are given in parentheses: erythrulose (*glycero*-tetrulose), xylulose (*threo*-pentulose), ribulose (*erythro*-pentulose).

pound, supplied exogenously, as the sole major source of carbon (for review, see Kreger-van Rij, 1962). Most of the test substrates act as a source both of energy and of carbon for growth. The tests are simple: the usual criterion of substrate utilization is growth; and the results are generally presented in an all-or-none fashion (+ or —). For brevity, the methods of testing are summarized in Table II.

III. MODES OF CATABOLISM OF THE TEST SUBSTRATES

This section gives some account of the routes by which the substrates may be catabolized, as such knowledge is essential in order to answer the three questions posed in the first paragraph. For the most part, the discussion is limited to the aerobic utilization of certain carbohydrates, and derivatives of carbohydrates, that are employed as test substrates.

The intermediary metabolism of the carbohydrates and their derivatives is described in Chapters 10 and 11 of Volume I. Consequently only those features are given here that should help to make the argument clear. The metabolism of these compounds appears to involve a few distinct central pathways, and depends on the cells' ability to convert the substrates into intermediary metabolites of one of these pathways (Krebs and Kornberg, 1957; Wood, 1961; Kornberg, 1965). A yeast may fail to grow aerobically on a substrate either (1) because the substrate does not enter the cells (see Volume I, Chapter 15), or (2) because the yeast lacks one or more enzymes necessary to convert the substrate into an intermediary metabolite of a central pathway (cf. Barnett, 1960, 1966a). For the most part, it seems likely that only minor differences in carbohydrate catabolism are concerned in the tests, not differences in central metabolic pathways. As these central pathways are frequently referred to, their interrelationships are shown in Fig. 1.

A. Hexoses and Glucosides

1. D-*Glucose*

All species of yeasts can grow aerobically on glucose (see Lodder and Kreger-van Rij, 1952; Kudriavzev, 1954; Novák and Zsolt, 1961; Kreger-van Rij, 1964); and the metabolism of the other test substrates can be related to that of glucose.

Yeasts break down glucose to pyruvate by the Embden-Meyerhof (EM) glycolytic pathway (Fig. 2), the overall reaction of which may be summarized as follows:

$$\text{Glucose} + 2\,\text{ADP} + 2\,\text{NAD}^+ + 2\,\text{P} \rightarrow 2\,\text{pyruvate} + 2\,\text{ATP} + 2\,\text{NADH} + 2\,\text{H}^+ + 2\,\text{H}_2\text{O} \quad (1)$$

TABLE II

NUTRITIONAL TESTS FOR CLASSIFYING YEASTS: SOME METHODS FOR ASSESSING UTILIZATION OF CARBOHYDRATES AND THEIR DERIVATIVES

Test	Criterion for positive test	Medium	Substrate	Method	Comments
Anaerobic[w]	Bubbles of gas formed in medium collected in tube	Yeast water[a,b,c] (sometimes with peptone and bromthymol blue[d])	0.1–0.2 M sugar (approximately 2% w/v): glucose, galactose, maltose, sucrose, lactose, raffinose, inulin;[a] melezitose, cellobiose, trehalose[e]	(1) Einhorn tubes[f,g,h] (also called Smith tubes[g], Dunbar tubes[h,i]) (2) Durham tubes[g,t,u,d]	*Tubes open to air* (via cotton-wool plug). Cells grow aerobically at surface and fall to bottom of tube where O_2 concentration is low, gas is collected in closed part of bent tube (Einhorn) or in smaller tube inserted upside down (Durham)
				(3) Clarke-Cowan tubes[j,k] (4) Winge fermentometer[h] (5) Van Iterson-Kluyver fermentometer[h] (6) Guerra tubes[l,m]	*Tubes closed to air*. Relatively large-cell suspension added initially. Little growth; O_2 in solution quickly used: sugar used at very low O_2 concentration. CO_2 cannot diffuse out of system. For method (3), washed cell-suspension in saline (not yeast-water)[k]
Aerobic[w]	Growth	Salts, yeast extract, bromphenol blue	Many substrates (e.g., see Table I) 0.01–0.1 M	(1) Agar slopes[b]	1. Substrate in agar medium 2. Surface of slope inoculated with yeast to be tested For critical comments see reference n
		Salts, vitamins, trace metals, NH_4^+ (N-source)	Many substrates (e.g., see Table I)	(2) Auxanograms[a,o,p,q]	1. Agar medium + inoculum poured into petri dishes 2. Crystals of test substrates placed on agar surface

	3. Growth observed after 1–6 days of incubation *Advantages:* (i) Sterile substrate unnecessary; (ii) differential response to varying substrate concentration observable; (iii) substrates with low solubility can be used *Disadvantages:* (i) assessment of growth subjective; (ii) unsuitable for volatile substrates	
(3) Test-tubes unshaken[d] (i.e. unaerated)	*Disadvantages:* (i) test is slow; (ii) undefined O_2 and CO_2 concentration; (iii) varying conditions within any tube; (iv) positive response may depend on selection of mutant or on autolysis[v]	For both shaken and unshaken tubes growth can be measured; but critical substrate concentration (e.g., toxicity) may obscure ability to utilize (T-tubes not used widely for yeast identification)
(4) T-tubes[o,p] or L-tubes[r]	*Advantages:* (i) can ensure that aeration is not limiting; (ii) can achieve homogeneous conditions throughout tube; (iii) can record growth automatically[s]	

[a] Lodder and Kreger-van Rij (1952)
[b] Kudriavzev (1954)
[c] Bouthilet *et al.* (1949)
[d] Wickerham (1951)
[e] van der Walt and van Kerken (1959)
[f] Einhorn (1885)
[g] Windisch (1960)
[h] Roberts (1950)
[i] Mishustin and Trisvyatski (1960)
[j] Clarke and Cowan (1952)
[k] Morris and Kirsop (1953)
[l] Langeron and Guerra (1938)
[m] Martin *et al.* (1937)
[n] Lodder and Kreger-van Rij (1962)
[o] Barnett and Ingram (1955)
[p] Barnett and Kornberg (1960)
[q] Beyerinck (1889)
[r] Gorrill and Gray (1956)
[s] Wentink and la Rivière (1962)
[t] Durham (1898)
[u] Henrici (1941)
[v] Barnett (1966b) cf. Knight (1938)

[w] A technique for studying aerobic growth of a large number of yeasts on different sources of carbon that has become popular is the replica plating method of Lederberg and Lederberg (1952), developed for yeasts by Shifrine *et al.* (1954) and by Beech *et al.* (1955).

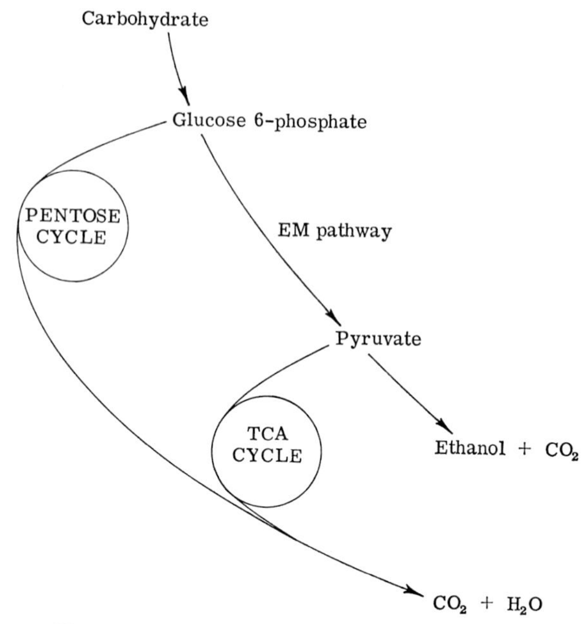

FIG. 1. Pathways of carbohydrate breakdown.

a. Anaerobic Metabolism. Anaerobically, yeasts capable of anaerobic metabolism convert the pyruvate produced by glycolysis to ethanol via acetaldehyde (Fig. 3).

b. Aerobic Metabolism. Aerobically, the pyruvate is converted to acetyl coenzyme A, not to ethanol, the net reaction being as follows:

$$\text{Pyruvate} + \text{CoA} \xrightarrow{\text{NAD}^+ \rightarrow \text{NADH}} \text{acetyl CoA} + CO_2 \quad (2)$$

The tricarboxylic acid (TCA) cycle (Fig. 4) is the principal route by which carbohydrate is oxidized to carbon dioxide and water (see Volume I, Chapter 11); and it is as acetyl CoA that the carbohydrate enters the cycle. The effect of one turn of this cycle is the complete oxidation of one molecular unit of acetate:

$$CH_3COOH + 2\ O_2 \rightarrow 2\ CO_2 + 2\ H_2O \quad (3)$$

c. The Pentose Phosphate Cycle. Saccharomyces cerevisiae and *Candida utilis* are capable of anaerobic metabolism and have been shown to break down most of the glucose they metabolize via the Embden-Meyerhof pathway (Fig. 2). However, under aerobic conditions, nonproliferating cells of these yeasts also appear to catabolize a substantial amount of the glucose by means of the pentose phosphate cycle (Fig. 5) (see Volume

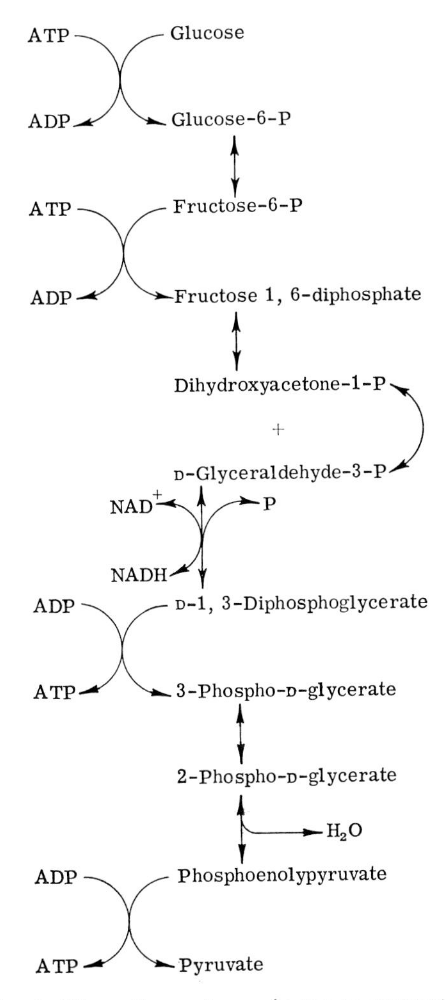

FIG. 2. The pathway from glucose to pyruvate.

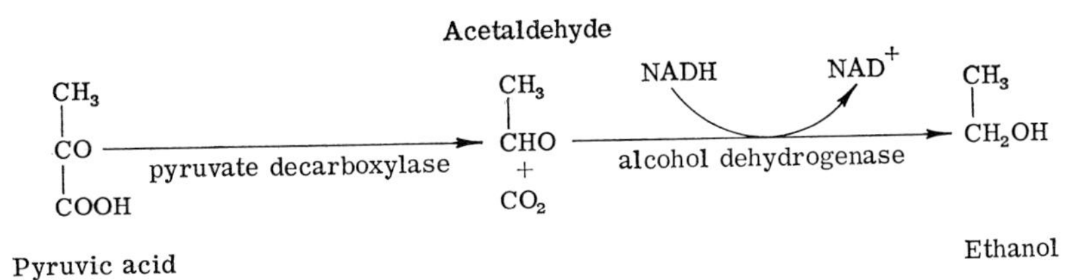

FIG. 3. Conversion of pyruvate to ethanol.

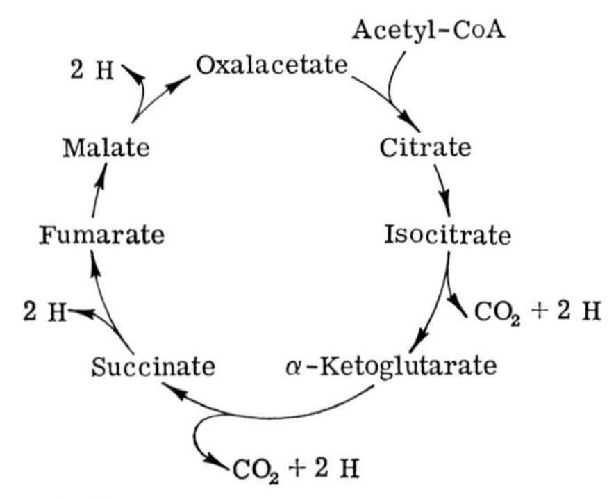

FIG. 4. Stages of the tricarboxylic acid cycle.

I, p. 252). As in the Embden-Meyerhof pathway (Fig. 2), the initial step of this cycle is the phosphorylation of glucose. The glucose phosphate is then converted via phosphogluconate to pentose phosphate:

$$\text{glucose} \rightarrow \text{glucose-6-P} \rightarrow \text{6-phosphogluconolactone} \rightarrow \text{6-phosphogluconate} \rightarrow \text{ribulose-5-P} \quad (4)$$

d. The Inability to Use Glucose Anaerobically. All species of yeasts that can use a sugar anaerobically can also do so aerobically. The converse does not hold; many species that metabolize sugars aerobically are described as unable to "ferment" any of them (Lodder and Kreger-van Rij, 1952; Kudriavzev, 1954) (see Table III). Barnett (1968) found that

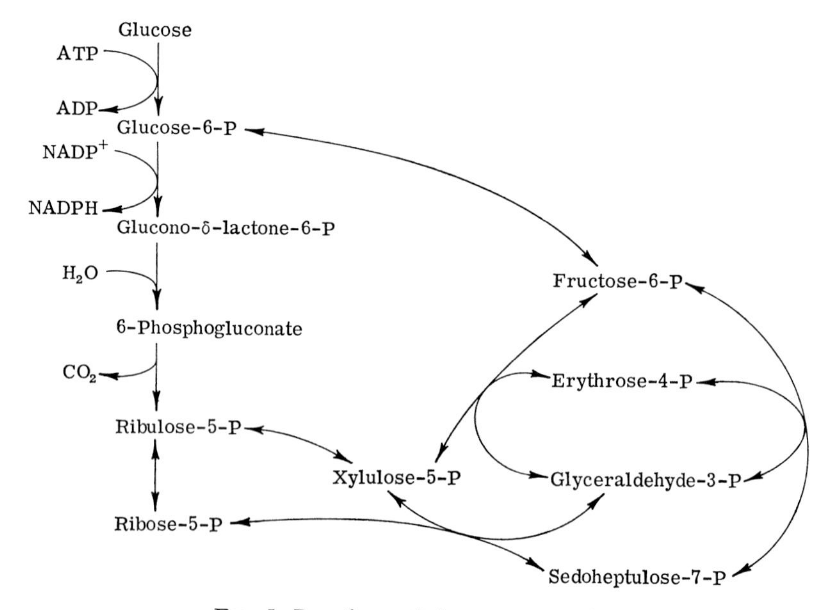

FIG. 5. Reactions of the pentose cycle.

TABLE III

USE OF FIVE SUGARS BY SIX SPECIES OF YEAST[a]

Yeasts	Substrates[b]				
	Glucose	Galactose	Sucrose	Maltose	Lactose
Candida albicans	F	F	G	F	—
Candida scottii	G	G	G	G	—
Trichosporon behrendii	F	F	F	F	—
Trichosporon pullulans	G	G	G	G	G
Saccharomyces cerevisiae	F	F	F	F	—
Cryptococcus neoformans	G	G	G	G	—

[a] Data from Lodder and Kreger-van Rij (1952).

[b] Symbols: F: substrate utilized anaerobically (i.e., "fermented") and aerobically with growth as criterion (often called "assimilated"); G: substrate utilized aerobically but not anaerobically; —: substrate not used, either aerobically or anaerobically.

there was no NAD- or NADP-linked alcohol dehydrogenase activity in cell-free extracts of a strain of *Torulopsis candida,* which is an obligate aerobe. Thus, perhaps, lack of either (1) alcohol dehydrogenase or (2) pyruvate decarboxylase (see Fig. 3) could explain the inability of many yeasts to "ferment" any sugars (cf. Hill and Mills, 1954; Cochrane, 1958). (3) Another reason for failure to use a substrate anaerobically could be the dependence of the cell on aerobic processes for the passage of that substrate across the plasma membrane. However, Kotyk and Höfer (1965) found that in a strain of *Rhodotorula gracilis* (which metabolizes sugars only aerobically) the translocation of monosaccharides into the cells is not the limiting step, either aerobically or anaerobically.

2. D-*Fructose*

Fructose is not often used as a test substrate for classifying yeasts. Those that can metabolize glucose anaerobically can nearly always ferment fructose too; and the ability to use fructose aerobically is probably as general as it is for glucose. Whether fructose is supplied independently or liberated from sucrose, it enters the glycolytic pathway by the action of a hexokinase which converts it to fructose 6-phosphate (Nord and Weiss, 1958), an intermediate of the glycolytic pathway (cf. Fig. 2, reactions 1 and 3):

$$\text{D-Fructofuranose} + \text{ATP} \xrightarrow{\text{hexokinase}} \text{D-fructose-6-P} + \text{ADP} \qquad (5)$$

3. D-*Galactose*

The yeasts *Saccharomyces cerevisiae* and *S. fragilis* convert D-galactose to glucose 6-phosphate, an intermediary metabolite of the Embden-Meyerhof pathway (Fig. 2). This conversion (Fig. 6), which was first

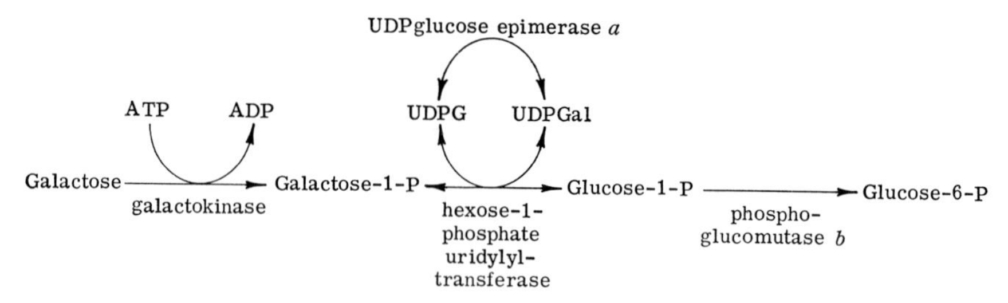

FIG. 6. Conversion of galactose to glucose 6-phosphate. Cofactors: *a*, protein-bound NAD; *b*, glucose 1,6-diphosphate.

elucidated by Leloir and his colleagues, involves (i) the phosphorylation of galactose to galactose 1-phosphate by galactokinase; (ii) the conversion of galactose 1-phosphate into glucose 1-phosphate by hexose 1-phosphate uridylyltransferase; and (iii) the conversion of glucose 1-phosphate to glucose 6-phosphate by phosphoglucomutase (Kalckar, 1958, 1960; de Robichon-Szulmajster, 1958; Maxwell and de Robichon-Szulmajster, 1960; Alvarado, 1960; Maxwell, 1961; Dixon and Webb, 1964).

De Robichon-Szulmajster (1958) showed that a mutant strain of *S. cerevisiae,* unable to use galactose as a substrate, could not synthesize galactokinase. A deficiency of this kind may possibly characterize species that cannot metabolize galactose, as indeed could the lack of any enzyme of the route to glucose 6-phosphate (Fig. 6). Douglas (1961) has found that cell-free extracts of certain galactose-negative mutants of the genus *Saccharomyces* were very low in phosphoglucomutase activity, though the levels of galactokinase, transferase, and epimerase were high (see also Tsoi and Douglas, 1964).

4. *Glucosides*

The initial step in the metabolism of an oligosaccharide is usually its enzymatic hydrolysis (Gottschalk, 1949) into the hexoses of which it is composed (Table IV). The metabolism of these hexoses, namely, glucose, fructose, or galactose, has already been discussed. The actions of different glycosidases on the oligosaccharides are summarized in Table IV, although it should be emphasized that difficulty in purifying these enzymes often casts doubt on their specificities (Fischer and Stein, 1960).

Kluyver and Custers (1940) confirmed earlier reports that some yeasts could metabolize the component hexoses of certain disaccharides anaerobically, but were able to use these disaccharides themselves only aerobically. For example, *Torulopsis dattila* can metabolize maltose only aerobically, although it is able to use glucose both aerobically and anaerobically (Lodder and Kreger-van Rij, 1952). A possible explanation

TABLE IV
THE ENZYMATIC CLEAVAGE OF CERTAIN GLUCOSIDES

Enzyme	Glucoside	Products
β-Fructofuranosidase	Raffinose	Fructose, melibiose
	Sucrose	Glucose, fructose
α-Glucosidase	Sucrose	Glucose, fructose
	Maltose	2 Glucose
	Methyl α-D-glucoside	Glucose, methanol
	Melezitose	2 Glucose, 1 fructose
Trehalase	Trehalose	2 Glucose
α-Galactosidase	Melibiose	Glucose, galactose
β-Galactosidase	Lactose	Glucose, galactose
β-Glucosidase	Cellobiose	2 Glucose
	Arbutin	Glucose, hydroquinone
	Salicin	Glucose, saligenin

is that oxygen is necessary for the entry of the disaccharides into the cells of these yeasts.

a. Sucrose. This may be considered as both a β-fructofuranoside and an α-glucoside; hence it is split into glucose and fructose (Fig. 7) by two

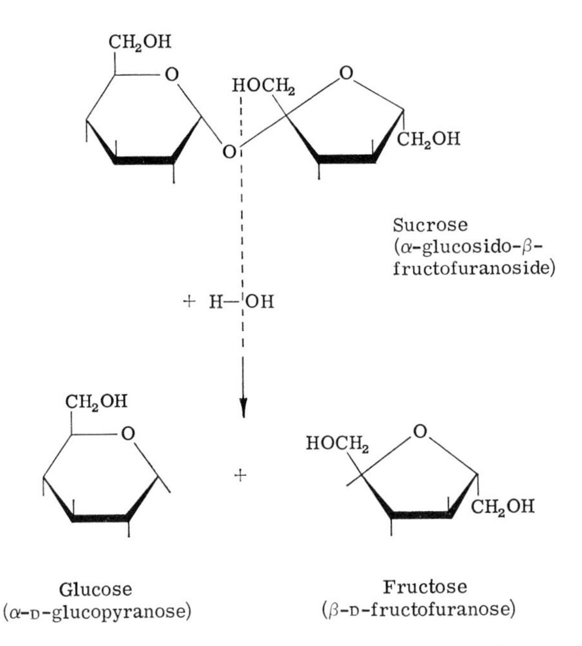

FIG. 7. The cleavage of sucrose to glucose and fructose.

different kinds of glycosidase; (1) a β-fructofuranosidase ("invertase") or (2) an α-glucosidase (Myrbäck, 1960; Dixon and Webb, 1964). Both types of enzyme have been reported in strains of *Saccharomyces cerevisiae*. β-Fructofuranosidase occurs also in *S. carlsbergensis,* but it may be absent from some species that can use sucrose, such as *Candida albicans* (Neuberg and Mandl, 1950) and *C. solani* (Novák, 1963), which may split sucrose by means of an α-glucosidase. Snyder and Phaff (1960) reported that the β-fructofuranosidase of *S. fragilis,* unlike that of *S. cerevisiae,* also hydrolyzes inulin, which accounts for the ability of the former yeast to use this compound (Lodder and Kreger-van Rij, 1952). β-Fructofuranosidase usually acts outside the cell membrane of *S. cerevisiae* and certain other yeasts that have been studied (Myrbäck, 1960; de la Fuente and Sols, 1962; Islam and Lampen, 1962; Weimberg and Orton, 1966), so that yeasts which are impermeable to sucrose may nevertheless be able to metabolize it.

Avigad (1960) has described a yeast which (1) cannot utilize sucrose, (2) contains a sucrose-hydrolyzing α-glucosidase, and (3) accumulates exogenously supplied sucrose in its cells. He explained these findings in terms of the presence of an intracellular barrier (within the cell membrane) separating the intracellularly accumulated sucrose from the α-glucosidase.

b. Maltose. α-Glucosidases that cleave maltose into two molecules of glucose have been found in various species of yeast (for review, see Larner, 1960). At least for *S. cerevisiae,* these enzymes appear to act within the cell membrane (de la Fuente and Sols, 1962; Sutton and Lampen, 1962; Millin, 1963). The specificities of the α-glucosidases may vary from one yeast to another (Larner, 1960); and a single strain may have two or more α-glucosidases with different specificities (Millin and Springham, 1966).

c. Trehalose. This glucoside has been reported as being hydrolyzed intracellularly, to form two glucose molecules, by a glucosidase of fairly high specificity and distinct from the maltose hydrolyzing enzymes (Myrbäck, 1949; Trevelyan, 1958; Frohwein and Leibowitz, 1962; Birch, 1963; Panek and Souza, 1964; Avigad *et al.,* 1965).

d. Lactose. Yeasts that can use lactose probably hydrolyze the molecule within the cell membrane into glucose and galactose by means of a β-galactosidase (reviews: Wallenfels and Malhotra, 1960, 1961; Hestrin, 1953; Veibel, 1950; de la Fuente and Sols, 1962).

e. Melibiose. S. carlsbergensis, but not *S. cerevisiae,* is known as one of the best sources of α-galactosidase which hydrolyzes melibiose, forming galactose and glucose (reviews: Veibel, 1950; Hassid and Ballou, 1957; Baumann and Pigman, 1957; Wallenfels and Malhotra, 1961). Like sucrose, melibiose is hydrolyzed outside the cell membrane (de la Fuente and Sols, 1962) in those cases that have been investigated.

f. Raffinose. The trisaccharide raffinose is composed of a molecule of glucose, one of fructose, and one of galactose:

α-D-Galactopyranosyl-(1→6)-α-D-glucopyranosyl-(1→2)-β-D-fructofuranoside

(Fig. 8) (French, 1954; Hassid and Ballou, 1957).

When a yeast metabolizes raffinose, it may use only the fructose part of the molecule, leaving the melibiose part intact (Fig. 8), or it may attack all three component hexoses. Consequently taxonomists have designed tests to distinguish not only those yeasts that cannot ferment

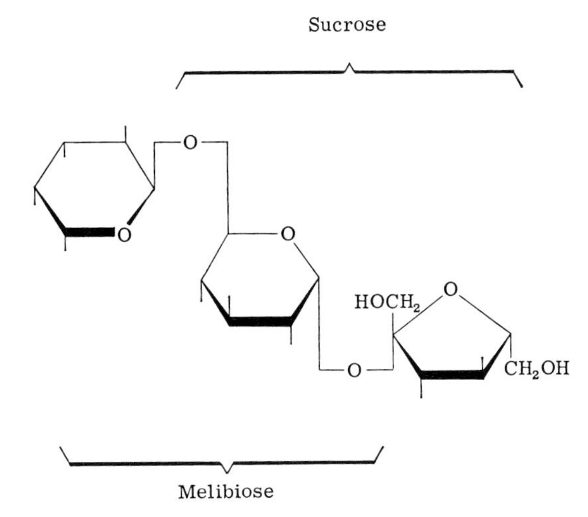

FIG. 8. The structure of raffinose.

raffinose at all, but also those that hydrolyze the raffinose molecule in different ways (e.g., Lodder and Kreger-van Rij, 1952).

At least two kinds of enzyme may hydrolyze raffinose: (1) an α-galactosidase cleaves the melibiose part, leaving galactose and sucrose; or (2) a β-fructofuranosidase splits the sucrose portion, leaving fructose and melibiose. It is possible, however, for the sucrose part of the molecule to be metabolized even if no β-fructofuranosidase is present. After the action of an α-galactosidase, the sucrose that remains can be hydrolyzed by an α-glucosidase (Winge and Roberts, 1958), if the sucrose can enter the cell or the enzyme acts at the cell surface. Insofar as both sucrose and melibiose may be hydrolyzed outside the cell membrane, it seems likely that raffinose may be too.

For various reasons, the situation may be more complicated than has been described. (1) The relevant enzymes may not always be accessible to the substrates. (2) Other enzymes than those considered may act on raffinose. For example, levansucrase of *Aerobacter levanicum* (Hestrin *et al.*, 1956) catalyzes a glycosyl transfer in the reaction between raffinose and glucose (Eisenberg and Hestrin, 1963):

$$\text{Glc} + \underset{\text{(raffinose)}}{\text{Gal-Glc-Fru}} \xrightarrow{\text{levansucrase}} \underset{\text{(melibiose)}}{\text{Gal-Glc}} + \underset{\text{(sucrose)}}{\text{Glc-Fru}} \qquad (6)$$

g. Arbutin, Salicin, and Cellobiose. These are β-D-glucopyranosides (Baumann and Pigman, 1957); their hydrolysis is catalyzed by β-glucosidases. The products of hydrolysis are (1) for arbutin and salicin, a phenolic compound and glucose, and (2) for cellobiose, two molecules of glucose (Table V).

TABLE V
THE β-GLUCOSIDES AND PRODUCTS OF THEIR HYDROLYSIS

β-Glucoside	Products	
	Glucose	Aglycon
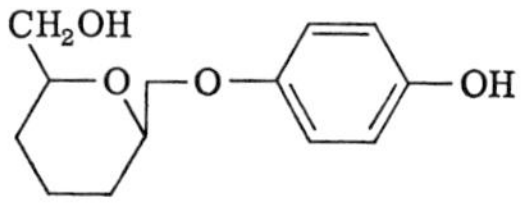 Arbutin	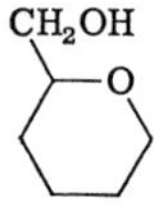 CH_2OH (glucose)	 Hydroquinone
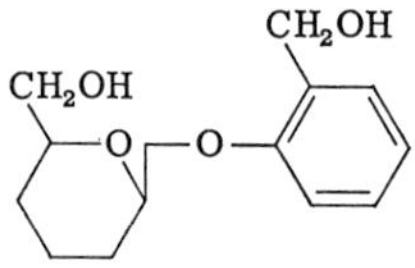 Salicin	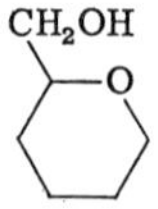 CH_2OH (glucose)	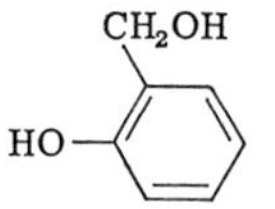 Saligenin
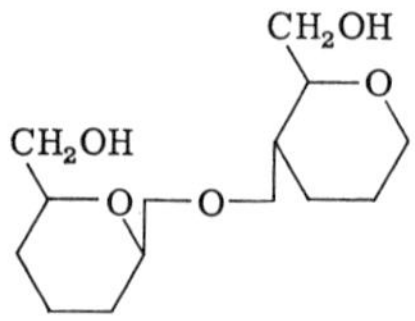 Cellobiose	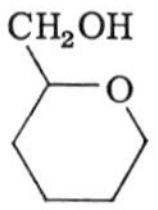 [2 Molecules]	

Barnett *et al.* (1956) suggested that the β-glucosidases of yeasts might be found to vary in their specificity. In agreement with this suggestion, Herman and Halvorson (1963) have published evidence that some strains of *Saccharomyces lactis* may have two β-glucosidases: one is active against arbutin and salicin, but not cellobiose; the other enzyme is active against cellobiose. However, the β-glucosidases of *Rhodotorula minuta* (Duerksen and Halvorson, 1958; A. S. L. Hu *et al.*, 1960; Herman and Halvorson, 1963) and of a hybrid between *S. fragilis* and *S. dobzhanskii* (A. S. L. Hu *et al.*, 1960) hydrolyzed all three glucosides, though the activity against cellobiose was low (Table VI). Furthermore, Kaplan

TABLE VI

SPECIFICITY OF β-GLUCOSIDASE OF *Rhodotorula minuta*[a] FOR SUBSTRATES AND INDUCERS

Substrate or inducer	Maximum rate of hydrolysis[b] (μmoles/mg protein/10 min)	Inducing activity[c] (enzyme/mass)
Cellobiose	12	13
Methyl β-D-glucoside	33	500
Salicin	82	19
Arbutin	187	8

[a] Originally called *Saccharomyces cerevisiae* by Duerksen and Halvorson, but corrected later (e.g., Herman and Halvorson, 1963).

[b] Duerksen and Halvorson (1958).

[c] Duerksen and Halvorson (1959).

(1965), Kaplan and Tacreiter (1966), and Inamdar and Kaplan (1966), working with a cellobiose-utilizing yeast which they named *S. cerevisiae,* present evidence of two distinct systems of β-glucosidase activity in this yeast. First, there is an intracellular enzyme, like that of *Rhodotorula minuta;* but, second, Kaplan and his colleagues found a membrane-bound β-glucosidase, with a high affinity for cellobiose, that cleaves the glucosides at the cell membrane so that they do not enter the cells intact. The role of the first (intracellular) enzyme, if any, is unknown.

Duerksen and Halvorson (1958, 1959) showed that for an inducible β-glucosidase of *Rhodotorula minuta,* arbutin was the best substrate they tested, and methyl β-D-glucoside was the best inducer (Table VI). Hence for testing the activity of yeasts against, say, salicin or arbutin, it might be worth investigating the addition to the test medium of compounds such as methyl β-D-glucoside to act as inducers of β-glucosidase activity. Such a procedure would be closely comparable to one used for bacterial classification by Clarke and Steel (1966). These authors employ lactose to induce β-galactosidase activity in bacteria; and the activity is detected by its action on *o*-nitrophenyl-β-D-galactoside as substrate.

B. Pentoses and Polyols

The initial step of polyol metabolism by yeasts connects the utilization of polyols with that of the pentoses. The reasons for this connection (see Touster and Shaw, 1962) are as follows.

1. As shown in Fig. 9, yeasts probably first oxidize each polyol to the corresponding ketose or aldose by means of a coenzyme-linked dehydrogenase. There is no evidence that yeasts phosphorylate polyols before oxidation.

Kind of reaction	Example
(a) CH_2OH–CHOH–R (Polyol) + NAD^+ (or $NADP^+$) ⇌ CH_2OH–C=O–R (Ketose) + NADH + H^+ (or NADPH)	CH_2OH–HCOH–HCOH–HCOH–CH_2OH (Ribitol) ⇌ [NAD^+ → NADH + H^+] CH_2OH–C=O–HCOH–HCOH–CH_2OH (D-Ribulose)
(b) CH_2OH–CHOH–R (Polyol) + $NADP^+$ ⇌ CHO–CHOH–R (Aldose) + NADPH + H^+	CH_2OH–HCOH–HOCH–HOCH–CH_2OH (L-Arabinitol) ⇌ [$NADP^+$ → NADPH + H^+] HCO–HCOH–HOCH–HOCH–CH_2OH (L-Arabinose)

FIG. 9. Two kinds of reaction catalyzed by polyol dehydrogenases.

2. The polyol dehydrogenases which catalyze reactions (a) and (b) in Fig. 9, although usually highly specific for either NAD or NADP, often have low specificity toward their polyol substrates. For example, the constitutive NAD-linked polyol dehydrogenase of a strain of *Torulopsis candida,* which from electrophoretic and kinetic evidence appears to be a single enzyme, catalyzes the oxidation of four polyols; namely, D-glucitol to D-fructose, L-iditol to L-sorbose, ribitol to D-ribulose, and xylitol to D-xylulose (Table VII). The specificity of this enzyme is closely comparable with that of the purified and crystallized L-iditol dehydrogenase of sheep liver (Smith, 1962).

3. By reason of their low substrate specificity, a single polyol dehydrogenase may be responsible for the conversion of more than one hexitol

TABLE VII

Reactions Catalyzed by Constitutive NAD-Linked Polyol Dehydrogenase of *Torulopsis candida* (NCYC 576)[a,b]

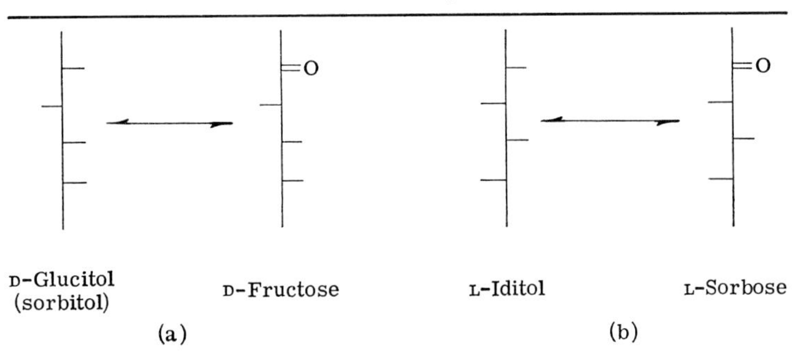

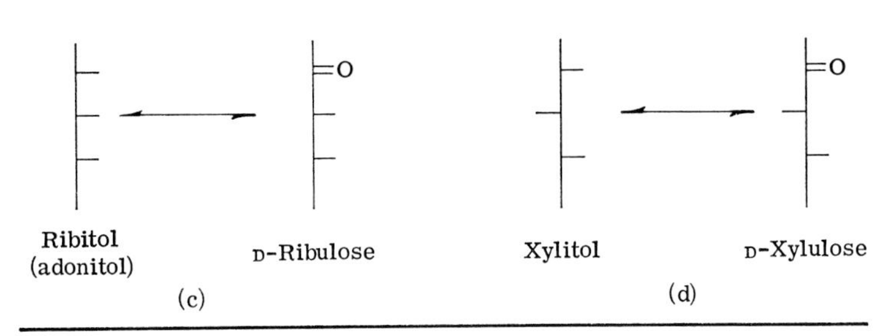

[a] This yeast is listed in the NCYC catalog (1963) as *Torulopsis famata*.
[b] Observations by Barnett (1968).

to its corresponding hexose (e.g., D-mannitol to D-mannose) and also of pentitols to pentoses (e.g., ribitol to D-ribose).

4. Yeasts appear to convert pentoses to D-xylulose by a series of alternating reductions and oxidations, each reduction and oxidation involving a polyol dehydrogenase.

For these four reasons, the metabolism of polyols and that of pentoses are interconnected, as well as that of one polyol with another and one pentose with another.

1. D-*Xylose and* L-*Arabinose*

Candida albicans and *C. utilis* appear to convert D-xylose to xylulose by the two kinds of reactions shown in Fig. 9. Xylulose is phosphorylated to xylulose 5-phosphate (Fig. 10) which is an intermediate of the pentose cycle (Veiga *et al.*, 1960; Chakravorty *et al.*, 1962; Horecker, 1962):

$$\text{Xylose} \rightarrow \text{xylitol} \rightarrow \text{xylulose} \rightarrow \text{xylulose phosphate} \quad (7)$$

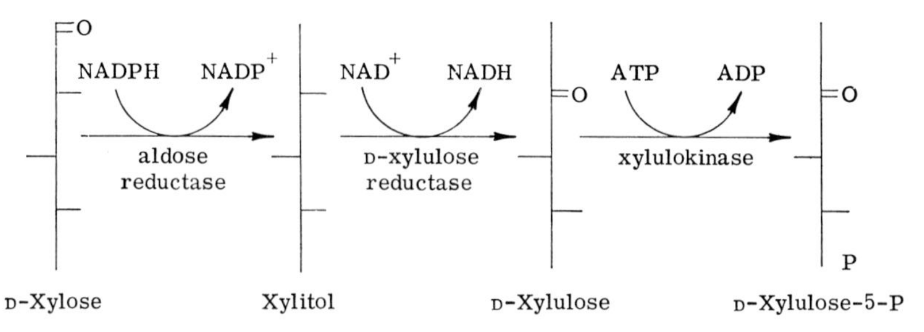

FIG. 10. Enzymatic conversion of D-xylose to D-xylulose 5-phosphate.

Onishi and Perry (1965) have reported that *Pichia farinosa* (*P. miso*), too, forms xylitol from D-xylose, but they did not examine the mechanism of formation.

The *C. albicans* strain used by Veiga *et al.* (1960) could grow on L-arabinose and also on D-xylose as sole source of carbon (Horecker, 1962); and the enzyme responsible for reducing D-xylose to xylitol (Fig. 10) also reduced L-arabinose to L-arabinitol (Fig. 9). The fate of the L-arabinitol and, consequently, the whole route is uncertain. However, some yeasts, such as certain strains of *Torulopsis pseudaeria, Torulopsis candida, Debaryomyces vanriji,* and *Debaryomyces phaffii,* can utilize L-arabinitol as sole carbon source for growth and for respiration (Barnett, 1968). Although no enzyme that oxidizes L-arabinitol to L-xylulose has yet been reported in yeasts, it is likely that the route of L-arabinose metabolism proposed by Chiang and Knight (1960) for *Penicillium chrysogenum* (Fig. 11) applies to yeasts too. This route for L-arabinose, as for D-xylose, leads to D-xyulose.

Bacteria generally convert D-xylose to D-xylulose by the action of xylose isomerase, not by oxidoreduction via xylitol (see Karasevich, 1965; Wood, 1966). Horecker and his colleagues stated explicitly that xylose isomerase was absent from *C. utilis* extracts (Chakravorty *et al.*, 1962; Horecker, 1962), but Tomoeda and Horitsu (1964) claim to have purified that enzyme from this yeast. Such apparently conflicting results might be explained by the use of different strains of yeast.

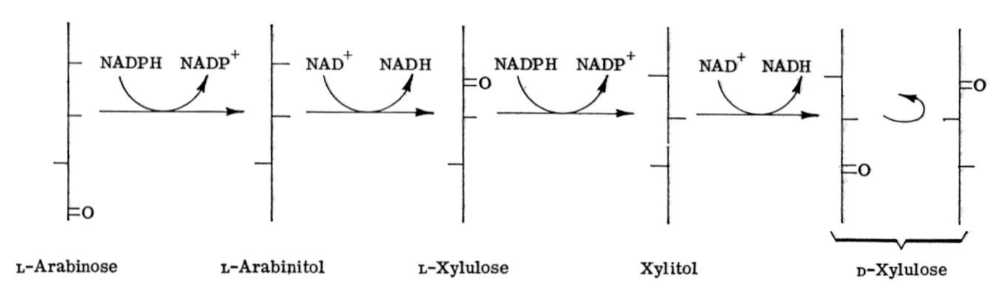

FIG. 11. Proposed pathway for conversion of L-arabinose to D-xylulose.

Although the routes of pentose catabolism in species of *Candida* discussed by Horecker (1962) are aerobic, it should be mentioned that Karczewska (1959) has reported the anaerobic metabolism of L-arabinose by *C. tropicalis.*

2. D-*Ribose and Ribitol* (*Adonitol*)

Veiga *et al.* (1960) found that the NADP-linked dehydrogenase of *C. albicans,* which reduced D-xylose to xylitol and L-arabinose to L-arabinitol, also reduced D-ribose to ribitol. In *C. utilis,* Chakravorty *et al.* (1962) found that the same enzyme which oxidized xylitol to D-xylulose, also converted ribitol to D-ribulose. Two comparable enzymes, (NADP- and NAD-linked, respectively) have also been detected in cell-free extracts of *Torulopsis candida* (Barnett, 1968), and an NADP-linked ribose-ribitol enzyme in *Geotrichum candidum* (Moret and Sperti, 1962). Observations on the two species of *Candida* led Horecker (1962) to suggest that these yeasts could interconvert D-ribose and D-ribulose:

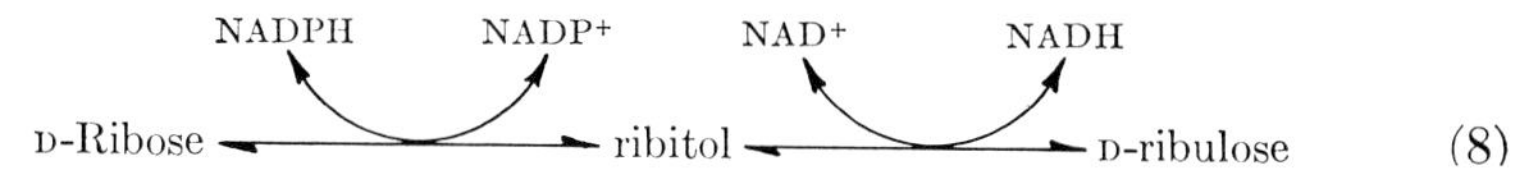

As Horecker pointed out, neither *C. utilis* nor *C. albicans* will grow on ribose as sole carbon source: in neither yeast could kinase activity be detected for either ribose or ribulose. Those yeasts, such as *T. candida* or *Debaryomyces vanriji,* which can utilize D-ribose and ribitol, probably convert these substrates either to ribulose phosphate or to ribose phosphate (Fig. 12) which are thence catabolized via the pentose cycle (Figs. 5 and 13).

3. D-*Arabinose*

The metabolism of D-arabinose by yeasts does not seem to have been investigated. Two hypothetical routes by which yeasts may catabolize D-arabinose are shown in Fig. 14. These routes are comparable with that

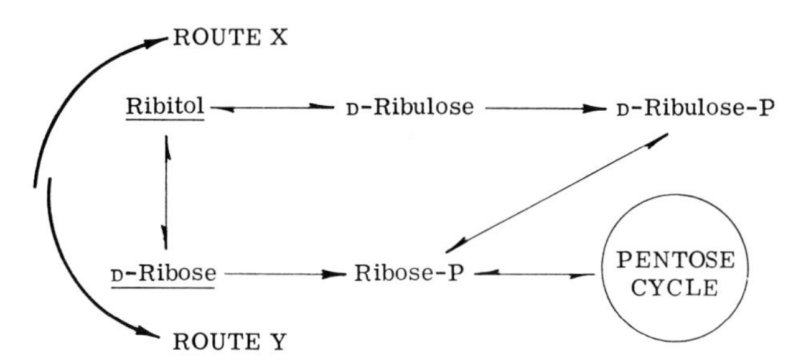

FIG. 12. Scheme for catabolism of D-ribose and ribitol. Substrates used for taxonomic tests are underlined.

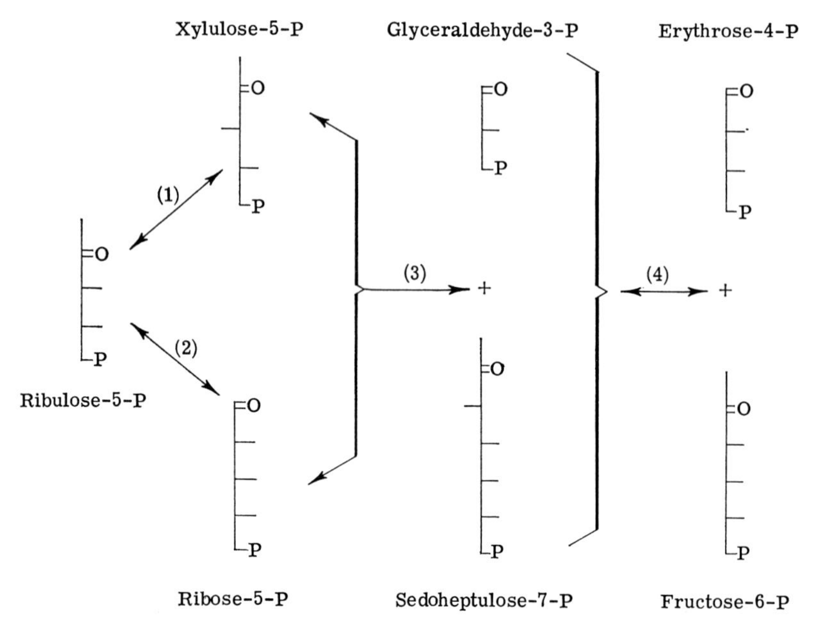

FIG. 13. The formation of fructose-6-P from pentose phosphate: (1) ribulose-phosphate 3-epimerase; (2) ribosephosphate isomerase; (3) transketolase; (4) transaldolase. After Horecker (1962).

for L-arabinose (Fig. 11): D-arabinose is reduced to D-arabinitol, which is oxidized either to D-xylulose or to D-ribulose. Ingram and Wood (1965) have found in *Saccharomyces rouxii* an NADP-linked D-arabinitol dehydrogenase, forming D-ribulose. However, alternative routes have been described for this substrate in other organisms. In *Aerobacter aerogenes,* for example, Wood and his colleagues have shown that D-arabinose is isomerized to D-ribulose which is then phosphorylated; and the D-ribulose 5-phosphate formed undergoes epimerization to give D-xylulose 5-phosphate (Mortlock *et al.,* 1965). Such alternative routes of pentose metabolism by microorganisms are reviewed by Horecker (1962), Hollmann (1964), Karasevich (1965), and Wood (1966).

4. D-*Mannitol and* D-*Glucitol* (*Sorbitol*)

Extracts of *Pichia farinosa* (*P. miso*), a yeast capable of utilizing D-mannitol and D-glucitol (Kreger-van Rij, 1964) have NAD-linked dehydrogenase activity for the conversion of both polyols to D-fructose (Onishi and Saito, 1962). A strain of *Torulopsis candida* can similarly convert D-mannitol and D-glucitol to D-fructose, but also to D-mannose and D-glucose, respectively, by means of an NADP-linked enzyme (Barnett, 1968). Oxidations of D-mannitol have been reported as NADP-linked for *Geotrichum candidum* (Chang and Li, 1964), and as both NAD- and NADP-linked for *Rhodotorula glutinis* (Deinema, 1967).

A good deal of work has been done on the polyol dehydrogenases of *Candida utilis,* the intact cells of which can use neither D-mannitol nor D-glucitol (Brady, 1965). Cell extracts of this yeast possess NAD-linked dehydrogenase activity which can interconvert both these polyols and D-fructose and L-sorbose (Fig. 15) (Arcus and Edson, 1956; Chakravorty *et al.,* 1962; Horecker, 1962; Horitsu and Tomoeda, 1966). Two such NAD-linked enzymes may be separated electrophoretically from extracts of *C. utilis:* one enzyme oxidizes both D-mannitol and D-glucitol, and the other enzyme oxidizes D-glucitol but not D-mannitol (Barnett, 1968). The same yeast contains an NADP-linked dehydrogenase which converts D-glucitol to D-glucose, but for which D-mannitol is not a substrate (Scher and Horecker, 1966).

NAD-linked dehydrogenases which oxidize D-mannitol have been found in other yeasts that do not use polyols; namely, *Saccharomyces carlsbergensis* (Müller, 1937) and *S. cerevisiae* (Wolff and Kaplan, 1956).

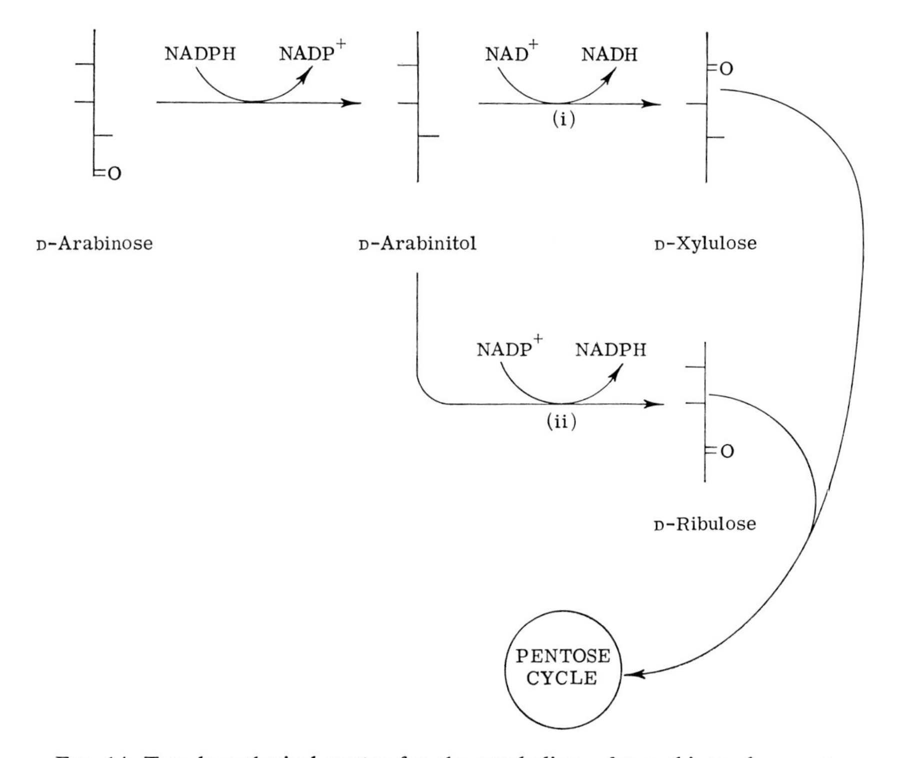

FIG. 14. Two hypothetical routes for the catabolism of D-arabinose by yeasts.

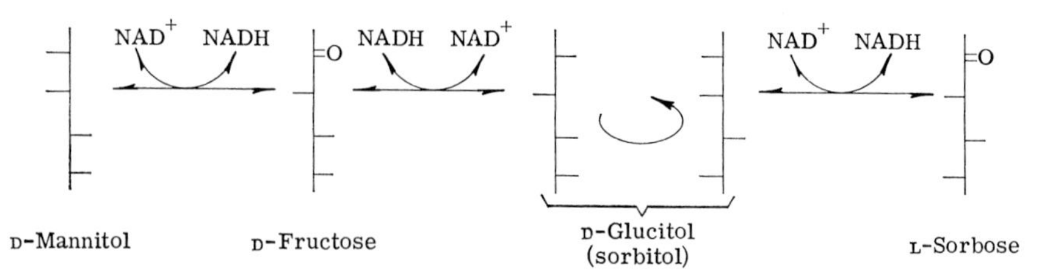

FIG. 15. NAD-linked interconversions of D-mannitol, D-fructose, D-glucitol, and L-sorbose by cell extracts of *Candida utilis.*

5. *Erythritol and Galactitol (Dulcitol)*

There is no obvious metabolic connection between erythritol and galactitol, but work with a number of species (Barnett, 1968) suggests that the metabolism of both polyols is initiated by specific inducible dehydrogenases, and that these two polyols are not oxidized by those enzymes, constitutively present in the cells, which can oxidize other polyols such as D-glucitol, mannitol, and so on. Specific induction of enzymes for galactitol and erythritol probably explains why only erythritol-grown cells of *Torulopsis candida* respire erythritol and only galactitol-grown cells respire galactitol (Table VIII). (Comparable observations have been made on the respiration of *Debaryomyces phaffii, Pichia vanriji,* and *Hansenula anomala.*) Cell-free extracts of *T. candida* contained an NAD-linked dehydrogenase which oxidized erythritol to erythrulose; and there is some evidence that this yeast possesses an NADP-linked enzyme for the conversion of galactitol to D-galactose, as described for the non-galactitol-, non-galactose-utilizing *Candida utilis* by Scher and Horecker (1966).

TABLE VIII

RATES OF RESPIRATION OF POLYOLS BY *Torulopsis candida* (NCYC 576)[a,b]

Carbon source for growth of yeast	Substrate for respiration					
	D-Glucose	D-Glucitol	D-Mannitol	Galactitol	Erythritol	Endogenous
D-Glucitol	80	60	27	7	5	5
D-Mannitol	80	46	45	4	5	4
Galactitol	60	39	28	**76**[c]	9	5
Erythritol	67	50	24	4	**65**	4
Succinate	70	42	28	4	4	3

[a] Barnett (1968).

[b] Each figure in the table represents the Q_{O_2} (uptake of oxygen in microliters per milligram dry weight of yeast per hour).

[c] Boldface type draws attention to the high rates for galactitol and erythritol, depending on their presence in the growth medium.

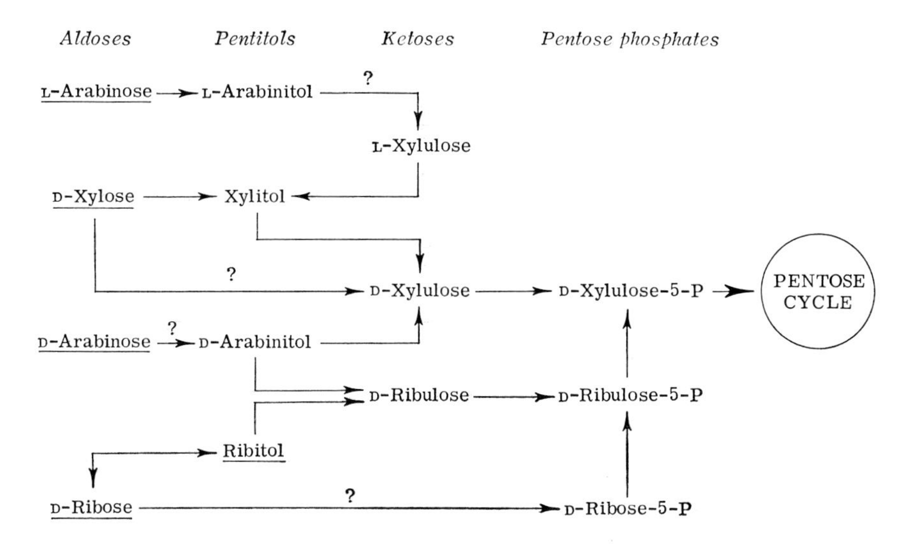

FIG. 16. Routes of pentose and pentitol catabolism by yeasts: a hypothetical scheme. Substrates used for taxonomic tests are underlined.

Erythritol is converted to L-erythrulose by *T. magnoliae* (Spencer and Gorin, 1960) and by species of *Acetobacter* (Ley, 1963; C. L. Hu *et al.*, 1965).

6. *Summary of Pentose and Polyol Metabolism*

Figures 16 and 17 show schemes summarizing the routes by which pentose and polyol substrates may be catabolized by yeasts. Ribitol and the pentoses are converted to D-xylulose 5-phosphate, an intermediary metabolite of the pentose cycle. D-Mannitol and D-glucitol, on the other hand, are oxidized to hexoses which are catabolized by the Embden-

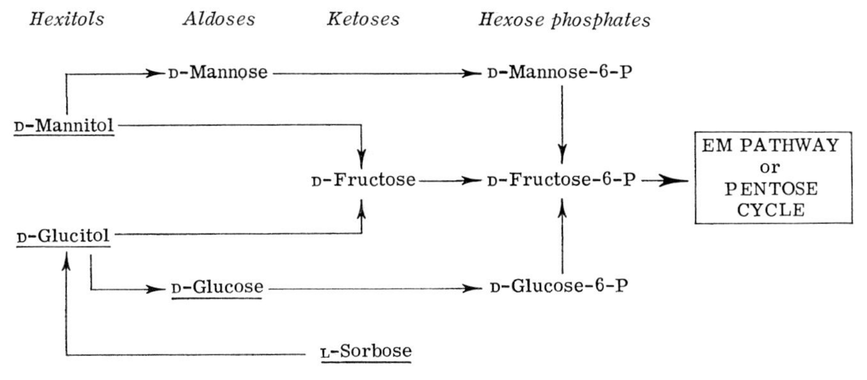

FIG. 17. Scheme for routes of hexose and hexitol catabolism by yeasts. Substrates used for taxonomic tests are underlined.

Meyerhof or pentose phosphate pathways. The fate of erythritol and galactitol is more obscure. Erythritol is probably converted to erythrulose and perhaps thence via erythrose catabolized by way of the pentose cycle. Galactitol may well be oxidized initially to galactose.

At the beginning of this section on pentoses and polyols, the point was made that the low substrate specificity of the polyol dehydrogenases provided connections between the ability to catabolize both six- and five-carbon compounds. This point is illustrated in Table IX, which shows

TABLE IX
SPECIFICITIES OF FOUR POLYOL DEHYDROGENASES FROM A STRAIN OF *Torulopsis candida*[a]

Polyol oxidized	Oxidation products with			
	Enzyme No. 1[b] NAD-linked	Enzyme No. 2[b] NADP-linked	Enzyme No. 3[c] NAD-linked	Enzyme No. 4[c] NADP-linked
D-Glucitol (sorbitol)	D-Fructose	L-Sorbose	L-Sorbose	D-Glucose
D-Mannitol	None	D-Fructose	D-Fructose	D-Mannose
L-Iditol	L-Sorbose	None	None	None
Ribitol (adonitol)	D-Ribulose	None	None	D-Ribose
Xylitol	D-Xylulose	L-Xylulose	L-Xylulose	D-Xylose
D-Arabinitol	None	D-Xylulose	D-Xylulose	D-Arabinose

[a] Barnett (1968).
[b] From succinate-grown yeast, enzymes separated electrophoretically.
[c] From D-glucitol-grown yeast, enzymes separated electrophoretically.

the specificities of four of eight such enzymes found in cell extracts of a strain of *Torulopsis candida* (Barnett, 1968).

C. *Acids of the Tricarboxylic Acid Cycle*

Citric, succinic, fumaric, and malic acids have in recent years been used as sole carbon sources for growth tests in identifying yeasts. Barnett and Kornberg (1960) examined causes of the differences between K+ yeasts (those that can use tricarboxylic acid cycle intermediates supplied exogenously) and K— yeasts (those that cannot). These workers pointed out that many K+ yeasts, though they can use succinate, are unable to use all the TCA cycle intermediates (Table X and Fig. 4); they compared the patterns of isotope incorporation from acetate-1,2-^{14}C by a K+ yeast (*Kluyveromyces* [*Saccharomyces*] *drosophilarum*) with those of K— yeasts (*Saccharomyces cerevisiae* and *S. acidifaciens*). Similarities between the patterns found for the two kinds of yeast supported the findings of Demoss

TABLE X

ABILITY OF FOUR YEASTS TO GROW ON ACIDS OF THE TRICARBOXYLIC ACID CYCLE[a]

Yeast	Substrate				
	Citrate	Fumarate	Malate	Succinate	Acetate
Saccharomyces cerevisiae	−	−	−	−	+
Saccharomyces lactis[b]	−	+	−	+	+
Saccharomyces marxianus[b]	−	+	+	+	+
Hansenula anomala	+	+	+	+	+

[a] Data from Barnett and Kornberg (1960).

[b] In future these yeasts will be classified in the genus *Kluyveromyces* (van der Walt, 1965).

and Swim (1957), who showed that the TCA cycle is of major importance in the oxidation of acetate by baker's yeast, a typical K− yeast. The difference between K+ and K− yeasts is thus not in a major metabolic pathway, but in the permeability of the intact cells (or parts of the cells) to the TCA cycle acids.

IV. TRANSLOCATION: THE ENTRY OF SUBSTRATES INTO THE CELLS

The consideration of metabolic pathways would be pointless if the substrates did not enter the cells. Investigations into the mode of entry of sugars into yeast cells have led to the following picture.

1. Each sugar that enters the cells intact does so by means of a special carrier system, without which the cell membrane is impermeable to sugars.

2. Entry depends on configuration rather than size of the sugar molecule: that is to say, translocation systems are stereospecific. Cirillo (1961a), for example, found that D-arabinose enters the cells of *Saccharomyces cerevisiae* (baker's yeast) more than twice as fast as L-arabinose.

3. The carrier systems are likely to be specific for more than one substrate. The maltose translocation system in *S. cerevisiae,* for instance, is probably responsible also for the entry of α-methyl D-glucoside (Harris and Thompson, 1961).

4. The carrier system may often be the limiting factor in the utilization of a substrate. Translocation may limit the use of the acids of the TCA cycle (see above), sugars, and also certain polyols, such as D-glucitol (sorbitol). As described earlier, intact cells of *Candida utilis* cannot use D-glucitol, though (a) their extracts contain an enzyme which oxidizes D-glucitol to D-fructose and (b) the yeast can use D-fructose for growth

and for respiration. It is a reasonable inference from these facts that exogenous D-glucitol does not penetrate intact cells of this yeast; and this inference has been confirmed using ^{14}C-labeled D-glucitol (Barnett, 1968).

As already mentioned, sucrose and melibiose are probably hydrolyzed outside the cell membrane, whereas maltose may enter the cells of *S. cerevisiae,* and lactose those of *Kluyveromyces* (*Saccharomyces*) *fragilis,* intact.

The uptake of metabolites by yeast cells is reviewed by Rothstein in Volume I, Chapter 15. Other discussions of this subject of special relevance include those of Cirillo (1961a,b,c, 1962), Sols and de la Fuente (1961), de la Fuente and Sols (1962), Jennings (1963), and Kotyk and Höfer (1965).

V. A BIOCHEMICAL INTERPRETATION OF THE RESPONSES TO GROWTH TESTS

A. Correlation of Responses to Different Substrates

Section III described the routes by which yeasts may catabolize certain of the test substrates. The descriptions of the routes have been given as a basis for explaining differences between yeasts in their responses to the tests. The evidence for these routes comes from biochemical studies on only a few strains of yeasts, as well as on other kinds of organisms. Hence, in order to decide whether these explanations are true for yeasts in general, it is necessary to examine the behavior of a large number of different yeasts. Consequently, Barnett (1966a,b) proposed a method for examining associations between the results of the nutritional tests. He used this method to deduce the routes by which yeasts convert the test compounds into intermediate metabolites of the central metabolic pathways. The proposed method may be compared to that by which information on biosynthetic pathways has been obtained from auxotrophic mutants. The principle of the latter technique is that, if the requirements of two mutant strains are satisfied by the same substrate x, and of only one of the strains by substrate y, then y is the precursor of x (Srb and Horowitz, 1944).

Accordingly, Barnett (1966a,b) considered biochemical schemes which follow logically from the results of taxonomic tests and which may explain these results. He discussed, particularly: (1) enzymes like β-glucosidases or polyol dehydrogenases, the presence of which in some yeasts and absence in others would lead to correlations between the results of a number of the tests; and (2) how analysis of the results of large numbers of tests could reveal the biochemical features that are likely to underlie these correlations. It is hoped to use an analysis of this kind for making generalizations about the initial catabolic steps for many substrates with large numbers of yeasts.

The method for scrutinizing the results of the tests is illustrated by the examples which follow. These examples give some evidence as to how far certain biochemical theories of the utilization of particular substrates apply to yeasts in general. The examples given here, most of which were considered by Barnett (1966a), are based on the data from two surveys which form part of the new major taxonomic study of the yeasts being carried out under the direction of Dr. J. Lodder. The two surveys are (1) the investigation by Kreger-van Rij (1964) of the genera *Endomycopsis, Pichia,* and *Debaryomyces;* and (2) unpublished observations of van Uden and his colleagues on *Candida* and *Torulopsis* (Brady, 1965).

B. *Reasons for Correlations of Responses to Different Substrates*

As previously mentioned, a yeast fails to grow aerobically on a substrate either (1) because the substrate does not enter the cells, or (2) because the yeast lacks one or more enzymes necessary to convert the substrate into an intermediate of a central pathway. It is important to emphasize that it may be quite impracticable from growth tests alone to distinguish between these two alternative reasons for failure.

Taxonomists often find that most organisms which can utilize a certain substrate, A, can also use another, B, and those that cannot use A cannot use B. Three alternative conditions may be responsible for such an association of responses to different substrates: (1) a catabolic enzyme, often that responsible for the initial attack on the test substrate, may have wide specificity; (2) substrate A is converted into B as a step in A's catabolic path; (3) both A and B may be converted into C, a common metabolite of the route to the central pathway for both substrates.

1. *A Common Initial Enzyme*

a. β-Glucosides. It has been seen that a single β-glucosidase may hydrolyze arbutin, salicin, and cellobiose. Yeasts with such an enzyme would be expected to use all three glucosides, provided that they enter the cells or, alternatively, that the enzyme acts outside the cell membrane. Those yeasts that lack the enzyme would fail to use all three substrates.

Suppose a number of yeasts were tested for their ability to use these substrates, it would be found that those able to use one of the substrates could also use the others; and, conversely, those that do not use any of the substrates do not use the others. A tabular form, in which the yeasts are divided into four categories, is used to examine the associations between the tests. If, for example, of 100 yeasts tested, 50 used substrate *A* and also substrate *B*, and the remaining 50 used neither substrate, this example may be expressed in tabular form as follows:

		Substrate *A* +	Substrate *A* −
Substrate *B*	+	50	0
	−	0	50

Results of the survey of the genera *Endomycopsis, Pichia,* and *Debaryomyces* by Kreger-van Rij (1964) are given in the above form in Table XI. This table clearly exemplifies the kind of association expected if a single β-glucosidase were responsible for attacking these substrates. With only two (4%) exceptions, those yeasts which use one β-glucoside also use the other β-glucosides. The results are consistent with the view that a single enzyme is responsible for hydrolyzing the β-glucosides, rather than that these yeasts contain a number of β-glucosidases of varying specificity. The exceptions (e.g., *Debaryomyces coudertii*), which use arbutin but not salicin, may be explained either (1) by failure of salicin to enter the cells, or (2) by the greater specificity of the β-glucosidase in these yeasts.

b. Sucrose and Raffinose. The results with sucrose and raffinose from the same survey (Table XII) show two facts of special significance in the present context. (1) None of these yeasts are [raffinose +, sucrose −], and this fact is consistent with the hypothesis that raffinose is hydrolyzed by an enzyme which also attacks sucrose, presumably a β-fructofuranosidase. (2) Ten yeasts are [sucrose +, raffinose −]; and

TABLE XI

RESULTS OF TESTING *Endomycopsis*, *Pichia*, AND *Debaryomyces* WITH THREE β-GLUCOSIDES[a,b]

		Cellobiose +	Cellobiose −	Salicin +	Salicin −
Arbutin	+	33	0	32	2
	−	0	14	0	14

[a] Entries in the table are numbers of species. +, Substrate utilized; −, substrate not utilized. From Barnett (1966a): observations of Kreger-van Rij (1964).

[b] Of the 51 species studied, certain of them gave variable results from one strain to another: results with these species have been omitted.

TABLE XII

RESULTS OF AEROBIC GROWTH TESTS WITH SUCROSE AND RAFFINOSE[a]

		Sucrose +	Sucrose −
Raffinose	+	18	0
	−	10	21

[a] Explanation as for Table XI.

these yeasts may hydrolyze sucrose with an α-glucosidase which does not attack raffinose.

c. L-*Sorbose and* D-*Mannitol* provide an interesting association which can be seen in Table XIII for *Candida* and *Torulopsis*. Only eight of 388 strains (about 2%) use L-sorbose but not D-mannitol. Five of these exceptional strains are of *C. ingens* and two of *C. curvata*. According to Kreger-van Rij (1964), *Endomycopsis ovetensis* provides another exception.

The association between L-sorbose and D-mannitol may be explained by the hypothetical scheme shown in Fig. 18. Two transformations, namely, (i) L-sorbose → D-glucitol and (ii) D-mannitol → D-fructose could be under the control of one enzyme with a specificity such as that described for enzymes 2 and 3 (Table IX) of *Torulopsis candida*. If yeasts that utilize L-sorbose always do so by the route shown in Fig. 18, then (ignoring any effects of permeability) such yeasts should use D-mannitol too. The converse, however, would not be expected: D-mannitol may be oxidized by enzymes of other specificity, such as one that converts it to D-mannose (e.g., enzyme 4, Table IX). Theoretically, another possible route for the catabolism of L-sorbose is its phosphorylation (Hers, 1952; Cadenas and Sols, 1960) followed by conversion to glyceraldehyde and dihydroxyacetone phosphate (Krebs and Lund, 1966). If such a route

TABLE XIII

RESULTS OF AEROBIC GROWTH TESTS WITH L-SORBOSE AND D-MANNITOL[a]

		D-Mannitol +	D-Mannitol −
L-Sorbose	+	208	8
	−	105	67

[a] Entries in the table are numbers of strains of *Candida* and *Torulopsis* species. +, Substrate utilized; −, substrate not utilized. Data from Brady (1965).

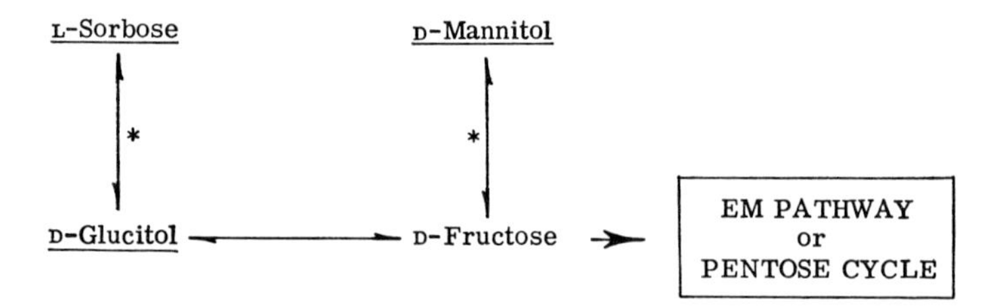

FIG. 18. Scheme for the catabolism of L-sorbose and D-mannitol. *The same enzyme is responsible for two transformations. Substrates used for taxonomic tests are underlined.

were operative, however, there would be no obvious reason for the observed association between L-sorbose and D-mannitol.

2. *Interconvertible Substrates: D-Ribose and Ribitol*

Enzymes have been found in yeasts which interconvert (i) D-ribose and ribitol (adonitol), and (ii) ribitol and D-ribulose (Fig. 12). Hence ribitol and D-ribose may be catabolized via two alternative routes (substrates are underlined):

(X) ribose→ribitol→ribulose→ribulose-P→pentose cycle

or (Y) ribitol→ribose→ribose-P→pentose cycle

Examination of Kreger-van Rij's survey confirms, for the genera she studied, that the utilization of ribitol is associated with that of D-ribose (Table XIV, panel a). Were the two tests independent, the chance of obtaining the figures in Table XIV, panel a is less than one in a thousand.

TABLE XIV

RESULTS OF AEROBIC GROWTH TESTS WITH RIBITOL AND D-RIBOSE[a]

	(a) Number of species of *Endomycopsis, Pichia,* and *Debaryomyces*		(b) Number of strains of 66 species of *Candida*		(c) Number of strains of 32 species of *Torulopsis*	
	Ribitol +	Ribitol −	Ribitol +	Ribitol −	Ribitol +	Ribitol −
D-Ribose +	18	0	96	13	22	17
D-Ribose −	7	18	89	95	7	50

[a] Panel a: explanation as for Table XI; panels b and c: explanation as for Table XIII.

If (i) the initial step in D-ribose catabolism were its reduction to ribitol (that is, route X, and not the formation of ribose phosphate); and (ii) the substrates were effectively unimpeded by cell membranes, then no yeast would be [D-ribose +, ribitol —]. The figures shown in Table XIV, panel a are consistent with route X. On the other hand, no yeast would be [ribitol +, D-ribose —] were ribitol first oxidized to D-ribose (route Y). The fact that seven yeasts are in this category is inconsistent with route Y. Hence analysis of the results of growth tests with *Endomycopsis, Pichia,* and *Debaryomyces* indicates that the first step in the catabolism of D-ribose is its conversion to ribitol.

The relationship between ribitol and D-ribose also holds for 293 strains (66 species) of *Candida* (Brady, 1965) with only 4% exceptions (Table XIV, panel b). The exceptions were mainly among strains of *C. mesenterica* and of *C. pseudotropicalis.* However, with 96 strains (32 species) of *Torulopsis* (Brady, 1965), there were 18% exceptions (Table XIV, panel c). Six strains of *T. magnoliae* provided the most clear-cut of the latter exceptions, that is of the ability to grow well on ribose accompanied by complete failure to use ribitol. Aspects of the polyol metabolism of this species have already been studied by Spencer and Gorin (1960), though they did not examine the enzymes of this yeast.

3. *Common Route to a Central Pathway:* L-*Arabinose and* D-*Xylose*

Likely routes for the catabolism of L-arabinose and D-xylose are given in Fig. 19. Both substrates are converted into a common metabolite, xylitol, so from this point they have a common route to the pentose cycle.

Although the metabolic relationship between L-arabinose and D-xylose clearly differs from that described for D-ribose and ribitol (compare Figs.

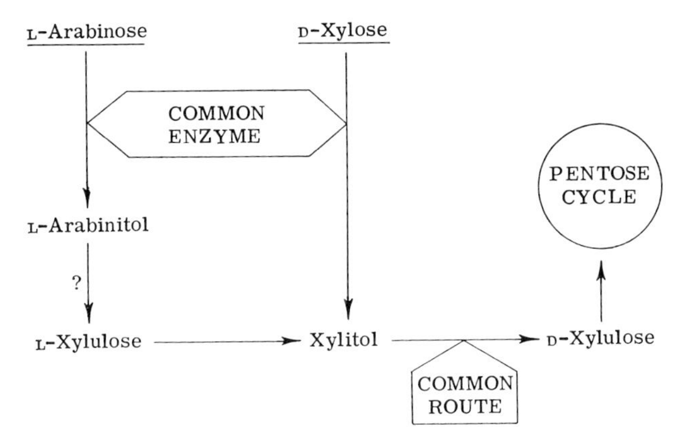

FIG. 19. Scheme for catabolism of L-arabinose and D-xylose (cf. Figs. 10, 11, and 15). Substrates used for taxonomic tests are underlined.

12 and 19), the figures from the taxonomic tests should be strictly comparable for both pairs of substrates. Provided that the scheme in Fig. 19 is true for yeasts and that the substrates can penetrate the cells, a yeast able to use L-arabinose can also use D-xylose. As can be seen from Table XV, panel a, this proposition is true for species of *Endomycopsis, Pichia,* and *Debaryomyces.* It is also true for many other yeasts: there were only 12 (4%) exceptions among 293 strains (66 species) of *Candida* (Table XV, panel b); and Santa María (1966) found only one exception among 1399 strains of different genera isolated mainly from living insects and frass. These exceptions should be examined for permeability to D-xylose; D-xylose is known to enter the cells of some yeasts, such as *Saccharomyces cerevisiae* (Cirillo, 1961a), which do not use this substrate.

Observations on the genus *Torulopsis* (Table XV, panel c) do not give

TABLE XV

RESULTS OF AEROBIC GROWTH TESTS WITH L-ARABINOSE AND D-XYLOSE[a]

(a) Number of species of *Endomycopsis, Pichia,* and *Debaryomyces*				(b) Number of strains of 66 species of *Candida*				(c) Number of strains of 32 species of *Torulopsis*			
		D-Xylose				D-Xylose				D-Xylose	
		+	−			+	−			+	−
L-Arabinose	+	17	0	L-Arabinose	+	160	12	L-Arabinose	+	22	17
	−	9	17		−	66	55		−	9	47

[a] Panel a: Explanation as for Table XI; panels b and c: explanation as for Table XIII.

the same picture as that for the other genera; 18% of the yeasts used L-arabinose but not D-xylose. It will be interesting to find out whether this generic difference exists because the cells of many *Torulopsis* strains (i) are impermeable to D-xylose, (ii) have a different pathway of pentose catabolism, or (iii) have a more specific enzyme reducing L-arabinose, but not D-xylose.

VI. CONCLUSION

In this chapter an attempt has been made to describe the kinds of metabolic differences which probably underlie the nutritional tests used for classifying yeasts. Not enough has yet been done to determine the extent or precise nature of such differences between particular taxa. However, the mechanisms by which many test substrates are utilized are clearly linked with each other. Shared enzymes and shared catabolic routes both are responsible for the correlated abilities between yeasts to use more than one substrate. The underlying mechanisms are linked, for instance, in the cases of the polyols, pentoses, and L-sorbose. These substrates constitute about one-third of the test substrates now in use for classifying yeasts. It is therefore obvious that tests using such substrates are far from "independent"; and as Stanier and his colleagues (1966) pointed out, when studying the pseudomonads: ". . . nutritional characters, which numerical taxonomists would treat as characters of equivalent weight, are in fact far from equivalent to one another when we examine them in terms of their underlying enzymatic mechanisms."

Evidence for associations between the tests, discussed in this chapter, has come both from metabolic studies by biochemists with only a few organisms and also from statistics drawn from taxonomic studies on very large numbers of yeasts. Some of the more striking associations between tests have been explained in terms of the catabolism of the substrates tested. Such associations must be examined further with more yeasts and more substrates. In order to make some headway toward understanding the biochemical bases of the nutritional tests and the biochemical differences between taxa, enzymatic studies must be made on selected strains of those yeasts that provide the general rules and also of those that have provided the exceptions. The mechanisms by which the substrates enter the cells must be investigated with respect to specificity: low specificity of a translocation system or of an initial catabolic enzyme could be equally responsible for associations between substrates. Perhaps such studies will help taxonomists decide whether or not they have been (to use Pasteur's words) "attaching too much importance to exterior characters."

REFERENCES

Alvarado, F. (1960). Substrate specificity of *Saccharomyces fragilis* galactokinase. *Biochim. Biophys. Acta* **41**: 233–238.

Arcus, A. C., and N. L. Edson. (1956). Polyol dehydrogenases. 2. The polyol dehydrogenases of *Acetobacter suboxydans* and *Candida utilis*. *Biochem. J.* **64**: 385–405.

Avigad, G. (1960). Accumulation of trehalose and sucrose in relation to the metabolism of α-glucosides in yeasts of defined genotype. *Biochim. Biophys. Acta* **40**: 124–134.

Avigad, G., O. Ziv, and E. Neufeld. (1965). Intracellular trehalase of a hybrid yeast. *Biochem. J.* **97**: 715–722.

Barnett, J. A. (1960). Comparative studies of yeasts. *Nature* **186**: 449–451.

Barnett, J. A. (1966a). A biochemical interpretation of some taxonomic differences between yeasts. *Nature* **210**: 565–568.

Barnett, J. A. (1966b). Biochemical differences between yeasts. *J. Gen. Microbiol.* **42**: i–ii.

Barnett, J. A. (1968). The catabolism of acyclic polyols by yeasts. *J. Gen. Microbiol.* **52**: 127–156.

Barnett, J. A., and M. Ingram. (1955). Technique in the study of yeast assimilation reactions. *J. Appl. Bacteriol.* **18**: 131–148.

Barnett, J. A., and H. L. Kornberg. (1960). The utilization by yeasts of acids of the tricarboxylic acid cycle. *J. Gen. Microbiol.* **23**: 65–82.

Barnett, J. A., M. Ingram, and T. Swain. (1956). The use of β-glucosides in classifying yeasts. *J. Gen. Microbiol.* **15**: 529–555.

Baumann, H., and W. Pigman. (1957). Naturally occurring glycosides and glycosidases. *In* "The Carbohydrates" (W. Pigman, ed.), pp. 536–601. Academic Press, New York.

Beech, F. W., J. G. Carr, and R. C. Codner. (1955). A multipoint inoculator for plating bacteria or yeasts. *J. Gen. Microbiol.* **13**: 408–410.

Beyerinck, M. W. (1889). L'auxanographie, ou la méthode de l'hydrodiffusion dans la gélatine appliquée aux recherches microbiologiques. *Arch. Neerl. Sci.* **23**: 367–372.

Birch, G. G. (1963). Trehaloses. *Advan. Carbohydrate Chem.* **18**: 201–225.

Bouthilet, R. J., N. E. Neilson, E. M. Mrak, and H. J. Phaff. (1949). The fermentation of trehalose by yeasts and its taxonomic implications. *J. Gen. Microbiol.* **3**: 282–289.

Brady, B. L. (1965). Personal communication: Data collated by Dr. Brady from unpublished observations of H. Buckley, N. van Uden, and M. Vidal-Leiria.

Cadenas, E., and A. Sols. (1960). The ketokinase activity of the intestinal mucosa. *Biochim. Biophys. Acta* **42**: 490–498.

Chakravorty, M., L. A. Veiga, M. Bacila, and B. L. Horecker. (1962). Pentose metabolism in Candida II. The diphosphopyridine nucleotide-specific polyol dehydrogenase of *Candida utilis. J. Biol. Chem.* **237**: 1014–1020.

Chang, S., and K. Li. (1964). Identification of D-mannitol in *Geotrichum candidum* Link and the mechanism of its formation. *Sci. Sinica (Peking)* **13**: 621–630.

Chiang, C., and S. G. Knight. (1960). A new pathway of pentose metabolism. *Biochem. Biophys. Res. Commun.* **3**: 554–559.

Cirillo, V. P. (1961a). The transport of non-fermentable sugars across the yeast cell membrane. *In* "Membrane Transport and Metabolism" (A. Kleinzeller and A. Kotyk, eds.), pp. 343–351. Academic Press, New York.

Cirillo, V. P. (1961b). The mechanism of sugar transport into the yeast cell. *Trans. N.Y. Acad. Sci* [2] **23**: 725–734.

Cirillo, V. P. (1961c). Sugar transport in microorganisms. *Ann. Rev. Microbiol.* **15**: 197–218.

Cirillo, V. P. (1962). Mechanism of glucose transport across the yeast cell membrane. *J. Bacteriol.* **84**: 485–491.

Clarke, P. H., and S. T. Cowan. (1952). Biochemical methods for bacteriology. *J. Gen. Microbiol.* **6**: 187–197.

Clarke, P. H., and K. J. Steel. (1966). Rapid and simple biochemical tests for bacterial identification. *In* "Identification Methods for Microbiologists: Part A" (B. M. Gibbs and F. A. Skinner, eds.), Vol. 1, pp. 111–115. Academic Press, New York.

Cochrane, V. W. (1958). "Physiology of Fungi." Wiley, New York.

Deinema, M. H. (1967). Extracellular lipid formation by yeasts. Paper given to *3rd Intern. Symp. Yeasts, Bratislava, 1966.*

de la Fuente, G., and A. Sols. (1962). Transport of sugars in yeasts. II. Mechanisms of utilization of disaccharides and related glycosides. *Biochim. Biophys. Acta* **56**: 49–62.

Demoss, J. A., and H. E. Swim. (1957). Quantitative aspects of the tricarboxylic acid cycle in baker's yeast. *J. Bacteriol.* **74**: 445–451.

de Robichon-Szulmajster, H. (1958). Induction of enzymes of the galactose pathway in mutants of Saccharomyces cerevisiae. *Science* **127**: 28–29.

Dixon, M., and E. C. Webb. (1964). "Enzymes," 2nd ed. Longmans, Green, New York.

Douglas, H. C. (1961). A mutation in *Saccharomyces* that affects phosphoglucomutase activity and galactose utilization. *Biochim. Biophys. Acta* **52**: 209–211.

Duerksen, J. D., and H. Halvorson. (1958). Purification and properties of an inducible β-glucosidase of yeast. *J. Biol. Chem.* **233**: 1113–1120.

Duerksen, J. D., and H. O. Halvorson. (1959). The specificity of induction of β-glucosidase in *Saccharomyces cerevisiae. Biochim. Biophys. Acta* **36**: 47–55.

Durham, H. E. (1898). A simple method for demonstrating the production of gas by bacteria. *Brit. Med. J.* **I**: 1387.

Einhorn, M. (1885). Die Gährungsprobe zum qualitativen Nachweise von Zucker im Harn. *Arch. Pathol. Anat. Physiol.* **102**: 263–285.

Eisenberg, F., and S. Hestrin. (1963). Glycosyl transfer by levansucrase and dextransucrase. *Bull. Res. Council Israel.* **A11**: 269–274.

Fischer, E. H., and E. A. Stein. (1960). Cleavage of O- and S-glycosidic bonds (survey). *In* "The Enzymes" (P. D. Boyer, H. Lardy, and K. Myrbäck, eds.), 2nd ed., Vol. 4, pp. 301–312. Academic Press, New York.

French, D. (1954). The raffinose family of oligosaccharides. *Advan. Carbohydrate Chem.* **9**: 149–184.

Frohwein, Y. Z., and J. Leibowitz. (1962). Yeast α-glucosidases. *Enzymologia* **24**: 211–229.

Gorrill, R. H., and R. A. Gray. (1956). The induction of bacteriophage in staphylococci. *J. Gen. Microbiol.* **14**: 167–173.

Gottschalk, A. (1949). "Direct" fermentation of disaccharides by yeast. *Wallerstein Lab. Commun.* **12**: 55–69.

Harris, G., and C. C. Thompson. (1961). The uptake of nutrients by yeasts. III. The maltose permease of brewing yeast. *Biochim. Biophys. Acta* **52**: 176–183.

Hassid, W. Z., and C. E. Ballou. (1957). Oligosaccharides. *In* "The Carbohydrates" (W. Pigman, ed.), pp. 478–535. Academic Press, New York.

Henrici, A. T. (1941). The yeasts, genetics, cytology, variation, classification and identification. *Bacteriol. Rev.* **5**: 97–179.

Herman, A., and H. O. Halvorson (1963). Identification of the structural gene for β-glucosidase in *Saccharomyces lactis. J. Bacteriol.* **85**: 895–900.

Hers, H. G. (1952). La fructokinase du foie. *Biochim. Biophys. Acta* **8**: 416–423.

Hestrin, S. (1953). Nonoxidative and nonproteolytic enzymes: Glycosidases. *Ann. Rev. Biochem.* **22**: 85–106.

Hestrin, S., D. S. Feingold, and G. Avigad. (1956). The mechanism of polysaccharide production from sucrose. 3. Donor-acceptor specificity of levansucrase from *Aerobacter levanicum. Biochem. J.* **64**: 340–351.

Hill, R. L., and R. C. Mills. (1954). The anaerobic glucose metabolism of *Bacterium tularense. Arch. Biochem. Biophys.* **53**: 174–183.

Hollmann, S. (1964). "Non-glycolytic Pathways of Metabolism of Glucose" (Transl. by O. Touster). Academic Press, New York.

Horecker, B. L. (1962). "Pentose Metabolism in Bacteria." Wiley, New York.

Horitsu, H., and M. Tomoeda. (1966). Pentose metabolism by *Candida utilis*. Part III. Polyol: NAD oxidoreductase. *Agr. Biol. Chem.* (*Tokyo*) **30**: 962–966.

Hu, A. S. L., R. Epstein, H. O. Halvorson, and R. M. Bock. (1960). Yeast β-glucosidase: Comparison of the physical-chemical properties of purified constitutive enzyme. *Arch. Biochem. Biophys.* **91**: 210–218.

Hu, C. L., E. A. McComb, and V. V. Rendig. (1965). Identification of altroheptulose and L-threitol as products of *meso*-erythritol oxidation by *Acetobacter suboxydans*. *Arch. Biochem. Biophys.* **110**: 350–353.

Inamdar, A. N., and J. G. Kaplan. (1966). Purification and properties of an inducible β-glucosidase of bakers' yeast. *Can. J. Biochem.* **44**: 1099–1108.

Ingram, J. M., and W. A. Wood. (1965). Enzymatic basis for D-arabitol production by *Saccharomyces rouxii*. *J. Bacteriol.* **89**: 1186–1194.

International Committee on Carbohydrate Nomenclature. (1952). Rules of carbohydrate nomenclature. *J. Chem. Soc.* p. 5108.

International Committee on Carbohydrate Nomenclature. (1962). Rules of carbohydrate nomenclature. *J. Chem. Soc.* p. 5307.

Islam, M. F., and J. O. Lampen. (1962). Invertase secretion and sucrose fermentation by *Saccharomyces cerevisiae* protoplasts. *Biochim. Biophys. Acta* **58**: 294–302.

Jennings, D. H. (1963). "The Absorption of Solutes by Plant Cells." Oliver & Boyd, Edinburgh and London.

Kalckar, H. M. (1958). Uridinediphosphogalactose: Metabolism, enzymology, and biology. *Advan. Enzymol.* **20**: 111–134.

Kalckar, H. M. (1960). Hereditary defects in galactose metabolism in man and microorganisms. *Federation Proc.* **19**: 984–990.

Kaplan, J. G. (1965). An inducible system for the hydrolysis and transport of β-glucosides in yeast. I. Characteristics of the β-glucosidase activity of intact and of lysed cells. *J. Gen. Physiol.* **48**: 873–886.

Kaplan, J. G., and W. Tacreiter. (1966). The β-glucosidase of the yeast cell surface. *J. Gen. Physiol.* **50**: 9–24.

Karasevich, Y. N. (1965). The initial stages of metabolism of pentoses in microorganisms. *Izz. Akad. Nauk SSSR, Ser. Biol.* **30**: 231–242.

Karczewska, H. (1959). Some observations on pentose utilization by Candida tropicalis. *Compt. Rend. Trav. Lab. Carlsberg* **31**: 251–258.

Kluyver, A. J., and M. T. J. Custers. (1940). The suitability of disaccharides as respiration and assimilation substrates for yeasts which do not ferment these sugars. *Antonie van Leeuwenhoek, J. Microbiol. Serol.* **6**: 121–162.

Knight, B. C. J. G. (1938). Bacterial nutrition. Material for a comparative physiology of bacteria. *Med. Res. Council, Spec. Rept. Ser.* **210**: 1–182.

Kornberg, H. L. (1965). The coordination of metabolic routes. *Symp. Soc. Gen. Microbiol.* **15**: 8–31.

Kotyk, A., and M. Höfer. (1965). Uphill transport of sugars in the yeast *Rhodotorula gracilis*. *Biochim. Biophys. Acta* **102**: 410–422.

Krebs, H. A., and H. L. Kornberg. (1957). A survey of the energy transformations in living matter. *Ergeb. Physiol., Biol. Chem. Exptl. Pharmakol.* **49**: 212–298.

Krebs, H. A., and P. Lund. (1966). Formation of glucose from hexoses, pentoses, polyols and related substances in kidney cortex. *Biochem. J.* **98**: 210–214.

Kreger-van Rij, N. J. W. (1962). The use of biochemical criteria in the taxonomy of yeasts. *Symp. Soc. Gen. Microbiol.* **12**: 196–211.

Kreger-van Rij, N. J. W. (1964). A taxonomic study of the yeast genera Endomycopsis, Pichia and Debaryomyces. Thesis. University of Leiden.
Kudriavzev, V. I. (1954). "The Systematics of Yeasts." Akad. Nauk S.S.S.R., Moscow (in Russian); German translation, Kudrjawzew, W. I. (1960). "Die Systematik der Hefen." Akademie Verlag, Berlin.
Langeron, M., and P. Guerra. (1938). Nouvelles recherches de zymologie. *Ann. Parasitol. Humaine Comparée* **16**: 36–84.
Larner, J. (1960). Other glucosidases. *In* "The Enzymes" (P. D. Boyer, H. Lardy, and K. Myrbäck, eds.), 2nd ed., Vol. 4, pp. 369–378. Academic Press, New York.
Lederberg, J., and E. M. Lederberg. (1952) Replica plating and indirect selection of bacterial mutants. *J. Bacteriol.* **63**: 399–406.
Ley, J. De. (1963). The use of *i*-erythritol for the classification of acetic acid bacteria *Antonie van Leeuwenhoek, J. Microbiol. Serol.* **29**: 177–179.
Lodder, J. (1934). "Die Anaskosporogenen Hefen." N. V. Noord-Hollandsche Uitgeversmaatschappij, Amsterdam.
Lodder, J., and N. J. W. Kreger-van Rij. (1952). "The Yeasts." North-Holland Publ., Amsterdam.
Lodder, J., and N. J. W. Kreger-van Rij, (1962). Book review: Kudrjawzew, W. I. (1960). Die Systematik der Hefen. *Z. Allgem. Mikrobiol.* **2**: 77–80.
Martin, D. S., C. P. Jones, K. F. Yao, and L. E. Lee. (1937). A practical classification of the Monilias. *J. Bacteriol.* **34**: 99–129.
Maxwell, E. S. (1961). Enzymic epimerizations. *In* "The Enzymes" (P. D. Boyer, H. Lardy, and K. Myrbäck, eds.), 2nd ed., Vol. 5, pp. 443–453. Academic Press, New York.
Maxwell, E. S., and H. de Robichon-Szulmajster. (1960). Purification of uridine diphosphate galactose-4-epimerase from yeast, and the identification of protein-bound diphosphopyridine nucleotide. *J. Biol. Chem.* **235**: 308–312.
Millin, D. J. (1963). Variation in α-glucosidase and α-glucoside permease systems of yeast. *J. Inst. Brewing* **69**: 389–393.
Millin, D. J., and D. G. Springham. (1966). Fermentative capacity of yeasts which metabolize maltotriose rapidly. *J. Inst. Brewing* **72**: 388–393.
Mishustin, E. N., and L. A. Trisvyatski. (1960). "The Microbiology of Grain and Flour." Technicheskoi i Ekonomicheskoi Literatury po Voprosam Chleboproduktov, Moscow (in Russian).
Moret, V., and S. Sperti. (1962). Pentose metabolism by cell-free extracts of *Oospora lactis. Arch. Biochem. Biophys.* **98**: 124–127.
Morris, E. O., and B. Kirsop. (1953). Rapid microtechniques for the fermentation of carbohydrates by yeasts. *J. Inst. Brewing* **59**: 486–491.
Mortlock, R. P., D. D. Fossitt, and W. A. Wood. (1965). A basis for utilization of unnatural pentoses and pentitols by Aerobacter aerogenes. *Proc. Natl. Acad. Sci. U.S.* **54**: 572–579.
Müller, D. (1937). Die Mannitdehydrase. *Enzymologia* **3**: 26–28.
Myrbäck, K. (1949). Trehalose and Trehalase. *Ergeb. Enzymforsch.* **10**: 168–190.
Myrbäck, K. (1960). Invertases. *In* "The Enzymes" (P. D. Boyer, H. Lardy, and K. Myrbäck, eds.), 2nd ed., Vol. 4, pp. 379–392. Academic Press, New York.
National Collection of Yeast Cultures, Catalogue of Cultures maintained at the Brewing Industry Research Foundation. Nutfield, Surrey. August, 1963.
Neuberg, C., and I. Mandl. (1950). Invertase. *In* "The Enzymes" (J. B. Sumner and K. Myrbäck, eds.), Vol. 1, Part I, pp. 527–550. Academic Press, New York.

Nord, F. F., and S. Weiss. (1958). Fermentation and respiration. *In* "The Chemistry and Biology of Yeasts" (A. H. Cook, ed.), pp. 323–368. Academic Press, New York.

Novák, E. K. (1963). Oligosaccharide decomposition by *Candida solani. Acta Microbiol. Acad. Sci. Hung.* **10:** 7–10.

Novák, E. K., and J. Zsolt. (1961). A new system proposed for yeasts. *Acta Botan. Acad. Sci. Hung.* **7:** 93–145.

Onishi, H., and M. B. Perry. (1965). The production of *meso-glycero-ido*-heptitol and D-*glycero*-D-*ido*-heptitol by *Pichia miso. Can. J. Microbiol.* **11:** 929–934.

Onishi, H., and N. Saito. (1962). Studies on osmophilic yeasts Part XIV. Partial purification of polyol dehydrogenase from *Pichia miso* and the properties of this enzyme. *Agr. Biol. Chem. (Tokyo)* **26:** 245–251.

Panek, A., and N. O. Souza. (1964). Purification and properties of bakers' yeast trehalase. *J. Biol. Chem.* **239:** 1671–1673.

Roberts, C. (1950). Methods in yeast genetics. *Methods Med. Res.* **3:** 37–50.

Santa María, J. (1966). Personal communication.

Scher, B. M., and B. L. Horecker. (1966). Pentose metabolism in *Candida* III. The triphosphopyridine nucleotide-specific polyol dehydrogenase of *Candida utilis. Arch. Biochem. Biophys.* **116:** 117–128.

Shifrine, M., H. J. Phaff, and A. L. Demain. (1954). Determination of carbon assimilation patterns of yeasts by replica plating. *J. Bacteriol.* **68:** 28–35.

Smith, M. G. (1962). Polyol dehydrogenases. 4. Crystallization of the L-iditol dehydrogenase of sheep liver. *Biochem. J.* **83:** 135–144.

Snyder, H. E., and H. J. Phaff. (1960). Studies on beta-fructosidase (inulinase) produced by *Saccharomyces fragilis. Antonie van Leeuwenhoek. J. Microbiol. Serol.* **26:** 433–452.

Sols, A., and G. de la Fuente. (1961). Transport and hydrolysis in the utilization of oligosaccharides by yeasts. *In* "Membrane Transport and Metabolism" (A. Keinzeller and A. Kotyk, eds.), pp. 361–377. Academic Press, New York.

Spencer, J. F. T., and P. A. J. Gorin. (1960). The biosynthesis of erythritol and glycerol by *Torulopsis magnoliae.* Studies with C^{14}-labelled glucose. *Can. J. Biochem. Physiol.* **38:** 157–164.

Srb, A. M., and N. H. Horowitz. (1944). The ornithine cycle in Neurospora and its genetic control. *J. Biol. Chem.* **154:** 129–139.

Stanek, J., M. Cĕrný, J. Kocourek, and J. Pacák. (1963). "The Monosaccharides" (Transl. by K. Mayer). Academic Press, New York.

Stanier, R. Y., N. J. Palleroni, and M. Doudoroff. (1966). The aerobic pseudomonads: A taxonomic study. *J. Gen. Microbiol.* **43:** 159–271.

Stelling-Dekker, N. M. (1931). Die sporogenen Hefen. *Verhandel. Koninkl. Ned. Akad. Wetenschap., Afdel. Natuurk., Sect. II* **28:** 1–547.

Sutton, D. D., and J. O. Lampen. (1962). Localization of sucrose and maltose fermenting systems in *Saccharomyces cerevisiae. Biochim. Biophys. Acta* **56:** 303–312.

Tomoeda, M., and H. Horitsu. (1964). Pentose metabolism by *Candida utilis.* Part I. Xylose isomerase. *Agr. Biol. Chem. (Tokyo)* **28:** 139–143.

Touster, O., and D. R. D. Shaw. (1962). Biochemistry of the acyclic polyols. *Physiol. Rev.* **42:** 181–225.

Trevelyan, W. E. (1958). Synthesis and degradation of cellular carbohydrates by yeasts. *In* "The Chemistry and Biology of Yeasts" (A. H. Cook, ed.), pp. 369–436. Academic Press, New York.

Tsoi, A., and H. C. Douglas. (1964). The effect of mutation on two forms of phosphoglucomutase in Saccharomyces. *Biochim. Biophys. Acta* **92**: 513–520.

van der Walt, J. P. (1965). The emendation of the genus *Kluyveromyces* v. d. Walt. *Antonie van Leeuwenhoek, J. Microbiol. Serol.* **31**: 341–348.

van der Walt, J. P., and A. E. van Kerken. (1959). The wine yeasts of the Cape part II. The occurrence of *Brettanomyces intermedius* and *Brettanomyces schanderlii* in South African table wines. *Antonie van Leeuwenhoek, J. Microbiol. Serol.* **25**: 145–151.

Veibel, S. (1950). Hydrolysis of galactosides, mannosides, and thioglycosides. *In* "The Enzymes" (J. B. Sumner and K. Myrbäck, eds.), Vol. 1, Part I, pp. 621–634. Academic Press, New York.

Veiga, L. A., M. Bacila, and B. L. Horecker. (1960). Pentose metabolism in *Candida albicans*. I. The reduction of D-xylose and L-arabinose. *Biochem. Biophys. Res. Commun.* **2**: 440–444.

Wallenfels, K., and O. P. Malhotra. (1960). β-Galactosidase. *In* "The Enzymes" (P. D. Boyer, H. Lardy, and K. Myrbäck, eds.), 2nd ed., Vol. 4, pp. 409–430. Academic Press, New York.

Wallenfels, K., and O. P. Malhotra. (1961). Galactosidases. *Advan. Carbohydrate Chem.* **16**: 239–298.

Weimberg, R., and W. L. Orton. (1966). Elution of exocellular enzymes from *Saccharomyces fragilis* and *Saccharomyces cerevisiae*. *J. Bacteriol.* **91**: 1–13.

Wentink, P., and J. W. M. la Rivière. (1962). An automatic turbidimeter for studies of microbial growth in aerated cultures. *Antonie van Leeuwenhoek, J. Microbiol. Serol.* **28**: 85–90.

Wickerham, L. J. (1951). Taxonomy of yeasts. *U.S. Dept. Agr., Tech. Bull.* **1029**: 1–56.

Wickerham, L. J., and K. A. Burton. (1948). Carbon assimilation tests for the classification of yeasts. *J. Bacteriol.* **56**: 363–371.

Windisch, S. (1960). Methoden zur Ermittlung der Gäreigenschaften. *In* "Die Hefen" (F. Reiff *et al.*, eds.), Vol. I, pp. 123–137, Verlag Hans Carl, Nürnberg.

Winge, Ö., and C. Roberts. (1958). Yeast genetics. *In* "The Chemistry and Biology of Yeasts" (A. H. Cook, ed.), pp. 123–156. Academic Press, New York.

Wolff, J. B., and N. O. Kaplan. (1956). Hexitol metabolism in *Escherichia coli*. *J. Bacteriol.* **71**: 557–564.

Wood, W. A. (1961). Fermentation of carbohydrates and related compounds. *In* "The Bacteria" (I. C. Gunsalus and R. Y. Stanier, eds.), Vol. 2, pp. 59–138. Academic Press, New York.

Wood, W. A. (1966). Carbohydrate metabolism. *Ann. Rev. Biochem.* **35**: 521–558.

CHAPTER 23

Serology as an Aid to Taxonomy

H. P. R. SEELIGER

Institut für Hygiene und Mikrobiologie der Bayerischen Julius-Maximilians-Universität Würzburg, Germany

I. INTRODUCTION

Since the beginning of the twentieth century immunological procedures have become an integral part of microbiology. Besides many useful applications in the study of human and animal microbial infections and intoxications, serological tests play an important role in the identification and classification of microorganisms. They surpass in sensitivity practically all chemical and biochemical methods used for this type of work (Shattock, 1955), and their value is recognized in the fields of bacteriology, virology, and protozoology. The general principles governing the serology of microorganisms are also valid for higher plants. The fundamental observations of Bertarelli (1904),[1] Magnus and Friedenthal (1906, 1907), and Kritschewski (1914) have, for instance, shown that the serological pattern of different species of Gramineae and Leguminosae reveals a striking resemblance to their phylogenetic relationships. Hence one can safely assume that the same principles will apply to lower organisms such as fungi. The correctness of this assumption is proved by more than a thousand contributions dealing with the serology of fungi and mycotic infections (cf. Kligman and DeLamater, 1950; Seeliger, 1958, 1960a, 1962a,b). The rapid development of mycology during recent years demonstrates that besides other methods serological procedures are increasingly appreciated by the mycologists as an aid in the taxonomy, classification, and identification of fungi.

II. HISTORICAL REMARKS

The first reports on the use of serological techniques in mycology appeared shortly after the detection of the antigen-antibody reaction and dealt

[1] For details of historical references up to 1930, see Seeliger (1958).

with attempts to distinguish yeasts of industrial importance, such as top and bottom yeasts used in brewing, wild yeasts, etc. (Bisserié, 1901; Malvoz, 1901; Schütze, 1903). Later the serological aspects of thrush and sporotrichosis were investigated by French workers (De Beurmann *et al.,* 1908, Widal *et al.,* 1910) while German workers continued to differentiate industrial yeasts by means of agglutination and complement-fixation reactions (Lichtenstein, 1914). Following reports on immune reactions of an antiserum against *Mucor racemosus* by Magnus and Friedenthal (1907) and Blakeslee *et al.* (see Blakeslee and Davenport, 1913; Blakeslee and Gortner, 1915) tried to differentiate serologically the sexual phases of *Mucor* V, a form similar to *M. hiemalis.* Fundamental contributions to the understanding of the immune response to dermatophytes were also made during this period by Bloch and his school. As early as 1916, Moses in Brazil reported on complement-fixing antibodies in human blastomycosis.

The many technical difficulties and discouraging findings, however, led to the statement expressed by several authors in Jadassohn's "Handbuch der Haut- und Geschlechtskrankheiten" that serological tests seemed to be of little value in mycology, with the possible exception of some deep fungous infections. Obviously this attitude represents mainly a reflection of the usefulness of fungous serology in the medical field.

Nevertheless numerous studies were performed during 1920–1930 with yeast-like organisms and on patients suffering from mycotic infections (Balls, 1925; Benedek, 1928; Biberstein and Epstein, 1932) as well as on aspergilli (Sartory, 1922; Matsumoto, 1929). These investigations introduced a more systematic approach to fungous serology which has only in recent years resulted in the elaboration of serological schemes of classification. Most of this work originated with a group of American mycologists led by Benham (1931, 1935), Almon and Stonvall (1934), and Martin and Jones (1940), but many of their studies coincided with similar investigations in Japan (Yukawa and Ohta, 1928; Yukawa *et al.,* 1931), Argentina (Negroni, 1934a,b), Canada, England (Stone and Garrod, 1931) and Hungary (Tomcsik, 1930).

The potential value of serological tests for the diagnosis of fungous diseases was not realized until the full extent of human systemic mycoses became known in certain areas of the United States, where a complement-fixation test (CFT) was developed for the diagnosis of North American blastomycosis as early as 1935 (Martin, 1935, 1941; Martin and Smith, 1936). The large-scale application of immunological and serological methods has, according to Campbell (1960), played a dominant role in changing the clinical concept of both coccidioidomycosis and histoplasmosis.

Lack of space prohibits a detailed description of the numerous and successful approaches to fungous serology during recent years, which are characterized by worldwide investigations on new or improved methods and their application.

Besides a great many individual workers some research groups have initiated long-term studies that have a major part in present-day concepts of fungous serology. Their work will be referred to in some of the subsequent sections.

This development corroborates the introductory statement that some of the serological procedures have been established as useful and reliable adjuncts to the antigenic analysis of certain groups of fungi, as well as to the investigation of mycotic diseases.

III. TEST PROCEDURES

Practically all serological methods used in mycology have been derived from similar or identical ones applied in other fields of microbiology. These are summarized in Table I.

The mycologist, however, has to cope with many more technical diffi-

TABLE I
TEST PROCEDURES USED IN IMMUNOLOGICAL STUDIES OF FUNGI AND MYCOTIC INFECTIONS

Type of reaction	Method	Antigen
Agglutination test (AT)	Slide, tube	Killed whole cells, sensitized particles (blood cells, collodion, latex, resin ion exchange particles)
Capsular reaction (CR)	Slide	Whole cells
Precipitin test (PT)	Classical ring test, agar gel diffusion test, immunoelectrophoresis	Culture filtrates, extracts, lysates, cell saps, chemical fractions of soluble substances
Castellani's absorption test	—	Whole cells or soluble antigens as above
Complement-fixation test (CFT)	Tube, slide, or plate	Killed whole cells, filtrates, lysates, cell saps, chemical fractions of soluble antigens
Fluorescent antibody staining (FAS)	Direct method, indirect method	Whole cells or soluble antigens on slide preparations or in tissue sections treated with fluorescent antibodies
Determination of fungicidal activity of patient's serum	Tube, slide	Living cells of test strain in stage of active growth

culties than the bacteriologist. The primary reason for this is that the cultural properties of many fungi are quite different from those of other microorganisms. Thus special procedures have to be devised before serological tests can be applied. The usefulness or applicability of any given immunological procedure is dependent upon the physical properties of the fungal antigen.

A. Preparation of Fungal Antigens

Numerous attempts have been made to produce antigens of high quality. Antigens for diagnostic purposes should be highly specific for a given organism or disease and are therefore often treated by various methods of chemical fractionation and purification. On the other hand, fungous serology as an aid in taxonomy and identification requires the analyses of *all* antigenic components. Hence antigens for diagnostic purposes may differ basically from those used in analytical procedures.

Experience has shown that antigens of different isolates of the same species may vary considerably not only in their composition, but also in antigenicity, antibody-binding capacity, and reacting power. Thus a high degree of standardization of antigen preparation is essential for obtaining comparable and significant results.

B. Preparation of Fungal Antisera

Three procedures of preparing fungal antisera have mainly been used, the third only recently: (1) intravenous injection of live or killed homogenized whole cell antigens of soluble substances; (2) infection of animals with pathogenic fungi; and (3) subcutaneous injection of homogenized antigens together with complete or incomplete Freund's adjuvants. The results vary considerably. Although antisera of excellent quality have been prepared in many instances, there is still a need for a reliable method to overcome the existing difficulties. Careful strain selection is of great help, for it has been shown that the antibody stimulating power may vary from isolate to isolate of one species. This holds particularly true for the capsulated cryptococci and some other fungi. According to recent experience a combination of methods (1) and (2) with procedure (3) may be of great help in solving this problem.

C. Serological Techniques

A detailed account of serological techniques has been given in two monographs (Seeliger, 1958, 1963) and in numerous reports by many workers. The most useful techniques are discussed under headings 1–10 below.

1. *Agglutination Test*

A prerequisite for the agglutination test (AT) is a homogeneous and stable suspension of the antigen. Homogenized antigens are likewise needed for agglutination-absorption studies, but primarily for the production of suitable immune sera. In the preparation of antigens such methods as continuous shaking of cultures during cultivation, choice of media and of temperature optimal for growth in the yeast phase, sonic oscillation, mechanical grinding and homogenization as well as the use of wetting agents such as Tween 80, have been of great value. Homogeneous suspensions of fungous cells can easily be prepared with conidia of many species, with the majority of yeasts and with the yeast phase of dimorphic fungi. Despite this, the AT, perhaps the simplest of all serological procedures, has been relatively little used by mycologists. In the hands of experienced

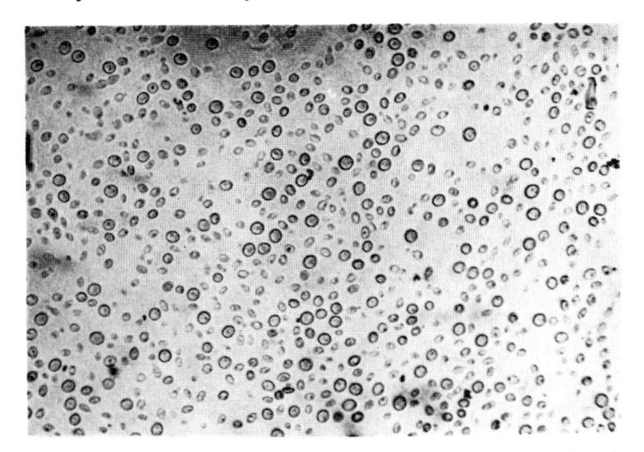

FIG. 1. Conidial suspension of *Trichophyton mentagrophytes* in the presence of normal serum.

workers it has given reproducible results particularly when used in conjunction with Castellani's absorption test (see Section 7, below). Typical examples of agglutination reactions with fungal cells are shown in Figs. 1–3. On the other hand, certain physicochemical peculiarities, the nature of which remains to be explored, may render whole-cell suspensions inapplicable in the AT although they are excellent immunizing agents. Yeast-phase antigens of *Blastomyces dermatitidis* and of *B.* [*Paracoccidioides*] *brasiliensis* will not be agglutinated by their homologous antiserum, and the one report by Cozad (1958) describing the use of whole yeast cells of *Histoplasma capsulatum* in the AT has not yet been further elaborated. Likewise Seeliger and Schröter (1963) reported that cell suspensions of some *Trichosporon* species gave poor or no agglutination with their immune sera. Contrary to this, other yeast-phase antigens—for

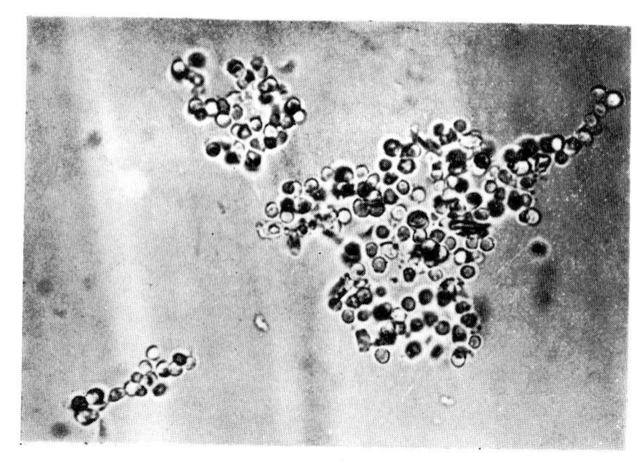

FIG. 2. Agglutination of conidial suspension of *Trichophyton mentagrophytes* in the presence of homologous antiserum.

instance from *Sporothrix schenckii*—can easily be used for the agglutination reaction (Nordén, 1951).

This occasional absence of agglutination with whole cells is not due to the failure of the combination between the antibody and the outer layers of the cell. Immunofluorescence has proved that such reactions take place, but they need not necessarily be followed by the second step of the reaction, i.e., the clumping which leads to the formation of agglutinates. The combination of the antigen with antibodies may in such cases also be proved by the complement fixation test for which homogeneous particulate suspensions of fungi are being widely used (see below).

2. *Capsular Reaction*

Although it is agreed that agglutination and complement fixation reactions are surface reactions, the changes occurring on the outer layers of the cell by the fixed antibody ordinarily remain invisible. If the cell, how-

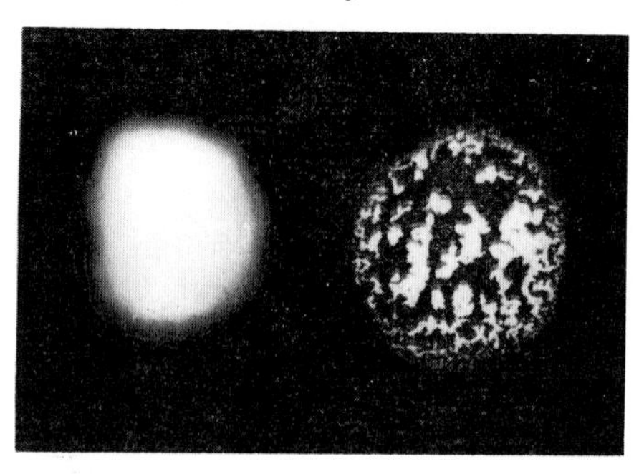

FIG. 3. Slide agglutination of *Cryptococcus neoformans* cells. *Left:* Negative reaction with antiserum of *Candida albicans*. *Right:* Positive reaction with antiserum of *Cryptococcus neoformans*. From Seeliger (1963).

ever, possesses a capsule, the antibody will be precipitated on its surface thereby altering its permeability to light. Thus a capsular reaction becomes visible (Figs. 4 and 5). In earlier days this reaction, first described by Neufeld (1902), was thought to be accompanied by capsular swelling, but it was conclusively shown that the capsular dimensions are not increased by the antigen-antibody reaction (Evans *et al.*, 1956).

3. *Precipitation Reaction*

The soluble antigens of fungi can be studied by a variety of classical serological methods, such as the complement fixation, the precipitin test

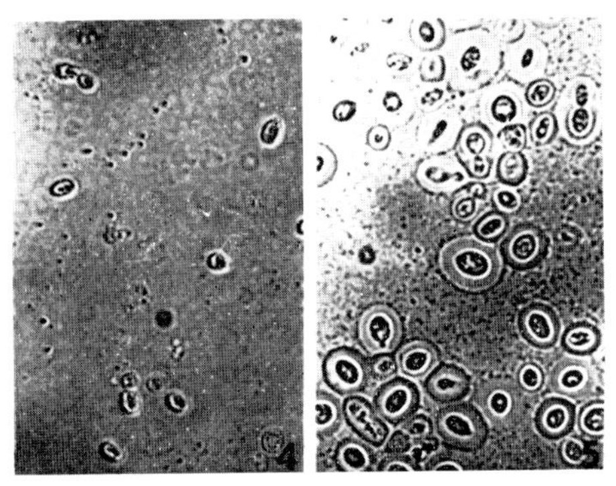

FIG. 4 (*Left*). Suspension of *Cryptococcus diffluens* in the presence of antiserum of *Lipomyces lipoferus;* negative reaction. From Seeliger (1958).

FIG. 5 (*Right*). Suspension of *Cryptococcus diffluens* in the presence of antiserum of *Cryptococcus neoformans;* distinct capsular reaction. From Seeliger (1958).

(PT), and microchemical procedures by means of which the nitrogen contents of the washed precipitates serve as a basis to measure the antigen-antibody reaction (Nordén, 1951; Jonsen, 1955). While the agglutination reactions are restricted to certain groups of fungi, precipitation tests may be performed with practically all kinds of fungi. Figure 6 gives an example of a typical ring precipitin test. Depending on the procedure used in the preparation of such soluble materials, all sorts of extracts can be investigated. These may range from crude cell saps and culture filtrates to highly purified fractions. Besides protein and lipid components, high molecular fungal polysaccharides containing only small amounts or traces of residual nitrogen determine the specifity of the reaction. As these purified polysaccharides are often not antigenic per se, they seem to represent haptenes which confer specifity but will act as antigens only after complexing.

Some more recently introduced procedures warrant special comment. Important among these are the various modifications of the agar-gel diffusion test originally elaborated by Bechold (1905) and later used by

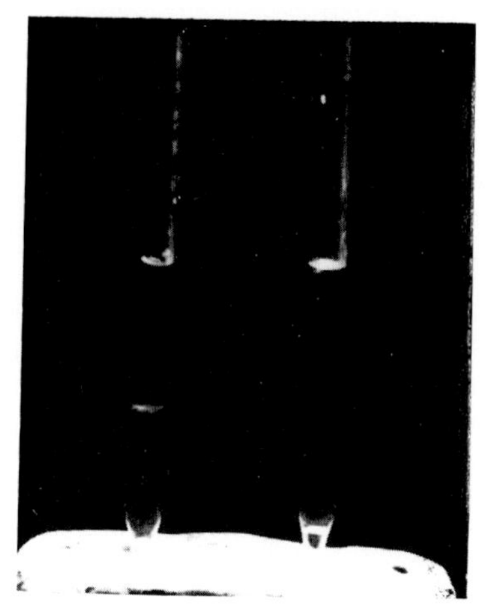

FIG. 6. Precipitation reaction, classical ring test, with *Candida albicans* antiserum. *Left:* Positive reaction in the presence of *C. albicans* polysaccharide. *Right:* Negative reaction in the presence of *Nocardia asteroides* polysaccharide. From Seeliger (1963).

Ouchterlony (1949) and others for investigation of toxins and antitoxins. The first application of this method to the study of fungal antigens was reported by Seeliger (1954, 1955), and its wide range of usefulness has been demonstrated by many subsequent reports (cf. Tempel, 1959; Seeliger, 1962a,b). In this test the complexity of the fungal precipitinogens can be revealed by a number of precipitation bands developing at the sites of the gel where soluble antigens or haptenes react with the antibodies in optimal proportions. In the case of antigenic identity these lines tend to form *arcades* (*coalescence-phenomenon*). If only some of several precipitation bands meet each other, this is interpretated as an indication of antigenic dissimilarity or common partial antigens. The evaluation of this test requires great care in order to avoid false positive reactions (cf. Feinberg, 1960), and the interpretation of precipitation lines of unknown specificity presents certain difficulties. In addition to its usefulness in the antigenic analysis of fungi, the agar-gel diffusion test has proved to be of value in the routine diagnosis of mycotic infections. Heiner (1958), Greene and Gordon (1959), and Schubert (1960) recommend this procedure—with certain limitations (Ball *et al.*, 1960)—in the examination of serum specimens for *Histoplasma capsulatum*, *Blastomyces dermatitidis*, and *Coccidioides immitis* antibodies, while Pepys *et al.* (Pepys, 1959, 1960; Pepys *et al.*, 1959) applied the agar-gel precipitation in the study of aspergillosis and *Candida* infections.

4. *Immunoelectrophoresis*

Further progress was made by the combination of agar-gel diffusion and electrophoresis. Electrophoretic patterns of fungal antisera were described by Jonsen (1955) and von Schrader-Beielstein and Seeliger (1956). Immunoelectrophoresis of fungal antigens [using techniques of Scheidegger (1955) and others] was successfully investigated by Tempel (1959) and by Biguet and co-workers (1959, 1961a,b). Their findings confirm and extend results obtained by other workers, for example Tsuchiya and his group (1959) using agglutination and agglutinin absorption tests. This method is very promising for the study of all fungi, particularly for the analysis of the complex antigenic structure of interrelated organisms.

5. *Agglutination with Sensitized Particles*

Soluble substances of fungi have also been used to sensitize serologically neutral particles. Red blood corpuscles treated with histoplasmin (Nordén, 1948; Coudert and Coly, 1956; McDearman *et al.,* 1958), or coated with yeast extracts (Vogel and Collins, 1955; Seeliger, 1958; Pospišil, 1959) have been used in serological studies with some success. Histoplasmin-coated collodion (Saslaw and Campbell, 1948, 1949, 1950) and latex particles (Carlisle and Saslaw, 1958) have likewise given reproducible results. Ion exchange resin particles readily adsorb cryptococcal polysaccharides.

6. *Complement-Fixation Test*

Both types of antigens, i.e., whole-cell suspensions or mycelial fragments and soluble substances, may be used for the complement-fixation test. This is a rather elaborate procedure which requires careful standardization of the various reagents (cf. Nordén, 1951; Seeliger, 1954, 1958, 1963). Although indispensable for the serological study of mycotic disease, this test seems to be of only limited value for the antigenic analysis of fungi. This is due to many cross-reactions caused by nonspecific lipid substances in addition to the more specific fungal polysaccharides.

7. *Castellani's Absorption Test*

In most fungi the antigenic mosaic is complex. Then antigenic analysis can be performed only by use of a set of *factor sera,* which are prepared by absorption of antisera with antigens of heterologous fungi. The value of this procedure originally devised by Castellani (1902), has conclusively been demonstrated in Japan by Tsuchiya *et al.* (1957a,b) during a long series of still continuing experiments with a great number of fungal species. Their results are in excellent agreement with many earlier observations (cf. Seeliger, 1954, 1957) and other more recent reports. The assumed serological identity of two fungi must always be confirmed by cross-absorption of their whole antisera with whole antigens. This makes the absorption test indispensable for any immunological approach to fungus identification.

8. *Immunofluorescence*

While all the above methods are primarily used for the detection and measurement of serum antibodies as well as for preparation of monovalent factor sera and subsequent analysis of the antigenic constituents of fungi, fungal antisera themselves can be conjugated with certain fluorescent dyes (such as fluorescein isothiocyanate) and used in this form for the rapid detection and even identification of fungal antigens in smears or tissues (Eveland *et al.,* 1958; Gordon, 1958; Kunz, 1958a,b; Kaplan and Kaufman, 1961). By means of the so-called "sandwich method" of indirect staining, antibodies may be detected even when all classical methods of investigation fail (Vogel *et al.,* 1961).

9. *Determination of Fungicidal Activity of Serum*

For the sake of completeness a method should be mentioned, by means of which the fungicidal activity of serum is determined (cf. Janke, 1959). This test may be of clinical interest, but it is of no help in the antigenic analysis of fungi.

10. *Skin Test*

Intracutaneous reactions performed with various kinds of antigens are of great importance in the study and diagnosis of mycotic infections.

IV. SPECIFICITY OF REACTION

As in other fields of microbiology, serological reactions with fungal antigens and antisera are not absolutely specific. Cross-reactions are quite frequent, particularly between species of one genus or between related fungi. The degree of serological specificity in a given antiserum depends very much on the length of the immunization procedure. The longer it is, the more overlapping antibodies may become demonstrable. By proper dilution of the antiserum or by Castellani's absorption test as applied by Almon and Stonvall (1934), Benham (1937), Martin (1942), Evans (1950), Kaufmann (1944–1945), Jonsen (1955), Nordén (1951), Seeliger (1954, 1957, 1958, 1959), and others, such cross-reactions can be eliminated to some extent.

Sometimes serological reactions with fungus antigens have been called "nonspecific," particularly in the study of fungal disease of man. For instance, a positive histoplasmin skin test was described in a patient suffering from cryptococcosis. From such and similar observations one may gain the erroneous impression that serological reactions are not specific.

From experimental studies it is known that antigens of *Histoplasma capsulatum* and *Cryptococcus neoformans* do not cross-react. It is, however, quite possible that a patient suffering from cryptococcosis may have acquired a persisting histoplasmin hypersensitivity many years earlier. This means that serological reactions are specific with regard to the antigen, but they need not necessarily be specific for a given disease. This applies particularly for the presence of antibodies against *Candida albicans* and *Trichophyton.* Owing to the spread of the organisms among the human population, a high number of positive reactors are usually found in skin testing and serum studies. This, of course, makes the interpretation of positive findings very difficult, if the attempt is made to use such procedures for diagnosis (Kligman and DeLamater, 1950; Janke, 1959; Seeliger, 1954, 1958; Winner, 1955).

There is no such thing as absolute antigenic specificity. The number of antigens or antigenic constituents in nature is limited. Therefore, it is not surprising to find serological cross-reactions even between antigens of rather different origin. For example, antisera of cryptococci give cross-reactions with certain pneumococcal serotypes (Rebers *et al.,* 1958) and with other substances of high molecular weight (Evans *et al.,* 1953). Similarly antisera against *Sporothrix schenckii* will precipitate polysaccharides of some pneumococci (Neill *et al.,* 1955). There are even common antigenic fractions between *Candida albicans* and salmonellae of O-group C (Aksoycan and Kauffmann, 1957). And yet from such findings, no one would doubt serological specificity as it exists in practice.

V. APPLICATION AND INTERPRETATION OF FUNGOUS SEROLOGY

In most genera so far investigated the antigenic materials are composed of various combinations of group-, species-, and even serotype-specific partial factors. Besides thermostable antigens, thermolabile components have been demonstrated. As stated above, Castellani's absorption test and the use of monovalent factor sera are required for determination of the antigenic formulas. Thus it was possible to work out antigenic schemes, many admittedly incomplete, for yeasts of the genera *Candida, Hansenula, Saccharomyces, Torulopsis,* etc. In such schemes the antigenic constituents are designated by symbols such as arabic or roman numbers or letters.

One of the best-investigated genera is *Candida.* The development of serological analysis within this group is shown by comparing the scheme published by Martin (1942) (see Table II) taking into account the quali-

TABLE II
ANTIGENIC COMPOSITION OF *Candida* SPECIES[a]

C. albicans	X	4Y	3Z
C. stellatoidea	X	2Y	2Z
C. tropicalis	X	4Y	
C. parapsilosis	X		4Z

[a] According to Martin (1942).

tative and quantitative differences of four species, with a more recent scheme compiling the results of the studies published by Tsuchiya and his group between 1957 and 1959 and other workers on 22 species (Table III). Immunoelectrophoretic studies indicate, however, that even more fractions than those designated by symbols may be present (Biguet *et al.,* 1959, 1961a,b).

In similar experiments Seeliger (1957) and Tsuchiya *et al.* (1957a) recognized several serogroups in *Rhodotorula* and *Sporobolomyces* (cf. Seeliger, 1960a). During these investigations standard cultures of all species described by Lodder and Kreger-van Rij (1952) and freshly isolated strains of these two genera were used. It may be of interest that no major antigenic communities could be detected between *Rhodotorula* and *Sporobolomyces,* although several species of both genera have many cultural and biochemical features in common. Agglutination and precipitation studies gave almost identical results. For *Rhodotorula mucilaginosa, R. ruba, R. minuta,* and *R. pallida* the Japanese and German investigators obtained very similar findings, and recently it was shown by the writer that the new species *R. texensis,* which culturally much resembles *R. minuta* and *R. pallida,* belongs to the same serological group.

Likewise a serological classification was elaborated for the genera *Torulopsis* (Tsuchiya *et al.,* 1961a), *Hansenula* (Tsuchiya *et al.,* 1957b, 1958a) and *Saccharomyces* (Tsuchiya *et al.* 1958b).

Antigenic analysis has proved an interesting tool in the demonstration of the identity of fungous species assigned in our present system of classification to different genera or even families. Thus it was confirmed serologically that some strains of *Candida pseudotropicalis* and *Saccharomyces fragilis* possess the same antigens; likewise *C. mycoderma* and *Pichia membranefaciens* (Seeliger, 1958). A specific serum of *C. krusei* likewise precipitated *P. fermentans* polysaccharide, but subsequent studies did not give evidence of complete serological identity of two strains of the latter two species (Seeliger and Gardini Tuesta, 1961). *Allescheria boydii* and its imperfect state *Monosporium apiospermum* gave serological reactions of identity (Seeliger, 1954, 1956), but these fungi could safely be separated on serological grounds from other agents of maduromycosis such as *Madurella grisea* and *M. mycetomi*. On the other hand, Tempel (1959) found it very difficult to distinguish serologically a series of *formae speciales* of *Fusarium oxysporum* although a few antisera, for instance that of *F. oxysporum* ff. sp. *pisi* and *lupini,* gave rather specific reactions in the gel precipitation test.

The first serological studies on black yeasts were reported in England by Stone (1930), who successfully applied the complement-fixation test. Later Conant and Martin (1937) again used this reaction in the study of the causal agents of chromoblastomycosis. These studies were extended by Trejos and Seeliger (see Seeliger, 1957, 1958), who employed the agglutination test with formolized suspensions of the yeast phases of various dematiaceous fungi. In addition, precipitin studies were performed with partially purified polysaccharide extracts from test cultures.

Table IV gives the results of tube-agglutination tests with strains of three *Pullularia* and two *Sporothrix* species. Besides species-specific reactions, one can observe some serological overlapping, which apparently is due to group or genus-specific factors of the antigens.

From Table V it will be seen that the precipitin reactions with partially purified carbohydrate extracts give similar results to the agglutination tests. A difference is the stronger cross-reactions between *P. pullulans* and *P. bergeri* in the former test.

From the outcome of these investigations extended by the study of a collection of cultures from Professor Lacaz, São Paulo, a tentative antigenic scheme was worked out based on the serological behavior of fifty-six strains.

It was of considerable interest to examine whether *Pullularia werneckii* might be related serologically to *Cladosporium mansonii,* as both organisms have been described as the cause of tinea nigra. An antiserum prepared from Castellani's original strain of *C. mansonii* precipitated homologous extracts, but also gave group reactions with extracts from *Phialophora verrucosa, Pullularia schawii,* and *Margarinomyces heteromorphus.* Such group reactions were not apparent with antigens from *Pullularia* [*Aureobasidium*] *pullulans, P. bergeri* and *P. werneckii.*

There was no serological evidence that *Cladosporium mansonii* and *P. werneckii* possess common antigenic factors. Antigenic relationship, however, was demonstrated between *C. mansonii* antiserum and two

TABLE III
ANTIGENIC STRUCTURE OF 22 *Candida* SPECIES[a,b]

Sero group	Species	Antigenic formula: Thermostable antigens[c]	Antigenic formula: Thermolabile antigens
I	*C. albicans*[d]	1, 2, 3, 4, 5, 6, 7,	
	C. clausenii	1, 2, 3, 4, 5, 6, 7,	
	C. tropicalis	1, 2, 3, 4, 5, 6,	
II	*C. pseudotropicalis*[e]	1, 8, (10)	a
	C. macedoniensis	1, 8, 10,	(a)
	C. scottii	1, 3, 4, 10, 26	
	C. robusta[f]	1, 2, 3, (10) (14) 18,	
	C. melinii	1, (2) (3) 5, 10, 17, 25,	a, e
	C. stellatoidea	1, 2, 3, 4, 5, (10)	
III	*C. krusei*[g]	1, 2, 5, (11)	b
	C. catenulata	1, 2, 5, 11,	b
	C. reukaufii	1, 2, (5) (11) (12)	b, f
	C. mycoderma	1, 2, 5, 11, 12,	
	C. rugosa	1, 2, 3, 4, 19,	g

IV	*C. parapsilosis* (*C. parakrusei*)	1,	2,	3,		5,								(13)	(14)	(15)						c
	C. pulcherrima	1,	2,	3,		5,								13,	14,	(15)						d
	C. zeylanoides	1,	2,	3,	4,									13,				17,				(a), c, h
V	*C. guilliermondii*	1,	2,	3,	4,					9,												
	C. melibiosi	1,	2,	3,	4,					(9)												
	C. tenuis	1,	2,	3,		(5)				(9)												
VI	*C. pelliculosa*[h]	1,	2,												14,	15,	16,				20	
	C. utilis[i]	(1)	(2)												(14)		16,	17,				c

[a] According to Tsuchiya *et al.* (1958c, 1959, 1961b).
[b] Obtained by slide-agglutination in absorbed monospecific sera diluted 1:10.
[c] In parentheses: weakly developed antigens, sometimes entirely absent.
[d] Antigenically identical with *C. clausenii* (Van Uden *et al.*, 1956).
[e] Antigenically identical with *Saccharomyces fragilis* (Seeliger, 1957).
[f] Antigenically identical with *Saccharomyces cerevisiae* (Tsuchiya *et al.*, 1958b).
[g] Serologically closely related to *Pichia fermentans* (Seeliger, 1957).
[h] Antigenically identical with *Hansenula anomala* (Tsuchiya *et al.*, 1957b, 1958a).
[i] Serologically closely related to the genus *Hansenula* (Tsuchiya *et al.*, 1958a).

TABLE IV
AGGLUTINATION REACTIONS WITH BLACK YEAST-LIKE FUNGI

Antigen	Antiserum				
	P. pullulans	*P. bergeri*	*P. werneckii*	*S. gougerotii*	*S. schenckii*
Pullularia [*Aureobasidium*] *pullulans*	320[a]	40	40	—[b]	—
P. bergeri	40	2560	—	—	—
P. werneckii	40	—	160	—	—
Sporothrix gougerotii	—	—	—	640	—
S. schenckii	—	—	—	—	640

[a] Reciprocal serum titer.
[b] Negative at 1:20.

strains of *M. heteromorphus*. With antigens and antisera from those three strains typical cross-precipitin reactions were observed. Whether this has any taxonomic or phylogenetic significance, remains to be seen.

Moreover, antisera of both these species agglutinated strongly, but in low dilutions only, a yeast-phase suspension of a strain of *Pullularia schawii*, and the yeast phase of this species was agglutinated very distinctly by antiserum from the so-called *Sporothrix gougerotii*.

These findings may have some importance for the taxonomy of certain morphologically similar black yeasts. It should be remembered that by

TABLE V
PRECIPITATION REACTIONS WITH BLACK YEAST-LIKE FUNGI

Antigen	Antiserum				
	P. pullulans	*P. bergeri*	*P. werneckii*	*S. gougerotii*	*S. schenckii*
Pullularia [*Aureobasidium*] *pullulans*	+++	±	±	±	−
P. bergeri	+++	+++	±	±	−
P. werneckii	+	−	+++	−	−
Sporothrix gougerotii	−	−	−	+++	−
S. schenckii	−	−	−	−	+++
Phialophora jeanselmei	−	−	−	+++	−
P. verrucosa, P. compacta, P. lignicola, Cladosporium pedrosoi, C. trichoides, C. carrionii	−	−	−	−	−

means of complement-fixation tests Stone (1930) first found that *S. gougerotii* and *Phialophora jeanselmei* could not be separated serologically. This also was borne out by Seeliger *et al.* (1958) by the use of precipitin tests. In the course of these experiments this serogroup could be differentiated distinctly from *Pullularia bergeri* (syn. *Torula bergeri*). This is in contrast to the assumption of Trejos that, on cultural and morphological grounds, *P. bergeri* belongs to *Phialophora jeanselmei.* The results with strains obtained from the collection of Professor Lacaz, São Paulo, again demonstrated that smooth and rough strains, both designated as *P. jeanselmei,* are apparently identical neither with each other nor with derivatives of each other. They are antigenically different and, therefore, in all probability members of two different species, only the smooth form of which is synonymous with *Pullularia bergeri.* It has also been shown by several investigators (Lurie, 1948; Nordén, 1951) that *Sporothrix schenckii* is serologically identical with its white variety, *S. beurmanii.*

TABLE VI
ANTIGENIC SCHEME OF SOME YEAST-LIKE DEMATIACEOUS FUNGI[a]

Species	Antigenic factors
Pullularia [*Aureobasidium*] *pullulans*	A B C . . . .
P. bergeri	. B . D . . . .
P. werneckii	. . C . E . . . .
Sporothrix gougerotii	. . . . . F . . . .
Phialophora jeanselmei	. . . . . F . . . .
S. schenckii	. . . . . . G . . . . . .

[a] After Seeliger (1957) in collaboration with Dr. Trejos.

There can be no doubt that *S. schenckii* strains from all parts of the world represent one homogeneous serogroup.

Furthermore, serological procedures were applied to the antigenic analysis of *Trichosporon* (Seeliger, 1957; Seeliger and Schröter, 1963) which resulted in the elaboration of the tentative antigenic scheme outlined in Table VII.

It should be noted that the three species of serogroup 1 gave cross-reactions with *Geotrichum candidum* and serologically related species such as *Nadsonia elongata* (Seeliger, 1954, 1958), whereas the three species of serogroup 2 shared a group antigen with many *Cryptococcus* strains and the two *Candida* species *C. humicola* and *C. curvata* (Seeliger, (1959). The latter species also have certain important biochemical properties in common, i.e., synthesis of starch and hydrolysis of urea. Thereby serology corroborates the correctness of Wickerham's view (1956) that

TABLE VII

TENTATIVE ANTIGENIC FORMULAS OF THE EIGHT SPECIES OF THE FORM GENUS *Trichosporon* BASED ON THE RESULTS OF PRECIPITATION, AGGLUTINATION, AND SOME AGGLUTININ-ABSORPTION TESTS[a]

Serogroup	Species	Proved by precipitation and agglutination				Proved by absorption and agglutination only					
1	*T. capitatum*	A				B	C				
	T. sericeum	A						D			
	T. fermentans	A					C				
Intermediate	*T. pullulans*	A	E			B		D?	G	(F)	J
2	*T. cutaneum*		(E)							F	J
	T. infestans		(E)						G	F	
	T. margaritiferum		(E)	H							
3	*T. behrendii*				I						

[a] After Seeliger and Schröter (1963).

some of the *Trichosporon* species may be phylogenetically related to *Geotrichum* and others to *Cryptococcus*. Taking this into consideration the present classification may be inadequate as it disregards important phyletic characters in favor of morphological resemblance. This led Seeliger (1958) to the position that the *present classification may eventually have to be revised if the fact is recognized that certain hereditary properties such as enzyme systems and antigens are more stable during the process of evolution than morphology.*

Likewise the serology of the genus *Geotrichum* has been investigated repeatedly (Seeliger, 1954; Cheek and Barrett, 1962; Torheim, 1963).

With capsulated *Cryptococcus* strains, capsular reactions have permitted the establishment of at least three antigenic capsule types of *C. neoformans,* according to Evans (1950) and Evans and Kessel (1951). These capsular reactions are not caused by a swelling, but by a precipitation of the antibody on the surface of the capsules (Evans *et al.,* 1956). However, nonpathogenic cryptococci likewise reacted with these capsular antisera. A serological diagnosis of *C. neoformans,* according to Tsuchiya *et al.* (1963), perhaps may be effected by combined use of absorbed factor sera, e.g., *C. neoformans* antiserum absorbed with heated cells of *Candida humicola,* and *C. curvata* antiserum absorbed with heated cells of *Cryptococcus neoformans.*

These findings clearly show the possibilities and limitations of fungus serology in this particular field. Until recently there was no way of distinguishing with certainty pathogenic from nonpathogenic cryptococci by use of agglutination, precipitation, or capsular reactions, but this has now become possible (Tsuchiya *et al.*, 1963). Also, it now is possible to separate serologically *Cryptococcus* from *Lipomyces,* which Benham (1955) suggested was the perfect state of the former (see Table VII).

A wide field still to be explored are the many genera of hyphomycetes, among which only a few have so far found the attention of serologists. The experience with agents of maduromycosis has already been mentioned. Others include the aspergilli first examined by Matsumoto (1929), and later by Seeliger (1958), who observed that some species are connected by group antigens as well as species-specific factors. Pepys *et al.* (1959) have extended this work with more refined techniques. They found common antigenic fractions among some fungi belonging to different genera such as *Aspergillus, Cladosporium,* and *Trichophyton* and Tran Van Ky, Biguet and Andrieu (1963) used immunoelectrophoresis successfully in the elucidation of the highly complex antigenic mosaic of dermatophytes which were earlier investigated by the Schultz-Dale technique (Jadassohn *et al.,* 1937) and by the classical methods of serology (Seeliger, 1954, 1958).

It should finally be mentioned that a great deal of serological work has been performed by many investigators on dimorphic pathogenic fungi of the genera *Histoplasma, Blastomyces, Paracoccidioides,* and *Coccidioides* (cf. Table VIII). Some of the essential findings on some selected groups of yeasts and hyphomycetes are summarized in Table VIII.

VI. CONCLUSIONS

As pointed out above, many investigators have succeeded in analyzing the antigenic composition of fungi. As a result several tentative antigenic schemes for a variety of genera already have been formulated. Serological analysis has proved to be exceedingly useful in taxonomic studies, and the results may eventually influence greatly the present system of classification by providing a better understanding of the phylogenetic relationships of morphologically different fungi. Thus, serological tests could help in the solution of some difficult taxonomic problems, particularly with the help of the highly specific and refined new test procedures such as agar-gel diffusion, immunoelectrophoresis, and fluorescent antibody techniques. But since serology is not yet an established procedure in mycology, it would be unwise to recommend it as *the* method to identify fungi. Evidence is accumulating, however, to indicate that serological diagnosis can be used with advantage as an additional, and perhaps more rapid, tool for this purpose, particularly in conjunction with other classical diagnostic procedures.

TABLE VIII

Antigenic Relationships of Some Pathogenic and Apathogenic Fungi, as Based on Results of Serological Studies

Genus or species	Method of investigation[a]	Antigenic relationships	Selected references[b]
Aspergillus fumigatus and other aspergilli	CFT-PT (+ agar-gel)	Species and group antigens, related to other aspergilli, but by common fractions also to *Penicillium*, *Cladosporium*, *Trichophyton*, etc.	Biguet *et al.* (1962); Matsumoto (1929); Pepys *et al.* (1959, 1960); Seeliger (1958)
Blastomyces dermatitidis	AT (sensitized particles) CFT-PT (+ agar-gel)-FAS	Both species serologically uniform, by group antigens strongly related to *H. capsulatum*, also weakly to *C. immitis*.	Brown *et al.* (1958); Campbell and Binkley (1953); Martin (1941); Salvin (1949, 1950); Seeliger (1954, 1958)
Blastomyces [*Paracoccidioides*] *brasiliensis*	AT (sensitized particles) CFT-PT (+ agar-gel)-FAS		D. T. Smith (1949); Fava Netto (1955); Friedman and Conant (1953); Seeliger (1954, 1958)
Candida albicans and other *Candida* species	AT-CFT-PT (+ agar gel)-FAS	*C. albicans* rather uniform (two serotypes), composed of different antigenic factors. Serologically similar to *C. tropicalis*, related to some other spp. of *Candida*, *Hansenula*, *Pichia*, *Saccharomyces*, *Torulopsis*, etc. Serological classification of *Candida* by factor sera (serotyping)	Almon and Stonvall (1934); Balls (1925); Benham (1931); Biguet *et al.* (1959, 1961b); Gordon (1958); Hasenclever *et al.* (1961a,b); Jonsen (1955); Kunz (1958b); Lamb and Lamb (1935); Martin and Jones (1940); Seeliger (1954, 1958); Stone and Garrod (1931); Tomcsik (1930); Tsuchiya *et al.* (1959)
Cladosporium (and related genera)	CFT-PT (+ agar gel)	Species and group antigens, cross-reactions between certain *Cladosporium* and *Phialophora* spp., minor antigenic factors in common with *Penicillium*, *Aspergillus*, and *Trichophyton*	Conant and Martin (1937); Pepys *et al.* (1959); Seeliger *et al.* (1957, 1958, 1960a)

Coccidioides immitis	CFT-PT	Strains from different places serologically uniform, minor partial antigens in common with *H. capsulatum*, *B. dermatitidis*, and *P. brasiliensis*	Levine (1962); Salvin (1949, 1950); Seeliger (1954, 1958); Smith *et al.* (1948, 1958)
Cryptococcus neoformans and other cryptococci	AT-CFT-CR-PT-FAS	Three capsular types, strongly related to *C. albidus* (*innocuus*) and *C. diffluens*. By partial antigens related to other saprophytic cryptococci and to urea-hydrolyzing spp. of *Candida* and *Trichosporon;* not related to *Lipomyces*. Cross reactions with certain high molecular polysaccharides	Benham (1935); Evans (1950); Eveland *et al.* (1958); Kaufmann (1944–1945); Salvin (1949, 1950); Saslaw and Campbell (1949, 1950a,b); Seeliger (1954, 1958, 1959, 1960b)
Dermatophytes: *Epidermophyton*, *Microsporum* spp. *Trichophyton* spp.	CFT-PT (+ agar gel) Schulz-Dale technique	Strong cross-reactions among the three genera, common group antigens, specific factors, probably present, partial antigens in common with saprophytes (*Aspergillus*, *Cladosporium*, *Penicillium*)	Biguet *et al.* (1961a); Jadassohn *et al.* (1937); Kokushina, (1952); Kuroda (1958); Pepys *et al.* (1959); Seeliger (1954, 1958); Tran Van Ky *et al.* (1963)
Geotrichum candidum and related spp.	AT-CFT-PT (+ agar gel)	Serologically homogeneous, related by common group antigens to certain spp. of *Candida*, *Endomyces*, *Nadsonia*, and *Trichosporon*, unilateral cross reaction with *Lipomyces* spp.	Cheek and Barrett (1962); Seeliger (1954, 1958, 1962b); Torheim (1963)
Histoplasma capsulatum and *H. duboisii*	AT (sensitized particles), CFT-PT (+ agar gel) FAS	*H. capsulatum* serologically uniform, strongly related to *H. duboisii*. Closely related to *B. dermatitidis* and *P. brasiliensis* by common group antigens, minor relationships with *C. immitis* and possibly with other hyphomycetes and yeasts	Brown *et al.* (1958); Campbell (1953); Coudert and Coly (1956); Cozad (1958); Heiner (1958); Salvin (1949, 1950); Schubert *et al.* (1953, 1955, 1957); Seeliger (1954, 1955, 1958); Sorensen and Evans (1954)

(*Continued*)

TABLE VIII (*Continued*)

Genus or species	Method of investigation[a]	Antigenic relationships	Selected references[b]
Allescheria boydii (*Monosporium apiospermum*)	AT-CFT-PT (− agar gel)	Perfect and imperfect states serologically identical, related to apathogenic *Monosporium* spp. by group antigens. Slight cross-reactions with *Trichophyton* and *Penicillium*. Not related to *Madurella*	Seeliger (1954, 1956, 1958)
Pullularia [*Aureobasidium*] *pullulans* and related spp.	AT-PT (+ agar gel)	Various species related by group antigens, not related to *S. schenckii Phialophora jeanselmei*, or *Cladosporium*	Seeliger (1956, 1957); Seeliger *et al.* (1958)
Sporothrix schenckii	AT-CFT-PT (+ agar gel)	Pigmented and nonpigmented strains from various places serologically homogeneous. No antigenic relationships with *Pullularia*, *Cladosporium*, and *Phialophora*	Kaden (1956, 1957); Lurie (1948); Nordén (1951); Seeliger (1954, 1956, 1957, 1958, 1960a)
Sporothrix gougerotii	AT-CFT-PT (+ agar gel)	Identical with certain strains of *Phialophora jeanselmei;* related to other *Phialophora* spp.	Seeliger (1956, 1958, 1960a); Stone and Garrod (1931)
Trichosporon cutaneum and related spp.	AT-CFT-PT (+ agar gel)	At least three different serological groups in the genus *Trichosporon*, some spp. related to the *Cryptococcus* genus, others to *Geotrichum*	Seeliger (1957); (1960a) Seeliger and Schröter (1963)

[a] Abbreviations: CFT, complement fixation test; PT, precipitin test; AT, agglutination test; CR, capsular reaction; FAS, fluorescent antibody staining.

[b] Simplified-selected references, for detailed reviews, see Seeliger (1957, 1962a,b).

REFERENCES*

References marked with an asterisk (*) include comprehensive bibliographies.

Aksoycan, N., and F. Kauffmann. (1957). Antigenic relationship between *Salmonella* O group C 1 and *Candida albicans*. *Acta Pathol. Microbiol. Scand.* **40:** 345–346.

Almon, L., and W. D. Stonvall. (1934). Serologic reactions of cultures of *Monilia* and some other yeastlike fungi. *J. Infect. Diseases* **55:** 12–25.

Ball, O. G., F. L. Lummus, M. L. Sigrest, J. F. Busey, and F. Allison, Jr. (1960). An immunologic survey for systemic fungus infections in general hospital patients of Central Mississippi. *Am. J. Hyg.* **72:** 231–243.

Balls, A. K. (1925). The precipitin test in the identification of yeasts. *J. Immunol.* **10:** 797.

Benham, R. W. (1931). Certain monilias parasitic in man. Their identification by morphology and agglutination. *J. Infect. Diseases* **49:** 183–215.

Benham, R. W. (1935). Cryptococci—their identification by morphology and serology. *J. Infect. Diseases* **57:** 255–274.

Benham, R. W. (1937). The cryptococci: Their identification by morphology and serology. *Proc. Soc. Exptl. Biol. Med.* **89:** 243–245.

Benham, R. W. (1955). *Cryptococcus neoformans:* "An ascomycete." *Proc. Soc. Exptl. Biol. Med.* **89:** 243–245.

Biberstein, H., and S. Epstein. (1932). Immunreaktionen bei der menschlichen und tierexperimentellen Oidiomykose der Haut. *Arch. Dermatol. Syphilis* **165:** 716–742.

Biguet, J., R. Havez, and P. Tran Van Ky. (1959). Les possibilités d'application aux champignons pathogènes de la méthode d'Ouchterlony et de l'immunoélectrophorèse. Résultats encourageants d'une tentative première concernant l'étude des antigènes de *Candida albicans*. *Mykosen* **2:** 115–120.

Biguet, J., S. Andrieu, and P. Tran Van Ky. (1961a). Application des méthodes électrophorétiques et immunochimiques à l'étude des fractions antigéniques des dermatophytes. Premiers résultats concernant *Ctenomyces mentagrophytes* (*Trichophyton mentagrophytes*). *Compt. Rend.* **253:** 2167–2169.

Biguet, J., R. Havez, P. Tran Van Ky, and R. Degaey. (1961b). Etude électrophorétíque, chromatographique et immunologique des antigènes de Candida albicans. *Ann. Inst. Pasteur* **100:** 13–24.

Biguet, J., P. Tran Van Ky, A. Capron, and J. Fruit. (1962). Analyse immunochimique des fractions antigéniques solubles d'Aspergillus fumigatus. Ordre d'apparition des anticorps expérimentaux du lapin, comparaison de ces derniers avec des anticorps naturels humains. *Compt. Rend.* **254:** 3768–3770.

Brown, R., E. L. Hazen, and C. H. Green. (1958). Fungal antigens for complement-fixation tests. *Histoplasma capsulatum. N.Y. State Dept. Health, Ann. Rept. Div. Labs. Res.* pp. 46–47.

Campbell, C. C. (1953). Antigenic fractions of *Histoplasma capsulatum*. *Am. J. Public Health* **43:** 712–717.

Campbell, C. C. (1960). The accuracy of serologic methods in diagnosis. *Ann. N.Y. Acad. Sci.* **89:** 163–177.

Campbell, C. C., and G. F. Binkley. (1953). Serologic diagnosis with respect to histoplasmosis, coccidioidomycosis, and blastomycosis and the problem of cross reactions. *J. Lab. Clin. Med.* **42:** 896–906.

* Some of the first reports are not cited. For references see Seeliger (1958).

Carlisle, H. N., and S. Saslaw. (1958). A histoplasmin-latex agglutination test. I. Results with animal sera. *J. Lab. Clin. Med.* **51**: 793–801.

Castellani, A. (1902). Die Agglutination bei gemischter Infektion und die Diagnose der letzteren. *Z. Hyg.* **40**: 1–19.

Cheek, C. W., and J. T. Barrett. (1962). Antigenic relationship of Geotrichum candidum strains. *Mycopathol. Mycol. Appl.* **17**: 47–54.

Conant, N. F., and D. S. Martin. (1937). The morphologic and serologic relationships of the various fungi causing dermatitis verrucosa (chromoblastomycosis). *Am. J. Trop. Med.* **17**: 553–576.

Coudert, J., and M. Coly. (1956). Essai d'application de la réaction d'agglutination des particules de collodion à quelques parasitoses. *Ann. Parasitol. Humaine Comparée* **31**: 389–499.

Cozad, G. C. (1958). A study of the whole yeast cell agglutination test in rabbits experimentally infected with *Histoplasma capsulatum*. *J. Immunol.* **81**: 368–375.

Evans, E. E. (1950). The antigenic composition of *Cryptococcus neoformans*. I. A serologic classification by means of capsular and agglutination reactions. *J. Immunol.* **64**: 423–430.

Evans, E. E., and Y. F. Kessel. (1951). The antigenic composition of *Cryptococcus neoformans*. II. Serologic studies with capsular polysaccharides. *J. Immunol.* **67**: 109–114.

Evans, E. E., L. J. Sorensen, and K. W. Walls. (1953). The antigenic composition of *Cryptococcus neoformans*. V. A survey of cross-reactions among strains of *Cryptococcus* and other antigens. *J. Bacteriol.* **66**: 287–293.

Evans, E. E., H. P. R. Seeliger, L. Kornfeld, and C. Garcia. (1956). Failure to demonstrate capsular swelling in *Cryptococcus neoformans*. *Proc. Soc. Exptl. Biol. Med.* **93**: 257–260.

Eveland, W. C., J. D. Marshall, and A. M. Silverstein. (1958). Rapid identification of pathogenic microorganisms using fluorescent antibodies of contrasting colors. *Proc. 7th Intern. Congr. Microbiol. Stockholm, 1958* Abstr., p. 313. Almqvist & Wiksell, Uppsala.

Fava Netto, C. (1955). Estudos quantitativos sôbre a fixaçao do complemento na blastomicose sul-americana, com antígeno polisacarídico. *Arch. Cir. Clin. Exptl.* **18**: 197–254.

Feinberg, J. G. (1960). Misinterpretation of an agar-gel precipitation pattern. *Nature* **188**: 684.

Friedman, L., and N. F. Conant. (1953). Immunologic studies on the etiologic agents of North and South American blastomycosis. II. Comparison of serologic reactions. *Mycopathol. Mycol. Appl.* **6**: 317–324.

Gordon, M. A. (1958). Differentiation of yeasts by means of fluorescent antibody. *Proc. Soc. Exptl. Biol. Med.* **97**: 694–698.

Greene, C. H., and M. A. Gordon. (1959). Gel precipitin test for histoplasmosis. *N.Y. State Dept. Health, Ann. Rept. Div. Labs. Res.*, p. 39.

Hasenclever, H. F., and W. O. Mitchell. (1961a). Antigenic studies of *Candida:* 1. Observation of two antigenic groups in Candida albicans. *J. Bacteriol.* **82**: 570–573.

Hasenclever, H. F., W. O. Mitchell and J. Loewe. (1961b). Antigenic studies of *Candida:* 2. Antigenic relation of Candida albicans group A and group B to Candida stellatoidea and Candida tropicalis. *J. Bacteriol.* **82**: 574–577.

Heiner, D. C. (1958). Diagnosis of histoplasmosis using precipitin reactions in agar gel. *Pediatrics* **22**: 616–627.

Jadassohn, W., F. Schaaf, and G. Wohler. (1937). Analysis of composite antigens by the Schultz-Dale-technique. Further experimental analyses of trichophytins. *J. Immunol.* **32:** 203–227.

Janke, D. (1959). Eine methodische Verbesserung des Nachweises der "Serumfungistase." *Hautarzt* **10:** 422.

Jonsen, J. (1955). "Serological studies in genus Candida," Thesis, University of Oslo.

Kaden, R. H. (1956). Präzipitation von Sporotrichon-Antiserum im Agarmedium. *Z. Haut-Geschlechtskrankh.* **21:** 87.

Kaden, R. H. (1957). Precipitin studies for the identity of antigens in different species of *Sporotrichum. Mycopathol. Mycol. Appl.* **8:** 260–270.

Kaplan, W., and L. Kaufman. (1961). The application of fluorescent antibody techniques to medical mycology. A review. *Sabouraudia* **1:** 137–144.

Kaufmann, W. (1944–1945). Die serologische Differenzierung von *Torulopsis neoformans* und *Torulopsis albida* mittels der Präzipitation und Agglutination. *Zentr. Bakteriol., Parasitenk., Abt. II* **106:** 434–437.

*Kligman, A. M., and D. DeLamater. (1950). The immunology of the human mycoses. *Ann. Rev. Microbiol.* **4:** 283–312.

Kokushina, T. M. (1952). Cited by P. N. Kashkin in *Mycol. Mycol. Appl.* **10:** 246.

Kunz, C. (1958a). Untersuchungen mit fluoresceinmarkierten Antikörpern an Hefen. *Schweiz. Z. Allgem. Pathol. Bakteriol.* **21:** 892–899.

Kunz, C. (1958b). Fluoreszenz-serologische Untersuchungen zum Nachweis von *Candida albicans*-Antigen bei Frühgeburten-Pneumonien. *Zentr. Bakteriol., Parasitenk., Abt. I. Orig.* **172:** 446–448.

Kuroda, T. (1958). Complement fixation and precipitating reactions in patients with dermatomycosis, using crude polysaccharide from Trichophyton asteroids mechanically disintegrated as antigen. *Bull. Pharm. Res. Inst.* **15:** 5–8.

Lamb, J. H., and M. L. Lamb. (1935). A grouping of the *Monilias* by fermentation and precipitin reactions. *J. Infect. Diseases* **56:** 8–10.

Levine, H. B. (1962). Immunogenicity of experimental vaccines in systemic mycoses. *In* "Fungi and Fungous Diseases." Pp. 254–276. Thomas, Springfield, Illinois.

Lodder, J., and N. J. W. Kreger-van Rij. (1952). "The Yeasts: A Taxonomic Study," 713 pp. North-Holland Publ., Amsterdam.

Lurie, H. J. (1948). A common antigenic factor in different species of Sporotrichum. *Mycologia* **40:** 106–113.

McDearman, S. C., V. F. McClure, E. D. Cherry, and E. W. Ulrich. (1958). Hemagglutination of histoplasmin-sensitized erythrocytes by sera from patients with culturally proved histoplasmosis. *Bacteriol. Proc.* p. 66.

Martin, D. S. (1935). Complement fixation in blastomycosis. *J. Infect. Diseases* **57:** 291–295.

Martin, D. S. (1941). Practical application of some immunologic principles to the diagnosis and treatment of certain fungus infections. *J. Invest. Dermatol.* **4:** 471–481.

Martin, D. S. (1942). Studies on the immunologic relationships among various species of the *Candida* (Monilia). *Am. J. Trop. Med.* **22:** 295–303.

Martin, D. S., and C. P. Jones. (1940). Further studies on the practical classification of the monilias. *J. Bacteriol.* **39:** 609–630.

Martin, D. S., and D. T. Smith. (1936). The laboratory diagnosis of blastomycosis. *J. Lab. Clin. Med.* **21:** 1289–1296.

Matsumoto, T. (1929). The investigation of Aspergilli by serological methods. *Trans. Brit. Mycol. Soc.* **14:** 69–88.

Negroni, P. (1934a). La fijación del complemento en la moniliasis cutáneomucosa. *Rev. Inst. Bacteriol. Dept. Nacl. Hig. (Buenos Aires)* **6:** 159–163.

Negroni, P. (1934b). Valor comparativo de la reacciones biológicas en las moniliasis cutáneomucosas. *Rev. Inst. Bacteriol. Dept. Nacl. Hig. (Buenos Aires)* **6**: 164–169.

Neill, J. M., C. G. Castillo, and A. H. Pinkes. (1955). Serological reactions between fungi and bacteria. I. Cross-reactions of *Sporotrichum schenckii* with pneumococci. *J. Immunol.* **74**: 120–125.

Nordén, A. (1948). Agglutination of sheep's erythrocytes sensitized with histoplasmin. *Proc. Soc. Exptl. Biol. Med.* **70**: 218–220.

*Nordén, A. (1951). Sporotrichosis. *Acta Pathol. Microbiol. Scand.* Suppl. 89. Pp. 1–119.

Ouchterlony, Ö. (1949). Antigen-antibody reactions in gels. *Acta Pathol. Microbiol. Scand.* **26**: 507.

Pepys, J. (1959). Immunological aspects of allergic disorders. *Nature* **183**: 296–297.

Pepys, J. (1960). The role of human precipitins to common fungal antigens in allergic reactions. *Acta Allergol.* Suppl. **7**: 108–111.

Pepys, J., R. W. Riddell, K. M. Citron, Y. M. Clayton, and E. I. Short. (1959). Clinical and immunologic significance of Aspergillus fumigatus in the sputum. *Am. Rev. Respirat Diseases* **80**: 167–180.

Pospišil, L. (1959). Agglutinations-, Komplementbindungs- und Hämagglutinationsreaktion bei der Bestimmung von Candida-Arten. *Dermatologica* **118**: 65–73.

Rebers, P. A., S. A. Barker, M. Heidelberger, Z. Dische, and E. E. Evans. (1958). Precipitation of the specific polysaccharide of *Cryptococcus neoformans* A by types I and XIV antipneumococcal sera. *J. Am. Chem. Soc.* **80**: 1135–1137.

Salvin, S. B. (1949). The serologic relationship of fungus antigens. *J. Lab. Clin. Med.* **34**: 1096–1104.

Salvin, S. B. (1950). Quantitative studies on the serologic relationships of fungi. *J. Immunol.* **65**: 617–626.

Saslaw, S., and C. C. Campbell. (1948). A method for demonstrating antibodies in rabbit sera against histoplasmin by the collodion agglutination technique. *Proc. Soc. Exptl. Biol. Med.* **68**: 559–562.

Saslaw, S., and C. C. Campbell. (1949). A collodion agglutination test for histoplasmosis. *Public Health Rept.* **64**: 424–429.

Saslaw, S., and C. C. Campbell. (1950a). Serologic studies in histoplasmosis. *Am. J. Public Health* **40**: 427–435.

Saslaw, S., and C. C. Campbell. (1950b). Studies on the stability of the histoplasmin collodion agglutination test. *J. Lab. Clin. Med.* **35**: 780–785.

Scheidegger, J. J. (1955). Une micro-méthode de l'immunoélectrophorèse. *Intern. Arch. Allergy* **7**: 103–110.

Schubert, J. (1960). The agar-gel precipitin test for histoplasmosis. *Proc. 5th Biennial Planning Conf. Instrumentation Course, Atlanta, 1960.*

Schubert, J., L. Ajello, S. Stanford, and V. R. Grant. (1953). Variation in complement fixation antigen production by two different strains of *H. capsulatum* grown on two media. *J. Lab. Clin. Med.* **41**: 91–97.

Schubert, J. H., L. Ajello, J. S. Cooper, and L. C. Runyon. (1955). Evaluation of histoplasmin and yeast phase antigens derived from a single strain of *Histoplasma capsulatum* in the complement fixation test. *J. Bacteriol.* **69**: 558–562.

Schubert, J. H., L. Ajello, and J. Hall. (1957). Variation in complement fixation antigenicity of different yeast phase strains of *Histoplasma capsulatum. J. Lab. Clin. Med.* **50**: 304–307.

Seeliger, H. P. R. (1954). "Experimentelle Untersuchungen zur mykologischen Serodiagnostik," Habilitations-Schrift, University of Bonn.

Seeliger, H. P. R. (1955). Zur Anwendungsmöglichkeit der Präzipitation im Agar-Gel bei der O-Antigenanalyse von Bakterien und Pilzen. *Z. Hyg. Infektionskrankh.* **141**: 110–121.

Seeliger, H. P. R. (1956). A serologic study of hyphomycetes causing mycetoma in man. *J. Invest. Dermatol.* **26**: 81–93.

Seeliger, H. P. R. (1957). Die Serologie schwarzer und roter Hefen. *Zentr. Bakteriol., Parasitenk., Abt. I. Orig.* **167**: 396–408.

*Seeliger, H. P. R. (1958). "Mykologische Serodiagnostik." Barth, Leipzig.

*Seeliger, H. P. R. (1959). Das kulturell-biochemische und serologische Verhalten der Cryptococcus-Gruppe. *Ergeb. Immunitätsforsch.* **32**: 23–72.

*Seeliger, H. P. R. (1960a). Advances in the serology of fungi. *Brit. Mycol. Soc. Trans.* **43**: 543–555.

Seeliger, H. P. R. (1960b). Les phénomènes d'immunité dans les cryptococcoses. *Pathol. Biol., Semaine Hop.* [N.S.] **8**: 297–306.

*Seeliger, H. P. R. (1962a). Serology of fungi and deep fungous infections. *In* "Fungi and Fungous Diseases" (G. Dalldorf, ed.), pp. 158–186. Thomas, Springfield, Illinois.

*Seeliger, H. P. R. (1962b). Serodiagnostik der Pilze und mykotischen Infektionen. *Zentr. Bakteriol., Parasitenk., Abt. I. Orig.* **184**: 203–226.

*Seeliger, H. P. R. (1963). Immunbiologisch-serologische Nachweisverfahren bei Pilzerkrankungen. *In* "Handbuch der Haut- und Geschlechtskrankheiten. Ergänzungsband" (A. Marchionini and H. Götz, eds.). Vol. IV, pp. 605–734.

Seeliger, H. P. R., and W. E. Gardini Tuesta. (1961). Unpublished studies.

Seeliger, H. P. R., and R. Schröter. (1963). A serological study on the antigenic relationships of the form genus *Trichosporon. Sabouraudia* **2**: 248–263.

Seeliger, H. P. R., C. da Silva Lacaz, and C. M. Ulson. (1958). Further serologic studies with dematiaceous fungi. *Proc. 6th Intern. Congr. Trop. Med. Malaria 1958* **4**: pp. 636–643.

Shattock, P. M. F. (1955). The use of serology in the classification of microorganisms. *J. Gen. Microbiol.* **13**: 367.

Smith, C. E., E. G. Whiting, E. E. Baker, H. G. Rosenberg, R. R. Beard, and M. T. Saito. (1948). The use of coccidioidin. *Am. Rev. Tuberc.* **57**: 330–360.

Smith, C. E., M. T. Saito, C. C. Campbell, G. B. Hill, S. Saslaw, S. B. Salvin, J. E. Felton, and M. A. Krupp. (1958). Comparison of complement fixation tests for coccidioidomycosis. *Public Health Rept.* (*U.S.*) **72**: 888–894.

Smith, D. T. (1949). Immunologic types of blastomycosis: A report of 40 cases. *Ann. Internal. Med.* [N.S.] **31**: 463–469.

Sorensen, L. J., and E. E. Evans. (1954). Antigenic fractions specific for *Histoplasma capsulatum* in the complement fixation reaction. *Proc. Soc. Exptl. Biol. Med.* **87**: 339–341.

Stone, K. (1930). A study of yeasts by the complement fixation test. *Lancet* **218**: 577.

Stone, K., and L. P. Garrod. (1931). The classification of monilias by serological methods. *J. Pathol. Bacteriol.* **34**: 429–436.

*Tempel, A. (1959). Serologisch onderzoek bij *Fusarium oxysporum. Mededel. Landbouwhogeschool Wageningen* **59**: 1–60.

Tomcsik, J. (1930). Über die Rolle des Hefegummis in der serologischen Differenzierung einzelner Hefearten. *Z. Immunitaetsforsch.* **66**: 8–16.

Torheim, B. J. (1963). Immunochemical investigations in Geotrichum and certain related fungi. II. Isolation and chemical analysis of polysaccharides. *Sabouraudia* **2**: 155–163.

Tran Van Ky, P., J. Biguet, and S. Andrieu. (1963). Etude par l'électrophorèse et la double diffusion en gélose des substances antigéniques excrétées dans le milieu de culture de *Candida albicans. Sabouraudia* **2:** 164–170.

Tsuchiya, T., Y. Fukazawa, S. Amemiya, M. Yonezawa, and K. Suzuki. (1957a). Serological classification of the genus Rhodotorula. *Yokohama Med. Bull.* **8:** 215–224.

Tsuchiya, T., Y. Fukazawa, J. Hayashi, Y. Nishikawa, and M. Doi (1957b). Serological classification of the genus Hansenula. *Japan. J. Microbiol.* **1:** 339–346.

Tsuchiya, T., Y. Fukazawa, I. Sato, S. Amemiya, and T. Murata (1958a). Further studies on the classification of the genus *Hansenula. Japan. J. Exptl. Med.* **28:** 105–114.

Tsuchiya, T., Y. Fukazawa, I. Sato, S. Kawakita, M. Yonezawa, and Y. Yamase. (1958b). Serologic classification of the genus *Saccharomyces. Yokohama Med. Bull.* **9:** 359–370.

Tsuchiya, T., S. Kawakita, J. Hayashi, and T. Kobayashi. (1958c). Serological classification of the genus Candida. *Jap. J. Exptl. Med.* **28:** 345–352.

Tsuchiya, T., Y. Fukazawa, and S. Kawakita. (1959). A method for the rapid identification of the genus Candida. *Mycopathol. Mycol. Appl.* **10:** 191–206.

Tsuchiya, T., Y. Fukazawa, and S. Kawakita. (1961a). Serological classification of the genus Torulopsis. *Sabouraudia* **1:** 145–153.

Tsuchiya, T., Y. Fukazawa, and S. Kawakita. (1961b). Serological classification of the genus *Candida. In* "Studies on Candidiasis in Japan," Research Committee of Candidiasis, pp. 34–46.

Tsuchiya, T., S. Kawakita, and M. Udagawa. (1963). Rapid identification of Cryptococcus neoformans by serology. *Sabouraudia* **2:** 209–214.

Van Uden, N., M. de Matos-Faia and L. Assis-Lopes. (1956). The relationship between *Candida clausenii* and *C. albicans. Rev. Bras. Port. Biol.* **1:** 68–75.

Vogel, R. A., and M. E. Collins. (1955). Hemagglutination test for detection of *C. albicans* antibodies in rabbit antiserum. *Proc. Soc. Exptl. Biol. Med.* **89:** 138–140.

Vogel, R. A., T. F. Sellers, and P. Woodward. (1961). Fluorescent antibody techniques applied to the study of human cryptococcosis. *J. Am. Med. Assoc.* **178:** 921.

von Schrader-Beielstein, H. W., and H. P. R. Seeliger. (1956). Papierelektrophoretische Untersuchungen an Pilzseren. *Z. Immunitätsforsch.* **113:** 328–332.

Wickerham, L. J. (1956). Personal communication.

Winner, H. I. (1955). A study of *Candida albicans* agglutinins in human sera. *J. Hyg.* **53:** 509–512.

Yukawa, M., and M. Ohta. (1928). Serological identification of yeasts (First report, Second report). Sci. Rep. Kyushu Imp. Univ., Fac. Agr. 3: 187–199, 209–216.

Yukawa, M., W. Yositome, and S. Misio. (1931). Serological identification of yeasts. (Third Report.) *Sci. Rept. Kyushu Imp. Univ. Fac. Agr.* **4:** 267–281.

CHAPTER 24

Genetical and Cytological Aspects of Taxonomy

MORTEN LANGE

Institut for Sporeplanter
Copenhagen, Denmark

I. INTRODUCTION

The modern taxonomy of higher plants is strongly dependent on utilization of cytological and genetical information. "Cytotaxonomy" is even considered a special discipline. The characters obtained from chromosome counts are important for the delimitation of species and influence also the arrangement of higher taxa, as do also the studies of chromosome morphology. The classical Mendelian genetics have had a strong influence on the evaluation of the significance of morphological characters.

The taxonomy of fungi is much less affected by such studies. It is evident that there are similar possibilities for taxonomic progress by studying fungal cytology and genetics, but the obstacles are several, especially as far as chromosome studies are concerned. The cytological studies of taxonomic importance have thus been mainly confined to other features.

II. CYTOLOGY

If cytology is taken in a very broad sense, as a study of the single cell, it is evidently a field of utmost taxonomic significance in mycology. Spore morphology is a character of highest rank, as are such finer cytomorphological features as the development of clamp connections. More recently pigmentation and incrustation of the cell wall also have been taken into account. But these characters are hardly to be considered cytological in the more usual sense of the word.

When cytology is more narrowly conceived—the features of the organelles, the plasma, and, probably, the cell wall structures—then it is obvious that such characters have been sparingly used in fungal taxonomy.

In the Phycomycetes, the structure and biochemical composition of the cell wall have for long been important taxonomic criteria. Occurrence of chitin or cellulose seems to be a distinguishing character of the main groups. Cellulose is present in the Oomycetidae and the Hyphochytriales. The latter group also has chitin, which is characteristic of the remaining fungal groups; for detailed references, see Volume I, Chapter 3. Cytochemical characters, reflecting less fundamental differences, are used widely in taxonomic mycology. As a marginal sector of cytology they will not be dealt with here.

The microstructure of the cell wall has attracted much recent interest, and the results are very promising for taxonomy, but the number of organisms studied will hardly permit general taxonomic conclusions to be drawn as yet. The same applies to a number of other microstructural features.

It is only a very mild overstatement that chromosome numbers have as yet had no importance in mycological taxonomy. One of the few exceptions to this rule is the genus *Allomyces,* studied by Emerson and Wilson (1954). From the information published it appears that while *Allomyces* species have a rather high chromosome number, the large majority of ascomycetes and basidiomycetes have low numbers, generally $n = 4$ (Burges, 1955), but most species have small chromosomes, tending to agglomerate, and several of the chromosome counts published may be regarded with some scepticism. For fungi even the nature of the mitotic division has hardly as yet been made clear, and also the features of the meiotic division are controversial. A recent account of this is given by Rossen and Westergaard (1966); see also Volume I, Chapters 6 and 7.

In spite of the limited knowledge of the meiotic division, it still contributes certain characters of great taxonomic importance. The spindle orientation in the basidium provides a solid taxonomic distinction among main groups of Heterobasidiomycetes, as in the transverse spindle in the chiastobasidium of the Tremellales as opposed to the arrangement in the stichobasidium of the Auriculariales, and the same character seems useful in distinguishing stichobasidial Cantharellaceae and related groups from the remaining, chiastobasidial Aphyllophorales.

A. Nuclear Number, Arrangement, and Phase

Although with the above exception, little taxonomical significance is applied to the karyological features, there is a quite different situation prevailing for the arrangement of the nuclei. Some general features support the major taxonomic divisions. The Basidiomycetes is characterized by the prevailing dikaryotic phase, the Ascomycetes by a more restricted dikaryon stage. Most phycomycetes were believed to be coenocytic and haploid, but recent studies by Sansome (1965) indicate that oomycetes are in diplophase in their vegetative stage.

The Blastocladiales have since long been outstanding among fungi because of their haplodiplontic nature. It is highly possible that further cytological studies on the various groups of phycomycetes will set them further apart from each other and from the other main groups of fungi.

Certain special features of the nucleus seem to characterize major groups. A nuclear cap is found in the Blastocladiales, while the Monoblepharidales have a similar but more diffuse arrangement around the nucleus (Fuller, 1966).

Deviations from the overall pattern outlined above are known, but hardly any of these have specific taxonomic consequences, although they may lend further support to certain arrangements. The genetic aspect of some of these will be discussed later.

Remaining for consideration is the number of nuclei in each mycelial cell and especially in the spores. Here we find characters of well-established taxonomic value.

The use of these characters in taxonomy has been given central importance through the studies of Kühner and his school. Kühner (1945) proved that the number of nuclei in the spores provided a valuable character on the familial or generic levels in the Agaricales. The fusion nucleus undergoes three divisions. If they all take place in the basidium, there will often be degeneration of four nuclei and the spores will receive only one nucleus. In other cases the third division will take place in the spore, which will then be binucleate. The pattern is not without exceptions, but the Hygrophoraceae and Tricholomataceae have mostly uninucleate spores while the spores in most of the chromosporous agaricales are binucleate. For certain genera, for instance *Rhodocybe,* the binucleate spore is regarded as a key character.

A number of students from Kühner's school have studied similar traits in other groups of fungi (Boidin, 1964; Lamoure, 1954). Lately Berthet (1964) found the number of nuclei in the spores to be a leading character in the Pezizales where most genera have uninucleate spores whereas they are four-spored in the Sarcoscyphaceae and Helvellaceae and have more than thirty nuclei in the Morchellaceae.

III. GENETICS

The restricted use of cytological characters is paralleled by a similar feeble exploitation of genetics in mycological taxonomy. The genetic study of fungi is certainly a well-developed field, and a number of fungi are classical genetical objects: *Neurospora* is preeminent but *Saccharomyces, Schizophyllum, Coprinus,* and others are important. Two facts restrict the taxonomic use of these studies: the number of fungi studied is quite limited, and the characters have to a large extent been of a biochemical nature.

These characters are of leading importance in the classification of the Saccharomycetaceae and similar fungi, where the definition of the species often is mainly genetic, and the genetical stability often is well studied (cp. Winge, 1957).

Physiological specialization, or host relationship is a taxonomic character to which high taxonomic value often is ascribed. Genetical studies have facilitated the evaluation of the taxonomic significance of such characters. The main emphasis often is placed on the establishment of taxa below the specific level, described as physiologic races, although their morphological traits might sometimes have given them status as varieties.

The studies in question have to a large part dealt with rusts (Flor, 1959), and further studies will probably here greatly help in establishing a balanced species concept for this group which is severely burdened with specific names. The same holds true for the smuts and for many of the Fungi Imperfecti (cp. Fincham and Day, 1963, p. 240).

At the specific level and above, morphological characters are preeminent among most groups of fungi, and the genetical evaluation of these characters, their constancy and stability is not a very widely studied field. The nature of the pigmentation of the spores is regarded as a taxonomic character of high rank. It is thus noteworthy, that the black pigmentation of the spores of *Sordaria macrospora* depends on a single gene, and similar findings have been made for other ascomycetes. The same studies have shown that another character, often ascribed high taxonomic value, can be dependent on a single mutable gene. Many taxa are defined *i.a.* by the uniseriate arrangement of spores in the ascus. But biseriate arrangement can occur on mutation of a single gene (for a survey, see Esser and Kuenen, 1965). These authors also list examples of genetical variation in morphological characters among fungi (Esser and Kuenen, 1965, p. 39). Even if examples like the ones quoted imply characters of value for morphological taxonomy, they are as yet too few to have impact on current taxonomy.

The formation and study of hybrids at the specific level have been an important part of the genetic contribution to the taxonomy of higher plants. Among fungi, such studies are extremely few. There is the very clear example of *Allomyces arbuscula* × *A. macrogynus* (Emerson and Wilson, 1954), and some *Saccharomyces* hybrids have been made by Winge (1942), who has reviewed older alleged cases of hybridization among fungi, finding many of them loosely based. It seems to be a reasonable deduction that intersterility is a very stable feature which can greatly facilitate delimitation of fungus species.

This applies both to the incompatibility of mycelia of two different species and to the pattern of compatibility within a species (cf. Chapter 27).

Patterns of compatibility have recently been examined by several workers, some of whom have proposed a more refined terminology (Esser and Kuenen, 1965; Burnett, 1956). From a taxonomic standpoint, the classical distinction between heterothallic and homothallic species still seems useful enough. Homothallic species occur in all major groups of fungi and even if the cytological and genetical background may not always be the same, it still can be considered a taxonomic character of value. Certain homothallic species may occasionally produce incompatible mycelia (*Neurospora tetrasperma,* five-spored asci), and others seem regularly to produce spores which give rise to both compatible and incompatible mycelia: amphithallic species. They are frequently basidiomycetes with two-spored basidia, but four-spored types can also react in this way (Lange, 1952; Lamoure, 1960).

In most groups studied it seems that the homothallic species form a minor part of the species. Ahmad (1965), however, found homothallism to be most common in 94 out of 133 yeast strains studied. He further found the character to be somewhat unreliable in certain species.

Heterothallism offers further possibilities for use in the classification of fungi. The Phycomycetes, Ascomycetes, and Uredinales have a one-locus, bipolar type of heterothallism. The remaining groups of Basidiomycetes may have the same, but more frequently have a two-locus, tetrapolar heterothallic system. The type of system seems to be a stable specific character, and may even be, in certain cases, a supporting character for higher taxonomic units. Thus Boidin (1956) found all members of *Peniophora* sect. Coloratae to be tetrapolar, while sect. Membranaceae had bipolar members only. The study of this character is now so broadly performed that its value above the level of species can be evaluated.

The species concept in fungi is a very delicate problem. This is certainly to a large extent due to a very limited use of genetical characters to test the stability of the morphological criteria employed. However, heterothallic species offer rich possibilities for a species concept based on sterility borders between related taxa.

It seems to be a rule with few exceptions, that positive results of confrontation among mycelia from different sources proves that the material tested belongs to the same species, while negative results—if not due to identical alleles—prove a specific difference. A few cases of hybridization have been established, as mentioned above. Several more examples are known, where incompatibility divides a well-defined species into two intersterile groups (a list of such cases is given by Burnett, 1965). From the material studied until now it appears that intersterility borders support a rather narrow species concept (Lange, 1952). A few cases where the groups are separated by reduced compatibility are also known (*Fomes pinicola,* Mounce and Macrae, 1938; *Auricularia auricula-judae,* Barnett, 1937).

The use of incompatibility in establishing differences between closely related species is made easy by the large number of alleles at each locus. For most species, it will be a real exception if two mycelia from different sources have a factor in common. A notable exception seems to be found in the species of Nidulariaceae (Fries, 1940).

IV. CONCLUSIONS

In conclusion, it is emphasized that the present account primarily deals with cytological and genetical results which have proved their significance for taxonomy. Other points could have been included, but most of these have very limited consequences. It is, however, evident that the use of the electron microscope is more likely to change this picture within the next few years.

REFERENCES

Ahmad, M. (1965). Incompatibility in yeast. *In* "Incompatibility in Fungi" (K. Esser and J. R. Raper, eds.), pp. 12–23. Springer, Berlin.

Barnett, H. L. (1937). Studies on the sexuality of the Heterobasidiae. *Mycologia* **29:** 626–649.

Berthet, P. (1964). "Essai biotaxinomique sur les Discomycètes," 158 pp. Thesis, Université de Lyon.

Boidin, J. (1956). Polarité dite "sexuelle" et systématique chez les Basidiomycètes Théléphoracés. *Rev. Mycol.* **21:** 121–131.

Boidin, J. (1964). Valeur des caractères culturaux et cytologiques pour la taxinomie des Théléphoraceae résupinés et étalés-réfléchis (Basidiomycètes). *Bull. Soc. Botan. France* **111:** 309–315.

Burges, A. (1955). Problems associated with the species concept in mycology. *In* "Species Studies in the British Flora" (J. E. Lousley, ed.), pp. 65–82. Buncle, Arbroath.

Burnett, J. H. (1956). The mating systems of fungi. I. *New Phytologist* **55:** 50–90.

Burnett, J. H. (1965). The natural history of recombination systems. *In* "Incompatibility in Fungi" (K. Esser and J. R. Raper, eds.), pp. 13–23. Springer, Berlin.

Emerson, R., and C. M. Wilson. (1954). Interspecific hybrids and the cytogenetics and cytotaxonomy of *Euallomyces. Mycologia* **46:** 393–434.

Esser, K., and R. Kuenen. (1965). "Genetik der Pilze," 496 pp. Springer, Berlin.

Fincham, J. R. S., and P. R. Day. (1963). "Fungal Genetics," 300 pp. Blackwell, Oxford.

Flor, H. H. (1959). Genetic control of host-parasite interaction in rust diseases. *Plant Pathol., Probl. Progr., 1908–1958* Chapter 14.

Fries, N. (1940). Researches into multipolar sexuality of *Cyathus striatus* Pers. *Symbolae Botan. Upsalienses* **4**(1): 1–39.

Fuller, M. S. (1966). Structure of the uniflagellate zoospores of aquatic Phycomycetes. *Proc. Symp. Colston Res. Soc.* **18**: 67–84.

Kühner, R. (1945). Nouvelle recherches sur les divisions nucléaires dans la basidie et les spores des Agaricales. *Compt. Rend.* **220**: 618–620.

Lamoure, D. (1954). Contributions à l'étude cytologique des germinations et du mycélium de quelques Agaricales, en particulier des Coprins de la section Setulosi (Lange). *Ann. Univ. Lyon* **C8**: 21–55.

Lamoure, D. (1960). "Recherches cytologiques et expérimentales sur l'amphithallie et la parthénogénèse chez les Agaricales," 119 pp. Thesis, Université de Lyon.

Lange, M. (1952). Species concept in the genus *Coprinus*. A study on the significance of intersterility. *Dansk Botan. Arkiv* **14**(1): 1–64.

Mounce, I., and R. Macrae. (1938). Interfertility phenomena in *Fomes pinicola*. *Can. J. Res.* **C16**: 354–376.

Rossen, J. M., and M. Westergaard. (1966). Studies on the mechanism of crossing over. I. Meiosis and the time of meiotic chromosome replication in the Ascomycete *Neottiella rutilans* (Fr.) Dennis. *Compt. Rend. Trav. Lab. Carlsberg* **35**: 233–260.

Sansome, E. R. (1965). Meiosis in diploid and polyploid sex organs of *Phytophthora* and *Achlya*. *Cytologia* **30**: 103–117.

Winge, Ö. (1942). Croisement inter-specific chez les champignons. *Scientia Genet.* **2**: 171–189.

Winge, Ö. (1957). The inheritance of fermentative ability in yeasts through complementary gene action. *Proc. Intern. Genet. Symp., Tokyo Kyoto, 1956* pp. 651–655. Sci. Council Japan, Tokyo.

Taxonomy

POSSIBLE EVOLUTIONARY PATTERNS

CHAPTER 25

The Origin and Status of Fungi (with a Note on the Fossil Record)

G. W. MARTIN

Department of Botany
University of Iowa
Iowa City, Iowa

I. THE ORIGIN AND STATUS OF FUNGI

A. *Early Views to Micheli*

1. The Classical Period

The early records of fungi are scattered and difficult to interpret. Certainly some fungi were eaten by the Greeks and Romans as they surely were by their less civilized contemporaries. *Amanita caesaria* owes its specific epithet to the tradition that it was prized by the Roman emperors although the actual mushroom referred to in ancient writings may have been something quite different, possibly a bolete. Truffles were highly esteemed, although their nature was completely misunderstood, one common belief associating their formation with thunderbolts. There were records of mushroom poisoning, and antidotes were suggested. The references are too vague to identify the species concerned, and the antidotes were of value only so far as they were purgatives. Buller (1915) summarizes fully the references to fungi in classical writings. They would be of purely historical interest had not the early herbalists passed them on to later times. While written records are lacking, there is evidence that hallucinogenic fungi were used in Siberia and in Mexico and Central America at a time not far from contemporary with the Greek and Roman cultures (Wasson and Wasson, 1957; Heim and Wasson, 1958).

Plant diseases caused by fungi were known to agriculturalists, but until late in the seventeenth century it was not suspected that they were caused by fungi. To the ancient writers, fungi were restricted to the fleshy or woody forms known as mushrooms or puffballs. Since they grew attached to the substratum after the manner of plants, they were considered plants, albeit aberrant forms.

2. *Renaissance to the Beginning of Modern Mycology*

With the revival of learning, numerous botanical works were published, at first annotated reprints of classical authors, especially Dioscorides, in the original or in translation; later, these tended to show more and more originality, and there was increasing mention of fungi. De Tournefort (1719) and Adanson (1763) give extended accounts of these writers, and Ramsbottom (1941), although his classical paper is chiefly concerned with Linnaeus and post-Linnaean authors, gives an excellent account of pre-Linnaean writers. There was vigorous controversy as to whether fungi were propagated by "seeds." Those who denied that such was the case included Caesalpinus, writing in 1583, and L. F. Marsigli, in 1714. G. della Porta, as early as 1588, supported the "seed" theory, and was followed by Malpighi in 1679, Tournefort in 1707, and A. D. de Jussieu in 1728. Although the balance was in favor of the "seed" theory, the idea that some organisms could arise spontaneously from decaying materials persisted until late in the nineteenth century. Oparin (1957) discusses this fully in his first chapter. See also Ainsworth's summary in Chapter I of the first volume of the present work.

Although de Tournefort's last published paper was on the culture of mushrooms, the fungi are treated only briefly in the third edition of his great work *Institutiones Rei Herbariae* (1719), published posthumously. Nine pages out of 565 and seven plates out of 333 are devoted to the fungi, which are grouped with the mosses and algae in his Class XVII. Two pages and one figure are given to the lichens, which are grouped with the ferns in his Class XVI.

B. *Micheli*

If de Tournefort is in many ways the precursor of modern botany, Micheli (1729) may be regarded as the first modern mycologist. He followed the system of de Tournefort, to which his book is essentially a supplement. All major groups except gymnosperms are represented, but over half the text and nearly three-quarters of the illustrations are devoted to fungi, including lichens. Most of the fungi discussed are the larger fleshy or woody forms such as mushrooms, puffballs, and a few slime molds, but perhaps the most notable feature is the description and illustration of microfungi, including *Botrytis, Aspergillus,* and what is now known as *Penicillium,* basidiospores in groups of four, and asci with ascospores. He was the first to attempt pure culture methods. Using a clean knife, he cut sound melons and sowed on the exposed surfaces "seeds" of various molds, noting that colonies of the same molds developed on the inoculated areas. This should have put an end to the theory of the origin of fungi from decaying materials, but, as usual in such cases, did not. Like others of his time, Micheli regarded the lichens as being clearly plants, quite distinct from the fungi and closest to the liverworts.

C. *Linnaeus and Contemporaries*

The treatment of the fungi by Linnaeus in the all-important first edition of the *Species Plantarum* of 1753 was very perfunctory and far less discriminating than that of Micheli. The importance of this work for mycology is that in it Linnaeus formalized binomial nomenclature and applied it to the relatively few species of fungi (less than 100) which he recognized. He included the fungi as the last, and lowest, group of his Class XXIV, Cryptogamia, and this is essentially the place they held for a century and a half. The lichens, with the liverworts, some gelatinous fungi, and a few sponges, were included in the algae. In the later editions of the *Species Plantarum,* under various editors, the treatment of the fungi was greatly improved. Adanson (1763) placed a few simple fungi, including *Aspergillus* and *Botrytis,* in his first family Byssi with the filamentous algae. The great majority were combined in his second family Fungi, divided into seven sections comprising 55 genera. In the case of the majority of these he cites Micheli's figures. Adanson's system, which stresses the inadequacy of classifications based on one or few characters, is frequently referred to by modern advocates of computer analysis.

Despite the work of Micheli, the controversy about the nature of the fungi persisted. O. von Muenchhausen, shortly after the middle of the eighteenth century, proposed a theory that the fungi were composed of aggregations of "zoophytes" which separated out when the fungi were soaked in water. According to Ramsbottom, Linnaeus was greatly impressed by Muenchhausen's view and conducted an extensive correspondence with him. Somewhat later, Hedwig supported the sap and decay theories. Many besides Linnaeus had doubts about the affinity of the fungi with plants, including Weiss (1770) and G. H. Weber (see Wiggers, 1780), so much so that Willdenow (1792) wrote a vigorous denunciation of these theories and came to the conclusion, wholly logical on the basis of the information he had, that the fungi were indubitably plants.

While the work of Linnaeus, and particularly his establishment of a uniform system of binomial nomenclature, was a stimulus to the study of the fungi, many other factors, including increasing use of the compound microscope, certainly played a part. Their study was pursued diligently by a number of able systematists of whom J. B. F. Bulliard, A. J. G. C. Batsch, D. C. H. Persoon, H. F. Link, L. D. de Schweinitz, and Fries are perhaps worthy of special mention. The number of species increased so rapidly that Fries (1825, p. 47) suggested that the total number might well be as great as that of the species of insects.

D. Phylogenetic Theories

1. Derivation from Algae

a. Polyphyletic Theories. Once the nature of the fungi as living organisms originating and reproducing in essentially the same way as others had been established, attempts were made to fit them more accurately into the general schemes of classification. The existence of thread-like filaments, the antheridial branches and oogonia of the water molds and particularly the zoospores produced by these forms naturally suggested algae as their nearest relatives. Alexander Braun (1847) declared that the fungi were no more than collateral groups of algae, and Pringsheim (1858) put the great weight of his authority behind this view.

The wide acceptance of evolution following Darwin's proposal of natural selection in 1858 and 1859 to explain how it might have occurred naturally stimulated phylogenetic theory. The view of fungi as derived from various algal groups was well adapted to treatment from this standpoint and was supported by Cohn (1872), Sachs (1875), Brefeld (1889), C. E. Bessey (1895), Harper (1899), Lotsy (1907), E. A. Bessey (1935, 1942, 1955) and, with increasing emphasis on the red algae as a possible source, particularly with reference to the Ascomycetes and rusts, by Dodge (1914), Orton (1927), Jackson (1944), Chadefaud (1944, 1960),[1] and Dennison and Carroll (1966). These theories in one form or another have probably represented until very recently the dominant opinion as to the origins of the fungi. Brefeld's derivation of the higher Fungi in two lines, one through the Zygomycetes and the other through the Oomycetes, both regarded as unquestionably offshoots from distinct groups of algae, is of special importance because of the wide acceptance it received for many years.

b. Monophyletic Theories. The polyphyletic views were not unchallenged. What are essentially monophyletic derivations of at least the great majority of the fungi from algae were advanced by Winter (1879), de Bary (1881, 1884), and Gäumann (1926). Fischer (1892) and Atkinson (1909) tended to support a similar origin, but both suggested that the source might possibly be sought in nonchlorophyllous unicellular forms. Zuck (1953) argued that three nutritional roads, the autotrophic,

[1] Chadefaud (1944) cites the French translation of Sachs' *Lehrbuch* of 1872 as the first suggestion of the origin of the Ascomycetes from red algae. I have been unable to verify this.

the lysotrophic, and the phagotrophic, may well have been followed by plants, fungi, and animals from very early time, hence we should recognize the three kingdoms Phyta, Myketes and Zoa. Copeland (1956) placed the great majority of the fungi in his phylum Inophyta but excluded the water molds and the Myxomycetes, distributing the former among three other phyla and including the latter with the rhizopod groups. He restricted the Kingdom Plantae to those plants whose pigments are restricted to chlorophyll *a* and *b*, carotene, and xanthophyll, that is the green algae, bryophytes, and vascular plants, and the Kingdom Animalia to multicellular animals. He accepted Enderlein's Kingdom Mychota for the bacteria and blue-green algae, and Hogg's Kingdom Protoctista for the red and brown algae, all pigmented flagellates and algae other than the green algae, the Protozoa, and the fungi included in the Inopyhta. Ingold (1959) remarked, with apparent approval, that many present-day students would favor the division of organisms into four kingdoms: Plant, Animal, Fungal, and Bacterial, essentially a simplification of Copeland's treatment.

2. *Derivation from Protozoa*

In establishing the Kingdom *Protista* in 1886, Haeckel emphasized the difficulty of distinguishing plants and animals at the lower levels of these groups and paved the way for reconsideration of the classifications then in use. Cornu (1872) pointed out errors in Pringsheim's arguments, but Gobi (1884; see Borodin, 1885) seems to have been the first to propose an independent derivation of the fungi from simple protozoans. Dangeard (1886) adopted this view and supported it in a number of subsequent papers. Others who have favored it include Scherffel (1901, 1925), Cavers (1915), Cook (1928), Martin (1932, 1955), Ramsbottom (1941), Langeron (1945), Langeron and Vanbreuseghem (1952), Heim (1952), Moreau (1954), and Ingold (1959). Some tended to favor a monophyletic, others a polyphyletic, system, but all agreed that the derivation of the fungi from the algae presents more difficulties than does a theory of protozoan origin.

3. *Phylogeny and Classification*

In recent years there has been a tendency to disparage phylogenetic speculation. Certainly, all previous systems based on such speculation have proved to be faulty in the light of new information, and there is no reason to expect that newer ones will be any more permanent. What is more serious is that when any such system becomes widely accepted and is used as a basis for classification it tends to become regarded as factual rather than theoretical and thus impedes rather than contributes to progress. Witness the persistence in current literature of the terms Thallophyta and Pteridophyta long after their application to modern systems has ceased to be relevant.[2] Yet until the idea of evolutionary development is divorced from classification—and there is no evidence that that is imminent—phylogenetic concepts will serve, explicitly or implicitly, as the basis for any attempt to formulate a natural classification and, if they are in accordance with the current knowledge of their time, will serve both as a guide and a challenge to contemporary students. Coulter's comment of 1898, cited by Lotsy (1907) on the title page of the *Vorträge,* is still true.[3]

E. *Theories as to Origin of Life and Their Relevance to Fungi*

1. *Older Views*

The idea that some living organisms developed from nonliving material is rooted in antiquity. Pasteur's experiments of a century ago served to show the fallacy of the evidence on which it was based in his time, and since then the aphorism that all life comes from life has frequently been quoted as settling the matter when, in reality, it merely evades the issue. The idea of such origin is, in fact, implicit in the concept of evolution. Huxley, in 1868, thought he had discovered a form very close to such a beginning in his *Bathybius* and, in 1870, in an important statement quoted by Oparin (1957, p. 73), he clearly recognized that the conditions under which life might be supposed to have arisen must have been quite different from those prevailing at the present time, that light need not be presumed to have been necessary, and that the hypothetical early manifestations of life might have much in common with fungi. Haeckel held similar views. Engels (1939), in a highly polemical work first published in the late 1870's, stated that "science is only able to say that [life] must have arisen as a result of chemical action," and in an unfinished book written in the early 1880's and read by Marx in manuscript, although not published

[2] In all recent editions of the International Code of Botanical Nomenclature, the starting point for the nomenclature of lichens is 1753; that of the fungi to which they are most closely related is 1821–1832. The starting point of the gasteromycetes is 1801; that of the fungi to which they are in many cases certainly related is also 1821–1832. Few modern systematists believe that either the lichens or the gasteromycetes constitute a natural group as that term is used in classification, hence these rules are based on classifications derived from phyletic opinions now very generally believed to be incorrect. There is, of course, no objection to the use of these terms, preferably not capitalized, as convenient generalizations.

[3] "The most difficult as well as the most fascinating problem in connection with any group is its phylogeny. The data upon which we base opinions concerning phylogeny are never sufficient but such opinions usually stimulate research and are necessary to progress."

until 1927 (Engels, 1940), he expressed this more formally. In his first three chapters, Oparin deals at length with these matters.

2. *Current Views*

The view that is now widely held is also most completely developed by Oparin. For the present discussion the most important points are (1) that when life first appeared, conditions on the earth's surface, including the atmosphere, must have been very different, as Huxley had suggested, from what they are at present; (2) that amino acids can be produced from inorganic materials in an environment in which the attempt is made to approximate such conditions, and that in dilute solutions in sea water such amino acids may be polymerized to form polypeptides at ordinary temperatures and pressures; and (3) that the earliest living material need not have possessed capacity for photosynthesis. Recent discussion of this question in the light of later information may be found in the papers by Cloud (1965) and by Ponnamperuma and Mack (1965). This seems to demolish the argument frequently advanced in the earlier literature that fungi must have been derived from algae since otherwise they would have had no source of nutrition.

The increasing emphasis on the biochemical approach to the understanding of living organisms has quite naturally had an impact on theories of relationship. The discovery of the remarkable similarity of the DNA molecule in widely different organisms is perhaps the most striking result of these studies. If this fundamental material is as similar in all organisms as present evidence indicates, then, it has been argued, all living things must be closely related. This is often extended to imply that all organisms have been derived from a single fortuitous chemical event. That is by no means a necessary part of the theory, which is in reality no more than a conviction that under suitable environmental conditions, such as may have existed on the earth at a remote time, matter must inevitably have assumed by gradual stages, and certainly at a subcellular level, the characteristics which we now associate with life. The details of such a process are still speculative, but the possibility of a multiple origin of life is at least strongly indicated by Cloud (1965). The important thing is that the very wide acceptance of this view within the last quarter of a century has brought about a change in our concepts of the nature of life far more revolutionary in its effect on traditional thinking than was Darwin's proposal, yet with very little popular opposition, in striking contrast with the reception accorded his hypothesis. This must ultimately affect any theory of development, but as yet the evidence as to the single or multiple origin of life is too scanty to permit more than an expression of opinion based on theoretical grounds, which were, of course, the basis for my own advocacy

(Martin, 1955) of the necessity to consider the possibility of multiple origins.

F. *Summary and Conclusion*

The belief that fungi are basically no more than algae which in the course of their evolution have dispensed with chlorophyll, while still held, has in recent years been less favored. The idea that the earliest organisms must have been photosynthetic has been shown to be unnecessary in the light of current theories as to the origin of life. It is becoming common to regard the Fungi as an essentially homogeneous group, at least conceivably monophyletic if, as is often the case, certain aberrant forms are excluded. Many would exclude the Myxomycetes; nearly as many, those water molds with cellulose walls. Other doubtful groups could be added, the Eccrinales, for example. This may point the way to future clarification of our concept as to what is meant by fungi. Flowering plants, red algae and a few apparent green algae have long been known to lack chlorophyll. It is possible that some groups still generally included in the Fungi, the Oomycetes for example, may have to be removed to algal groups. But on the whole, the bulk of the fungi may be regarded, in the light of present information, as constituting a very large, extremely variable, but on the whole remarkably coherent group of organisms, which may reasonably be treated as a discrete major taxonomic unit.

II. NOTE ON FOSSIL FUNGI

A. *The Nineteenth Century*

Fungi or organic remnants which suggested fungi have been recognized in fossil materials for well over a century. A number of paleobotanists from the 1840's to the end of the century, of whom some of the better known were Brongniart, Heer, Lesquereux, Renault, Schimper, and Unger, published notes on what they regarded as fungi which occurred as mycelium embedded in wood and sometimes bearing what were regarded as spores or sporangia, or, much more commonly, spots on leaves and twigs which were believed to be similar to the leaf-spots and molds which occur today. Some dated as far back as the Carboniferous. Some were certainly not fungi. *Polyporites bowmanni* (Lindl. & Hutton) Mesch., one of the earliest, described in 1831 from the Carboniferous of Wales, is now believed to be based on a fish scale. Others, suggesting mycelium, are now believed to be worm tunnels; still others, corals. Nevertheless, a substantial number of them apparently are fungi, many quite similar, in outward appearance at least, to fungi now living. It was this that prompted Gardner (1886) to remark: "The fungi are destitute of chlorophyll and hence, or owing to their parasitic and saprophytic habits, any further development in them seems to have been arrested."

The knowledge of fossil fungi to the end of the nineteenth century was summarized by Meschinelli, first in volumes 10 and 11 of Saccardo's *Sylloge Fungorum* (1892, 1895) and then in his beautifully illustrated *Fungorum Fossilium Omnium* (1902). As of the end of the nineteenth century, it may be said that clear records of mycelium and more doubtful records of fructifications were known from as early as the Carboniferous, although in rather scanty amount, and that there were abundant relics of what appeared to be leaf and stem fungi from the Tertiary and the Pleistocene. Many of the latter were so like modern forms as to be indistinguishable from them, particularly as spores and spore-bearing structures were largely lacking and identification in such cases had to be on the basis of the form of the fructification, with much doubt as to whether some of the closed fruiting bodies were ascocarps or pycnidia.

Meschinelli's work marks the end of one epoch and the beginning of a new one. Many of the names he introduced were based on well-known modern genera, interpreted widely, with the termination *-ites* replacing the original ending, and the new names credited to the authors of the original names on which they were based, who had, of course, never heard of them. These names have recently been criticized by Holm (1959). A discussion of this question is beyond the scope of the present treatment, but it may be proper to suggest that Meschinelli had good palaeontological tradition to justify his usage and it is to be hoped that his names can be regularized to make them acceptable under the current Code. Holm has already done this for *Phacidites*.

In order to explain the apparent scarcity of fungi in the Carboniferous strata, it was suggested that the fungi were not adapted to live on hosts at or below the pteridophyte level; also that the large amount of carbon dioxide in the air was probably unfavorable to their growth. Others contended that fungi were, by their nature, unlikely to be preserved except in rare and exceptional instances. This last explanation may well apply to the soft, fleshy, hymenomycetous fungi, but it is difficult to see how it could be important in the case of some of the tough or woody forms which, in modern species, may resist decay almost as well as do the wood or leaves on which they grow.

B. *Modern Developments*

The next important addition to our knowledge of fossil fungi was the appearance of the classical studies of Kidston and Lang on the fossils of the Rhynie beds of middle Devonian age. In their fifth paper (1921) they summarize the thallophytes which occurred in the ancient equivalent of a modern peat bed. The rhizomes and decaying stems of the primitive vascular plants which composed the bed are permeated by fungal hyphae. They state: "The fungal hyphae are so generally distributed that they can be regarded as forming an integral part of the peat." Most of the hyphae appear to be nonseptate, but in view of the difficulty in observing septa in many modern fungi which occur in similar situations, some of these conclusions may be accepted with reservation. Certainly some of the fungi were clearly septate (their Figs. 1 and 3) and do not suggest septate phycomycetous mycelium. Various types of vesicular bodies apparently represent sporangia and resting spores. There is a strong suggestion that at least one of these fungi found regularly in the inner cortex of the rhizomes of *Asteroxylon* may have been associated with the plant when it was living. Butler (1939) emphasized the strong resemblance of these fossil fungi to modern fungi referred to *Rhizophagus,* now regarded as a genus of the Endogonaceae and occurring under what appear to be comparable circumstances.

Material of possible organic origin suggesting the occurrence of plant life in Precambrian time has been known for many years and has usually been regarded as possible indication of the presence of bacteria and blue-green algae. For fungi, the most startling extension of time is revealed by the study of ancient cherts by Tyler and Barghoorn (1954), who found what they interpreted as two kinds of fungi, associated with blue-green algae and a possible flagellate, in material from the Gunflint formation of Ontario, with a possible age of nearly two billion years, verified by Hurley *et al.* (1962) using K-Ar and Rb-Sr measurements of the same material. Later studies on these fossils by Barghoorn and his associates (Tyler *et al.,* 1957; Barghoorn and Tyler, 1965; Barghoorn *et al.,* 1965; Schopf *et al.,* 1965), while extending these studies significantly, have emphasized bacteria and blue-green algae. Cloud (1965), in his careful survey of the Gunflint "microflora" seems somewhat uncertain about the presence of fungi. Barghoorn and Schopf (1966) present convincing evidence of the existence of bacteria in comparable cherts from South Africa with a well-authenticated age of over three billion years, and associated with them are what appear to be filamentous forms the nature of which still remains uncertain. This, and other recent evidence cited in the papers mentioned, pushes back the time at which life appeared on the earth to a much more remote period than has heretofore been thought possible, and suggests that fungi may have appeared at a very early stage.

It is frequently said that some of the Devonian rhizomes, of *Asteroxylon,* for example, were mycorrhizal. Most of the fungi associated with them are of the arbuscular type discussed by Butler. To what extent these constitute mycorrhizae in modern plants is as yet unsettled, but the relationship with the hosts in the case of the fossils may be presumed to be of the same nature.

Recent reports by Dilcher (1963, 1965) illustrate and describe fossil leaf fungi from the Lower Eocene of Tennessee, in which fruiting structures are so perfectly preserved as to permit their assignment in many cases to contemporary genera, such as *Meliola* and *Asterina,* thus bearing witness to the persistence of these genera for a period estimated as over fifty million years. In the later paper, Dilcher gives an invaluable summary of the epiphyllous fungi known from the fossil record.

In summary, it may be concluded that fungi have been present for over two billion years, from Precambrian time, in aquatic habitats, that they were abundant in association with land plants in the Devonian, and that despite wide gaps in the fossil record it is safe to assume they have been continuously present since that remote period and have maintained the same general relationships with other organisms that they do today.

REFERENCES

Adanson, M. (1763). "Familles des Plantes," Parts I and II. Vincent, Paris.

Atkinson, G. F. (1909). Some problems in the evolution of the lower fungi. *Ann. Mycol.* **7**: 441–472.

Barghoorn, E. S., and S. A. Tyler. (1965). Microorganisms from the Gunflint chert. *Science* **147**: 563–577.

Barghoorn, E. S., and J. W. Schopf. (1966). Microorganisms three billion years old from the Precambrian of South Africa. *Science* **152**: 758–763.

Barghoorn, E. S., W. S. Meinscher, and J. W. Schopf. (1965). Paleobiology of a Precambrian shale. *Science* **148**: 461–472.

Bessey, C. E. (1895). Synopsis of plant phyla. *Studies Veget. Nebraska* **7**: 275–373.

Bessey, E. A. (1935). "A Textbook of Mycology," 495 pp. McGraw-Hill (Blakiston), New York.

Bessey, E. A. (1942). Some problems in fungus phylogeny. *Mycologia* **34**: 355–379.

Bessey, E. A. (1955). "Morphology and Taxonomy of Fungi," 791 pp. Blakiston, Philadelphia, Pennsylvania.

Borodin, J. (1885). Review of Chr. Gobi: Ueber die Gruppe der Amoeboideae. (Original in Russian.) *Botan. Centr.* **22**: 35–38.

Braun, A. (1847). *Chara kokelii,* eine neue deutscher Art. *Flora* **30**: 17–29 (footnote, p. 23).

Brefeld, O. (1889). "Untersuchungen aus dem Gesammtgebiet der Mycologie. VIII. Basidiomyceten III und die Begründung des natürlichen Systemes der Pilze." 305 pp. Klein, Leipzig.

Buller, A. H. R. (1915). The fungus lore of the Greeks and Romans. *Brit. Mycol. Soc. Trans.* **5**: 21–66.

Butler, E. J. (1939). The occurrences and systematic positions of the vesicular-arbuscular type of mycorrhizal fungi. *Brit. Mycol. Soc. Trans.* **22**: 274–301.

Cavers, F. (1915). The interrelationships of Protista and primitive Fungi. *New Phytologist* **14**: 94–104, 164–168, 223–227, and 275–280.

Chadefaud, M. (1944). "Biologie des Champignons," 8th ed. 267 pp. Gallimard, Paris.

Chadefaud, M. (1960). Les végétaux non vasculaires. Cryptogamie. *In* "Traité de Botanique Systematiques" (M. Chadefaud and L. Emberger, eds.), Vol. 1, 1018 pp. Masson, Paris.

Cohn, F. (1872). Conspectus familiarum cryptogamarum secondum naturalem dispositarum. *Hedwigia* **1**: 17–20.

Cloud, P. E., Jr. (1965). Significance of the Gunflint (Precambrian) Microflora. *Science* **148**: 27–35.

Cook, W. R. I. (1928). The inter-relationships of the Archimycetes. *New Phytologist* **27**: 230–260 and 298–320.

Copeland, H. F. (1956). "The Classification of Lower Organisms," 302 pp. Pacific Press, Palo Alto, California.

Cornu, M. (1872). Monographie des Saprolegniées. *Ann. Sci. Nat.: Botan.* [5] **15**: 5–198.

Dangeard, P. A. (1886). Recherches sur les organisms inférieurs. *Ann. Sci. Nat.: Botan.* [7] **4**: 241–341.

de Bary, A. (1881). Zur Systematik der Thallophyten. *Botan. Ztg.* **39**: 1–17 and 33–36.

de Bary, A. (1884). "Vergleichende Morphologie und Physiologie der Pilzen, Mycetozoen und Bakterien," 558 pp. Engelmann, Leipzig.

Denison, W. C., and G. C. Carroll. (1966). The primitive Ascomycetes: A new look at an old problem. *Mycologia* **58**: 249–269.

de Tournefort, J. P. (1719). *In* "Institutiones rei herbariae" (A. de Jussieu, ed.), 3rd ed., Vols. I, II and III. Typographia Regia, Paris.

Dilcher, D. L. (1963). Eocene epiphyllous fungi. *Science* **142**: 667–669.

Dilcher, D. L. (1965). Epiphyllous fungi from Eocene deposits in western Tennessee, U.S.A. *Palaeontographica* **B116**: 1–54.

Dodge, B. O. (1914). The morphological relationships of the Florideae and the Ascomycetes. *Bull. Torrey Botan. Club* **41**: 157–202.

Engels, F. (1939). "Herr Eugen Dühring's Revolution in Science (Anti-Dühring)" (English transl. by E. Burns), 365 pp. International Publishers, New York. Originally published in periodical form in Vorwärts, Leipzig, 1877–1878.)

Engels, F. (1940). "Dialectics of Nature" (transl. by Clemens Dutt with a preface and notes by J. B. S. Haldane), 383 pp. International Publishers, New York. (Originally published in German in 1927.)

Fischer, A. (1892). Phycomycetes. *Kryptogamen Flora* **1**: 1–105.

Fries, E. (1825). "Systema Orbis Vegetabilis. I. Plantae Homonemeae," 374 pp. Typographia Academica, Lund.

Gardner, J. S. (1886). *In* "A Monograph of the British Eocene Flora" (J. S. Gardner and C. B. Ettingshausen, eds.), p. 159. London.

Gäumann, E. A. (1926). "Vergleichende Morphologie der Pilze," 626 pp. Fischer, Jena.

Harper, R. A. (1899). Cell-division in sporangia and asci. *Ann. Botany* (*London*) **13**: 467–525.

Heim, R. (1952). Les voies de l'évolution chez les champignons. *Colloq. Intern. Centre Nat. Rech. Sci.* (*Paris*). pp. 27–28.

Heim, R., and R. G. Wasson. (1958). "Les champignons hallucinogènes du Mexique," 322 pp. Mus. Nat. d'Hist. Nat., Paris.

Holm, L. (1959). Some remarks on Meschinelli's fungus-names. *Taxon* **8**: 66–67.

Hurley, P., H. W. Fairbairn, H. W. Pinson, Jr., and J. Hower. (1962). Unmetamorphosed minerals in the Gunflint formation used to test the age of the Animikie. *J. Geol.* **70:** 489–492.

Ingold, C. T. (1959). Fungi. *In* "Vistas in Botany" (W. B. Turrill, ed.), pp. 348–385. Pergamon Press, Oxford.

Jackson, H. S. (1944). Life cycles and phylogeny in the higher fungi. *Trans. Roy. Soc. Can., Sect. V* [3] **38:** 1–32.

Kidston, R., and W. H. Lang. (1921). On Old Red Sandstone plants showing structure, from the Rhynie chert bed, Aberdeenshire. V. The Thallophyta occurring in the peat-bed. *Trans. Roy. Soc. Edinburgh* **52:** 855–902.

Langeron, M. (1945). "Précis de mycologie," 672 pp. Masson, Paris.

Langeron, M., and R. Vanbreuseghem. (1952). "Précis de mycologie," 703 pp. Masson, Paris.

Lotsy, J. P. (1907). "Vorträge über botanische Stammegeschichte. I. Algen und Pilzen," 828 pp. Fischer. Jena.

Martin, G. W. (1932). Systematic position of the slime molds and its bearing on the classification of the fungi. *Botan. Gaz.* **93:** 421–435.

Martin, G. W. (1955). Are fungi plants? *Mycologia* **47:** 779–792.

Meschinelli, A. (1892). Fungi Fossiles. *Sylloge Fungorum* **10:** 747–808.

Meschinelli, A. (1895). Fungi Fossiles (Addenda). *Sylloge Fungorum* **11:** 657–659.

Meschinelli, A. (1902). "Fungorum Fossilium Omnium hucusque cognitorum Iconographia," 144 pp. Vicentiae.

Micheli, P. A. (1729). "Nova Plantarum Genera iuxta Tournefortii Methodum disposita," 232 pp. Florence.

Moreau, F. (1954). "Les Champignons," Vol. 2, pp. 941–2120. Lechevalier, Paris.

Oparin, A. I. (1957). "The Origin of Life on Earth." (transl. by A. Synge), 3rd ed., 495 pp. Oliver & Boyd, Edinburgh and London.

Orton, C. R. (1927). A working hypothesis on the origin of the rusts, with special reference to the phenomena of heteroecism. *Botan. Gaz.* **84:** 113–138.

Ponnamperuma, C., and R. Mack. (1965). Nucleotide synthesis under possible primitive earth conditions. *Science* **148:** 1221–1223.

Pringsheim, N. (1858). Beiträge zur Morphologie und Systematik der Algen. I. Die Saprolegnieen. *Jahrb. Wiss. Botan.* **1:** 284–306.

Ramsbottom, J. (1941). The expanding knowledge of mycology since Linnaeus. *Trans. Linnean Soc. London* (*Botany*) **151:** 280–367.

Sachs, J. (1875). "A Textbook of Botany" (transl. by A. W. Bennett and W. T. Thistelton Dyer), 858 pp. Oxford Univ. Press, London and New York.

Scherffel, A. (1901). Kleiner Beitrag zur Phylogenie einiger Gruppen niederer Organismen. *Botan. Ztg.* **59:** 143–158.

Scherffel, A. (1925). Endophytische Phycomyceten-Parasiten der Bacillariaceen und einige neue Monadinen. *Arch. Protistenk.* **52:** 1–141.

Schopf, J. W., E. S. Barghoorn, N. D. Maser, and R. O. Gordon. (1965). Electron microscopy of fossil bacteria two billion years old. *Science* **149:** 1365–1367.

Tyler, S. A., and E. S. Barghoorn. (1954). Occurrence of structurally preserved plants in pre-Cambrian rocks of the Canadian shield. *Science* **119:** 606–608.

Tyler, S. A., E. S. Barghoorn and L. S. Barrett. (1957). Anthracitic coal from Precambrian Upper Huronian black shale of the Iron River district, northern Michigan. *Bull. Geol. Soc. Am.* **68:** 1293–1304.

Wasson, V. P., and R. G. Wasson. (1957). "Mushrooms, Russia and History," 2 vols., 433 pp. Pantheon Books, New York.

Weiss, F. G. (1770). "Plantae cryptogamicae Florae Gottingensis," 333 pp. Göttingen.

Wiggers, F. H. (1780). *"Primitiae Florae Holsaticae,"* 112 pp. Kiliae. (Often attributed to G. H. Weber.)

Willdenow, C. L. (1792). Etwas über die Entstehung der Pilze. *Ann. Botan. Usteri* **3**: 59–72.

Winter, G. (1879). Ueber ein naturliches System der Thallophyten. *Hedwigia* **18**: 1–12.

Zuck, R. K. (1953). Alternation of generations and the manner of nutrition. *Drew Univ. Studies* No. 6, pp. 1–19.

CHAPTER 26

Possible Interrelationships between Fungal Groups

D. B. O. SAVILE

Plant Research Institute
Central Experimental Farm
Ottawa, Canada

I. INTRODUCTION

A. Lack of Attention to Guiding Principles

Phylogenetic relationships are the ultimate basis of a satisfactory taxonomy, which in turn is central to all phases of mycology. Paleontologists criticize botanists for erecting phylogenies with inadequate fossil data, and mycologists are especially susceptible to such criticisms. For organisms with no adequate fossil record we must do the best possible without it. But the lack of such a record does not excuse unsupported guesswork. On the contrary we should follow the available guiding principles all the more carefully. The naïve, insupportable schemes often proposed for the fungi do not advance our understanding, but serve only to lower the prestige of mycology. De Bary showed an intuitive appreciation of evolutionary processes much greater than that of many of his successors.

The derivation of phylogenetic principles is beyond our scope. A minimal discussion accompanies the list presented below (Section I, B). The serious student of phylogeny and evolution in the fungi should study at least the elements of vertebrate paleontology in order to appreciate evolution within a group with an adequate fossil record. Some of these principles have been discussed in more detail elsewhere (Savile, 1954b, 1955). Together with a thorough appreciation of the problems faced by the fungi in entering new ecological niches, these principles may help the reader toward a realistic picture of evolution in the fungi.

B. *Phylogenetic Principles*

General principles are presented first, followed by ones that refer particularly to fungi.

1. New groups do not spring from climax groups, but always from less specialized, genetically plastic groups, and generally diverge early in the parental lineage. This fundamental principle is repeatedly ignored by mycologists.

2. Because new groups diverge from plastic ancestral groups, most connecting links fail to survive. The *direct* descendants within the parental group, in balance with a stable environment, evolve slowly. But in the *divergent* group a critical mutation releases a series of other mutations, and many casualties occur before stability is reestablished.

3. Thresholds and barriers: these concepts help us to understand principle 2 and to recognize the direction of evolution. When an evolutionary sequence passes the point where it is better adapted to a new than to an earlier environmental condition, it crosses a threshold. The threshold may or may not include an appreciable barrier; but barriers, both physiographic and physiological, are an important stimulus to rapid evolution (Savile, 1959). When, after prolonged restriction, an organism penetrates a barrier it enters a new environment with which it is not in balance. Often it is promptly eliminated, but, if it does survive, its progeny radiate into new niches. If we bear this process in mind and consider the problems of dispersal and water retention faced by the fungi as they penetrated terrestrial niches, their evolutionary sequences become easier to visualize.

4. If there are few possible ways of attaining important ends, convergent evolution is probable if not inevitable. However, appreciable convergence is to be expected only in adaptive characters. Every marked convergence in plants or animals that I have studied in detail has proved to be adaptive once the function was recognized. See also Section II.

5. A vacant ecological niche tends to be filled from several unrelated sources. Because particular structures are adapted to a given niche, such ecologically related organisms often show marked convergence.

6. In a single lineage the direction of evolution of a character is not randomly reversed; that of a functional character is never reversed unless an altered environment destroys its function. When there is reversal of a trend, we may see a substitute for an original structure; but the structure itself is not restored, for this would require many reverse mutations in the appropriate sequence.

7. In a group markedly different from its forerunners we see increasingly elaborate morphology, until the species are well adapted to the available habitats. Simplification then tends to set in, often accompanied by apomixis or a similar device.

8. It is true that ontogeny generally recapitulates phylogeny; but even with complex organisms this rule must be used with discretion. In the fungi the meager anatomical detail in immature structures usually makes it useless. It can occasionally be used with caution; e.g., the ontogeny of the sori in the Uredinales confirms other clues to their origins. Lamentably this is the one principle that mycologists, in asserting the homology of the ascus hook and clamp connection, have generally used (see Section II, especially C). When I previously included it, for completeness, but belittled its mycological value, it was the one principle mentioned by a reviewer.

9. Preadaptation. This term has been used in many ways, which are discussed by Simpson (1953) and Bock (1959). Provided, of course, that we avoid any inference of specific preparation for future adaptation, the term is useful in describing a variety of common evolutionary sequences. In this chapter it refers to a structure or mechanism adapted to one function in an ancestral group being, without change, adaptive in some degree for a new function in a derived group. Even if it functions imperfectly it provides the basis for refinement by future mutations. Thus the early uredinial peridium in the rust fungi, adapted to protection from insects, was preadapted to a new role in the first heteroecious rusts, in which a rigid domed structure served to rupture the heavy epidermis of the coniferous aecial host. Later, as forcible aeciospore discharge developed, the rigid lateral wall of the peridium was preadapted to maintain lateral pressure on the developing spores; and the final refinement was the development, on the inner faces of the peridial cells, of long slender warts that serve as compression springs.

10. In simple organisms biochemistry often proves more reliable than gross morphology in indicating genetic relationship. In conjunction with microscopic anatomy it long ago clarified algal classification, and it is yielding important results in the Basidiomycetes. It provides the final blow to attempts to derive the fungi from superficially similar algae.

11. Elaborate sexual mechanisms and self-sterility are generally ancient, as is shown by their occurrence in primitive algae and fungi. Simple sexual mechanisms and self-fertility or apomixis occur later, in species well adapted to a specialized niche; but these changes are potentially self-destructive, for reduced gene flow may make it difficult for such organisms to adapt to a changing environment.

12. As the fungi became increasingly terrestrial an elaboration of dispersal systems occurred to offset the loss of motile cells and transport by waves and currents. Similarly numerous devices to reduce desiccation evolved.

13. Obligate parasitism in the fungi is not a belated evolutionary

bypath, but a fundamental attribute of primitive groups; and saprophytism arose repeatedly from it. The first typical fungi were probably parasites; and it was as parasites that the fungi left the water protected by the tissues of their hosts. Destructive parasites, which are facultative saprophytes, may in some cases be derived from saprophytes. The common view that parasitic animals are generally derived from free-living species has no bearing on the fungi, which always had quite different physical and nutritional problems.

14. In strict parasitism the antiquity of the host reflects that of the parasite and vice versa. Hosts and parasites evolve together, apparently in balanced polymorphism (Mode, 1958). A new parasitic association is most likely to occur when host and parasite are genetically plastic, e.g., in the period of rapid evolution that follows establishment of a new group. Although hitherto used largely to show details of relationship and relative age among related genera of flowering plants (Savile, 1954a, 1961), this principle reveals the approximate relative ages of groups of parasitic fungi.

C. *Historical Review*

Fitzpatrick (1930) discussed most of the early phylogenetic speculations, and they will be only briefly summarized here. Pringsheim (1858) scattered the genera of Saprolegniales among the Siphonales, on the basis of gross morphology. Cohn (1872) and Sachs (1874) extended Pringsheim's scheme until all the fungi were hopefully disposed as offshoots of seemingly appropriate algae. These connections were based on superficial resemblances, occasionally even between sexual and asexual states. In the infancy of biochemistry these resemblances were plausible to the casual observer and the schemes were hailed as a natural system. De Bary (1881) pointed out that the various groups of fungi show considerable coherence in their physiology but differ sharply from all algae. His knowledge of comparative morphology gave him an insight into relationships that, in broad outline, is still of value. But for the efforts of Sachs' student C. E. Bessey, later supported by E. A. Bessey (e.g., 1942, and references therein), the algal hypothesis would surely have passed into history with de Bary's reasoned attack.

Today most of the alga-fungus resemblances are such palpable examples of convergence that, even without the clues from physiology and biochemistry, they present no problem to the student of evolutionary mechanisms. Stagnant water, devoid of violent agitation, encourages the formation, in algae and fungi, of large coenocytic cells that would be prone to critical damage in many habitats. In an evolutionary series devoid of motile cells, fertilization may be guaranteed either by the male cells having large food reserves (a more serious waste in small than in large organisms) and growing toward the female elements, or by means of a trichogyne or similar receptive hypha that will catch passively transported sperm cells that are produced in great numbers but have no appreciable food reserve. We need not wonder that this simple device appeared independently in the red algae, in some ascomycetes, and in the rust fungi.

Rejection of the algal hypothesis left no remaining doubt that the typical fungi are monophyletic, the Phycomycetes giving rise to the Ascomycetes and the latter to the Basidiomycetes. We shall try to elucidate the details of some of the connections between and within the classes.

II. CONVERGENCE AND HOMOLOGY

A. Recognition of Convergence

In complex organisms, such as vertebrates or flowering plants, convergence is usually easily recognized because the correlation of various functionally unrelated characters, often agreeing in elaborate detail, clearly indicates the related organisms. If we understand the biology of the organisms adequately we find that markedly convergent structures are strongly adaptive. Probably the only exceptions are characters that persist for some time after an ecological shift in the lineage has destroyed their function.

In simple organisms we find fewer characters and no wealth of fine detail. Consequently a relatively crude convergence may pass easily for homology. Our first question must then be: Has the supposedly homologous character an important function, and in how many ways may that function be performed? If the function is important and the means of performing it are limited, the probability of convergence is strong. If it also opposes two or more correlated characters of detailed anatomy or biochemistry, convergence is nearly certain. Finally, if it necessitates a phylogenetic arrangement that runs counter to phylogenetic principles it must be abandoned.

B. Examples

There are various examples of obvious convergence in the fungi. No one today would seriously suggest that all the hypogeous macrofungi (*Endogone, Elaphomyces,* Tuberales, and various gasteromycetes) are closely related. The striking superficial similarity of the sporocarps reflects their adaptation to a highly specialized niche. They mature underground and are dispersed by fossorial rodents with a keen olfactory sense.

The primitive hymenomycete with a smooth hymenium could increase its surface, without enlarging the sporocarp, in only a few ways. The surface could be thrown into shallow lobes or folds, as in *Leptotus,* a curious genus parasitic on mosses, whose affinities are uncertain but whose morphology and host relationship suggest it to be ancient. From such a start we may have the development of lamellae, teeth, or tubes. With so few alternatives it should not surprise us if some of these methods have been used more than once. In fact an increasing amount of study, much of it reviewed by Nobles (1958), shows that many of the classical genera and families of the higher basidiomycetes are polyphyletic; the lineages indicated by detailed anatomy and biochemistry cut across groups based on gross morphology. These studies are leading to a clearer picture of evolution within these fungi, and should eventually allow a more rational classification.

In earlier discussions (Savile, 1954b, 1955) various striking examples of convergence in other organisms were presented. I present here one more, to emphasize that we must not underestimate this process where the end is important and the means limited. Paleontological advances have essentially closed the gap between the reptiles and mammals. Recent summaries by Olson (1959) and Simpson (1959) clearly show that various lineages of reptiles approached the mammal grade skeletally and probably physiologically. Different characters naturally do not all advance synchronously. For convenience the initiation of mammal grade is defined by the paleontologist as the level at which the quadrate-articular jaw hinge is replaced by the more efficient dentary-squamosal hinge. This grade has been reached by at least five separate lines. Even more startling is the fact that in the two surviving groups, the monotremes and the typical mammals, the surplus quadrate and articular bones have passed, greatly reduced, into the inner ear where they serve as extra ossicles in an improved hearing mechanism. These little bones are generally lost in fossilization, and their fate in the extinct lineages is uncertain. Here we have one complex change that has occurred five times, and a correlated one that has followed it at least twice.

C. *The Gordian Knot*

In a dikaryotic mycelium there are three ways in which the daughter nuclei can be arranged in compatible pairs after simultaneous division. The cell can be wide enough for the spindles to lie side by side, as is seen in the basal cells of the aecia or uredinia of many rusts and in the pileus tissue of many agarics; or, in narrower cells, the spindles may lie end to end and the two central daughter nuclei slide past each other, as occurs regularly in *Taphrina,* in the typical mycelium of all rusts and in various other basidiomycetes; or a mechanical bypass may be constructed. The first alternative would be disadvantageous in distributive mycelium, because a hypha with twice the normal diameter and four times the cross-sectional area would be very wasteful. It is thus scarcely to be thought miraculous that such an adaptive device as a bypass should have arisen more than once. It is also difficult to visualize such a device, constructed economically, that would look much unlike the ascus hook or clamp connection. There is no more morphological basis for the claim that these two structures are homologous than for the other two means of nuclear reassortment being so. All that is involved is the initiation of a hyphal branch whose direction is controlled by the compatible nuclei.

The homology of such structures might be accepted with some confidence if they were correlated with other characters that seem to link the Ascomycetes and Basidiomycetes genetically, and if acceptance allowed a phylogenetic connection in harmony with evolutionary principles. Neither of these conditions holds. No relationship between hook-forming ascomycetes and clamp-forming basidiomycetes has ever been demonstrated that was not plainly ecological rather than genetic. The members of the two classes that show correlated unifying characters are simple organisms that lack these and other refinements.

If we cut this Gordian knot we can devise a rational phylogeny and extend our mycological vista. Perhaps we cannot, like Alexander, conquer the world; but let us at least try to do better than Gordus' son Midas, upon whom Apollo fixed asses' ears as the mark of his mentality.

III. THE PHYCOMYCETE–ASCOMYCETE CONNECTION

There can be little doubt that the connection between these classes was through simple parasites not unlike Protomycetales and Endomycetales. Some of these organisms can be placed equally well in either class. I suggested (Savile, 1955) that Taphrinales are only slightly more advanced than such borderline groups. Kramer (1958) later reexamined the two species of *Taphrina* attacking *Osmunda* (the most ancient extant ferns). He has assigned them to a more primitive genus, *Mixia,* which almost closes the gap between Taphrinales and the borderline phycomycetes.

Only to a supporter of the floridean ancestry of the ascomycetes does this connection present difficulties. That viewpoint demands either that these resemblances are convergent or that an ascomycetous lineage suffered simplification into aquatic phycomycetes that are palpably more primitive and, from their parasitic relationships, more ancient than the supposed parental group.

Marked similarities in storage products link the Phycomycetes with the Ascomycetes, with increasing amounts of chitin or some similar material (lacking in all algal groups) in the latter. In green algae and red algae, from which attempts were made to derive these classes, respectively, we find different cytological details. I have shown at some length (Savile, 1955) that the Florideae are much too specialized and in other respects quite impossible as a source of any ascomycetes. They are a climactic group, fully adapted to a marine habitat, have high chromosome numbers, and are biochemically and anatomically unlike any fungi. We have seen in Section I, C that the few superficial resemblances are easily recognized as convergent.

The phycomycetous origin of the ascomycetes, based on comparative morphology and biochemistry, allows a rational explanation for the difficult transition from aquatic to terrestrial habitats. The transition almost certainly occurred in simple parasites of early vascular plants, more or less synchronously with invasion of the land by the latter. The change into ascomycetes was in fact, apparently a response to a change in habitat: relinquishing the aquatic habitat rendered motile cells almost useless, and new dispersal devices had to be developed. Emergence from the water constituted penetration of a pronounced ecological barrier, and carried with it all the consequences of barrier penetration: rapid extinction of most transitional forms, which were inadequately adapted to the new conditions; radiation of the survivors into vacant ecological niches; and consequently rapid and extensive evolution. Possibly more serious than the dispersal problem for these fungi was the desiccation problem, which plagued all groups of plants and animals that invaded the land. For delicate filamentous fungi the problem might have been insuperable but for the parasitic habit. By emerging from the water within the tissues of their host plants, in a saturated atmosphere, the fungi were shielded from desiccation during the transitional period. Eventually the adaptation was improved, e.g., by the development of wall pigments that, more important than their protection against visible and ultraviolet radiation, are extremely impervious to water (see Chapter 17).

As we have seen in Section I, B, principle 13, parasitism is an old, perhaps original characteristic of the fungi, rather than a belated acquisition. It goes back at least to Olpidiaceae and Rhizidiaceae. The transition to Ascomycetes emphasizes its importance. The phycomycetes reached the land at least twice, the second (and seemingly much later) invasion being from *Phythium*-like ancestors to the Peronosporales, once more as parasites.

The Protomycetales, which include parasites of quite modern plants, suggest what the connecting forms looked like but may represent a separate lineage. The real connecting links, like the early vascular plants that they parasitized, disappeared as their derivatives quickly evolved into unequivocal and more stable ascomycetes. With the multiple crossing of the reptile–mammal intergrade as a warning (Section II, B), it is easy to suppose that both emergence from the water and approach to the ascomycete grade occurred repeatedly as the primitive vascular plants gradually invaded first swamps and then exposed low ground. This may be the explanation of the Protomycetales, which perhaps approached the ascomycete grade independently and much later than the first true ascomycetes.

Among the simplest, and apparently oldest, true ascomycetes Taphrinales are conspicuous. Here is a coherent group of parasites, almost all on ferns and the older dicotyledons. *Taphrina* has simple asci that grow out of rounded cells formed in a dikaryotic mycelium. There are no ascocarps, paraphyses, or ascus hooks. Paraphyses became adaptive only with the development of a firmly delimited ascocarp (Section VI). Similarly the ascus hook, a device to simplify conjugate division in narrow hyphae, probably became significantly adaptive only with the development of close packing of asci in the ascocarp. *Taphrina* is thus seen to be essentially devoid of morphological specialization. It appears to be truly primitive, its host associations show it to be of ancient origin, and it provides a clue to the origins of both the basidiomycetes and the higher ascomycetes.

IV. THE ASCOMYCETE–BASIDIOMYCETE CONNECTION

It is generally agreed that the Basidiomycetes are derived from the Ascomycetes, but there the agreement ends. To those who insist upon the homology of ascus hook and clamp connection, the search for a link is disheartening, for one must connect a highly evolved ascomycete with a highly evolved basidiomycete, doing violence to various principles. It should be clear to an experienced biologist that the morphological similarities between members of the two classes are largely responses to similar ecological conditions or functional needs. Yet superficial resemblances have instigated some fantastic hypotheses. Linder (1940) derived the Uredinales from ascolocular ascomycetes, homologizing the bitunicate ascus with the (modern) pucciniaceous teliospore and basidium, and the pycnidium with the pycnium. The pycnium, an organ unique to the rusts, is flask-shaped only in advanced genera on modern hosts; and its relationship to the pycnidium is purely mathematical. This scheme completely inverts the evolutionary sequence in the rusts, and, while insisting on the homology of hook and clamp, derives the basidiomycetes through an order lacking clamps. Greis (1938), on the basis of the hook-clamp homology, confidently derived the gasteromycetes (and other basidiomycetes) from *Tuber* and related ascomycetes; and a few others have even more recently toyed with such a scheme. This proposal ignores the inevitable convergence in gross morphology among angiocarpic and, particularly, hypogeous macrofungi (Section II, A; Savile, 1955). It derives the basidiomycetes from a climactic, specialized and quite recent group, by means of similarly specialized gasteromycetes. The fundamental change in spore production is postulated to occur in closed, hypogeous sporocarps, i.e., in extremely stable conditions that could not stimulate such a change even in plastic, unspecialized fungi. The fantastic difficulties resulting from the pursuit of such a scheme are detailed in Section V.

Forgetting this alleged homology, let us seek a connection in the only logical place, among the older and morphologically simple ascomycetes. The basidiomycetes and complex ascomycetes both reflect the struggle to disperse their spores effectively in relatively dry habitats. We should seek both their origins in groups lacking special adaptations, rather than deriving one forcible discharge mechanism from another fully established one. Inevitably we come to *Taphrina* as the closest survivor of the common ancestor. The asci burst under saturation and the spores are dispersed by rain. Although Lohwag (1934) noted that the *Taphrina* ascus somewhat resembled a basidium, he dismissed it as a degenerate basidium. Donk (1962) countenanced Lohwag's extraordinary suggestion, despite the demonstration by Kramer (1958) that Taphrinales are inseparably linked with the phycomycetes through *Mixia,* a genus close to Protomycetaceae. Donk's argument concerning spindle orientation is of little value, because orientation largely reflects basidium shape. A slender basidium can only be stichic. Linder (1940) brushed aside *Taphrina* in his obsession to homologize specialized structures of advanced ascomycetes and Pucciniaceae. Bessey (1942, 1950) did place *Taphrina* close to the line leading to the Basidiomycetes, but without consideration of its characters and in a scheme otherwise untenable: simple, parasitic Taphrinales were derived from complex, saprophytic Pezizales and ultimately Florideae. Although he later conceded (*in litt.*) that my proposal (Savile, 1955) seemed closer to the truth than any other, Bessey clung to the hook and clamp homology. Yet his own scheme actually links groups having these structures by simple-septate intermediates.

I showed (Savile, 1955) that the ancestral rust must have been a fungus that produced self-sterile, simple-septate, dikaryotic mycelium parasitic in fern fronds; and that it fruited by the rounding up of some cells, from which basidia developed that bore four subspherical spores upon sterigmata. This description exactly fits the more primitive species of *Taphrina* but for the method of spore formation. Sadebeck (1884) noted that, under abnormal conditions, the asci of *Taphrina* may bud externally, producing subspherical spores on sterigma-like projections. In an organism with such a tendency a quite minor mutation might easily stabilize the process of external spore production. When I first proposed this evolutionary sequence I did not fully appreciate that the level at which external spore production became stabilized is a threshold (Section I, B, 3). Before crossing this threshold the lineage was adapted to spore release and dispersal in free water. After the crossing, adaptation was at once for spore release in moist air. Although rain presumably did at first often scatter the spores, dispersal could be achieved by air currents. Given the initial adaptation, selection pressure must quickly have perfected it and led to the distinctive discharge mechanism. The way was then open for penetration of the barrier to many new upland niches, and a spectacular evolutionary radiation occurred. As always occurs in barrier penetration, the first, weakly adapted, members were quickly displaced by better adapted species. Thus there is a substantial gap between the ascomycetous ancestor and extant basidiomycetes, but only a small gap between that ancestor and *Taphrina,* which has remained essentially in the ancestral niche (see Fig. 1).

V. RELATIONSHIPS WITHIN THE BASIDIOMYCETES

A. Heterobasidiomycetidae

I am unable to offer, in this group, much advance over the scheme previously presented (Savile, 1955), summarized in Fig. 1 (left). Starting with a *Taphrina*-like protobasidiomycete, parasitic upon ferns and distinguished mainly by its assumption of externally produced spores that were forcibly discharged, I visualize an early bifurcation. One branch led to the Uredinales in which early emphasis was upon the elaboration of accessory spore states. The other branch (or possibly branches) led to the remaining heterobasidiomycetes, with elaborate basidiocarps but little emphasis on conidia.

Within the Uredinales marked elaboration of uredinia and aecia occurred early, but the telia evolved only slightly. Eventually, increased exposure of the teliospores began and, once the trend was started, it proved so highly adaptive that it progressed in several lineages, giving rise to the polyphyletic assemblage that we call Pucciniaceae. The final stage in this process is the release of the teliospore as a diaspore and frequent suppression of the accessory spore states.

The basic heterobasidiomycetes are linked by the transversely septate basidium, simple fruiting structures, parasitic habit, and lack of clamp connections. The trend has been toward various changes in basidium structure (so extensive that the homologies of the parts become doubtful), elaborate basidiocarps, assumption of saprophytism, and frequent but erratic development of clamp connections.

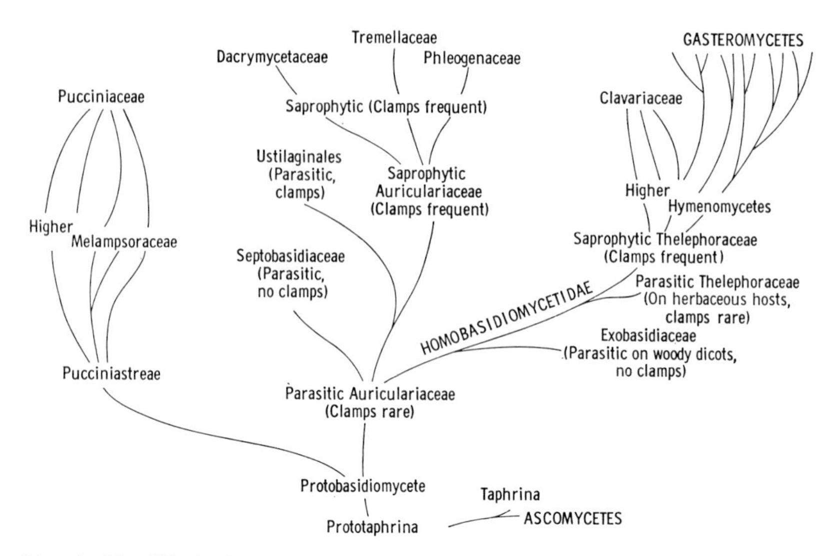

FIG. 1. Simplified phylogenetic diagram of the Basidiomycetes. Trends are from parasitism to saprophytism and from simple to clamp-bearing mycelium; but the latter character becomes confined to particular lineages in the advanced hymenomycetes.

B. *Homobasidiomycetidae*

1. *Introduction*

I suggested (Savile, 1955) that homobasidiomycetes arose from a source close to the parasitic Auriculariaceae. The trend was toward saprophytism, increased development of clamp connections and increased hymenial surface. The right-hand part of Fig. 1 demonstrates the broad evolutionary pattern. These tendencies accompanied penetration into the many ecological niches provided by the newly evolving upland forests, which contrasted markedly with those provided by ancient swamp forests. Inevitably the need to increase hymenial surface and to protect it from rain led to the few conceivable devices evolving repeatedly. Recent studies using microscopic anatomy and biochemistry show lineages that repeatedly cut across the genera and families based upon gross morphology. Nobles (1958) brings together much of the literature in this field and demonstrates the progress that is being made. These studies are allowing the splitting of various heterogeneous groups, and may eventually yield a workable natural classification.

Two aberrant groups must be considered. The Clavariaceae represent hymenomycetes that have somehow overcome the need to protect the hymenium from rain. As soon as this restriction is removed an indeterminate growth habit, with the hymenium closely following the growing point, becomes adaptive. With this habit some hymenium is produced with a minimum of structural tissue; and there is little risk of complete failure if unfavorable conditions halt growth. Although there is probably a valid family in this group, some unrelated lineages have certainly converged into the clavarioid habit under similar evolutionary pressures.

A second, plainly polyphyletic group are the gasteromycetes, which most mycologists regard as derived from the Agaricales and Boletales. A contrary view has recently been expressed, and this connection must therefore be examined in detail.

2. *The Hymenomycete–Gasteromycete Connection*

a. Introduction. Recent detailed studies, latterly by Singer and Smith in particular, make it clear that the family Secotiaceae links Agaricales and typical gasteromycetes through numerous lineages. Each new study further emphasizes the multiplicity of these connections. Table I, from data by Heim (1948) and Singer and Smith (1960, and earlier references therein), shows connections that seem adequately documented. Others may yet be added. If we accept Singer and Smith's suggestion that *Thaxterogaster* is connected separately with two subgenera of *Cortinarius*, we have fifteen lineages. For this discussion we may assume the total to be fourteen. Whatever its origin, Secotiaceae is plainly not a natural family, but a polyphyletic assemblage of organisms at nearly the same

TABLE I
CONNECTIONS BETWEEN HYMENOMYCETES AND SECOTIACEAE

Nearest extant hymenomycetes	Corresponding secotiaceous or gasteromycetous genera
Boletales	*Gastroboletus, Truncocolumella, Chamonixia, Rhizopogon*
Pholiota, Pleuroflammula, Kuehneromyces	*Nivatogastrum*
Naematoloma, Psilocybe	*Weraroa*
Coprinus	*Montagnites, Gyrophragmium*
Rhodophyllus	*Richoniella*
Conocybe, Bolbitius	*Setchelliogaster*
Chlorophyllum, Macrolepiota	*Secotium, Neosecotium*
Agaricus	*Endoptychum*
Cortinarius (2 subgenera)	*Thaxterogaster* (diphyletic)
Gomphidius	*Brauniellula*
Laccaria	*Hydnangium*
Lactarius	*Arcangeliella, Zelleromyces, Octavianina*
Russula	*Macowanites, Martellia, Gymnomyces*
Russulaceae	*Cystangium, Elasmomyces*

evolutionary level; i.e., an evolutionary *grade,* not a lineage. In this sense the term has continued usefulness.

b. The Case for Agaricoid Origin. The following arguments support derivation of the gasteromycetes, through secotiaceous intermediates, from Agaricales or other hymenomycetes.

1. The hymenomycetes are connected to most other basidiomycetes by their very distinctive spore-discharge mechanism. Other groups of fungi have developed discharge devices, but none have duplicated the basidiomycetous mechanism. In the many dry-spored genera of hyphomycetes, in which discharge would be of value, and in some of which the conidiophore tip approaches the form of a sterigma, discharge is relatively rare and is completely unrelated (Meredith, 1963). The chance of the process evolving more than once even in such an unspecialized basidiomycetous ancestor as I have postulated seems small. That it should develop even once from a gasteromycete with sterigmata adapted to passive fracture for spore release would be remarkable. That it should do so fourteen times without exception is beyond belief. If there were an even chance of its being adopted once, the chance of it being adopted in each of fourteen lines would be $1:2^{14}$ or 1:16,384. As the actual probability of a single occurrence must be less than 1:100, the chance of its occurrence in every series is astronomical.

2. Despite some exceptions, the agarics and boletes are, in general, adapted to substantially moister conditions than are the gasteromycetes. Under unduly dry, or possibly otherwise unfavorable, conditions, some agarics remain more or less hypogeous and mature their spores while in the button stage. If a widespread drying trend persists, mutations that reinforce such tendencies will generally be adaptive to agarics in the region. If the population is isolated, then speciation may occur. If only part of the total parental population is isolated, we may expect to see a recognizable agaric-secotioid pair. If the penetration of this physiological barrier occurred very recently, we might hope to match species to species; but the farther back in time that the penetration occurred, the less precise is such pairing likely to be. This mechanism of derivation of gasteromycetes is essentially the catastrophic selection shown by Lewis (1962) to be responsible for the origin of some flowering plants under increased aridity in marginal situations in California. As Lewis points out, the reverse process does not occur, because increased rainfall does not cause the sudden extinction of whole populations, which would be necessary for speciation in an outbreeding species.

3. During the perhaps two million years of the Pleistocene there were several pronounced, and many minor, fluctuations of temperature and

moisture. Somewhat similar fluctuations seem to have occurred repeatedly in late Tertiary and perhaps earlier; and the process still continues. The last glaciation was followed by a xerothermic interval much warmer and drier than today, and smaller fluctuations have since occurred. Relict "islands" of various plant communities emphasize the importance of these fluctuations. If aridity is the chief stimulus for adoption of the secotioid habit, as it seems to be, there has been ample opportunity for its repeated occurrence. With the mechanism for initiation of the secotioid habit freely available, we see why the American Cordillera, where mountain ranges stand isolated by desert or steppe, is so productive of these fungi. A humid coniferous forest clothing a mountain range may be transformed into dry ponderosa pine parkland, in which most agarics will become extinct, but incipient secotioid forms may speciate because isolated from the parental species. The situation in South Africa must be very similar. Regardless of what arrests normal gymnocarpic development, the end product can only approach the secotioid habit.

4. With the assumption of angiocarpy several characteristics of the parental group cease to be adaptive: elevation of the sporocarp upon a stipe, regular form and spacing of lamellae or tubes, positive geotropism of lamellae or tubes, and forcible spore discharge. Mutations deleterious to such structures or mechanisms, promptly eliminated in the gymnocarpic organism, are now neutral or beneficial. Thus it is not surprising that the energy-consuming process of spore discharge quickly disappears.

5. If we postulate the gasteromycetous origin, we must visualize a plausible adaptive function for the evolution of lamellae or tubes, of a stipe, and of vertical orientation of lamellae or tubes in every series, *before gymnocarpy is achieved.* No such function has been demonstrated for any of these characters. Without such function the postulated development is not preadaptation in the legitimate sense, but preordination; and the argument abandons logic for mysticism. The chance of one of these characters evolving in one of our fourteen series seems small. Even if we assume equal chances for each character, the chance of one character occurring in all series is, as before, 1:16,384. But, if we are to assume the independent universal adoption of all three characters and the distinctive spore discharge mechanism, the odds reach about $1{:}7.1 \times 10^{16}$. If we reduce the individual initial odds to a more reasonable figure, e.g., 1:100, the final odds are beyond comprehension.

6. Despite the inevitable gaps of any large group of organisms with few fossils, the Basidiomycetes seem to be a natural class. The distinctive spore discharge mechanism is almost universal except in the gasteromycetes, the gastroid heterobasidiomycete *Hyaloria,* and one or two other

xerophytes. Various other characters link individual orders or families together. Some of the simple, apparently primitive basidiomycetes parasitize primitive land plants and must be of ancient stock. If we base a phylogenetic scheme upon the primitiveness of these simple organisms, we must conclude that the typical hymenomycetes are relatively advanced. We must then conclude that gasteromycetes are derived from hymenomycetes. The alternative is to derive some Agaricales from simple hymenomycetes, but others, by at least fourteen routes, from various gastroid groups, with a precise matching of numerous correlated characters in all cases against odds even greater than those estimated in paragraph 5.

7. In the more complex gasteromycetes, adaptation to particular niches has been accompanied by varied dispersal mechanisms: carrion insects in Phallales, splash-cup in Nidulariales, explosive discharge by imbibition pressure in Sphaerobolales, bellows and wind action in Lycoperdales, and transport by rodents in the polyphyletic Hymenogastrales. All these mechanisms are relatively specialized, suggesting that these are climactic groups unlikely to give rise to a diversified new group.

8. If we derive the agarics from the gasteromycetes, we must find an origin for the latter. A few authors, notably Greis (1938), have supported the derivation of the gasteromycetes from Tuberales. This suggestion is based on the resemblance of the sporocarps to those of various hypogeous gasteromycetes, and on the reported occurrence in some *Tuber* spp. of apparently typical clamp connections. The sporocarp form is simply an adaptation to transport by rodents, and has occurred several times in Phycomycetes, Ascomycetes, and Basidiomycetes (Savile, 1955). The occurrence of clamps, questioned by several authors, may be due to the presence in *Tuber* of extensive dikaryotic mycelium. If extension of the dikaryophase from the hymenium to vegetative mycelium is the means of transforming the apothecium into a closed sporocarp, the bypass that we call an ascus hook must inevitably closely duplicate the basidiomycetous clamp, which evolved to perform exactly the same function. Holm (1949) remarked that *Tuber* is nearly unique among ascomycetes in having an extensive dikaryophase; but *Taphrina* is also predominantly dikaryotic, and is a much more feasible link between the classes. Adaptation to transfer by rodents gives us an approximate limit for the antiquity of both Tuberales and hypogeous gasteromycetes. The rodents originated in the Paleocene, but did not radiate strongly until late Eocene. Fossorial, food-hoarding rodents with an exceptional sense of smell presumably became available appreciably later still. It is thus probable that invasion of the hypogeous niche could not start until 40 million years ago or less. Such a date is more than 200 million years too late to account for the origin of

the primitive basidiomycetes, which we can roughly date by their host plants.

Tuber is an inconceivable source of any gasteromycete or other basidiomycete on other grounds. First, Tuberales are highly specialized and thus unlikely to be able to produce the various supplementary mutations needed to reinforce any critical mutation initiating an important new character. In specialized organisms such dangerous experiments are doomed to extinction. Second, spectacular changes in a lineage result from strong evolutionary pressure, usually the need to adapt to a changed environment, as we have seen in Sections III and IV. In stable conditions the first mutation is generally inadaptive. Only under altered conditions is it likely to be adaptive and to be incorporated into the gene pool. Then the organism can utilize reinforcing mutations. A hypogeous habitat is second only to a fully aquatic one in stability. In it a change from internally formed ascospores to externally formed basidiospores, within a closed sporocarp, would almost certainly lack even the smallest advantage; and the first mutation toward the change would be eliminated. Third, even if the sculpturing of an ascospore is laid down internally into a gelatinous matrix as in externally borne spores (Savile, 1954b), as the inconclusive account of Dodge (1957) suggests for *Neurospora,* it is difficult to imagine the change from internal to external spore production occurring in organisms with markedly thickened and often sculptured walls. The transition almost certainly occurred in a group (like *Taphrina*) with simple, delicate spore walls, in which one or a few mutations might stabilize the change.

9. The distorted hymenium and reduced stipe of the secotioid fungi do not reflect the ontogeny of the agarics and boletes, in which the stipe develops early and the pileus and lamellae or tubes grow radially outward from it.

c. The Arguments for Gastroid Origin

1. Singer (1951) originally objected to agaricoid origin because the agaric veil anticipates angiocarpy. This argument would be valid if the veil had no function, but it seems to protect the young hymenium both from desiccation (by reducing air movement) and from the depredations of small animals. Change in function commonly accompanies invasion of of new niche. The tetrapod forelimb anticipates the avian wing, but the reptiles are not derived from the birds!

2. *Cystangium* is stated (Singer and Smith, 1960) to be off the main astrogastraceous series, with characters not combined in *Russula* and *Lactarius,* and thus to be in a complex that gave rise to both genera. The argument implies that extant species must arise from extant species. Even ancestral lineages that are not extinguished after fostering a divergent

lineage must inevitably evolve, although often slowly. *Cystangium* is evidently derived from an extinct agaric close to the common ancestor of *Russula* and *Lactarius*.

3. "*Cystangium sessile* simply cannot be interpreted as a direct line in the 'reduction' of any known agaric." The competent evolutionist knows extinction to be an integral part of evolution. The conditions that made the secotioid habit adaptive made the status of the ancestral agaric precarious. As Mayr (e.g., 1942, 1954) has repeatedly shown, isolation is essential for speciation in organisms with normal sexual reproduction. In this type of speciation extinction of at least the local population of the agaric provides the isolation. It is remarkable that so many connections can be made even at the generic level (see above, points 2 and 3 in Section b). Smith and Reid (1962) use the same fallacious argument in discussing the New South Wales genus *Cribbea*. (If the agaric counterpart of *Cribbea* did survive, it is probably isolated in the inadequately studied Australasian humid tropics.)

4. Singer and Smith are surprised that the species of *Macowanites* do not match individual species of *Russula*. This is not an argument in favor of either origin, but merely explicit support of derivation from extant species implied in arguments (2) and (3).

5. It is claimed that, if the astrogastraceous series is derived from Russulaceae, *Cystangium* and *Elasmomyces* must have retrogressed toward the agaric form. As shown under arguments (2) and (3), the anatomical data suggest an independent origin from a precursor of *Russula* and *Lactarius*.

6. It is claimed that the occurrence of clamp connections in *Hydnangium*, interpreted by Singer and Smith as the first member of the astrogastraceous series, but not in the other genera, makes agaric origin impossible. This argument is invalidated by their own revelation that *Hydnangium* is linked by several characters (including clamps) to *Laccaria*. It is evidently derived from an agaric close to *Laccaria* and must be excluded from this series. Clamps do disappear in some hymenomycetous series; but it would be surprising if they always occurred in *Hydnangium*, yet never in a single species of the ten genera that Singer and Smith would derive from it.

7. In dry frost duff. *Russula* buttons may remain hypogeous and simulate *Macowanites*. These observations merely emphasize the relationship and suggest how the secotiaceous habit originated.

8. It is proposed that in Russulaceae spore discharge arose not in a single mutation but by a "series of minor mutational steps" from gastroid ancestors. Whatever such a process led to it could scarcely lead to typical basidiospore discharge, unless the gastroid ancestors produced, in antici-

pation, the double septum demonstrated by Prince (1943), functionless in the gasteromycetes in which turgor need not be maintained in the basidium. The chance of such a process occurring once is very small, and that of it occurring in all fourteen or more series is fantastic.

9. "It can at once be recognized that if this pattern holds for this group, it could equally well apply to the other series." This claim ignores elementary probability. If the odds against a single occurrence are p, the odds against occurrence n out of n times are p^n.

10. It is claimed that the gastroid origin readily explains development of the diagnostic characters of Russulaceae, and that proponents of the agaricoid origin can show no source for this group. Certainly the precise origin of Russulaceae is in doubt, although its general affinity with other Agaricales is clear. There is also doubt about the precise origin of almost every genus and family of plants or animals that lacks a good fossil record. If failure to find their immediate agaricoid ancestors means that none existed, what must we do with the much more numerous agaric and bolete genera that show no gasteromycetous affinity? And where are the "living ancestors" of various gasteromycetes? When carried beyond a special case such arguments merely confound their proponents.

11. Singer and Smith put great faith in the amyloid reaction to support the gastroid origin of *Russula* and *Lactarius*. If it were limited to this series the point might have some merit. However, the reaction is widespread at least among white-spored agaric genera (a color reaction is difficult to confirm in colored spores), and also occurs sporadically in some other hymenomycetes. (It even shows in the ascus and spores of some ascomycetes.) The reaction is a useful diagnostic aid at the species or sectional level; but the independent occurrence of an amyloid layer in various groups suggests that it is adaptive under some circumstances. Its disappearance in *Octavianina* suggests that it may be connected with maintenance of turgor in the gymnocarpic hymenomycetes.

C. *General Pattern of Evolution*

Figure 2 is presented to epitomize the evolutionary pattern of the Basidiomycetes. It is purely diagrammatic. The vertical coordinate is time, and the horizontal coordinate represents both ecological variation and morphological change, which is dependent on it. The vertical lines are pronounced ecological barriers. Arrows reaching the top of the diagram represent extant organisms. Note that organisms restricted to the narrow ancestral niche at left change little in morphology, so that surviving species give good clues to the ancestral stock. Escape from this niche allows rapid radiation in upland niches. The right-hand column represents the dry-land niche reached repeatedly by the assumption of angiocarpy. Note that

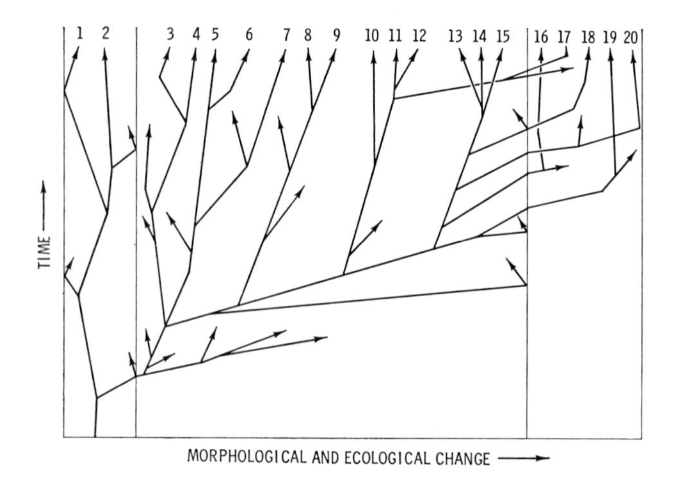

FIG. 2. Simplified diagram of evolutionary patterns in the Basidiomycetes. Vertical lines are ecological barriers. Numbered arrows at top represent survivors. Note that distantly related organisms may show convergent morphological similarity.

adjacent arrows represent comparable morphological evolution but not always genetic relationship. Thus 9 and 10, 12 and 13, and 18 and 19 are only distantly related. On the other hand 15 and 18, which may look very different, are quite closely related. The diagram is severely simplified, but it does give a realistic picture of the evolution of any group of organisms as a continual struggle against environmental limitations.

VI. RELATIONSHIPS WITHIN THE ASCOMYCETES

Detailed studies, particularly in the last thirty-five years, have shown remarkable convergent similarities to occur within the two main evolutionary series of Ascomycetes. We cannot consider the class in detail, but must examine these two series. Although the disposition of some aberrant groups remains in doubt, it is clear that all but the simplest ascomycetes fall into two large groups: the true pyrenomycetes and discomycetes; and a parallel group that often closely copies the pyrenomycetes and occasionally approaches the discomycete form. If we follow the classification of Luttrell (1955), but use the approved terminations for this rank, we may recognize the following subclasses. Hemiascomycetidae includes the simple and primitive Pericystales, Dipodascales, Endomycetales, and Taphrinales. Euascomycetidae includes all those orders with unitunicate asci and true, but occasionally reduced, perithecia or apothecia. Loculoascomycetidae includes those orders with bitunicate asci and ascostromatic ascocarps. The ascocarps of the last subclass may closely resemble perithecia, but are distinguishable in ontogenetic studies. Similarly some fungi with unitunicate asci have what seem to be ascostromatic ascocarps; but all whose development has been studied prove actually to have reduced perithecia. Thus the distinction between these two subclasses is evidently valid, being based upon two fundamental characters, although one of them is not always evident at maturity. Some supplementary characters reinforce the separation. Thus most Euascomycetidae possess true paraphyses, which are never formed in Loculoascomycetidae.

How did these very similar series of fungi evolve? When the fungi emerged from their ancestral aquatic habitats spore dispersal immediately became a critical problem. Motile cells lost almost every chance to function and were quickly abandoned. (In some Peronosporales they persist as an alternative to germination by germ tube.) Passive dispersal by wind or water allowed the early land invaders to persist in favorable niches. But ample dispersal in most land niches demanded the development of spore discharge, or of conidia, or both. We have seen that one discharge mechanism led to the Basidiomycetes. The alternative was to develop the spores within the ascus and eject them from the tip. The bursting ascus of *Taphrina* foreshadows such a process, but achieves dispersal by water splash rather than by air. Effective ejection demands not only turgor within the ascus, but an elastic support that will maintain the internal pressure until the ascus is empty. This may be accomplished in several ways. By being grouped together and surrounded by a stout wall, the asci press upon each other so that the first few, at least, are adequately squeezed. The operation is simplified if turgor can be maintained throughout the ascocarp rather than only within the asci. This end may be achieved by the production of a hygroscopic gel, which will swell by imbibition and exert continuing pressure on the asci. The bitunicate ascus, with gelatinous material between the inner and outer walls, seems to have two functions. First, it increases turgor within the ascocarp. Second, the outer wall ruptures just before discharge, allowing the inner sac to elongate until the ascus tip extends into the ostiole of the ascocarp; the tip then ruptures, the spores are forcibly ejected, and the collapsed ascus is withdrawn by the elasticity of the inner wall. The first was probably the original function, for it would be adaptive from the start of the evolution of the double wall, but the second may now be the more important.

In the Euascomycetidae the paraphysis, a filament arising from the hymenium and free at the tip, developed early, probably mainly in response to the need for increased and sustained turgor. Paraphyses generally have a small lumen, but the walls are often thick and apparently hygroscopic; and, in mass, they seem to supply the needed pressure. They also seem to guide the ascus into the ostiole just before spore discharge, which is probably a secondary function. In many ascostromatic species pseudoparaphyses, not derived from the hymenium, simulate paraphyses and probably function similarly. In discomycetes the paraphyses may assume further functions. Occasionally, as in *Hysteropezizella,* those near the margin cut out a disk of epidermis, exposing the hymenium. In some discomycetes the paraphysis tips are clavate and pigmented, and protect the hymenium from desiccation. Here we have a simple case of preadaptation. The paraphysis could scarcely have arisen *de novo* to protect the discomycete hymenium; but, having evolved through other functions until they regularly overtopped the asci, they were preadapted to supply some protection in the first discomycetes.

This brief consideration of the functions of various structures may grant the reader a realistic vision of evolution in the Ascomycetes. The enclosed ascocarp was presumably a prerequisite to improving spore discharge by turgor maintenance. With its initiation arose the need for close packing of the asci, for which the ascus hook was more effective than the simple dikaryotic mycelium of the *Taphrina*-like ancestors. With improved ascospore dispersal came the need for more elaborate fertilizing devices, offsetting the decreased probability of compatible mycelia developing contiguously. The marked reduction of the dikaryophase perhaps resulted from the delayed fertilization. (The evolutionary pressure upon elaboration of fertilizing devices parallels that in the Uredinales, where perfection of the pycnia was stimulated by evolution first of the uredinia and later of heteroecism and the aecia). Given a simple closed ascocarp, other turgor-inducing devices became adaptive. Turgor maintenance in the Euascomycetidae finally became so perfect that it was possible to develop cupulate, plane, or even everted ascocarps with greatly increased hymenial area.

VII. THE ASCOMYCETE–DEUTEROMYCETE CONNECTION

The Fungi Imperfecti as generally understood are almost all of ascomycetous affinity, for most conidial states of phycomycetes and basidiomycetes are readily assigned to family or even genus of the parental group. This discussion can do little but indicate the need for detailed work in a neglected field (cf. Tubaki, 1966).

The initiation of conidia in all classes of fungi emphasizes their adaptive value. They serve as agents for dispersal, population increase, and the bringing together of compatible haploid mycelia. Their repeated evolution in fungi whose perfect states had restricted mobility was almost inevitable. We need to know how often and in what pattern conidial states arose in the ascomycetes.

Saccardo (1884, 1886), under the urgent need to catalog all the described species, erected a frankly artificial system for the Fungi Imperfecti. Only in recent years have a few mycologists seriously attempted to demonstrate the interrelationships of these numerous and important fungi. Hughes (1953) laid the foundation for a more rational classification of the hyphomycetes by proposing eight sections based upon conidiophore morphology and the method of conidium production. Although it may prove that some of these sections are not strictly natural, this study gives us a basis for the grouping of related genera.

Some ascomycetous genera possess a variety of conidial states; and some conidial form-genera have ascigerous states in different, occasionally distantly related genera. If all such genera were natural we should have to postulate a reticulate evolutionary pattern, which would demand the repeated production of fertile hybrids at about the genus level. Simulated reticulate patterns suggest that some of our genera are based on two or more convergent lineages. Such polyphyletic genera are probably not uncommon in the Fungi Imperfecti. A good example is *Gloeosporium* in the classical sense, to which were referred the conidial states of various discomycetes and pyrenomycetes. The detailed study of von Arx (1957) shows that these organisms may be distributed among 29 genera. Even if the complex should prove to be somewhat oversplit, the treatment reveals various natural groups that eliminate the discordant ascomycetous relationships.

Tubaki (1958) tabulated the ascigerous states of numerous hyphomycetes, which were grouped by Hughes' system with slight modifications. To make full use of his data we must divide Tubaki's "Sphaeriales" between the ascohymenial and ascolocular groups. We then find that the discomycetes and true Sphaeriales are connected with sections IA, IB, II, IVA, IVB, VII, IX, and in one doubtful case, VI; the last being a state assigned to *Helminthosporium,* a spore type found in both II and VI. The ascolocular species are connected with sections II, IIIA, IIIB, and VI. If the *Helminthosporium* assignment to VI should prove to be erroneous, the only section common to both subclasses in this admittedly somewhat small sample would be II, which is well represented in both. Unless this section proves to be diphyletic it must be regarded as a basic type. This conclusion is supported by the occurrence of type I, II, III, and IV conidial states in Eurotiales, which seem to be close to the common ancestors of the two major subclasses.

Some apparently natural ascomycetous genera are connected with several imperfect genera. This situation presents no serious problem when the conidial states are assignable to a single section. *Mycosphaerella,* however, has conidial states that have been assigned to *Phoma, Phyllosticta,*

Ascochyta, Septoria, Cercospora, Cladosporium, Cercosporella, Didymaria, and *Ramularia* (including *Ovularia*). *Mycosphaerella* seems to be essentially natural, and attempts to divide it according to conidial states have merely confused the issue. Specimens virtually indistinguishable from *M. tassiana* (stat. conid. *Cladosporium herbarum*) are confined to single hosts and have *Cercosporella* or *Didymaria* connections. Some of these conidial states are mutable, appearing as *Cercosporella, Ramularia* or *"Ovularia"* (an untenable name), with minor environmental changes. Pigmentation, although often a significant character, is also highly variable in some species, e.g., *Ramularia montana.* Thus the production of various conidial states in section II is easily understood. More puzzling is the production of pycnidial states by this genus. Probably all the states assigned to *Phyllosticta* and *Phoma* are not true members of these genera, but only microconidial (spermatial) states. The occurrence of true pycnidia in *Mycosphaerella* is probably explained by the occurrence of ancestral pleomorphic species. At least one pleomorphic species probably exists today. *Cercospora streptopi* and *Septoria streptopodis* are repeatedly found together on leaves of *Disporum,* not only on the same lesions, but often with hypophyllous *Cercospora* conidiophores growing from the bases of the epiphyllous pycnidia. They seem to be alternative states of a *Mycosphaerella,* the one adapted to wind- and the other to rain-dispersal. Many early ascomycetes may similarly have been broadly adapted; but isolated populations must have shed whichever state was least adapted to a restricted range of habitats. Thus the progeny of two populations of a single pleomorphic species might have very different conidial states.

However, diversification of a single hyphomycetous state must frequently have accompanied speciation. Within a single hyphomycete section the possible morphological variation is somewhat limited. Some convergence is thus inevitable and we must not expect all the genera to be strictly monophyletic.

Following diversification of early ascomycetes with simple conidia, and of conidial states associated with individual genera, came diversification of conidial states no longer associated with any ascomycete. It is believed that about one-third of the Fungi Imperfecti have no perfect state. Diversification within such a group may thus have been very extensive. This simplification of the life cycle, potentially yielding both independent ascomycetes and conidial fungi, seems to reflect adaptation to a specialized niche. In arctic and alpine habitats the short summer largely deprives pleomorphism of any adaptive value, and it becomes relatively scarce. The Pleistocene climatic fluctuations may have stimulated much recent cleavage of related states, a process that is probably still continuing. *Mycosphaerella tassiana* is genetically connected with *Cladosporium herbarum.*

Both states occur profusely in the arctic, with subtle morphological variations; but they seldom occur in close association, and one receives the impression that each is independently evolving into a complex of slightly divergent races.

ADDENDUM

Since the completion of this chapter, a few papers have appeared that merit brief comment. Smith (1965) discusses the variations observed in amyloid, pseudoamyloid, and dextrinoid reactions, and admits the danger of using amyloidy as a taxonomic character above the species level.

Ubrizsy and Vörös (1966) give a fairly orthodox broad classification of the fungi, deriving the ascomycetes from the phycomycetes, but they present some detailed dispositions that seem to be untenable. Thus Heterobasidiomycetes and Exobasidiales are derived from Homobasidiomycetes without supporting evidence; Acrospermaceae are placed in Ascoloculares, but, from repeated examination, I find *Acrospermum compressum* to have unitunicate asci and true paraphyses; and Sporobolomycetaceae are surprisingly placed in Moniliales. The authors recognize Mycota as a separate kingdom, a view that has considerable merit.

Denison and Carroll (1966) have rehashed the arguments in favor of floridean ancestry but have failed to consider the fundamentals of evolutionary theory and paleontology.

REFERENCES

Bessey, E. A. (1942). Some problems in fungus phylogeny. *Mycologia* **34**: 355–379.

Bessey, E. A. (1950). "Morphology and Taxonomy of Fungi." Blakiston, Philadelphia, Pennsylvania.

Bock, W. J. (1959). Preadaptation and multiple evolutionary pathways. *Evolution* **13**: 194–211.

Cohn, F. (1872). Conspectus familiarum cryptogamarum secundum methodum naturalem dispositarum. *Hedwigia* **11**: 17–20.

de Bary, A. (1881). Zur Systematik der Thallophyten. *Botan. Z.* **39**: 1–17.

Denison, W. C., and G. C. Carroll. (1966). The primitive ascomycete: A new look at an old problem. *Mycologia* **58**: 249–269.

Dodge, B. O. (1957). Rib formation in ascospores of *Neurospora* and questions of terminology. *Bull. Torrey Botan. Club* **84**: 182–186.

Donk, M. A. (1962). Notes on the basidium. II. *Persoonia* (*Leiden*) **2**: 211–216.

Fitzpatrick, H. M. (1930). "The Lower Fungi: Phycomycetes." McGraw-Hill, New York.

Greis, H. (1938). Die Entstehung der Basidiomycetenschnallen aus der Ascomycetenhaken. *Jahrb. Wiss. Botan.* **86**: 81–106.

Heim, R. (1948). Phylogeny and natural classification of macrofungi. *Brit. Mycol. Soc. Trans.* **30**: 161–178.

Holm, L. (1949). Some aspects on the origin of the Gastromycetes. *Svensk Botan. Tidskr.* **45**: 65–71.

Hughes, S. J. (1953). Conidiophores, conidia and classification. *Can. J. Botany* **31**: 577–659.

Kramer, C. L. (1958). A new genus in the Protomycetaceae. *Mycologia* **50**: 916–926.

Lewis, H. (1962). Catastrophic selection as a factor in speciation. *Evolution* **16**: 257–271.

Linder, D. H. (1940). Evolution of the Basidiomycetes and its relation to the terminology of the basidium. *Mycologia* **32**: 419–447.

Lohwag, H. (1934). Zu *Lycoperdellon. Ann. Mycol. Notitiam Sci. Mycol. Univ.* **32**: 244–255.

Luttrell, E. S. (1955). The ascostromatic Ascomycetes. *Mycologia* **47**: 511–532.

Mayr, E. (1942). "Systematics and the Origin of Species." Columbia Univ. Press, New York.

Mayr, E. (1954). Changes of genetic environment and evolution. *In* "Evolution as a Process" (J. Huxley, A. C. Hardy, and E. B. Ford, eds.), pp. 157–180. Allen & Unwin, London.

Meredith, D. S. (1963). Violent spore release in some Fungi Imperfecti. *Ann. Botany* (*London*) [N.S.] **27**: 39–47.

Mode, C. J. (1958). A mathematical model for the co-evolution of obligate parasites and their hosts. *Evolution* **12**: 158–165.

Nobles, M. K. (1958). Cultural characters as a guide to the taxonomy and phylogeny of the Polyporaceae. *Can. J. Botany* **36**: 883–926.

Olson, E. C. (1959). The evolution of mammalian characters. *Evolution* **13**: 344–353.

Prince, A. E. (1943). Basidium formation and spore discharge in *Gymnosporangium nidus-avis. Farlowia* **1**: 79–93.

Pringsheim, N. (1858). Beiträge zur Morphologie und Systematik der Algen. II. Die Saprolegnieen. *Jahrb. Wiss. Botan.* **1**: 284–306.

Saccardo, P. A. (1884, 1886). "Sylloge Fungorum," Vols. III and IV. Padua.

Sachs, J. (1874). "Lehrbuch der Botanik." Engelmann, Leipzig.

Sadebeck, R. (1884). Untersuchungen über die Pilzgattung *Exoascus. Jahrb. Hamburg Wiss. Anstalt* **1**: 93–124.

Savile, D. B. O. (1954a). The fungi as aids in the taxonomy of the flowering plants. *Science* **120**: 583–585.

Savile, D. B. O. (1954b). Cellular mechanics, taxonomy and evolution in the Uredinales and Ustilaginales. *Mycologia* **46**: 736–761.

Savile, D. B. O. (1955). A phylogeny of the Basidiomycetes. *Can. J. Botany* **33**: 60–104.

Savile, D. B. O. (1959). Limited penetration of barriers as a factor in evolution. *Evolution* **13**: 333–343.

Savile, D. B. O. (1961). Evolution of Saxifragaceae from a mycologist's viewpoint. *In* "Recent Advances in Botany," pp. 169–172. Univ. of Toronto Press, Toronto, Canada.

Simpson, G. G. (1953). "The Major Features of Evolution." Columbia Univ. Press, New York.

Simpson, G. G. (1959). Mesozoic mammals and the polyphyletic origin of mammals. *Evolution* **13**: 405–414.

Singer, R. (1951). The Agaricales (mushrooms) in modern taxonomy. *Lilloa Rev. Botan.* **22**: 5–832.

Singer, R., and A. H. Smith. (1960). Studies on secotiaceous fungi. IX. The astrogastraceous series. *Mem. Torrey Botan. Club* **21**: 1–112.

Smith, A. H. (1965). New and unusual basidiomycetes with comments on hyphal and spore wall reactions with Melzer's solution. *Mycopathol. Mycol. Appl.* **26**: 385–402.

Smith, A. H., and D. A. Reid. (1962). A new genus of Secotiaceae. *Mycologia* **54**: 98–104.

Tubaki, K. (1958). Studies on Japanese Hyphomycetes. V. Leaf and stem group with a discussion of the classification of Hyphomycetes and their perfect stages. *J. Hattori Botan. Lab.* **20**: 142–244.

Tubaki, K. (1966). Sporulating structures in Fungi Imperfecti. *In* "The Fungi" (G. C. Ainsworth and A. S. Sussman, eds.), Vol. 2, 113–131. Academic Press, New York.

Ubrizsy, G., and J. Vörös. (1966). A new conception in the review of the phylogeny and system of fungi. *Acta Botan. Acad. Sci. Hung.* **12**: 199–220.

von Arx, J. A. (1957). Revision der zu *Gloeosporium* gestellten Pilze. *Verhandel. Koninkl. Ned. Akad. Wetenschap., Afdel. Natuurk., Sect. II* **51**: 1–153.

CHAPTER 27

On the of Evolution Fungi

JOHN R. RAPER

Department of Biology
Harvard University
Cambridge, Massachusetts

In the preceding chapter, Saville has set forth in some detail the principles that determine the course of evolution in all organisms, the fungi included, and the detailed characteristics of the vast assemblage of extant fungi should be largely explicable in terms of these principles. These principles, however, derive from the incredible capacity of the genetic endowment to generate random variations which are either conserved or eliminated under the selective pressures imposed by the environment. The present chapter will attempt to deal more generally with those features of the fungi, particularly certain genetic aspects, that appear to have played major roles in the evolutionary history of the group.

I. SIGNIFICANCE OF BASIC FUNGAL CHARACTERISTICS

Two all too often overlooked but major characteristics of the fungi have undoubtedly been of basic importance: their essentially aquatic habit and their predominant haploidy. The first of these features severely restricts the range of ecological niches which the fungi can penetrate, while the latter affects significantly the operational details of the evolutionary process in many ways.

A majority of fungi occur in a land environment and are generally considered to be terrestrial organisms, but their dependence upon water, at least during the vegetative phase, is continuous and critical. Among aquatic phycomycetes, water is essential for all life processes, growth, asexual and sexual reproduction, and dispersal. In these forms, ordinarily only the spores derived through sexual reproduction can withstand desiccation. In other forms that have achieved a terrestrial existence, the dependence upon water is no less critical. The vegetative mycelium in most cases not only requires a source of water, it must be either submerged in or in intimate contact with an aqueous milieu: the tissue of a host if parasitic, or in or upon a wet substrate if saprophytic. Even mild desiccation results, at best, in total cessation of growth. Asexual reproduction requires spores or other propagative elements that can withstand exposure to dry air, but these are borne either directly upon the vegetative mycelium or upon specialized hyphal structures in close proximity to a wet substrate. It is only in the more highly developed forms—predominantly the higher basidiomycetes, many of which form rhizomorphs—that large sporulating structures are formed in the open air at some distance from their subtending vegetative mycelia, and even here, the geometry of the hymenium provides sheltered recesses for the critical stages of spore formation.

Although many life cycles of fungi include diploid or dikaryotic vegetative phases of some duration, an independent haploid vegetative phase is present in a majority of forms. The known exceptions to this occur in the *Cystogenes* sections of *Allomyces* and *Blastocladiella,* in certain (possibly all) of the biflagellate phycomycetes, in a very few yeasts, in those smuts (e.g., *Tilletia*) with routine sporidial conjugation, and in the secondarily homothallic species scattered throughout the Ascomycetes and Basidiomycetes. In these few cases, diploidy or dikaryosis persists, in effect, throughout the life cycle. In all other cases, either asexual or sexual propagules generate an independent haploid phase, unbuffered by heterozygosity or by genetic complementation, which is particularly subject to the rigors of natural selection. Actually, diploidy or dikaryosis may afford no benefits in this respect in homothallic species, as their exactly duplicated genomes provide no heterozygosity. Because most fungi lack such a balanced system that can mask genetic deficiencies during an obligatory haplophase of the life cycle, the effects of natural selection are more immediate and more rigorous than in most other organisms.

A third factor should be added to the restrictions to easy colonization imposed by their continuing need for water and by their unbuffered haploidy. Despite the many, and often elaborate, mechanisms for the dispersal of spores, these devices merely remove the spores from their immediate source, and any longer-range dispersal is totally haphazard. Various fungi attract insects, snails, burrowing animals, etc., and the spores of such forms are likely to be deposited in locations similar to those in which they originated. Coprophilous fungi commonly deposit their spores, by an intriguing variety of highly specialized devices, on nearby vegetation, where they have a maximal chance of being recycled through the alimentary tract of a browsing animal. But for a majority of fungi, no such favorable odds are provided for the dispersal of their reproductive elements. Most species deposit their spores in the air by one means or another: (a) conidia, oidia, chlamydospores, uredospores, etc., are simply detached at maturity and are committed to the vagaries of local currents of air; (b) ascospores are often discharged to some distance into the air, where supporting air currents are more likely; (c) basidiospores of the larger and more conspicuous fungi may be either actively or passively deposited in the open air. Air currents or winds are thus the major dispersal agent for the spores of most fungi, and chance alone is the factor that determines the deposition of any spore upon a suitable substrate or upon a susceptible host.

When these three features are recognized, it is obvious that the prospects of the individual fungal spore are indeed dim. To this handicap of all but total mortality of fungal propagules, natural selection has provided the only reasonable solution: the production of prodigious numbers of spores, including asexual, sexual, or both. Generally, asexual spores are the predominant reproductive elements in the lower fungi, the Phycomycetes and those ascomycetes that lack large fruiting bodies, whereas sexual spores are the dominant elements of the Discomycetes and Basidiomycetes. In the simpler phycomycetes, most or even all of the protoplasm of the thallus is converted directly into spores, and in many filamentous forms, a large fraction of the protoplasm may become incorporated into asexual spores. It is only in the higher fungi, with the production of elaborate fruiting bodies, that the vegetative and reproductive functions typically remain distinct, but even here fruiting constitutes a major drain on the organisms' resources. There are, of course, many exceptions in both directions to this generalization. There are many species scattered throughout the major groups of fungi that produce vast numbers of asexual as well as sexual spores. Conversely, some few forms produce no asexual spores and only modest numbers of sexual spores, but such fungi, e.g., the coprophile, *Sordaria,* and the insect-parasites, the Laboulbeniales, occupy particularly stable niches in which high reproductive potential appears to afford no critical selective advantage. Taken as a group, however, the fungi are typically heavy spore bearers, and the number of spores produced by one individual can be tremendous: Buller's (1931) estimates for a variety of basidiomycetes range from 10^9 to $>10^{12}$ spores per fruiting body.

Another major factor in the evolution of the fungi has undoubtedly been the fact of their obligate heterotrophy, by which their total biology is inextricably tied to that of other organisms. There is no reason to think that protoplasm has changed drastically in nature or in composition during the period that fungi have existed, and the direct or indirect dependence of fungi upon protoplasm or metabolic products has to a large extent circumscribed the evolutionary possibilities. On the other hand, the appearance of each new specialization or product in the evolution of other organisms has created a new ecological niche for fungi, and the ability to overcome new defensive specializations or to utilize novel metabolic products would confer obvious selective advantages. The result of this relationship between fungi and other organisms is clear: the fungi are versatile in the extreme in their degradative abilities and, as a group, they can degrade and use the entire catalog of biological products as food. That the organic debris about us is only of very recent origin bespeaks not only the efficacy of the fungi (and bacteria) in recycling the components of living matter, but also the efficiency of the evolutionary process.

These several common characteristics differentiate the fungi rather sharply from other groups of plants and from all but the very simplest animals. Accordingly it is quite reasonable to suspect that the fundamental causes and processes of evolution—though they are undoubtedly the same here as elsewhere—may have certain features that differ significantly from their counterparts in higher plants and animals, upon which groups the modern theory of evolution is largely based. The causes and processes that comprise what Stebbins (1966) terms the synthetic, modern theory of evolution are: gene mutation, changes in chromosome structure and number, recombination, natural selection, and reproductive isolation, together with the accessory factors of migration, hybridization, and chance. An evaluation of the relative importance of the basic causes and processes of evolution in the fungi as compared with other organisms, however, must remain for the present an intuitive and intellectual exercise, because the information presently available is fragmentary and insufficient to support rigorous comparisons.

II. VARIABILITY IN FUNGAL POPULATIONS

Consider, for example, the matter of variability in fungal populations. Gene mutations, recombination, gene flow, migration, hybridization, and genetic drift are all involved in the generation and maintenance of the potential for variation upon which evolutionary change by natural selection depends. No mycologist needs to be told that any species of fungus is highly variable, but what studies with fungi can be cited that adequately define this variation within and between populations? One can cite numerous studies with fungi at the population level devoted to mating systems and the associated phenomena of hybridization, inbreeding *vs.* outbreeding, barriers to heterokaryosis and other devices to promote reproductive isolation, etc. [cf. Burnett (1965) and Mather (1965) for review and discussion]. Beyond the central concern with mating systems and corollary phenomena, relatively little attention has been paid to population biology in the fungi. This slight was pointed out by Mather (1965), ". . . indeed the fungi have not yet been made the subject of any investigations in biometrical and population genetics on a major scale . . ."—a slight that a group of British workers, who were strongly influenced by Mather, is industriously working to rectify. A series of recent papers (Croft and Simchen, 1965; Simchen and Jinks, 1964; Jinks *et al.*, 1966; Simchen, 1965, 1966a,b, 1967) report detailed analyses of the variability of several fungal characteristics such as homokaryotic and dikaryotic growth rate, mycelial morphology, "heterokaryon incompatibility," time of fruiting, and recombination. From all the available information, however, no significant features that are clearly distinctive to the fungi are evident from these investigations. Polygenic systems are rather prominent as a major basis for variability—whether to a greater extent than elsewhere is uncertain—but, as pointed out by Papa *et al.* (1966), this is to be expected in haploid organisms lacking a diploid basis for heterosis. Although heterokaryosis provides a reasonably effective substitute for heterosis in "heterokaryotic vigor" (Dodge, 1942), the substitution is temporary, because heterokaryons are disassociated to a greater or lesser extent in asexual reproduction and completely in sexual reproduction. There is a possible distinction between fungi and most other organisms in this respect, for any significant accumulation in most fungal populations of even mildly deleterious mutations is quite effectively prevented by their selective disadvantage in the haploid phase—whether transient or extended—through which practically all fungal life cycles pass. Relatively greater value may well accrue to the occurrence and interrelations among what Stebbins (1966) terms "mutations with small effects" than might be the case with diploid organisms.

III. CRITICAL EVENTS IN THE EVOLUTION OF FUNGI

Minor differences, such as the suspected one above, may well eventually be found as regards any and all facets of the evolutionary process. However, their documentation at the present time is impossible, and speculation about them is bootless. A more fruitful pursuit is the identification of a number of innovations in the evolutionary history of the fungi and the evaluation of their significance in relation to features of, and relationships among, present-day fungi. Little agreement could be expected in the choice, by different students of the fungi, of the more important evolutionary advances that have been made. Four are selected here that appear to have provided the greatest opportunities for explosive adaptive radiations: (a) saprophytism, (b) incompatibility, (c) heterokaryosis, and (d) dikaryosis and its incorporation as an integral phase of the sexual cycle.

A. Saprophytism

Obligatory heterotrophy as a universal characteristic of the fungi would seem to justify Savile's theses (Chapter 26) that all fungi have been derived from parasitic ancestors and that the major lines of fungal evolution have occurred in parasitic forms or in forms that had recently "escaped" from the parasitic habit. Primeval fungi are accordingly visualized as generalized obligate parasites, their growth and survival dependent upon a number of protoplasmic constituents common to all hosts. Two pathways for slow change in nutritional requirements would have been available to such forms, and both would confer significant selective advantages: (a) A gradual loss of competence to synthesize certain compounds would result in the establishment of requirements for complex protoplasmic constituents that could be provided only by a restricted range of host organisms—a process that would lead eventually to highly specific host-parasite associations, with the fungus uniquely adapted to a single, or a few closely related, host species. (b) Conversely, a gradual acquisition of synthetic competence, through which the fungus would be able to utilize progressively simpler protoplasmic constituents or products, would finally lead to the saprophytic habit. Such an escape from obligate parasitism would proceed through several stages, each of which would confer a significant advantage. The competence to synthesize each specific nutrilite formerly required from the host would decrease the dependence of the fungus upon the living host and thereby would increase the range of acceptable substrates. The eventual competence of an escaping parasite to continue to flourish on the remains of its dead host inevitably increased its reproductive and dispersal potential and conferred enhanced fitness in competition with related forms that remained totally dependent upon living host tissue.

The gradual escape from the parasitic habit must have occurred repeatedly to establish numerous types of primitive, plastic forms leading to the several great assemblages of saprophytic fungi. The degree of independence from living matter—or, conversely, the degree of residual dependence, for true autotrophy has not evolved in the fungi—could have varied widely in different independent lines. Present-day saprophytes vary tremendously in their needs for organic materials, from those relatively few that require only a single, simple source of organic carbon, e.g., acetate or a sugar, to the majority that must be provided with one or more compounds including organic nitrogen, reduced sulfur, vitamins, organic iron-containing compounds, fatty acids, amino acids, nucleotides, etc. (Fries, 1965). Such deficiencies are commonly interpreted as the loss of synthetic competence in ancestral forms having high synthetic capacity (Cantino, 1966). This seems quite reasonable in cases where varied specific compounds are required by scattered species in groups that are generally autotrophic for these compounds. Divergent evolutionary lines would arise in circumstances in which particular compounds were readily available, and the ability to synthesize the corresponding compounds would have little or no selective advantage. Requirements that characterize large fungal taxa, such as biotin in the higher ascomycetes and thiamine in the Basidiomycetes, could well have had quite a different origin. These could perhaps more reasonably represent lines that never achieved the synthesis of the particular substances required. To be sure, biotin and thiamine are required in very small amounts, and they are practically universal in organic materials, but the same applies to other equally necessary substances for which deficiencies are far less generally distributed. Furthermore, when biochemical mutations are induced in forms, such as *Aspergillus* and *Penicillium,* that require no organic substances beyond a source of carbon and energy, deficiencies for biotin and thiamine are no more frequent than those for numerous other vitamins, amino acids, bases, etc. (Fincham and Day, 1965).

Facultative parasitism could have originated in either of two ways and has probably done so repeatedly by both routes. In the first place, a critical stage in the postulated escape to saprophytism is represented by a parasite with a newly acquired competence for continued life without the living host, i.e., a facultative parasite; alternately and in other cases, facultative parasitism could have originated from saprophytic forms by the *de novo* acquisition of the competence to overcome the inherent resistance to infection by prospective host organisms. In either case, facultative parasites have rather the best of the situation, as they can take full advantage of the rich substrate provided by living tissue yet are able to grow and develop normally on nonliving matter.

The great success of saprophytic fungi lies in the fact that their metabolic processes have been successfully uncoupled from those of other *living* organisms and, indeed from those of specific *dead* organisms. The degree of independence from requirements for specific and complex constituents of living matter that is achieved by saprophytic and facultatively parasitic fungi, however, is probably not too critical, because most available natural substrates are richly provided with the necessities of fungal life, and any incidental nutritional deficiencies, of whatever origin, are of minor importance for growth, propagation, and survival.

B. *Incompatibility*

Perhaps the most important development in the evolution of the fungi was the emergence of the complex and interrelated features of incompatibility, hterokaryosis, and the incorporation of the dikaryon—a precisely regulated expression of heterokaryosis—as an integral phase of the sexual cycle. Both the means by which these characteristics appeared and the point(s) in the evolutionary sequence of their origins are uncertain. Heterokaryosis of an accidental sort—which actually appears to be disadvantageous under normal circumstances—occurs in *Phycomyces* of the Mucorales along with an incompatibility system consisting of two alleles at a single locus that determines mating competence (Blakeslee, 1906; Burgeff, 1914). In the yeasts, a one-locus two-allele, *a* and α, incompatibility system is characteristic of many species (Lindegren and Lindegren, 1943; Ahmad, 1965), and a more complex type of incompatibility is known in one species, *Schizosaccharomyces pombe* (Leupold, 1958). Heterokaryosis is not known in this group, but diploidy, which serves essentially the same functions, is very common. Otherwise, the three features of incompatibility, heterokaryosis, and a dikaryotic sexual phase appear together in association. This constellation of features appears to have provided extraordinary potential for adaptation and radiation, as it is characteristics of all groups of the Euascomycetes and Basidiomycetes. It should be emphasized, of course, that all three features are not characteristic of all species in these larger groupings: incompatibility systems are lacking in homothallic and imperfect forms, and a dikaryotic phase is also lacking in the latter. The generalization holds, however, for in these groups the sequence of events comprising nuclear fusion, meiosis, and the production of ascospores or basidiospores invariably terminates a dikaryotic phase, and heterothallism, wherever present, is determined by incompatibility systems.

Incompatibility is defined as a genetic system that determines mating competence in the absence of any morphological differentiation (Esser, 1966). Incompatibility systems are known in several groups of plants—the Myxomycetes, the fungi, at least one fern, and the flowering plants—and their significance lies in the regulation of the outbreeding-inbreeding potential. Among the fungi, two different types of incompatibility have been recognized (Esser, 1962): *homogenic incompatibility,* the more widely distributed and better-known type, limits interfertility to pairings that bring together *different* factors, with the result that inbreeding is severely restricted and outbreeding is enhanced; *heterogenic incompatibility,* by contrast, limits interfertility to pairings that bring together *like* factors, with a consequent restriction of outbreeding and a promotion of inbreeding. The evolutionary effects of the two types are thus diametrically opposed: the former, by the promotion of outbreeding, enhances gene flow between populations and guarantees that the species *per se* participates as the evolutionary unit, whereas the latter, by the promotion of inbreeding, restricts gene flow and makes the race the evolutionary unit and is probably a significant factor in speciation (Raper and Esser, 1964; Burnett, 1965). The concept of sterility between races as an incompatibility system is a recent development, and, indeed, the information available about it is insufficient for any assessment of its significance as a factor in the evolution of the fungi. Its occurrence, in widely different groups of fungi, appears to be quite sporadic, and it is not a basic characteristic of any particular group or groups of fungi. The case is quite different for homogenic incompatibility, the distribution of which implicates it as a major evolutionary factor. Further consideration of incompatibility is accordingly restricted to this type.

A number of different incompatibility systems characteristically occur in the various groups of the higher fungi. These systems are most easily differentiated by their underlying genetical structures: (a) a *one-locus, two-allele* system occurs generally among the Euascomycetes and the rusts and most smuts of the Basidiomycetes, as well as in the Mucorales and the yeasts; (b) a *one-factor, multiple-allele* system, or bipolar incompatibility, is common in the saprophytic heterobasidiomycetes (*Auricularia, Exidia, Tremella,* etc.) and throughout the Homobasidiomycetes; (c) a *two-factor, multiple-allele* system, or tetrapolar incompatibility, is unique to, and characteristic of, a majority of the species of the Homobasidiomycetes; and (d) a *two-factor, two-alleles* at one and *multiple-alleles* at the other, system has been found only in a few smuts (Rowell and DeVay, 1954; Rowell, 1955) and in *Tremella mesenterica* (Bandoni, 1965).

The interrelations, if any, between these different incompatibility systems are completely obscure, as are the means by which they might have evolved. Wheeler (1954) and Olive (1958) would derive a simple incompatibility system, such as (a) above, repeatedly from homothallic ancestors, by mutations of genes affecting distinct but complementary functions in the sexual process. This view is supported by the observations that in homothallic forms mutations to self-sterility commonly permit interfertility and by the demonstration of complete fertility between strains carrying two very closely linked mutations that disrupt the sexual process in *Sordaria fimicola* (El Ani and Olive, 1962). Furthermore, the different means by which incompatibility factors impose their control on the sexual processes in the few ascomycetes for which information is available (Bistis, 1965) are consistent with polyphyletic origins of incompatibility in this group. Beyond this, however, no reasonable suggestions have been advanced to explain the origins of the multiple-allelic incompatibility systems. The increased outbreeding potential accruing from the accumulation of multiple alleles at a single incompatibility locus could well account for the evolution of such a system, but whether such a *one-locus,* multiple-allelic system exists or not is problematic. No genetic resolution has yet been made of the single, multiple-allelic factor of any bipolar form. Detailed information about the genetic structure of multiple-allelic systems is available only for the tetrapolar or two-factor system, in which each factor, *A* and *B*, is constituted of two distinct loci, each with multiple alleles (Raper, 1966).

Not only is the origin of tetrapolar incompatibility unknown; its biological significance is somewhat uncertain. Raper and Esser (1964) summed up these uncertainties: "It is certainly an effective outbreeding system (Mather, 1942; Whitehouse, 1949; Papazian, 1951), but the number of alternate factors (e.g., ca. 450 *A* and 90 *B* factors in *Schizophyllum commune*) far exceeds the minimal number that would seriously limit the selective advantage of new factors. Furthermore, the existence of a second series of factors restricting inbreeding to 25% would appear to have little critical advantage. . . . The compound structure of the factors is also puzzling. . . . In brief, the probable or even possible evolutionary history of tetrapolar incompatibility is completely obscure, and the selective advantages of the system, though qualitatively obvious, are quantitatively puzzling."

Simchen (1967), in a recent evaluation of the two-locus structure of incompatibility factors has given estimates of certain advantages of a two-locus factor as compared with a one-locus factor containing the same number of allelic specificities—though he ventures no suggestion of *how* the dual factor could have originated: (a) The two-locus factor has the greater outbreeding efficiency, and the greatest benefit for the compound factor would obtain when the number of allelic specificities was low—a maximal absolute difference in outbreeding efficiency of 6.25% would obtain between eight alleles at a single locus (87.5%) as compared with four alleles at each of two loci (93.7%). Likewise, maximal benefit would accrue from the addition of a second locus when the alleles at the original locus were few. (b) The two-locus factor is far superior for the maintenance of outbreeding potential in small populations. "Thus for the 450 *A* factors (ca. 9 α's and 50 β's) of *S. commune*, for instance, a bottle-neck population of 178 monokaryons can still maintain all potential specificities in 99% of the cases, while 4822 monokaryons will be required in a single locus system. Hence the two-locus structure permits a much higher number of factor specificities (and higher out-breeding level) to be maintained in the population than the latter's size and size fluctuations otherwise determine" (Simchen, 1967).

C. *Heterokaryosis*

But whatever the origins of the several incompatibility systems, one or another of them is characteristic of each group of fungi in which heterokaryosis occurs, and wherever it is present, incompatibility determines the type(s) of heterokaryosis (Raper and San Antonio, 1954). For example, generally in the Ascomycetes, e.g., *Neurospora crassa,* stable heterokaryons are readily formed between strains of like mating type, $A \times A$ and $a \times a$, whereas only highly unstable heterokaryons are formed between strains of unlike mating type, $A \times a$ (Sansome, 1946; Gross, 1950). In homothallic ascomycetes and imperfect fungi, heterokaryosis generally resembles that between incompatible strains of *Neurospora.* In the rusts and smuts, in which a simple two-allele incompatibility system is present, the relationship is reversed as compared with the Ascomycetes: only a single type of heterokaryon, the dikaryophase, is known, and this is formed only in pairings that bring together unlike incompatibility factors. In the higher basidiomycetes, however, two and four characteristic types of heterokaryons are formed in bipolar and tetrapolar species, respectively, dependent upon the combinations of incompatibility factors (Raper, 1955). Thus there is very good reason to consider the association of heterokaryosis and incompatibility to be one of very ancient origin.

The biological significance of heterokaryosis follows from a number of more or less distinct functions (Raper, 1955): (a) it provides a mechanism, i.e., complementation, for the restoration of normal form and function in associated, deficient genomes; (b) it is the basis for adaptive response to changing conditions; (c) it is the prerequisite for somatic recombination and parasexuality; and (d) it provides, in the form of the stable and highly specialized dikaryophase, an integral phase of the sexual cycle of all higher fungi. The first three of these functions have been treated in detail in this treatise (Davis, 1966; Roper, 1966). The fourth, the integration of a specialized heterokaryon, the dikaryophase, in the life cycle of the higher fungi, deserves further consideration.

D. *The Dikaryon*

An alternation of generations is characteristic of a large majority of all plants, and in the higher fungi, the Euascomycetes and Basidiomycetes, the dikaryophase, or dikaryon, replaces the prolonged diploid phase common to most other plants and to a few groups of fungi as well (e.g., *Allomyces,* probably most of the biflagellate phycomycetes, and the yeasts). The advantages of diploidy are numerous and obvious, and the same advantages generally accrue to the dikaryon: it is a genetically balanced system with the same intergenomic relations that obtain in the diploid. Why, then, is the life cycle of the most highly developed fungi based on the dikaryon rather than on diploidy, a feature that is established in several groups of fungi that are commonly conceded to be more primitive? Mather (1965) suggests ". . . that these fungi have not, so to speak, mastered the problem of managing a diploid nucleus, that they do not possess the fine genetic balance to secure the accurate timing in relation to one or another of the cycles of chromosome division necessary for diploid mitosis to follow a normal path. . . ." An alternate view that the dikaryon has critical selective advantages over the diploid, however, has some merit. Diploid strains are well known in numerous ascomycetes (cf. Roper, 1966) and in a few basidiomycetes (Casselton, 1965; Prud'-homme, 1965; Parag and Nachman, 1966), and certain of the latter have now remained stable during extended culture. Inability of these fungi "to manage" diploidy apparently does not explain the dikaryon.

Although it is difficult to see any advantage of the dikaryon *vs.* diploidy in the ascogenous hyphae of the Ascomycetes, a very significant advantage of the dikaryon of the higher basidiomycetes is readily apparent. Buller's (1931) concept of the vegetative mycelia of *Coprinus,* etc., as dikaryotic mosaics has been substantially confirmed in nature (Burnett and Partington, 1957). Such mosaics are probably established in large part by the dikaryotization of homokaryons by previously established dikaryons (Raper, 1966) in interactions that afford a high degree of internuclear selection (Ellingboe and Raper, 1962; Crowe, 1963). In the higher basidiomycetes, at least, the dikaryon, by its retention of the combined mating capacities of its two component genomes, affords a type of selective advantage that is not possible in a diploid. The exchange of nuclei between contiguous dikaryons of *Coprinus* (Swiezynski, 1961) and of rusts, with consequently enhanced potentiality for somatic recombination (Vakili and Caldwell, 1957; Ellingboe, 1961), further attest to a genetic plasticity of the dikaryon as compared to the diploid. Comparable phenomena are unknown in ascomycetous dikaryons, but their universal persistence strongly suggests some critical if subtle advantage(s) for the maintenance of the component genomes in separate nuclei.

The simple fact that the dikaryon is common to the Euascomycetes and Basidiomycetes and is found in no other groups of organisms justifies an assumption of a common ancestry to these two large classes of fungi. Furthermore, in view of the basic heterokaryotic structure of the dikaryon, its stabilization by the intimate pairing of its component nuclei and their synchronous or conjugate division could have occurred only after heterokaryosis *per se* was firmly established in the ancestral forms. Divergence of the two lines that gave rise to the Euascomycetes and Basidiomycetes, however, must have occurred quite early in the history of the dikaryon, as the characteristics of the dikaryons in the two classes are quite distinct. The dikaryophase in the former group is parasitic upon the haploid phase, is restricted in its development to the confines of a single fruiting structure, of which it forms only the fertile elements, and its function is strictly sexual. By contrast, the dikaryophase of the Basidiomycetes is independent of any haploid phase, is capable of indefinite propagation, is the sole component of the fruiting structure, and performs both vegetative and sexual functions. It is difficult to see by what processes one type of dikaryophase might have been derived from the other, and the parallel evolution in time of the two groups seems the more probable explanation of the marked divergence in the characteristics of a shared and unique feature. Savile's proposal (Chapter 26) of a very primitive, plastic, parasitic form, similar to *Taphrina,* as a likely ancestral base for the Basidiomycetes is very attractive. It is parasitic, has a simple type of incompatibility system, has a prolonged, independent dikaryotic phase (quite unlike that typical of the Ascomycetes), and displays a remarkable lack of morphological differentiation. Such a form provides, as Savile points out, precisely the constellation of characteristics that result in adaptive radiation. The various characteristics of the Basidiomycetes can be rationalized from such an ancestor far more easily than from more highly specialized ascomycetous forms. Even the outlandishly complex tetrapolar incompatibility system so ubiquitous in the higher groups can be rationalized from such beginnings by an improbable series of developments, for each of which precedent is available in the literature of population genetics. The sequence is improbable, but tetrapolar incompatibility is a fact.

IV. CONCLUSION

Because of the lack of all but the most fragmentary fossil record (cf. Martin, Chapter 25), any understanding of the evolutionary history of the fungi is almost exclusively a matter of deduction, and any worthwhile clarification of this history will be achieved only through the most careful evaluation of many fungal characteristics at all levels of organization, from major groupings to subspecific populations, in relation to known evolutionary processes. The result of this long-term and arduous task, however, cannot be a definitive history, as is that of the vertebrates; the best that can be hoped for is a consensus of plausibility, which must be tempered by an appreciation of probability. It must be assumed that novel evolutionary processes, peculiar to the fungi, will not be found, and it must thus be further assumed that irretrievably lost are most if not all of the critical stages in fungal evolution—the primitive unspecialized, plastic forms ideally suited to penetrate a wide range of different niches and there to generate divergent lines. Present-day fungi are the products of processes that involve both progressive and regressive tendencies, not only in the constellations of characteristics of large assemblages of related forms but also in specific characteristics which occur sporadically in widely separated groups. The various phylogenetic systems amply reflect the difficulties inherent in judgment on these matters: a primitive group according to one authority is often a highly specialized, but degenerate group of another. The prospects for *a* definitive evolutionary history of the fungi are vanishingly improbable.

Studies on evolutionary processes with fungi, however, afford a far brighter prospect. The basic characteristics of many fungi—ease of culture, short generation-time, and many special features such as haploidy, heterokaryosis, and the dikaryon—admirably suit them for high-resolution analysis of a variety of specific evolutionary processes. Fungi have already been used to extremely good effect in the clarification of certain phenomena of basic evolutionary significance. Preeminent in this regard are the contributions from fungal studies to the present knowledge of mutations, physiological genetics, and the mechanics of recombination. Contributions from such studies to the understanding of evolutionary processes, however, have been largely incidental, as the underlying experimentation was seldom designed with their primary objectives the evaluation of the evolutionary significance of the phenomena under investigation. Most studies with fungi having evolutionary considerations as a central interest have been carried out by taxonomists, the more venturesome doubling as phylogeneticists. Basic experimentation in this area has been meager and represents a field that is now ripe for effective exploration and exploitation. A modicum of familiarity with a few fungal systems rather than presumptiousness prompts the following examples. As mentioned above, polygenic systems appear to be rather prominent in the fungi; whether more or less than elsewhere is problematic. What is not problematic, however, is that studies on the evolution of polygenic systems can be made more expeditiously and effectively with haploid organisms having short generation-times than with higher, diploid forms. The dikaryon is a feature unique to the fungi and, at least in the Basidiomycetes, affords opportunities for experimentation that are impossible with any other group of organisms. Of particular interest here is the interaction between dikaryons and homokaryons, a very complex interaction that is still imperfectly understood, in which occur numerous phenomena of undoubted but unassessed evolutionary significance, such as internuclear selection and somatic recombination. Furthermore, the Basidiomycetes now provide the only known possibilities for the direct comparison of genic or genomic interactions in haploid, dikaryotic, and diploid phases in the same organism. Other groups of fungi with distinctive features afford comparable opportunities, and when the fungi are considered in their totality, the opportunities for basic evolutionary studies are endless.

REFERENCES

Ahmad, M. (1965). Incompatibility in yeasts. *In* "Incompatibility in Fungi" (K. Esser and J. R. Raper, eds.), pp. 13–23. Springer, Berlin.

Bandoni, R. J. (1965). Secondary control of conjugation in *Tremella mesenterica*. *Can. J. Botany* **43**: 627–630.

Bistis, G. N. (1965). The function of the mating type locus in filamentous Ascomycetes. *In* "Incompatibility in Fungi" (K. Esser and J. R. Raper, eds.), pp. 23–31. Springer, Berlin.

Blakeslee, A. F. (1906). Zygospore germinations in the Mucorineae. *Ann. Mycol. (Berlin)* **4**: 1–28.

Buller, A. H. R. (1931). "Researches on Fungi," Vol. IV, 329 pp. Longman's Green, New York.

Burgeff, H. (1914). Untersuchungen über Variabilität, Sexualität, und Erblichkeit bei *Phycomyces nitens*. I. *Flora (Jena)* **107**: 259–316.

Burnett, J. H. (1965). The natural history of recombination systems. *In* "Incompatibility in Fungi" (K. Esser and J. R. Raper, eds.), pp. 98–113. Springer, Berlin.

Burnett, J. H., and M. Partington. (1957). Spatial distribution of fungal mating type factors. *Proc. Roy. Phys. Soc. Edinburgh* **26**: 61–68.

Cantino, E. C. (1966). Morphogenesis in aquatic fungi. *In* "The Fungi" (G. C. Ainsworth and A. S. Sussman, eds.), Vol. 2, pp. 283–330. Academic Press, New York.

Casselton, L. A. (1965). The production and behavior of diploid strains of *Coprinus lagopus*. *Genet. Res.* **6**: 190–208.

Croft, J. H., and G. Simchen. (1965). Natural variation among monokaryons of *Collybia velutipes*. *Am. Naturalist* **99**: 451–462.

Crowe, L. K. (1963). Competition between compatible nuclei in the establishment of a dikaryon in *Schizophyllum commune*. *Heredity* **18**: 525–533.

Davis, R. H. (1966). Mechanisms of inheritance. 2. Heterokaryosis. *In* "The Fungi" (G. S. Ainsworth and A. S. Sussman, eds.), Vol. 2, pp. 567–588. Academic Press, New York.

Dodge, B. O. (1942). Heterokaryotic vigor in *Neurospora*. *Bull. Torrey Botan. Club* **73**: 410–416.

El Ani, A. S., and L. S. Olive. (1962). The induction of balanced heterothallism in *Sordaria fimicola*. *Proc. Natl. Acad. Sci. U.S.* **48**: 17–19.

Ellingboe, A. H. (1961). Somatic recombination in *Puccinia graminis tritici*. *Phytopathology* **51**: 13–15.

Ellingboe, A. H., and J. R. Raper. (1962). The Buller phenomenon in *Schizophyllum commune:* nuclear selection in fully compatible dikaryotic-homokaryotic matings. *Am. J. Botany* **49**: 454–459.

Esser, K. (1962). Die Genetik der sexuellen Fortpflanzung bei den Pilzen. *Biol. Zentr.* **81**: 161–172.

Esser, K. (1966). Incompatibility. *In* "The Fungi" (G. C. Ainsworth and A. S. Sussman, eds.), Vol. 2, pp. 661–676. Academic Press, New York.

Fincham, J. R. S., and P. R. Day. (1965). "Fungal Genetics," 326 pp. F. A. Davis, Philadelphia, Pennsylvania.

Fries, N. (1965). The chemical environment for fungal growth. Vitamins and other organic growth factors. *In* "The Fungi" (G. C. Ainsworth and A. S. Sussman, eds.), Vol. 1, pp. 491–525. Academic Press, New York.

Gross, S. R. (1950). Heterokaryosis between opposite mating types of *Neurospora crassa*. *Biol. Bull.* **99**: 331–332.

Jinks, J. L., C. E. Caten, G. Simchen, and J. H. Croft. (1966). Heterokaryon incompatibility and variation in wild populations of *Aspergillus nidulans*. *Heredity* **21**: 227–239.

Leupold, U. (1958). Studies on recombination in *Schizosaccharomyces pombe*. *Cold Spring Harbor Symp. Quant. Biol.* **23**: 161–169.

Lindegren, C. C., and G. Lindegren. (1943). Segregation, mutation and copulation in *Saccharomyces cerevisiae*. *Ann. Missouri Botan. Garden* **30**: 453–468.

Mather, K. (1942). Heterothally as an outbreeding mechanism in fungi. *Nature* **149**: 54.

Mather, K. (1965). The genetic interest of incompatibility in fungi. *In* "Incompatibility in Fungi" (K. Esser and J. R. Raper, eds.), pp. 113–117. Springer, Berlin.

Olive, L. S. (1958). On the evolution of heterothallism in fungi. *Am. Naturalist* **92**: 233–251.

Papa, K. E., A. M. Srb, and W. T. Federer. (1966). Selection for increased growth rate in inter- and intrastrain crosses of *Neurospora*. *Heredity* **21**: 595–615.

Papazian, H. P. (1951). The incompatibility factors and a related gene in *Schizophyllum commune*. *Genetics* **36**: 441–459.

Parag, Y., and B. Nachman. (1966). Diploidy in the tetrapolar heterothallic basidiomycete *Schizophyllum commune*. *Heredity* **21**: 151–154.

Prud'homme, N. (1965). Somatic recombination in the basidiomycete *Coprinus radiatus*. *In* "Incompatibility in Fungi" (K. Esser and J. R. Raper, eds.), pp. 48–52. Springer, Berlin.

Raper, J. R. (1955). Heterokaryosis and sexuality in fungi. *Trans. N.Y. Acad. Sci.* [2] **17**: 627–635.

Raper, J. R. (1966). "Genetics of Sexuality in Higher Fungi," 283 pp. Ronald Press, New York.

Raper, J. R., and K. Esser. (1964). The fungi. *In* "The Cell" (J. Brachet and A. E. Mirsky, eds.), Vol. 6, pp. 139–245. Academic Press, New York.

Raper, J. R., and J. P. San Antonio. (1954). Heterokaryotic mutagenesis in Hymenomycetes. I. Heterokaryosis in *Schizophyllum commune*. *Am. J. Botany* **41**: 69–86.

Roper, J. A. (1966). Mechanisms of inheritance. 3. The parasexual cycle. *In* "The Fungi" (G. C. Ainsworth and A. S. Sussman, eds.), Vol. 2, pp. 589–617. Academic Press, New York.

Rowell, J. B. (1955). Functional role of incompatibility factors and an *in vitro* test for sexual compatible haploid lines of *Ustilago zeae*. *Phytopathology* **45**: 370–375.

Rowell, J. B., and J. E. DeVay. (1954). Genetics of *Ustilago zeae* in relation to basic problems of its pathogenicity. *Phytopathology* **44**: 356.

Sansome, E. R. (1946). Heterokaryosis, mating-type factors, and sexual reproduction in *Neurospora*. *Bull. Torrey Botan. Club* **73**: 397–409.

Simchen, G. (1965). Variation in a dikaryotic population of *Collybia velutipes*. *Genetics* **51**: 709–721.

Simchen, G. (1966a). Monokaryotic variation and haploid selection in *Schizophyllum commune*. *Heredity* **21**: 241–263.

Simchen, G. (1966b). Fruiting and growth rate among dikaryotic progeny of single wild isolates of *Schizophyllum commune*. *Genetics* **53**: 1151–1165.

Simchen, G. (1967). Genetic control of recombination and the incompatibility system in *Schizophyllum commune*. *Genet. Res.* **9**: 195–210.

Simchen, G., and J. L. Jinks. (1964). The determination of dikaryotic growth-rate in the basidiomycete, *Schizophyllum commune:* A biometrical analysis. *Heredity* **19**: 629–649.

Stebbins, G. L. (1966). "Processes of Organic Evolution," 191 pp. Prentice-Hall, Englewood Cliffs, New Jersey.

Swiezynski, K. M. (1961). Exchange of nuclei between dikaryons in *Coprinus lagopus*. *Acta Soc. Botan. Polon.* **30**: 535–552.

Vakili, N. G., and R. M. Caldwell. (1957). Recombination of spore color and pathogenicity between uredial clones of *Puccinia recondita* f. *tritici*. *Phytopathology* **47**: 536.

Wheeler, H. E. (1954). Genetics and evolution of heterothallism in *Glomerella*. *Phytopathology* **44**: 342–345.

Whitehouse, H. L. K. (1949). Multiple-allelomorph heterothallism in the fungi. *New Phytologist* **48**: 212–244.

Author Index

Numbers in italics refer to the pages on which the complete references are listed.

C

I

J

N

O

P

T

U

V

Subject Index

An asterisk (*) after a page number indicates an illustration.

G

V

W

Y

Z

Index to Fungi, Lichens, and Actinomycetes

An asterisk (*) after a page number indicates an illustration.

B

F

G

H

Z

B 5
C 6
D 7
E 8
F 9
G 0
H 1
I 2
J 3